AS YOU EXAMINE

HOLT ALGEBRA 1

PLEASE NOTICE   This Algebra 1 text provides a balanced course designed to be mastered by all first-year algebra students. All the basic concepts that are usually covered in a first-year algebra course are found in HOLT ALGEBRA 1.

FORMAT

A significant innovation in HOLT ALGEBRA 1 is the format of each lesson involving a five-part presentation (see any lesson):

- Lesson Objective
- Review Capsule
- Worked-out Examples in black type (right-hand column)
- Hints, Suggestions, and Comments in blue type (left-hand column)
- Graded Exercises

CONTENT

1. Reading is kept to a minimum through the use of a two-column format. (See any lesson.)
2. Begins with a review of fundamental mathematical skills and concepts. (See pp. 1-19.)
3. Worked-out examples focus on the mathematics, thus eliminating long, wordy explanations. (See pp. 135-137.)
4. Suggestions, hints, and comments in color on the left-hand side of the page help clarify the development of the mathematics in the right-hand column. (See any lesson.)
5. Oral exercises appear before many written exercise sets. These provide readiness for the written exercises. (See pp. 5, 195, 439.)
6. Exercises are plentiful and are grouped in three levels of difficulty: A, B, C. Examples in the lesson match every type of exercise in Part A and Part B. (See pp. 17, 291, 403.)
7. Each chapter ends with a Chapter Review and Chapter Test. The Review is diagnostic and is keyed to lesson pages. The Test is an alternate form of the Review.
8. Special Topics pages vary the pace and enrich the course. They include applications of algebra in the everyday world, as well as careers that use mathematics. (See pp. viii, 12, 63, 202, 377, 413.)
9. Flow-chart approach to calculator and computer activities. (See pp. 97, 149.)
10. Answers to odd-numbered exercises are provided in the back of the pupil edition. (See pp. 483-500.)
11. Teacher's Edition with Commentary for Teachers and Lesson Commentaries with Cumulative Review exercises (see pp. T-15 to T-47), Pacing Chart with assignments for three levels of difficulty (see pp. T-49 to T-60), and a complete set of answers (see pp. T-61 to T-96).

SUPPLEMENTARY MATERIALS ON D⬛⬛⬛⬛⬛ERS

- A set of alternate chapter tests.
- A set of 60 Skillmasters provides two daily quizzes or additional exercise sets on each master, as well as two Cumulative Reviews.
- F⬛⬛⬛⬛⬛⬛⬛⬛⬛⬛⬛⬛⬛⬛⬛, there is a set of d⬛⬛⬛⬛⬛⬛⬛⬛⬛⬛gnment sheets, placement tests, and record-keeping forms as well as a Teacher's Guide.

Eugene D. Nichols

Mervine L. Edwards

E. Henry Garland

Sylvia A. Hoffman

Albert Mamary

William F. Palmer

TEACHER'S
EDITION

HOLT ALGEBRA 1

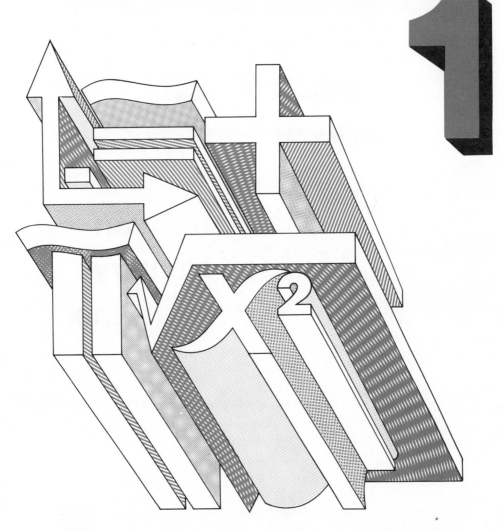

 HOLT, RINEHART AND WINSTON, PUBLISHERS
New York · Toronto · London · Sydney

About the Authors

Eugene D. Nichols is Professor of Mathematics Education and Lecturer in the Department of Mathematics at Florida State University, Tallahassee, Florida.

Mervine L. Edwards is Chairman of the Mathematics Department, Shore Regional High School, West Long Branch, New Jersey.

E. Henry Garland is Head of the Mathematics Department at the Developmental Research School, and Associate Professor of Mathematics Education at Florida State University, Tallahassee, Florida.

Sylvia A. Hoffman is Curriculum Coordinator for the Metropolitan Chicago Region of the Illinois Office of Education, State of Illinois.

Albert Mamary is Assistant Superintendent of Schools for Instruction, Johnson City Central School District, Johnson City, New York.

William F. Palmer is Professor and Chairman of the Department of Education, Catawba College, Salisbury, North Carolina.

ISBN: 0–03–018906–3

890123456 071 98765432

Teacher's Edition

CONTENTS

HOLT ALGEBRA 1

BENEFITS

1. CONTAINS ALL BASIC SKILLS AND CONCEPTS

2. TEACHES BY WORKED-OUT EXAMPLES

3. SINGLE CONCEPT LESSONS

4. FIVE-PART PRESENTATION OF LESSONS

5. OPEN FORMAT

6. REDUCED READING

7. SPECIAL TOPICS WITH PROJECTS

8. GRADED EXERCISES

9. CHAPTER REVIEWS AND TESTS

10. EXTENSIVELY FIELD TESTED

11. SUPPLEMENTARY TESTS AND SKILLMASTERS

12. HELPFUL TEACHER'S EDITION

13. MANAGEMENT SYSTEM FOR INDIVIDUALIZING

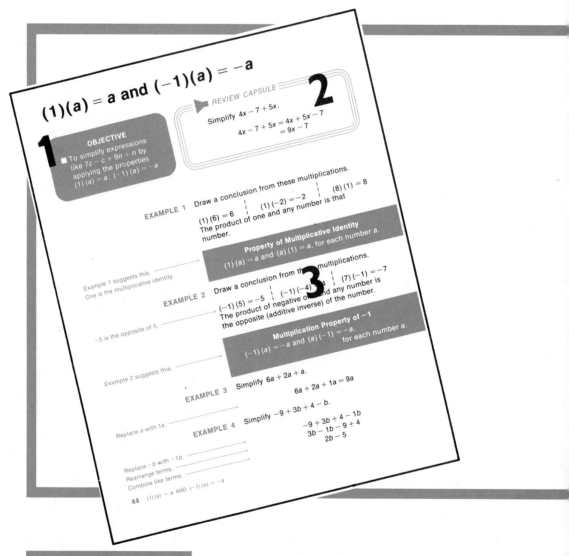

$(1)(a) = a$ and $(-1)(a) = -a$

2 ▶ REVIEW CAPSULE

Simplify $4x - 7 + 5x$.

$4x - 7 + 5x = 4x + 5x - 7$
$= 9x - 7$

1 **OBJECTIVE**
■ To simplify expressions like $7c - c + 9n + n$ by applying the properties $(1)(a) = a$; $(-1)(a) = -a$

EXAMPLE 1   Draw a conclusion from these multiplications.

$(1)(6) = 6$ │ $(1)(-2) = -2$ │ $(8)(1) = 8$
The product of one and any number is that number.

Property of Multiplicative Identity
$(1)(a) = a$ and $(a)(1) = a$, for each number a.

Example 1 suggests this.
One is the multiplicative identity.

3 EXAMPLE 2   Draw a conclusion from the multiplications.

$(-1)(5) = -5$ │ $(-1)(-4)$ │ $(7)(-1) = -7$
The product of negative one and any number is the opposite (additive inverse) of the number.

−5 is the opposite of 5.

Multiplication Property of −1
$(-1)(a) = -a$ and $(a)(-1) = -a$, for each number a.

Example 2 suggests this.

EXAMPLE 3   Simplify $6a + 2a + a$.

$6a + 2a + 1a = 9a$

Replace a with 1a.

EXAMPLE 4   Simplify $-9 + 3b + 4 - b$.

$-9 + 3b + 4 - 1b$
$3b - 1b - 9 + 4$
$2b - 5$

Replace −b with −1b.
Rearrange terms.
Combine like terms.

44   $(1)(a) = a$ AND $(-1)(a) = -a$

FIVE-PART PRESENTATION OF EACH LESSON

1. OBJECTIVE
2. REVIEW CAPSULE
3. WORKED-OUT EXAMPLES
4. HINTS, COMMENTS, AND SUGGESTIONS
5. GRADED EXERCISES

_____ IS ORGANIZED

1. Expected performance is stated simply in the language of the student.
2. Summarizes a skill or concept the student needs to recall for this lesson.
3. The use of words is cut to a minimum so the mathematical ideas stand out.
4. Hints on the left-hand side of the page direct attention to key parts of the development.
5. Oral exercises provide readiness for the written exercises.
   Exercises are graded according to level of difficulty, A, B, and C.

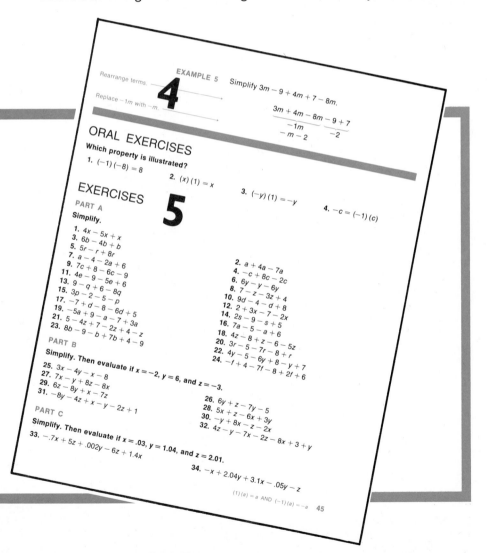

Rearrange terms.

Replace −1m with −m.

EXAMPLE 5 Simplify $3m - 9 + 4m + 7 - 8m$.

$$3m + 4m - 8m - 9 + 7$$
$$-1m \quad -2$$
$$-m - 2$$

4

ORAL EXERCISES

Which property is illustrated?

1. $(-1)(-8) = 8$

2. $(x)(1) = x$

3. $(-y)(1) = -y$

4. $-c = (-1)(c)$

EXERCISES

5

PART A

Simplify.

1. $4x - 5x + x$
3. $6b - 4b + b$
5. $5r - r + 8r$
7. $a - 4 - 2a + 6$
9. $7c + 8 - 6c - 9$
11. $4e - 9 - 5e + 6$
13. $9 - q + 6 - 8q$
15. $3p - 2 - 5 - p$
17. $-7 + d - 8 - 6d + 5$
19. $-5a + 9 - a - 7 + 3a$
21. $5 - 4z + 7 - 2z + 4 - z$
23. $8b - 9 - b + 7b + 4 - 9$

2. $a + 4a - 7a$
4. $-c + 8c - 2c$
6. $6y - y - 6y$
8. $7 - z - 3z + 4$
10. $9d - 4 - d + 8$
12. $2 + 3x - 7 - 2x$
14. $2s - 9 - s + 5$
16. $7a - 5 - a + 6$
18. $4z - 8 + z - 6 - 5z$
20. $3r - 5 - 7r - 8 + r$
22. $4y - 5 - 6y + 8 - y + 7$
24. $-f + 4 - 7f - 8 + 2f + 6$

PART B

Simplify. Then evaluate if $x = -2$, $y = 6$, and $z = -3$.

25. $3x - 4y - x - 8$
27. $7x - y + 8z - 8x$
29. $6z - 8y + x - 7z$
31. $-8y - 4z + x - y - 2z + 1$

26. $6y + z - 7y - 5$
28. $5x + z - 6x + 3y$
30. $-y + 8x - z - 2x$
32. $4z - y - 7x - 2z - 8x + 3 + y$

PART C

Simplify. Then evaluate if $x = .03$, $y = 1.04$, and $z = 2.01$.

33. $-.7x + 5z + .002y - 6z + 1.4x$

34. $-x + 2.04y + 3.1x - .05y - z$

$(1)(a) = a$ AND $(-1)(a) = -a$ **45**

ALGEBRAIC SKILLS

English Phrases to Algebra

- Prerequisite pages precede lessons on solving word problems.
- Page 70 is prerequisite for page 72.
- Page 304 is prerequisite for page 306.
- Page 350 is prerequisite for page 353.

OBJECTIVE
■ To write English phrases like 12 more than twice x in mathematical terms

▶ *REVIEW CAPSULE*

English phrase: 6 decreased by 2
Mathematical terms: 6   −   2
6 decreased by 2 means 6 made smaller by 2, or $6 - 2$

English phrase: 8 increased by 3
Mathematical terms: 8   +   3
8 increased by 3 means 8 made greater by 3, or $8 + 3$

EXAMPLE 1 Write in

7 dec

Decreased by means made smaller by.
Use −.

7 —

EXAMPLE 2 Write in

The value of x is not known.

EXAMPLE 3 Write in

Let a variable represent the number.

EXAMPLE 4 Write in

7 less than 10 does not mean $7 - 10$.
It means $10 - 7$.

70 ENGLISH PHRASES TO ALGEBRA

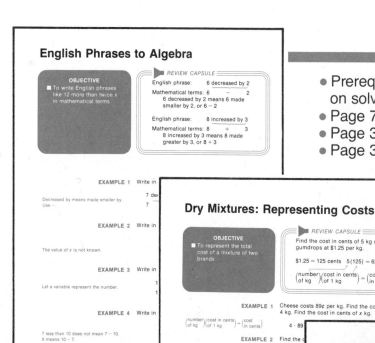

Dry Mixtures: Representing Costs

OBJECTIVE
■ To represent the total cost of a mixture of two brands

▶ *REVIEW CAPSULE*

Find the cost in cents of 5 kg of gumdrops at $1.25 per kg.

$1.25 = 125$ cents $5(125) = 625$ cents

$\binom{\text{number}}{\text{of kg}} \binom{\text{cost in cents}}{\text{of 1 kg}} = \binom{\text{cost}}{\text{in cents}}$

EXAMPLE 1 Cheese costs 89¢ per kg. Find the cost in cents of 4 kg. Find the cost in cents of x kg.

$\binom{\text{number}}{\text{of kg}} \binom{\text{cost in cents}}{\text{of 1 kg}} = \binom{\text{cost}}{\text{in cents}}$ $4 \cdot 89$

EXAMPLE 2 Find the c
coffee at
per kg.

Use $\binom{\text{number}}{\text{of kg}} \binom{\text{cost in cents}}{\text{of 1 kg}}$ twice. $3(32$
Thus, the

EXAMPLE 3 Find the c
at $1.35 p

Use $\binom{\text{number}}{\text{of kg}} \binom{\text{cost in cents}}{\text{of 1 kg}}$ twice.
Thus, the

EXAMPLE 4 Complete

| Brand A |
| Brand B |

$1.45 = 145$ cents
$1.95 = 195$ cents

| Brand A |
| Brand B |

304 DRY MIXTURES: REPRESENTING COSTS

Representing Amounts of Work

OBJECTIVE
■ To express the amount of work done on a job as a fraction

▶ *REVIEW CAPSULE*

Fractions are used to compare parts of an object with the whole.

What part of the diagram is shaded?

Four of the 5 squares are shaded.
Thus, $\frac{4}{5}$ of the diagram is shaded.

EXAMPLE 1 Sheila can mow a lawn in 3 hours. What part of the lawn can she mow in 1 hour?

Lawn
3 hours

1 hour
3 hours

In 1 hour, she can mow $\frac{1}{3}$ of the lawn.

EXAMPLE 2 Pedro can paint a house in 5 days. What part will he paint in 1 day? in 3 days? in 4 days? in x days?

He will have finished in

1 day $\frac{1}{5}$ of the job.

3 days $3 \cdot \frac{1}{5} = \frac{3}{5}$ of the job.
3 days

4 days $4 \cdot \frac{1}{5} = \frac{4}{5}$ of the job.
4 days

x days $x \cdot \frac{1}{5} = \frac{x}{5}$ of the job.

350 REPRESENTING AMOUNTS OF WORK

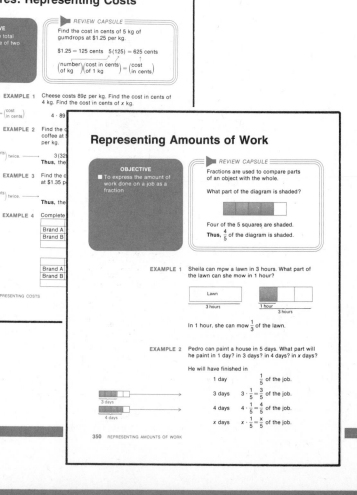

APPLIED TO PROBLEM SOLVING

Work Problems

▶ REVIEW CAPSULE

John can paint a house in 5 days.

Part of Job Done in 1 Day	Number of Days Worked	Part of Job Completed
$\frac{1}{5}$	x	$x \cdot \frac{1}{5} = \frac{x}{5}$

EXAMPLE 1 It takes Jack 5 hours and Joan 10 hours to paint a shed. How long will it take them to do the job if they work together?

	Part of Job Done in 1 Hour	Number Hours Working Together	Part of Job Completed
ck	$\frac{1}{5}$	x	$x \cdot \frac{1}{5} = \frac{x}{5}$
an	$\frac{1}{10}$	x	$x \cdot \frac{1}{10} = \frac{x}{10}$

Part Jack did + part Joan did = whole job.

$$\frac{x}{5} + \frac{x}{10} = 1$$

$$\frac{x}{5} + \frac{x}{5 \cdot 2} = 1$$

$$5 \cdot 2\left(\frac{x}{5} + \frac{x}{5 \cdot 2}\right) = 5 \cdot 2 \cdot \frac{1}{1}$$

$$5 \cdot 2 \cdot \frac{x}{5} + 5 \cdot 2 \cdot \frac{x}{5 \cdot 2} = 5 \cdot 2 \cdot 1$$

$$2x + 1x = 10$$
$$3x = 10$$
$$x = \frac{10}{3}$$

Thus, it takes $3\frac{1}{3}$ hours if they work together.

Solving Dry Mixture Problems

▶ REVIEW CAPSULE

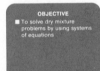

Write an equation.

y is 3 more than x

$y = x + 3$

y is twice x

$y = 2x$

y is 4 more than 3 times x

$y = 3x + 4$

y is 2 less than x

$y = x - 2$

One brand of candy costs $1.70 per kg. Another costs $1.50 per kg. The two brands are to be mixed to form a 5-kg gift box that will cost $8.10. How many kg of each should be included?

	Number of kg	Cost per kg	Cost in Cents
1st Brand	x	170	$x \cdot 170 = 170x$
2nd Brand	y	150	$y \cdot 150 = 150y$
	Total cost in cents		$170x + 150y$

total kg: $x + y = 5$

cost in cents: $170x + 150y = 810$

$x = -y + 5$ (1)   The two equations

$170x + 150y = 810$ (2)   form a system.

$170(-y + 5) + 150y = 810$
$-170y + 850 + 150y = 810$
$-20y + 850 = 810$
$-20y = -40$
$y = 2$

To find x, let $y = 2$ in equation (1).
$x = -y + 5$
$x = -2 + 5$
$x = 3$

Thus, 3 kg at $1.70 per kg and 2 kg at $1.50 per kg should be included in the mixture.

Number Problems

▶ REVIEW CAPSULE

7 increased by 2

5 less than 3 times x

$7 + 2$ $3x - 5$

6 more than twice a number

$2n + 6$

EXAMPLE 1 Write an equation for each sentence.

Three more than a number is 9.

$n + 3 = 9$

A number decreased by 7 is 8 times the number.

$n - 7 = 8n$

EXAMPLE 2 Seven more than 4 times a number is 31. Find the number.

Let n = the number

7 more than 4 times n is 31.

Write an equation. $4n + 7 = 31$
Add -7 to each side. $\dfrac{-7 \quad -7}{4n \quad = 24}$
Divide each side by 4. $n = 6$

Check 6 in the problem.   7 more than 4 times 6 is 31.

$$\begin{array}{c|c} 4(6) + 7 & 31 \\ 24 + 7 & \\ 31 & \end{array}$$

Thus, the number is 6.

A COMPLETE EVALUATION SYSTEM

- Chapter Review and Chapter Test for each chapter.
- The Test is an alternate form of the Review.
- Chapter Review is keyed back to the lesson indicating in second color the pages where the concepts were taught, thus serving as a diagnostic test.
- A pad of duplicating masters has a test for each chapter and five cumulative tests.

CHAPTER 13 TEST

Solve and check for extraneous solutions.

1. $\dfrac{6a-8}{21} = \dfrac{3a}{7} + \dfrac{1}{3}$ 2. $\dfrac{4}{5} + \dfrac{11}{x} = 3$

-5 5

3. $\dfrac{3}{5}(x-3) + \dfrac{x+7}{5} = \dfrac{x+17}{10}$

3

4. $\dfrac{7}{y-6} - \dfrac{2}{y+2} = \dfrac{46}{y^2-4y-12}$

4

Solve each problem.

5. Working together, Janet and James can paint a fence in 7 hours. It would take Janet 10 hours to do it alone. How long would it take James?

$23\frac{1}{3}$ hr

Solve.

7. $.6x + 3 = .2x + 4$

2.5

8. $.02(2 - .5x) = .32 - .03x$

14

Show that each is a rational number.

9. $.83\overline{3}$ 10. $.15\overline{15}$

$\dfrac{75}{90}$, or $\dfrac{5}{6}$ $\dfrac{15}{99}$, or $\dfrac{5}{33}$

Simplify.

11. $\dfrac{\frac{1}{m} - \frac{4}{m^2}}{\frac{1}{m} - \frac{6}{m^2}}$ 12. $\dfrac{\frac{5}{a-3} + \frac{4}{a}}{\frac{7}{a^2-3a}}$

$m+2$ $\dfrac{9a-12}{7}$

Solve for x.

Chapter Thirteen Test

Solve and check for extraneous solutions.

1. $\dfrac{3a-4}{15} = \dfrac{2a}{5} + \dfrac{1}{3}$ 2. $\dfrac{2}{3} + \dfrac{6}{x} = 2$

3. $\dfrac{4}{y-8} - \dfrac{3}{y+2} = \dfrac{4}{y^2-6y-16}$ 4. $\dfrac{2}{7}(x-2) + \dfrac{x+4}{7}$

5. Working together, Janice and Jack can mow a lawn in 4 hours. It would take Janice 7 hours to do it alone. How long would it take Jack?

6. Rodney can rep... 9 hours. If Lisa h... complete the job... long would it tak...

7. Working together, two men can build a shed in 15 hours. It would take one of them 4 times as long as the other to do it alone. How long would it take each alone?

8. By herself, Joan... 4 weeks. It woul... How long would... working togethe... complete the job...

Solve.

9. $.05x = 4$ 10. $.5x + 2 = .32x + 12$ 11. $.01(3...$

Show that each is a rational number.

12. -14 13. $8\frac{1}{3}$ 14. $.4\overline{4}$

Simplify.

16. $\dfrac{\frac{4}{7} + \frac{1}{3}}{\frac{2}{3} + \frac{5}{21}}$ 17. $\dfrac{\frac{7}{a-2} + \frac{5}{a}}{\frac{3}{a^2-2a}}$

18. $\dfrac{1 - \frac{5}{m} - \frac{14}{m^2}}{\frac{1}{m} - \frac{5}{m^2}}$ 19. $\dfrac{x - 2 + \frac{5}{x+3}}{\frac{7}{x+3} + 5}$

Solve for x.

20. $mx - 4 = 2a$ 21. $7 + 2x = tx$ 22. $5...$

Solve each formula for the variable indicated.

23. Solve $m = abd$ for b. Then find b if $m = 28$, $a = 2$, and $d = 7$.

24. Solve $I = \frac{1}{2}mp^2$ fo... if $p = 2$ and $I = 2$...

CHAPTE...

Chapter Thirteen Review

Solve and check for extraneous solutions. [p. 341, 346]

1. $\dfrac{2a-3}{6} = \dfrac{4a}{3} + \dfrac{1}{2}$ 2. $\dfrac{3}{5} + \dfrac{6}{x} = 1$

3. $\dfrac{2}{3}(x-4) + \dfrac{x+5}{2} = \dfrac{2x-1}{3}$ 4. $\dfrac{7}{y+3} - \dfrac{4}{y-7} = \dfrac{2}{y^2-4y-21}$

5. $\dfrac{x}{x-7} + \dfrac{3}{x} = \dfrac{-23}{x^2-7x}$ 6. $\dfrac{2}{b+2} + \dfrac{13}{b^2-4} = \dfrac{b}{b-2}$

[p. 350, 353]

7. Working together, Mona and Martin can mow a lawn in 5 hours. It would take Mona 9 hours to do it alone. How long would it take Martin?

8. George can repair a radio in 5 hours. If Tina helps him, they can do the job in 2 hours. How long would it take Tina to do it alone?

9. Working together, two women can build a house in 7 months. It would take one of them 3 times as long as the other to do it alone. How long would it take each alone?

10. By herself, Jane can build a table in 2 weeks. It would take Juan 5 weeks. How long would it take Irv if, working together, all three can complete the job in 1 week?

Solve. [p. 358]

11. $.03x = 7$ 12. $.6x + 3 = .21x + 18$ 13. $.01(2 - .5x) = .48 - .003x$

Show that each is a rational number. [p. 361]

14. -18 15. 0 16. $7\frac{1}{3}$ 17. $4.6\overline{6}$ 18. $.32\overline{2}$ 19. $.18\overline{18}$

Simplify. [p. 368, 371]

20. $\dfrac{\frac{3}{5} + \frac{1}{2}}{\frac{3}{10} + \frac{2}{5}}$ 21. $\dfrac{\frac{3}{b^2} + \frac{5}{b}}{\frac{2}{b} + \frac{7}{3b^2}}$ 22. $\dfrac{1 - \frac{2}{x} - \frac{15}{x^2}}{\frac{1}{x} - \frac{5}{x^2}}$

23. $\dfrac{\frac{6}{a-3} + \frac{4}{a}}{\frac{7}{a^2-3a}}$ 24. $\dfrac{\frac{3}{a-4} + \frac{5}{2a+3}}{\frac{4a}{2a^2-5a-12}}$ 25. $\dfrac{x - 5 + \frac{3}{x-2}}{\frac{3}{x-2} + 2}$

Solve for x. [p. 374]

26. $bx - 8 = 3m$ 27. $5a + mx = tr$ 28. $8 - 5x = kx$ 29. $6a + 5x = 4a + 3x$

Solve each formula for the variable indicated. Then evaluate. [p. 374]

30. Solve $a = mpq$ for p. Then find p if $a = 32$, $m = 2$, and $q = 7$.

31. Solve $k = \frac{1}{2}fd^2$ for f. Then find f if $k = 7$ and $d = 2$.

ADDITIONAL EVALUATION IN TEACHER'S EDITION AND ON SKILLMASTERS

- Cumulative Review exercises in the Teacher's Edition provide lesson-by-lesson practice or quiz.
- A pad of duplicating masters, SKILLMASTERS, provides two short quizzes for every lesson in the student book.
- Cumulative Reviews for every two lessons are also provided on the SKILLMASTERS.

QUADRATIC EQUATIONS: STANDARD FORM [162]

Students first put quadratic equations into standard form. Standard form implies:

(1) Coefficient of the x^2 term is positive.
(2) Polynomial is equal to 0.
(3) Terms are arranged in descending order of exponents.

Then they apply the method of the previous lesson to solve the equation.

You may use the middle column of the Part A and Part B exercises on page 164 as oral exercises on putting equations in standard form.

Cumulative Review
1. Solve $2x - (x + 1) = 0$.
2. Simplify $2a^3 + 8a^2 - 5a - (2a^3 + 6a^2 - 9a)$.
3. Factor $6x^2 + 27x - 15$ completely.
1. 1 2. $2a^2 + 4a$ 3. $3(2x - 1)(x + 5)$

CONSECUTIVE INTEGERS [165]

We are concerned with writing set-ups (algebraic representations) for consecutive integer problems in preparation for their solution in the next lesson. Students find it hard to accept that consecutive odd integers, as well as consecutive even integers, differ by 2. Students tend to want to add 1 to an integer to get the next consecutive odd integer.

Cumulative Review
1. Factor $4a^2 - 12a + 9$.
2. Evaluate $(x + 5)^2$ if $x = -2$.
3. Solve $a^2 - 7a = -6$.
1. $(2a - 3)(2a - 3)$ 2. 9 3. $1; 6$

HA1 [After p. 162]

Form A

Solve.

1. $x^2 + x = 30$
   $-6, 5$
2. $x^2 = 13x$
   $0, 13$
3. $-2x^2 = 5x - 3$
   $\frac{1}{2}, -3$
4. $x^2 = 64$
   $-8, 8$
5. $7x - x^2 = 10$
   $5, 2$
6. $4x + 3 = -x^2$
   $-3, -1$

HA1 [After p. 162]

Form B

Solve.

1. $x^2 - x = 20$
   $5, -4$
2. $x^2 = 11x$
   $0, 11$
3. $-2x^2 = 3x - 5$
   $-\frac{5}{2}, 1$
4. $81 = x^2$
   $9, -9$
5. $9x - x^2 = 14$
   $7, 2$
6. $7x + 10 = -x^2$
   $-5, -2$

HA1 [After p. 165]

Form A

Write an equation.

1. The sum of three consecutive integers is 54. $x + (x + 1) + (x + 2) = 54$

2. The product of two consecutive even integers is 48. $(x)(x + 2) = 48$

3. Six times the second of two consecutive integers, increased by the first is 48. $6(x + 1) + x = 48$

4. Five times the second of two consecutive even integers, decreased by 4 times the first is 0. $5(x + 2) - 4x = 0$

HA1 [After p. 165]

Form B

Write an equation.

1. The sum of three consecutive odd integers is 39. $x + (x + 2) + (x + 4) = 39$

2. The product of two consecutive integers is 56. $(x)(x + 1) = 56$

3. Nine times the first of two consecutive integers, decreased by the second is 31. $9x - (x + 1) = 31$

4. Four times the second of two consecutive integers, decreased by twice the first is 24. $4(x + 1) - 2x = 24$

HA1 CUMULATIVE REVIEW [After p. 165]

Form A

1. Solve $x^2 - 6x = -8$. $4, 2$

2. Solve $3m - (6 - 3m) = 8 + m$. $\frac{14}{5}$

3. Factor $16x^2 - 25y^2$. $(4x - 5y)(4x + 5y)$

HA1 CUMULATIVE REVIEW [After p. 165]

Form B

1. Solve $x^2 - 10x = -16$. $8, 2$

2. Solve $2m - (8 - 4m) = 9 + m$. $\frac{17}{5}$

3. Factor $49a^2 - 4b^2$. $(7a - 2b)(7a + 2b)$

Holt, Rinehart and Winston—Algebra 1—Skillmaster—23

SPECIAL TOPICS PAGES

- Careers using Mathematics

- Practical Applications of Algebra

- Extensions of Concepts

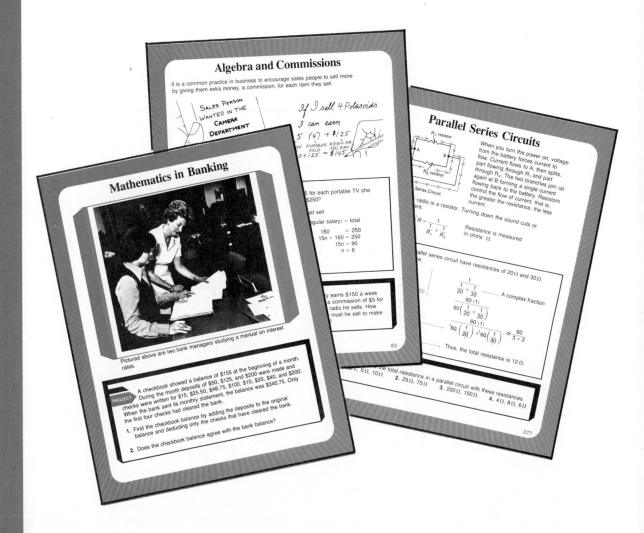

Algebra and Commissions

It is a common practice in business to encourage sales people to sell more by giving them extra money, a commission, for each item they sell.

SALES PERSON
WANTED IN THE
CAMERA
DEPARTMENT

If I sell 4 Polaroids
I can earn
5 (4) + $/25
ON NUMBER REGULAR
SOLD SALARY
0 + 125 = $145

...5 for each portable TV she
...$250?

...ust sell

...egular salary) = total

160 = 250
15n + 160 = 250
15n = 90
n = 6

...y earns $150 a week
...a commission of $5 for
...radio he sells. How
...must he sell to make

63

Mathematics in Banking

Pictured above are two bank managers studying a manual on interest rates.

PROJECT A checkbook showed a balance of $155 at the beginning of a month. During the month deposits of $50, $125, and $200 were made and checks were written for $15, $25.50, $48.75, $100, $10, $35, $40, and $200. Only the first four checks had cleared the bank. When the bank sent its monthly statement, the balance was $340.75.

1. Find the checkbook balance by adding the deposits to the original balance and deducting only the checks that have cleared the bank.

2. Does the checkbook balance agree with the bank balance?

Parallel Series Circuits

R_1 resistor

A   B

R_2 resistor

Series Circuit

...radio is a resistor. Turning down the sound cuts or

When you turn the power on, voltage from the battery forces current to flow. Current flows to A, then splits, part flowing through R_1 and part through R_2. The two branches join up again at B forming a single current flowing back to the battery. Resistors control the flow of current, that is, the greater the resistance, the less current.

$$R = \frac{1}{\frac{1}{R_1} + \frac{1}{R_2}}$$

Resistance is measured in ohms: Ω.

...allel series circuit have resistances of $20\,\Omega$ and $30\,\Omega$.

$$\frac{1}{\frac{1}{20} + \frac{1}{30}} \quad \longleftarrow \text{A complex fraction}$$

$$\frac{60\,(1)}{60\left(\frac{1}{20} + \frac{1}{30}\right)}$$

$$\frac{60\,(1)}{^{3}60\left(\frac{1}{20}\right) + {}^{2}60\left(\frac{1}{30}\right)}, \text{ or } \frac{60}{3+2}$$

$\longleftarrow$ Thus, the total resistance is $12\,\Omega$.

...he total resistance in a parallel circuit with these resistances.
1. $5\,\Omega,\ 10\,\Omega$ **2.** $25\,\Omega,\ 75\,\Omega$
3. $200\,\Omega,\ 150\,\Omega$ **4.** $4\,\Omega,\ 8\,\Omega,\ 6\,\Omega$

377

COMMENTARIES

The Commentary for Teachers describes the features of the text and offers suggestions for individualizing the course. A description of the supplementary materials that are available for use with the text is included also.

The Lesson Commentaries present a brief overview of each chapter, followed by a commentary for each lesson and Special Topic.

Beginning with the second lesson and with each succeeding lesson, a Cumulative Review, with answers, is included. You may use the Cumulative Review before, or after, the lesson is studied. The purpose of the Cumulative Review is to sharpen students' algebraic skills.

The authors of *Holt Algebra 1*, in offering this book, fully realize that many students entering the study of algebra do so with varied levels of proficiency in basic arithmetic skills. For this reason, the course begins very informally, giving students the opportunity to review and strengthen fundamental skills and concepts. The introduction to the basic algebraic ideas is quite gradual. The entire course, however, meets the standards of the algebra syllabi. It is a balanced course presented in such a manner that it can be mastered by all high school students enrolled in first year algebra.

Holt Algebra 1 contains all of the topics that are usually expected to be found in a first year algebra course. When these topics are first introduced, practice in arithmetic skills is also provided. This practice, however, is done for a purpose: to understand, verify, and extend new algebraic concepts.

One of the most significant innovations in *Holt Algebra 1* is the format, which results in a course that is easy to teach and lends itself easily to an individualized style of presentation. The features of this format are described below.

NEW FORMAT

Following are the features of the book that elicited much enthusiasm on the part of the pilot teachers and of the thousands of users of the first edition. Because of its unusual effectiveness with both the teachers and students, this format is being retained in this revised edition.

1. The *Objectives* of each lesson are given on the pupil page. These state very briefly and concisely the student's expected performance at the completion of the lesson.

2. A *Review Capsule* is supplied for each lesson. The capsule reintroduces a skill or concept that the student needs to recall for that lesson.

3. Each lesson is developed through a sequence of worked-out examples. The use of words is cut to the minimum so that mathematical ideas stand out.

4. *Hints and suggestions* along the left-hand side of the page are used to direct the students' attention to the key parts of the development. The hints and suggestions not only help the students who need help, but allow the students who grasp ideas quickly to move on without being slowed down by explanations that they do not need.

5. *Definitions* and other key statements are clearly set out in color for easy identification.

6. There is an abundance of worked-out *Examples* to introduce concepts and establish patterns. These serve as reference for problems of a similar nature that are to be done by students on their own. Over the years, teachers have ascertained the fact that students understand ideas better and feel more confident with mathematics if they see worked-out examples.

7. *Exercises* are plentiful in each lesson. They are presented in Parts A, B, and C according to level of difficulty. In this way, all students may work on material suited to their abilities. Part C exercises consist of more challenging problems and thus provide an enriched course. Columns of exercises are similar to each other. Successful performance in a given column implies that the student is ready to advance to the next level. Unsuccessful performance indicates the necessity for the student to restudy the illustrative examples.

8. *Oral Exercises* precede the exercise set in many lessons. The purpose of the Oral Exercises is to help the student recall basic facts that will be used in the exercise set. The Oral Exercises serve for practice on simple concepts and skills. Many of these simple concepts and skills can be practiced in a short time.

9. *Chapter Reviews* are keyed into lesson pages for quick reference. *Chapter Tests* exactly parallel the Chapter Reviews. This enables students to locate quickly the pages on which the items that they need to study further were taught.

It is a well-known fact that a significant number of high school students do not succeed in mathematics. The authors of *Holt Algebra 1* believe that part of the fault lies with the way in which mathematics is presented. For this reason, the radically different approach described above was adopted.

The use of the first edition of the book has proved the effectiveness of the new format. Students can read and understand what they are reading. They are able to solve problems on their own. Thus, very carefully sequenced experiences followed by immediate reinforcement do result in greater success.

IMPROVEMENTS IN THE PRESENT EDITION

While the thousands of teachers who used the first edition of *Holt Algebra 1* found that their students were succeeding remarkably well, they made suggestions for making the book even more teachable. These suggestions for improvements were incorporated in the 1978 edition of the book. Some of these improvements are the following:

1. The number and frequency of Part C exercises have been increased. In some instances, they have been made more challenging. Students are asked to apply the concepts to some novel situations.
2. Additional material concerning careers was incorporated.

3. Applications of algebra to real life problems were added. Many of these are directly tied in with career awareness pages.
4. An optional lesson on solving systems of linear inequalities by graphing has been added in Chapter 11. The prerequisite lesson on graphing inequalities has been moved from Chapter 12 to Chapter 10, thus providing the necessary background for the new lesson on simultaneous inequalities.
5. Suggestions for easier or alternate methods of handling some concepts have been provided in several lessons.
6. Answers to all odd-numbered exercises are provided in the student text.
7. The metric system of measurement is now used exclusively.

INDIVIDUALIZING THE COURSE

Holt Algebra 1 is designed in such a way that it lends itself easily to an individualized approach. Each lesson is designed so that it can be read and understood by each student.

Holt Algebra 1 provides for three different ways to individualize the course.

1. **By Lesson**   Each lesson has exercises arranged in three levels of difficulty: Part A, Part B, and Part C. Those students who wish to pursue the basic course would do some Part A exercises and some Part B exercises —usually the least difficult exercises in each section. Students who wish to pursue the average course would do some Part A exercises and some Part B exercises—usually those of medium difficulty. Students who are capable of handling the enriched course would do some exercises from each group: Part A, Part B, and Part C.
2. **By Course**   At the end of the Lesson Commentaries in the front of the Teacher's Edition, the Pacing Chart divides the year's work into three levels:
   Level A   provides the minimal course and allows time for reinforcement and recycling.
   Level B   provides the regular course.
   Level C   provides an enriched course.

You may choose to suggest that the basic student follow the Level A assignments; the average student, the Level B assignments; and the capable student, the Level C assignments. Each of the three groups of students would complete a different course throughout the year.

3. **Using the Individualized Guide** The Teacher's Guide for Individualizing the Holt Algebras is a rich source of ideas and aids for the means of providing for individual differences. Other components, in addition to the text, that can be used with the Individualized Guide are *Test Masters, Skillmasters,* and *Individualization Masters.*

PILOTING THE PROGRAM

While the first edition of this program was under development, it was tested in order to ascertain its effectiveness. Schools scattered throughout the United States used the materials under the ordinary classroom conditions. Both average and below average classes were included in pilot testing. The testing of materials extended over a two-year period. A systematic evaluation of results for each lesson, by the teachers, established the conclusion that the material is highly teachable to all students. One of the recurring comments from teachers was that students' achievement in the *Holt Algebra 1* program was higher than in other programs used previously or concurrently with other classes.

ORGANIZATION OF THE COURSE

The book begins with a review of the basic operations and an introduction to the central concept of algebra, that of variables. Chapter 2 deals with the four basic operations on integers with subtraction performed as related addition. Chapter 3 presents linear equations. Practice in translating between English and mathematical phrases is provided; verbal problem solving is introduced by means of number relation, coin, and perimeter problems. In Chapter 4, the study of linear equations is followed by the study of linear inequalities. Solution sets are described as unions and intersections. Chapters 5 and 6 introduce the laws of exponents, followed by factoring in preparation

for work with fractions and quadratic equations. Chapters 7 and 8 deal with fractions, including techniques for simplifying and combining fractions. The study of the number line through the concept of one-to-one correspondence between the real numbers and the points of a line is done in Chapter 9. This leads into the study of the coordinate plane, in which one-to-one correspondence between ordered pairs of real numbers and the points in the plane is established. Ratio and proportion, relations and functions, systems of linear equations, and direct and inverse variations are studied in Chapters 10–12. Fractional (including decimal) equations, complex fractions, and literal equations are studied in Chapter 13. Chapter 14 completes the real number system with irrational numbers. The Pythagorean relation is presented in this chapter also. Finally, in Chapter 15 the general method of solving quadratic equations is presented. Application is provided with area problems. Chapter 16 deals with right triangle trigonometry.

The contents, as described above, give a full course in first year algebra. In addition to the course described above, there are five optional problem-solving lessons: motion problems, age problems, digit problems, investment problems, and wet mixture problems. Another optional lesson on solving systems of linear inequalities by graphing is included.

Sixty-two pages of material are provided to vary the pace and enrich the course. These pages contain biographies, recreational mathematics, historical data, mathematical curiosities, career awareness, applications, flow-charting, and measurement. For a listing of the Special Topics, see page viii in the front of the pupil edition.

HOW TO USE THE BOOK

The format of *Holt Algebra 1* was developed on the basis of the conviction that no student should be penalized in the study of mathematics because of the lack of reading skills. Inability to read should not stand in the way of learning mathematics.

It is also recognized that teachers succeed with their students in many different ways. Each teacher's style of teaching should be respected.

Holt Algebra 1 provides the freedom to style your teaching in accordance with your individual preferences. The authors would not presume to impose any specific best way of teaching from this textbook. Some general guidelines are offered.

The textbook can be used in an individualized instruction situation. Individualization is made possible by guiding the student through the lesson developments by means of many examples. Exercises are arranged from simple to more complex. A multitude of practice material, much of a very basic nature, facilitates individual study.

Where group instruction takes place, the examples can be discussed in small groups or with an entire class. The exercises can be used in the usual manner, some for practicing new work and some for review and quizzes.

There should be no doubt that students will be attracted to the study of algebra if they are encouraged frequently. A definite and positive attitude as put forth in *Holt Algebra 1* will help keep students interested and active.

SUPPLEMENTARY MATERIALS

Holt Algebra 1 is a system that supplies the teacher with a variety of materials, making it easy to adjust the course to each individual student.

Holt Algebra 1 Tests The Test Masters are a means of evaluating a student's abilities to perform the objectives of the *Holt Algebra 1* program. The items on the Chapter Test sample the objectives covered in that chapter only. Each of the Chapter Test Masters is an alternate form of the Chapter Test found in the textbook.

The Chapter Test Masters can be used with students who have not satisfactorily succeeded with the Chapter Tests found in the textbook. Thus, the tests found in the Duplicating Masters can serve as a second chance for the students to succeed. They also provide an opportunity to use one of the tests (for example, chapter test in the textbook) as a pre-test, and the other test (Chapter Test Master) as a post-test.

The Test Masters also contain five cumulative tests that can be used for semester or trimester schedules.

Holt Algebra 1 Skillmasters Skillmasters are usable in a class or in an individualized situation. Each sheet has two parallel forms (A and B) for every lesson. They may be used as pre- or post-lesson self-tests, pre-tests for diagnosis, extra practice to set a skill, quizzes to test mastery, or assignments. At the bottom of each sheet, there are two parallel forms of a Cumulative Review that test skills and concepts previously presented.

REFERENCE CHART FOR ALGEBRA 1 SKILLMASTERS

LESSON PAGES	SKILL-MASTER NUMBER	LESSON PAGES	SKILL-MASTER NUMBER
1, 4	1	231, 234	31
6, 9	2	236, 240	32
14, 16	3	242, 246	33
21, 24	4	248, 251	34
28, 31	5	255, 261	35
36, 40	6	265, 268	36
42, 44	7	272, 276	37
46, 48	8	279, 281	38
50, 56	9	289, 294	39
59, 64	10	297, 300	40
68, 70	11	304, 306	41
72, 76	12	310, 317	42
80, 84	13	320, 323	43
91, 94	14	330, 334	44
98, 102	15	341, 346	45
105, 112	16	350, 353	46
119, 121	17	358, 361	47
124, 128	18	368, 371	48
132, 135	19	374, 382	49
141, 145	20	384, 388	50
150, 153	21	391, 394	51
156, 158	22	396, 399	52
162, 165	23	402, 404	53
168, 175	24	408, 411	54
180, 184	25	417, 420	55
188, 191	26	423, 427	56
194, 198	27	434, 437	57
203, 210	28	445, 448	58
214, 218	29	451, 456	59
221, 224	30	458, 461	60

Teacher's Guide for Individualizing Holt Algebra 1 and Holt Algebra 2 with Trigonometry The teacher's guide presents the different approaches for individualizing and the ways for implementing each approach. There is also an *Activity Reservoir* that contains suggestions for research projects, activities, and games.

The Activities can supply students with interesting diversions into topics that can satisfy the unique desires of various students.

Duplicating Masters for Individualizing Holt Algebra 1 and Holt Algebra 2
These duplicating masters assist the teacher in classroom management when individualizing the *Holt Algebra* programs. They contain *Placement Tests* which provide the teacher with the ready means to assess the student's standing and thus place her or him at the level where she or he will succeed.

Also included are an *Assignment Sheet* for each chapter, a teacher record sheet for the individual student, a class record sheet, and a parent report form to be sent to parents at marking periods. The Assignment Sheet for each chapter contains specific references to several sources of additional development and practice aids. Thus, it provides the work that is commensurate with the individual student's capabilities, interests, and needs.

ACKNOWLEDGEMENTS

We wish to thank and acknowledge the help of the pilot teachers and students for testing the first edition of *Holt Algebra 1*. Their comments and suggestions have been of invaluable help in making this a better and more teachable text. The following teachers and schools took part in the pilot:

Alton Black, Reading Memorial High School, Reading, Massachusetts; Agnes Krause, Phillip Livingston Junior High School, Albany, New York; Phyllis Solden, Shore Regional High School, West Long Branch, New Jersey; Catherine Halladay, North Hills Intermediate High School, Pittsburgh, Pennsylvania; Kathy Boyd, Greater Johnstown Area, Vocational-Technical Schools, Johnstown, Pennsylvania; Edith Nelson, Woodlawn Senior High School, Baltimore, Maryland; Bobbie Maness, Herndon High School, Herndon, Virginia; Jenet Creighton, Herndon High School, Herndon, Virginia; Carol Osborne, Ruffner Junior High School, Roanoke, Virginia; Luda Dixon, Jeffersontown High School, Louisville, Kentucky; Margaret Edenfield, Central High School, Macon, Georgia; Myron Goff, The University School, Tallahassee, Florida; E. Henry Garland, The University School, Tallahassee, Florida; William Bourjaily, Middleburg Heights Junior High School, Middleburg Heights, Ohio; Shirley Freeman, Waller High School, Chicago, Illinois; Linda Bourg, Irving Junior High School, Lincoln, Nebraska; Starr Hirschback, Robin Mickle Junior High School, Lincoln, Nebraska; George Bratton, Eastside Junior High School, Benton, Arkansas; Richard Henkel, Miraleste High School, Miraleste, California; James Hawkins, West Junior High School, Boise, Idaho; Frank Gould, Tappan Zee High School, Orangeburg, New York; Del Griffin, Escondido High School, Escondido, California; Linda LaFerrara, Frank Antonides School, West Long Branch, New Jersey; Annette O'Brien, Winter Park High School, Winter Park, Florida; Fred Cheney, Brockton High School, Brockton, Massachusetts; Katherine Gervais, Brockton High School, Brockton, Massachusetts; Dolores Jones, Central High School, Macon, Georgia; Leo Liebling, Oakwood Junior High School, East Detroit, Michigan; Tom O'Hara, Oakwood Junior High School, East Detroit, Michigan; Earl Cloud, Eastside Junior High School, Benton, Arkansas; Carl Duzen, Miraleste High School, Miraleste, California; Lawrence G. Isel, Nova High School, Fort Lauderdale, Florida; Gail Harris, Ruffner Junior High School, Roanoke, Virginia; Marvin Van Note, San Pasqual High School, Escondido, California; Meta Wahl, Shore Regional High School, West Long Branch, New Jersey.

We also want to thank the hundreds of teachers, supervisors, and administrators who participated in our surveys used for this new series.

LESSON COMMENTARIES

CHAPTER 1 *Basic Operations*

Students work with the operations of addition and multiplication in the set of whole numbers. The order of operations is developed in the first lesson, and then variables are introduced. Students study the properties of addition and multiplication, and special emphasis is given to the distributive property and combining like terms.

PUZZLES [x]
This page may be used at any time of the year. You may wish to use it on a Friday, or the day before a scheduled holiday, to serve as a break in the routine for all students.

ORDER OF OPERATIONS [1]
Example 1 shows the necessity for an agreement on the order in which addition and multiplication are to be performed. The abbreviated statement, "Multiply first, then add." is used in remembering the order of operations.

MATHEMATICS IN AVIATION [3]
This is the first of a series of pages on career awareness. These pages lend themselves to class discussion and open-ended projects.

Students who are interested in this field should be encouraged to do some research on it.

VARIABLES [4]
The order of operations still applies after a variable has been replaced. Students should understand the difference between a *term* and the *coefficient* of a variable.

Cumulative Review
Compute.
1. $7 + (6)(8)$ 2. $2 \cdot 3 + 5 \cdot 9$
3. $4 + 3 \cdot 7 + 4 \cdot 8 + 9$
1. *55*   2. *51*   3. *66*

COMMUTATIVE AND ASSOCIATIVE PROPERTIES [6]
The commutative and associative properties of addition and multiplication are first illustrated with specific examples and then generalized. In Examples 3 and 4, they are combined for each operation so that students can summarize that "Addition can be done in any order. Multiplication can be done in any order."

Cumulative Review
Evaluate.
1. $4 + 8x$ if $x = 7$ 2. $5m + 3$ if $m = 9$
3. $8a + 3 + 7b$ if $a = 5, b = 3$
1. *60*   2. *48*   3. *64*

DISTRIBUTIVE PROPERTY [9]
The distributive property is developed in four different forms:
$a(b + c)\quad = a(b) + a(c)$
$(a + b)c\quad = a(c) + b(c)$
$a(b) + a(c) = a(b + c)$
$a(c) + b(c) = (a + b)c$
It is also generalized to more than two addends.

Cumulative Review
Compute.
1. $8 + 4 \cdot 3 + 6 \cdot 9$ 2. $5 \cdot 137 \cdot 20$
3. $99 + 45 + 5 + 1$
1. *74*   2. *13,700*   3. *150*

THE METRIC SYSTEM [12]
Length, capacity, and weight are considered. Stress that the simplicity of the metric system of measurement is based on two factors: (1) It is based on ten. (2) Each unit of measurement is named by using a base and a prefix; for example, *centi*meter, meaning one hundredth of a meter.

The fraction technique illustrated for changing 5 km to cm is used frequently in science. As an extension, you may ask students to change 50 km/h to m/sec.

All students will benefit by doing all or part of this optional lesson.

DISTRIBUTIVE PROPERTY AND VARIABLES   [14]

The distributive property is shown as the justification for combining like terms. The word *simplify* is introduced to mean *combine like terms*.

Cumulative Review

1. Name the terms, the variables, and the coefficient of each variable for $6x + 7 + 2y$.
2. Evaluate $4a + 3b + 9$ if $a = 8$, $b = 3$.
1. Terms: 6x, 2y, 7; Variables: x, y; Coefficient of x, 6; Coefficient of y, 2   *2. 50*

APPLYING THE DISTRIBUTIVE PROPERTY   [16]

Students use the commutative and associative properties of multiplication to rewrite expressions like $(2y)3$ as $6y$. They also use the distributive property to remove parentheses before combining like terms.

Cumulative Review
Simplify.
1. $5y + 9 + 4y$ **2.** $8 + 3g + 9g$
3. $7r + 4 + 8s + 9r$
1. 9y + 9   *2. 12g + 8*   *3. 16r + 8s + 4*

CHAPTER 2   *Integers*

Addition of integers is first introduced with a heavy plus sign **+** to indicate the operation of addition. The regular plus sign $+$ indicates that a number is positive.

$$-10 \textbf{ + } +3 = -7$$

is read negative 10 *plus* positive 3 is equal to negative 7. Later it is agreed that the heavy plus signs may be dropped, but are still understood. Thus,

$$-8 + 7 - 2$$

is read negative 8 *plus* positive 7 *plus* negative 2. This approach was adopted since students have fewer difficulties when they can interpret a

problem like the one above as an addition problem. The operation of subtraction is not introduced until the last lesson.

TEMPERATURE   [20]

By using reference points on a thermometer marked in degrees Celsius, students estimate temperatures for given activities. Some students might be interested in preparing a report on the origin of the word "Celsius" and why this scale is preferred in the world of science.

ADDING INTEGERS   [21]

A number line is used for adding integers. No formal rules for addition are stated, but students can formulate their own rules in Exercises 81–84. Exercises 33–80 suggest some of the properties of addition.

Cumulative Review
Simplify.
1. $7x + 3(4 + 6x)$ **2.** $(2y + 8)3 + 4y$
3. $4(2c + 7) + 6(9 + 5c)$
1. 25x + 12   *2. 10y + 24*   *3. 38c + 82*

PROPERTIES OF ADDITION OF INTEGERS   [24]

In order to eliminate the necessity of redeveloping the properties of addition with each new set of numbers, the properties are stated for all *numbers* rather than for all *integers*. By all numbers, we mean all *real* numbers. We avoid using the word *real* because it has no meaning to students at this time. The real numbers will be treated in Chapter 14. Emphasis is given to reading "$-a$" as "the opposite of a" rather than "negative a."

Cumulative Review
Simplify. Then evaluate if $x = 7$ and $y = 4$.
1. $5x + 8x + 9 + 2y$ **2.** $3y + 2x + 6 + 5x + 7y$
1. 13x + 2y + 9; 108   *2. 7x + 10y + 6; 95*

PROBABILITY   [27]

The probability of an event is defined in terms of a sample space. You may wish to assign independent study on permutations and combinations. You may also ask students to research careers in which probability is used, such as actuarial work.

MULTIPLYING INTEGERS [28]
Examples 2, 3, and 5 develop rationales for the rules for multiplying integers. These rules are summarized at the end of the lesson.

Cumulative Review
Add.
1. $-14 + +8$ **2.** $+23 + -19$
3. $-36 + -27$
1. -6 *2.* 4 *3.* -63

DIVIDING INTEGERS [31]
The relationship between multiplication and division is reviewed in the Review Capsule. Examples 1–4 develop the rules for dividing integers. Exercises 39–46 suggest the properties $a \div 1 = a$ and $a \div a = 1$, $[a \neq 0]$.

Cumulative Review
Multiply.
1. $(-5)(-16)$ **2.** $(+3)(-29)$ **3.** $(-67)(0)$
1. 80 *2.* -87 *3.* 0

USING INTEGERS [34]
Applications of integers to some everyday situations are considered. Encourage students to make up problems to show applications of integers to everyday situations such as stock transactions and game penalties.

A NEW LOOK AT ADDITION [36]
The commutative and associative properties of addition are combined, and students conclude that addition can be done in any order. It is agreed that the heavy plus signs can be eliminated, but are understood. Thus,
$$-3 + 7 - 6$$
is interpreted as negative 3 *plus* positive 7 *plus* negative 6. $-3 + 7$, and -6 are considered as *terms* which are to be *added*. The operation of subtraction, which causes difficulty for many students, is postponed until the last lesson.

Cumulative Review
1. Simplify $4x + 5(9 + 7x)$.
2. Multiply $(-3)(+6)(-20)$.
3. Divide $-98 \div +2$.
1. $39x + 45$ *2.* 360 *3.* -49

MAGIC SQUARES [39]
This topic may be used at any time. As an additional activity, students may make up magic squares for their classmates to solve.

EVALUATING EXPRESSIONS [40]
In expressions like $3x - 7y$, students replace the variables with the integers and then evaluate.
$$3x - 7y$$
is interpreted as "positive 3 times *x plus* negative 7 times *y*." We avoid using 1 and -1 as numerical coefficients until page 44.

Cumulative Review
Which property is illustrated?
1. $0 + +6 = +6$ **2.** $-7 + +3 = +3 + -7$
3. $+4 + -4 = 0$
1. additive identity   2. commutative property of addition   3. additive inverse

COMBINING LIKE TERMS [42]
Students combine like terms in expressions with integer coefficients by using the distributive property.

Cumulative Review
Add the terms.
1. $-8 + 4 - 6$ **2.** $16 + 23 - 91$
3. $-42 + 23 + 70 - 68$
1. -10 *2.* -52 *3.* -17

$(1)(a) = a$ and $(-1)(a) = -a$ [44]
The properties $(1)(a) = a$ and $(-1)(a) = -a$ are useful in simplifying expressions like $-7a + a + 9b - b$. Students replace *a* with $1a$ and $-b$ with $-1b$ then combine like terms.

Cumulative Review
Evaluate.
1. $2x + 6y$ if $x = 3$, $y = -9$
2. $7a - 5b$ if $a = 2$, $b = 6$
3. $-4p + 2q - 7r$ if $p = -1$, $q = 8$, $r = 5$
1. -48 *2.* -16 *3.* -15

REMOVING PARENTHESES [46]
Students use the distributive property to remove parentheses before combining like terms. Expressions like
$$-6x - 7(4 + 3x)$$

are interpreted as negative 6x *plus* negative 7 times the quantity $(4 + 3x)$. The heavy plus sign is used in Example 1 to facilitate this interpretation. In the examples that follow, students think of the heavy plus sign but do not actually write it.

Cumulative Review
Simplify.
1. $-x + 9x - 5x$ **2.** $9y - 6 + 17 - 8y$
3. $6x - 5 - 2x + 18 - 5x$
1. 3x   *2. y + 11*   *3. -x + 13*

APPLYING THE PROPERTY $-a = -1(a)$ [48]
Students think of an expression like $7y - (3 + 2y)$ as $7y + -1(3 + 2y)$. Then they apply the distributive property to $-1(3 + 2y)$ and combine like terms.

Cumulative Review
Divide.
1. $-68 \div +4$ **2.** $+96 \div -16$
3. $-105 \div -5$
1. -17   *2. -6*   *3. 21*

SUBTRACTING INTEGERS   [50]
Subtraction is introduced for the first time in this lesson. "a subtract b" is defined as "a plus the opposite of b." For example, 6 subtract -1 means 6 plus the opposite of -1, or 6 plus 1.

Cumulative Review
Simplify.
1. $-8x + (7 - x) - 4$ **2.** $-(4 + 3y) - 8 + 9y$
3. $-7(2c + 3) - (8 - 5c)$
1. -9x + 3   *2. 6y - 12*   *3. -9c - 29*

CHAPTER 3   *Linear Equations*

The addition and division properties for equations are stressed as means for solving equations of the form $ax + b = c$ and $ax + b = cx + d$. Later, equations with parentheses are considered. The concept of *solution set* is not introduced until the next chapter. In this chapter, students simply *solve* equations (find the solution). A careful development of translating English phrases to algebra is given as a basis for solving verbal problems. Number problems, coin problems, and perimeter problems are presented.

COMPUTER PROGRAMS: FLOW CHARTS   [54]
This topic lends itself to discussion on career opportunities. Even if no computer is available, you might form a computer club in which you teach "BASIC." Frequently, a nearby college will allow you to run a computer program once a week so that students can see the workings of a computer.

OPEN SENTENCES   [56]
An open sentence is neither true nor false until the variable is replaced. Then it becomes either true or false. Students should realize that in a sentence like $4x + 3 = x + 9$, if x is replaced with 2, then x must be replaced with 2 in *both* places.

Cumulative Review
Evaluate for the given value of the variable.
1. $6x - 4$ if $x = -2$ **2.** $5 - 7y$ if $y = -7$
3. $-4z + 12$ if $z = 5$
1. -16   *2. 54*   *3. -8*

SOLVING EQUATIONS   [59]
Examples 1, 2, and 3 develop the addition, multiplication, and division properties for equations, respectively. Then these properties are used in solving equations of the form $ax + b = c$. Students are sometimes required to check their solutions.

Cumulative Review
Which property is illustrated?
1. $4(x + y) = (x + y)4$ **2.** $3(x + y) = 3x + 3y$
3. $(x + 4) + 9 = x + (4 + 9)$
1. Commutative property of multiplication
2. Distributive property
3. Associative property of addition

ALGEBRA AND COMMISSIONS   [63]
Percent is not used here. Commission is given as an amount per article sold. After decimal equations are studied, you may wish to extend this concept by expressing rate of commission as a percent of sales.

EQUATIONS: THE VARIABLE ON BOTH SIDES   [64]
Examples 1 and 2 show that students can solve an equation of the form $ax + b = cx + d$ by adding either $-cx$ or $-ax$ to each side.

Cumulative Review
Simplify. Then evaluate for the given values
of the variables.
1. $3(2 + 8x) + 7x$ if $x = 2$
2. $(5 + 3d)2 + 4d$ if $d = 3$
3. $5y + 4(2y + 6)$ if $y = 9$
1. $31x + 6$; 68   2. $10d + 10$; 40
3. $13y + 24$; 141

NUMBER MYSTERIES   [67]
This topic may be used as a change of pace any
time during the course.

EQUATIONS WITH PARENTHESES   [68]
Students learn to use the distributive property
to remove parentheses as a first step in solving
equations that contain them.

Cumulative Review
Simplify.
1. $7x - 3(2 + 4x)$ 2. $5y - (6 - 7y)$
3. $2(-3a + 2) + a - 9$
1. $-5x - 6$ 2. $12y - 6$ 3. $-5a - 5$

ENGLISH PHRASES TO ALGEBRA   [70]
This is a key lesson in developing problem-solving
skills. It provides basic terminology for all verbal
problems in both *Holt Algebra 1* and *Holt Algebra
2 with Trigonometry.* For Exercise 12, show why
the comma is necessary: 7 times a number, decreased by 2 means $7n - 2$. 7 times a number
decreased by 2 means $7(n - 2)$.

Cumulative Review
Solve.
1. $5x - 21 = 29$ 2. $3x - 8 = -8$
3. $6 + 2y = -8$
1. 10   2. 0   3. -7

NUMBER PROBLEMS   [72]
All of the problems in this lesson involve just one
number. The problems in Part B of the exercise
set require removing parentheses.

Cumulative Review
Solve.
1. $3x - 16 = 8 + 7x$ 2. $5x + 16 = 4x - 10$
3. $2y + 7 = 18 - 9y$
1. -6 2. -26 3. 1

MORE NUMBER PROBLEMS   [76]
The problems in this lesson involve two numbers.
One number should be expressed algebraically
in terms of the other before an equation is written.

Cumulative Review
Solve.
1. $4(-2x - 6) = 16$
2. $6(y + 2) = 3 - (3 - 2y)$
3. $10(14 - x) = 5(7 - x)$
1. -5 2. -3 3. 21

COIN PROBLEMS   [80]
The charts shown help students to understand the
relationship between the *number* of coins and the
value of the coins.

Cumulative Review
Write in mathematical terms.
1. 5 more than twice x
2. 9 decreased by 3 times a number
3. 2 less than 5 times y
1. $2x + 5$ 2. $9 - 3n$ 3. $5y - 2$

VACATIONING BY RENTAL CAR   [83]
Students might interview several traveling sales
representatives to find out their opinions on
whether it is more economical to rent a car or
purchase one.

PERIMETER PROBLEMS   [84]
Students need to understand the meaning of
perimeter. Many confuse perimeter and area. In
order to write an equation that they can solve,
students must express both length and width in
terms of the same variable.

Cumulative Review
Simplify.
1. $y - 3(2 + 6y)$ 2. $4x - (3 - 2x) + 8$
3. $-(-5c + 8) - 2(7 - 4c)$
1. $-17y - 6$ 2. $6x + 5$ 3. $13c - 22$

MATHEMATICS IN THE HOSPITAL   [87]
If possible, display samples of electrocardiograph
print outs to show a practical use of graphs. You
may wish to discuss the type of math required for
admission into nursing or other hospital related
careers.

CHAPTER 4 *Linear Inequalities*

The concept of the *solution set* of an open sentence is introduced, and students use the properties for inequalities to find solution sets of linear inequalities. Graphing is stressed as a visual means of understanding solution sets of linear inequalities and for determining intersections and unions of sets described by inequalities.

SEQUENCES [90]

Students are exposed to number patterns. You might wish to extend this concept by introducing arithmetic progressions.

SETS [91]

The concept of the *solution set* of an equation is introduced, and students are confronted with equations whose solution set is the *empty set*. In Part B of the exercise set, equations whose solution set is {all numbers} are introduced. By {all numbers}, we mean {all real numbers}.

Cumulative Review
Rewrite by using the distributive property.
1. $3(x + y)$ **2.** $6a + 6b$ **3.** $(c + d + e)7$
1. $3x + 3y$ 2. $6(a + b)$ 3. $7c + 7d + 7e$

INEQUALITIES [94]

Students should observe the use of the "circle" versus the dot in graphing solution sets of inequalities like $x < 2$ and $x \le 2$. Emphasize reading $4 < x$ as $x > 4$. It is easier for students to grasp the meaning if the variable is read first.

Cumulative Review
Name the terms and variables. Then name the coefficient of each variable.
1. $3x + 9$ **2.** $5a + 6b$ **3.** $7r + 9 + 8s$
1. Terms: 3x and 9; Variable: x; Coefficient of x: 3
2. Terms: 5a and 6b; Variables: a and b; Coefficient of a: 5; Coefficient of b: 6
3. Terms: 7r, 9, and 8s; Variables: r and s; Coefficient of r: 7; Coefficient of s: 8

COMPUTER PROGRAMS: INPUT AND OUTPUT [97]

The symbols used for input/output and store are introduced. For additional suggestions, see the commentary for page 54 of page T–26.

PROPERTIES FOR INEQUALITIES [98]

The addition, multiplication, and division properties for inequalities are developed. The only times that the inequality sign is reversed are when multiplying or dividing each side of an inequality by a *negative* number.

Cumulative Review
Divide.
1. $\dfrac{+27}{-3}$ **2.** $\dfrac{-52}{+13}$ **3.** $\dfrac{-96}{-16}$
1. -9 2. -4 3. $+6$

SOLVING INEQUALITIES [102]

Examples 3 and 4 point out that an inequality of the form $ax + b < cx + d$ can be solved by adding either $-cx$ or $-ax$ to each side.

Cumulative Review
Simplify.
1. $-7x - 5x$ **2.** $-(3y + 2) - 4y - 7$
3. $-4a - 6(1 + 2a)$
1. $-12x$ 2. $-7y - 9$ 3. $-16a - 6$

INTERSECTION AND UNION OF SETS [105]

Students may want to discuss the statements on page 105: "Every set is a subset of itself and the empty set is a subset of every set." Every set A is a subset of itself since every element of A is in A. The empty set is a subset of every set A since every element of the empty set (there are none) is in A.

For Example 2, interested students can examine sets with $0, 1, 2, 3, \ldots, n$ elements to determine the number of subsets that each has.

Cumulative Review
Describe each set by listing its elements.
1. {negative integers greater than -4}
2. {integers between 7 and 8}
3. {positive integers less than 2}
1. $\{-3, -2, -1\}$ 2. ϕ 3. $\{1\}$

MOTION PROBLEMS [108]

This is an optional lesson. In Example 3, stress that solving the equation for x does not produce the answer to the question. In order to answer the question it is necessary to multiply by the speed.

GRAPHING INTERSECTIONS AND UNIONS [112]

In Examples 1 and 2, the graphs of P and Q overlap on a number line, but go in *opposite* directions. In Examples 3 and 4, the graphs of R and S do *not* overlap. In Example 5, the graphs of C and D overlap and go in the *same* direction.

Cumulative Review
Solve.
1. $-17 - 3x = 1$ 2. $4x - 9 = -21 - 2x$
3. $3(x - 2) + 7 = 5x - 13$
1. -6 2. -2 3. 7

RENÉ DESCARTES [115]

You may wish to point out to students where elements of coordinate geometry have been or will be used in their current algebra course.

CHAPTER 5   *Factoring*

This chapter paves the way for work on general factoring in the following chapter. The generalizations

$$x^m \cdot x^n = x^{m+n} \text{ and } (x^m)^n = x^{mn}$$

are presented to facilitate simplifying polynomial expressions. The application of the distributive property to multiplying by a monomial is presented. After the concept of factoring is introduced, students again use the distributive property to factor out a common monomial.

SOPHIE GERMAIN [118]

For those students who are interested in reading more about Germain, you may wish to refer them to *Women in Mathematics* by Lynn M. Osen.

EXPONENTS [119]

Students frequently want to write 3^2 as $3(2)$. Another trouble spot is an example like, "Evaluate $3a^2$ for $a = 4$." Students tend to multiply 3 by 4, then square. To prevent this, we rewrite $3a^2$ as $(3)(a)(a)$. Similarly, $-a^2 = (-1)(a)(a)$.

Cumulative Review
1. Solve $3x + 1 = x - 7$.
2. Solve $2x + 5 = 2x + 7$.
3. Solve $3x - 2(3 - 4x) = x + 14$.
1. -4 2. ϕ 3. 2

PROPERTIES OF EXPONENTS [121]

The property $x^m \cdot x^n = x^{m+n}$ holds only if the bases are the same. Students should recognize that they cannot simplify $a^3 b^4$. The fact that $a = a^1$ is used to simplify expressions like $a^4 \cdot a$. Students can discover $(x^m)^n = x^{mn}$ by rewriting expressions like $(a^3)^4$ as $a^3 \cdot a^3 \cdot a^3 \cdot a^3 = a^{3+3+3+3}$, or a^{12}. In simplifying expressions like $(2a^2 b^4)^3$, students should be especially careful to distribute the power to each factor. Some students tend to forget to distribute the power to numerical coefficients. Urge these students to rewrite expressions like $(2a^2 b^4)^3$ as $(2^1 a^2 b^4)^3$.

Cumulative Review
1. Solve $2x - (5 - 7x) = 6x + 16$.
2. Find and graph the solution set of $3x - 2 < 5x + 4$.
3. Graph $R = \{x | x < 5\}$. Graph $S = \{x | x > -2\}$. Then graph $R \cap S$.
1. 7 2. $\{x | x > -3\}$
3. $R \cap S = \{x | -2 < x < 5\}$

POLYNOMIALS [124]

The ability to rewrite polynomials in descending order of exponents will be important in later lessons on factoring and solving quadratic equations. Students should see that the work on simplifying polynomials is just an extension of the concept of combining like terms.

Cumulative Review
1. One number is 5 more than another. Their sum is 23. Find the numbers.
2. Find 3 consecutive integers whose sum is 24.
3. The length of a rectangle is twice the width. The perimeter is 24 meters. Find the length and the width.
1. *9 and 14*   2. *7, 8, 9*   3. *8 meters; 4 meters*

FLOW CHART: ORDERING NUMBERS [126]

As a project, students may be interested in making a bulletin board display of pictures formed from the "dots" on computer printouts. For additional suggestions, see the commentary for page 54 on page T–26.

SIMPLIFYING POLYNOMIALS [128]

Application of the distributive property is extended to products involving exponents. Students tend to forget that $3x^2$ represents the product of two factors, 3 and x^2.

Thus, $3x^2(x + 5) = 3x^2(x^1) + 3x^2(5)$
$$= 3 \cdot x^2 \cdot x^1 + 3 \cdot 5 \cdot x^2$$

Cumulative Review

1. Simplify $(3a^2)^4$.
2. Find the value of $-2a^3$ for $a = -3$.
3. Solve $7m - (4 - m) = 2m + 5$.

1. $81a^8$ 2. 54 3. $\frac{3}{2}$ or $1\frac{1}{2}$

PERFECT NUMBERS [131]

Students who are interested in learning more about the properties of perfect numbers may be referred to the *History of Mathematics* by Howard Eves.

CONCEPT OF FACTORING [132]

The concept of factoring will be at the heart of many applications throughout the remainder of the course. Interested students might do research on topics such as the number of primes, perfect numbers, and amicable numbers. In Example 4, students should see that we are actually looking for two factors: a whole number (for 20) and a variable (for a^7).

Cumulative Review

1. Simplify $3a^2(4a^3 + 2a^2 - 5a + 2)$.
2. Find and graph the solution set of $2x + 3 < 3x + 7$.
3. Graph $\{x | x \neq 4\}$ on a number line.

1. $12a^5 + 6a^4 - 15a^3 + 6a^2$ 2. $\{x | x > -4\}$
3. *All points except the point for 4*

FACTORING OUT A COMMON MONOMIAL [135]

It appears easier for some students to factor out the greatest common whole number factor, if any, first. Then they look for a common variable factor. Students who catch on rapidly can factor out both whole number and variable common factors at the same time. Students should be sure to check that they have factored out the *greatest common factor* in each case.

Cumulative Review

1. Solve $3x - (5 - 2x) = 7x + 11$.
2. Find $\{2, 4, 6, 8, 10\} \cap \{3, 5, 6, 10, 11\}$.
3. Evaluate $-a^3b^2$ if $a = -2$, $b = 3$.

1. -8 2. $\{6, 10\}$ 3. 72

CHAPTER 6   *Factoring Trinomials*

Multiplying two binomials is shown in vertical form. Similarly, factoring is also presented in vertical form. Classroom testing has indicated that factoring using a vertical pattern is easier for most students. We avoid special cases of factoring at first. The general method for factoring trinomials works for all situations and means fewer rules to memorize. At the end of the chapter, students see applications of factoring to solving quadratic equations and to solving verbal problems leading to quadratic equations.

SCIENTIFIC NOTATION [140]

Ask students to see if they can discover a short cut for computing an exercise like $.0469 \times 10^{-23} + 72.3 \times 10^{-25}$. Someone may come up with the idea that the exponents must be the same in order to add. Thus, $.0469 \times 10^{-23} + 72.3 \times 10^{-25}$
$$= 10^2 \times .0469 \times 10^{-23} \times 10^{-2} + 72.3 \times 10^{-25}$$
$$= 100 \times .0469 \times 10^{-25} + 72.3 \times 10^{-25}$$
$$= 10^{-25}(4.69 + 72.3)$$

An interesting application of this arises in science when working with moles.

MULTIPLYING POLYNOMIALS [141]

Example 3 shows that the product of two binomials can be a binomial. Later, we shall interpret $x^2 - 25$ as a disguised trinomial $x^2 + 0x - 25$. Then factoring this trinomial will suggest a pattern for factoring the difference of two squares. Visually oriented students might benefit from seeing a geometrical interpretation of the multiplication of binomials. (See p. 144.)

Cumulative Review

1. Solve $-3x - 2(4 - 3x) = 7x - 28$.
2. Factor out the GCF: $6x^3 - 18x^2 - 12x$.
3. Simplify $(3a^2)(-7a^5)$.

1. 5 2. $6x(x^2 - 3x - 2)$ 3. $-21a^7$

RECTANGLE PRODUCTS [144]

To find the product $(a + 7)(a + 1)$, $a + 7$ and $a + 1$ are used as the length and width of a rectangle. The rectangle is then divided into 4 rectangles with areas a^2, $7a$, $1a$, and 7, respectively. The sum of these areas $a^2 + 8a + 7$ is the product $(a + 7)(a + 1)$.

FACTORING TRINOMIALS [145]

Contrary to the traditional method, we first try integral factors without regard to signs. Then we try to fill in signs to get the correct middle and end terms. Students may be disturbed by the trial and error method since they are used to direct procedures that always work. Getting students to accept this new trial and error procedure is important.

Cumulative Review

1. Find and graph the solution set of $10x + 2 > 12x - 5$.   2. $(+7m^3)(?) = -28m^5$
3. $R = \{x|2x + 5 < 9\}$ and $S = \{x|x > 3\}$. Graph $R \cap S$ on a number line.
1. $\left\{x|x < 3\frac{1}{2}\right\}$ 3. $-4m^2$ 3. $R \cap S = \phi$

FLOW CHART: SOLVING A SIMPLE EQUATION [149]

If at all possible, distribute a copy of the solution for $ax + b = c$ written in BASIC. Explaining each line as it appears in BASIC and translating it into ordinary language will provide students with some additional insights into the equation-solving techniques.

THE DIFFERENCE OF TWO SQUARES [150]

We now consider this special case as a direct application of general trinomial factoring.

Cumulative Review

1. Multiply $(3x + 2)(2x - 5)$.
2. Solve $3x - (2 - x) = 4x - 3$.
3. Factor out the GCF: $3x^3 - 9x^2 + 45x$.
1. $6x^2 - 11x - 10$ 2. ϕ
3. $3x(x^2 - 3x + 15)$

COMBINED TYPES OF FACTORING [153]

Factor completely means:
   (1) First, factor out the GCF, if any.
   (2) Then, factor the remaining polynomial.

Students sometimes do all the steps correctly but then forget to include the GCF as part of the final answer. They should be sure to check that they have included all of the factors.

Cumulative Review

1. The sum of two numbers is 24. The larger number is 8 more than the smaller. Find the numbers.
2. The length of a rectangle is 6 more than twice the width. The perimeter is 36 meters. Find the length and the width.
1. 8; 16   2. 14 meters; 4 meters

FACTORING POLYNOMIALS IN TWO VARIABLES [156]

The methods of the previous three lessons are extended to polynomials in two variables.

Cumulative Review

1. $(5x^4)(4x^5) = ?$
2. Find $\{3, 4, 6, 8\} \cap \{2, 5, 7\}$.
3. Evaluate $-a^3b^2$ if $a = -2$, $b = 4$.
1. $20x^9$ 2. ϕ 3. 128

QUADRATIC EQUATIONS [158]

This first lesson on quadratic equations is limited to equations with all terms on one side and the coefficient of the x^2 term positive. In Example 5, some students may have difficulty in interpreting results like $x(x - 7) = 0$. Since x is not a binomial, they tend to ignore it and write only one solution, 7. Suggest that these students rewrite $x(x - 7) = 0$ as $(x - 0)(x - 7) = 0$.

Cumulative Review

1. Factor $4x^2 - 100$ completely.
2. Multiply $(2x + 3)(x - 7)$.
3. Solve $3x - (4 - 2x) = 5x + 7$.
1. $4(x + 5)(x - 5)$ 2. $2x^2 - 11x - 21$
3. ϕ

COMPUTING MENTALLY [161]

In general, the square of a number ending in 5 is:

$$\underset{\text{first 2 digits}}{\underbrace{n(n + 1)}} \qquad \underset{\text{last 2 digits}}{\underbrace{25}}$$

Thus, $35^2 = 3(3 + 1)$ 25, or 1,225.

QUADRATIC EQUATIONS: STANDARD FORM [162]

Students first put quadratic equations into standard form. Standard form implies:

(1) Coefficient of the x^2 term is positive.
(2) Polynomial is equal to 0.
(3) Terms are arranged in descending order of exponents.

Then they apply the method of the previous lesson to solve the equation.

You may use the middle column of the Part A and Part B exercises on page 164 as oral exercises on putting equations in standard form.

Cumulative Review
1. Solve $2x - (x + 1) = 0$.
2. Simplify $2a^3 + 8a^2 - 5a - (2a^3 + 6a^2 - 9a)$.
3. Factor $6x^2 + 27x - 15$ completely.
1. *1*   2. *$2a^2 + 4a$*   3. *$3(2x - 1)(x + 5)$*

CONSECUTIVE INTEGERS [165]

We are concerned with writing set-ups (algebraic representations) for consecutive integer problems in preparation for their solution in the next lesson. Students find it hard to accept that consecutive odd integers, as well as consecutive even integers, differ by 2. Students tend to want to add 1 to an integer to get the next consecutive odd integer.

Cumulative Review
1. Factor $4a^2 - 12a + 9$.
2. Evaluate $(x + 5)^2$ if $x = -2$.
3. Solve $a^2 - 7a = -6$.
1. *$(2a - 3)(2a - 3)$*   2. *9*   3. *1; 6*

CONSECUTIVE INTEGER PROBLEMS [168]

In exercises such as the one in Example 3, students frequently forget the middle term in the expansion of $(x + 1)^2$. Emphasizing that $(x + 1)^2 = (x + 1)(x + 1)$ and using a vertical format for the multiplication should help avoid this error. Also, many students stop after solving the equation and neglect to go back to the algebraic representation in order to answer the question. Checking in the original problem may help eliminate this pitfall.

Cumulative Review
1. Find the solution set of $2(x + 5) = 10 - x$.
2. Solve $2x^2 - 50 = 0$.
3. If $x = y$, what is the value of $x(x - y)$?
1. *{0}*   2. *-5; 5*   3. *0*

BRAKING DISTANCE [171]

Stress the fact that .006 in the formula is an approximate value. Reaction time is also a factor that should be considered in braking distance.

CHAPTER 7 *Simplifying Fractions*

Students see another application of factoring, the simplification of fractions. The chapter builds on arithmetic concepts by showing a process in arithmetic first, then applying the process to variables. General proofs are suggested by arithmetic illustrations. Rules for multiplying fractions are developed through a sequence starting with $a \cdot \dfrac{1}{b} = \dfrac{a}{b}$. Then the principle $\dfrac{1}{a} \cdot \dfrac{1}{b} = \dfrac{1}{ab}$ is justified and is used to show that $\dfrac{a}{b} \cdot \dfrac{c}{d} = \dfrac{a \cdot c}{b \cdot d}$. Students learn the justification for writing fractions in simplest form by applying the last definition "in reverse," as well as the principle $\dfrac{a}{a} = 1$. A technique is introduced for simplifying expressions like $\dfrac{x - 3}{9 - x^2}$, where a factor of -1 is involved. Finally, the methods for multiplying, dividing, and simplifying fractions are put together in order to find products and quotients in simplest form.

MATHEMATICS IN MUSIC [174]

In cooperation with the physics department, demonstrate the use of an oscilloscope in showing graphs of sound waves.

FRACTIONS [175]

An intuitive foundation for defining $\dfrac{a}{b}$ as $a\left(\dfrac{1}{b}\right)$ is laid by referring to a number line. We have tried to stress that $b \neq 0$ in $\dfrac{a}{b}$ by showing that an expression like $\dfrac{6}{0}$ has no meaning. This concept will be important when we discuss undefined slopes for vertical lines in Chapter 9.

Cumulative Review
1. Solve $x^2 + 4x = 5$.
2. Simplify $-(2x^3 + 3x^2 - 2)$.
3. Factor $3x^2 - 21x + 36$.
1. $-5; 1$ 2. $-2x^3 - 3x^2 + 2$
3. $3(x - 4)(x - 3)$

ZERO AND NEGATIVE EXPONENTS   [179]
You may wish to use the following to show the basis for the definition $a^0 = 1$.
$$\frac{a^7}{a^7} = a^{7-7}$$
$$= a^0$$
But, $\frac{a^7}{a^7} = 1$.

So, we define a^0 as 1. Similarly, you may wish to show the basis for the definition $a^{-n} = \frac{1}{a^n}$.
$$a^{-5} = \frac{a^{-5}}{1}$$
Then, $\frac{a^{-5}}{1} \cdot \frac{a^5}{a^5} = \frac{a^0}{a^5}$
$$= \frac{1}{a^5}.$$
So, we define a^{-n} as $\frac{1}{a^n}$.

MULTIPLYING FRACTIONS   [180]
Example 1 is a numerical illustration that suggests a proof for $\frac{1}{a} \cdot \frac{1}{b} = \frac{1}{ab}$. More able students can try to write the general proof using the example as a model. Similarly, Example 3 may be used as a model of a proof for $\frac{a}{b} \cdot \frac{c}{d} = \frac{ac}{bd}$.

Cumulative Review
1. Find the solution set of $5x = 2x^2 + 3$.
2. Solve $-28 + 11 = 9r - 8$.
3. Find and graph the solution set of $3x - (5 - 2x) > 3x + 7$.
1. $\left\{\frac{3}{2}, 1\right\}$ 2. -1 3. $\{x|x > 6\}$

REWRITING FRACTIONS IN SIMPLEST FORM   [184]
Students proceed from rewriting
$\frac{20}{30} = \frac{2 \cdot 2 \cdot 5}{5 \cdot 3 \cdot 2} = \frac{2 \cdot 2 \cdot 5}{3 \cdot 2 \cdot 5} = \frac{2}{3} \cdot 1 \cdot 1 = \frac{2}{3}$ to the

more compact form, $\frac{20}{30} = \frac{2 \cdot \overset{1}{2} \cdot \overset{1}{5}}{\underset{1}{5} \cdot 3 \cdot \underset{1}{2}} = \frac{2}{3}$. Then they apply this procedure to variables. Example 5 is designed to stress that only common *factors* can be divided out. $\frac{x+3}{x+4}$ cannot be rewritten as $\frac{3}{4}$.

Cumulative Review
1. Find two consecutive integers whose sum is 61.   2. Find two consecutive integers whose product is 20.   3. Find three consecutive integers such that the third is equal to the square of the first.
1. $30; 31$ 2. $4, 5$ or $-5, -4$
3. $-1, 0, 1$ or $2, 3, 4$

THE GREAT AIRPLANE MYSTERY   [187]
Students are exposed to logical reasoning.

USING THE -1 TECHNIQUE   [188]
The concept of convenient form of a polynomial is a useful aid in factoring polynomials and simplifying fractions. The principle $-\frac{a}{b} = \frac{-1(a)}{b} = \frac{a}{-1(b)}$ is used here as well as in the next chapter for adding fractions like $\frac{2}{x^2 - 9} + \frac{x}{3 - x}$.

Cumulative Review
1. Multiply $\frac{a-2}{a+5} \cdot \frac{a+1}{a+4}$.   2. Factor $a^3 - 9a$.
3. $R = \{x|x - 1 < 8\}$ and $S = \{x|x > 2\}$. Find $R \cap S$.
1. $\frac{a^2 - a - 2}{a^2 + 9a + 20}$ 2. $a(a + 3)(a - 3)$
3. $R \cap S = \{x|2 < x < 9\}$

FRACTIONS WITH COMMON MONOMIAL FACTORS   [191]
In finding quotients of monomials, we have avoided stating a general rule. Students easily make the transition from
$\frac{x^3}{x^6} = \frac{x \cdot x \cdot x}{x \cdot x \cdot x \cdot x \cdot x \cdot x} = \frac{1}{x^3}$ to doing the process mentally. However, for students who work better with general formulas, you might consider giving the rule shown on the next page.'

$$\frac{x^m}{x^n} = \begin{cases} x^{m-n} & \text{if } m > n. \\ 1 & \text{if } m = n. \\ \dfrac{1}{x^{n-m}} & \text{if } m < n. \end{cases}$$

Cumulative Review

1. Find the solution set of $-3x + 9 < 2(x - 6)$.
2. Evaluate $-x^3y^2$ if $x = -1$, $y = 3$.
3. Multiply $(3x + 2)(x - 7)$.

1. $\left\{x \mid x > 4\frac{1}{5}\right\}$ **2.** 9   **3.** $3x^2 - 19x - 14$

SIMPLIFYING PRODUCTS OF FRACTIONS [194]

Once the student has written $\dfrac{a}{b} \cdot \dfrac{c}{d} = \dfrac{a \cdot c}{b \cdot d}$, all that is left to do is to write the result in simplest form. The methods of the previous three lessons are used. The technique of writing an expression like $6 - 6y$ in convenient form as $-1(6y - 6)$ is once again used in the process of simplifying.

Cumulative Review

1. Solve $9x^2 - 49 = 0$.
2. Graph $\{x \mid x \neq -2\}$ on a number line.
3. $A = \{x \mid x < 5\}$ and $B = \{x \mid 2x + 3 > 15\}$. Find $A \cup B$.

1. $-\frac{7}{3}; \frac{7}{3}$ **2.** *All points except* -2
3. $A \cup B = \{x \mid x < 5 \text{ or } x > 6\}$

PUZZLERS [197]

You may wish to ask students to make up exercises with missing digits for their classmates to solve. Addition and subtraction as well as multiplication and division may be used.

DIVIDING FRACTIONS [198]

The review capsule reminds students of the rule $\dfrac{a}{b} \div \dfrac{c}{d} = \dfrac{a}{b} \cdot \dfrac{d}{c}$. Once a division exercise is rewritten using this rule, it becomes exactly the same type of multiplication exercise as those handled in the previous lesson.

Cumulative Review

1. Find and graph the solution set of $5 - (2 - 3x) > 7x + 11$.
2. Solve $4x - 12 = 3(x - 6)$.
3. Simplify $(-2a^2b^3)^3$.

1. $\{x \mid x < -2\}$ **2.** -6 **3.** $-8a^6b^9$

CHAPTER 8 *Combining Fractions*

Students progress from first combining fractions with like denominators to combining fractions with different denominators. Heavy emphasis is given to a definite procedure for getting a common denominator. The subtraction $\dfrac{a}{b} - \dfrac{c}{d}$ is interpreted as $\dfrac{a}{b} + \dfrac{-1(c)}{d}$. An entire lesson is devoted to types that are frequently troublesome to students, for example,

$$\frac{4x}{x^2 - 4} + \frac{2}{2 - x} \text{ and } \frac{-6}{x^2 - 7x + 12} - \frac{x + 2}{4 - x}.$$

MATHEMATICS IN THE TRADES [202]

A discussion on the training requirements for the trades listed on this page would be worthwhile. Students should be encouraged to research other trades in which they may be interested.

ADDING FRACTIONS: SAME DENOMINATOR [203]

As in previous lessons, the first example can be used as a model to generate a proof for $\dfrac{a}{b} + \dfrac{c}{b} = \dfrac{a + c}{b}$. Encourage students to write results in simplest form.

Cumulative Review

1. Solve $4x - 2(3 - x) = 4x - 2$.
2. Solve $a^2 - 36 = 0$.
3. Multiply $\dfrac{x^2 - 36}{3x - 2} \cdot \dfrac{3x^2 + x - 2}{4x - 24}$.

1. 2   **2.** $6, -6$ **3.** $\dfrac{(x + 6)(x + 1)}{4}$

AGE PROBLEMS [206]

This is an optional lesson. Examples 1–3 provide experiences in representing ages algebraically in preparation for solving problems.

ADDING: DIFFERENT DENOMINATORS [210]

For students who have trouble following the procedure, more simple arithmetic examples like Example 2 might be helpful. Example 3 illustrates the technique to use if a given factor appears more than once in any one denominator. Students should remember to use the distributive property when a binomial numerator needs to be multiplied by a missing factor, as in Example 6. They should also be careful to combine like terms in the final result and to write the answer in simplest form. The oral exercises reinforce the idea of finding the LCD.

Cumulative Review
1. Find the solution set of $2x^2 - 3x = 5$.
2. Find and graph the solution set of $3x - 2 < 5x + 12$.
3. Simplify $\dfrac{x^2 - 36}{2x - 10} \div \dfrac{12 - 2x}{x^2 - 25}$.
1. $\left\{ \frac{5}{2}, -1 \right\}$ 2. $\{x | x > -7\}$
3. $\dfrac{(x + 5)(x + 6)}{-4}$

ADDING: POLYNOMIAL DENOMINATORS [214]
Factoring plays a key role in finding the LCD. Students will need to use all of the factoring patterns that they have learned. Example 1 uses the pattern for the difference of two squares; Example 2 has a common monomial factor; and Example 3 contains a general trinomial.

Cumulative Review
1. Simplify $\dfrac{3a^2b^4c^9}{12ab^6c^3}$.   2. Solve $3x^2 + 5x = 2$.
3. Divide $\dfrac{x^2 - 25}{x^2 + 7x + 10} \div \dfrac{x^2 - 2x - 15}{2x + 4}$.
1. $\dfrac{ac^6}{4b^2}$ 2. $\frac{1}{3}, -2$ 3. $\dfrac{2}{x + 3}$

OPERATIONS [217]
As an extension, you may wish to discuss addition in base five.

MORE ON ADDING FRACTIONS [218]
Students sometimes have difficulty with exercises that have prime denominators such as $\dfrac{9}{y + 4} + \dfrac{6}{y - 4}$. Example 2 shows the procedure in such cases. Examples 3 and 4 illustrate types involving monomial factors. The Part B exercises involve the need to multiply binomials. Stress being careful not to forget the middle term.

Cumulative Review
1. Multiply $\dfrac{4x - 8}{2x^2 + 3x - 2} \cdot \dfrac{1 - 2x}{x^2 - 4}$.
2. Multiply $3x^4(2x^3 - 7x^2 + 8x)$.
3. Simplify $\dfrac{4m^3p^5(x^2 - 7x + 12)}{8mp^7(4 - x)}$.
1. $\dfrac{-4}{(x + 2)(x + 2)}$ 2. $6x^7 - 21x^6 + 24x^5$
3. $\dfrac{m^2(x - 3)}{-2p^2}$

SUBTRACTING FRACTIONS [221]
Once students see that $\dfrac{a}{b} - \dfrac{c}{d}$ means $\dfrac{a}{b} + \dfrac{-1(c)}{d}$, they merely apply the methods of the previous lessons on adding fractions. Example 4 is a good summary exercise showing the use of $\dfrac{a}{b} - \dfrac{c}{d} = \dfrac{a}{b} + \dfrac{-1(c)}{d}$ as well as the procedure for writing the result in simplest form.

Cumulative Review
1. In a collection of coins there are 4 more quarters than dimes. If the total value is $3.10, find the number of coins of each type.
2. $5(x + 3) = 5x + 15$. Which property is illustrated?
1. *6 dimes; 10 quarters*
2. *distributive property*

SIMPLIFYING FRACTIONS: −1 TECHNIQUE [224]
The procedure of putting polynomials in convenient form is applied to the problem of simplifying sums and differences of fractions. Example 3 is especially interesting because students must use the property $\dfrac{a}{b} - \dfrac{c}{d} = \dfrac{a}{b} + \dfrac{-1(c)}{d}$ as well as having to rewrite the denominator $4 - x$ as $-1(x - 4)$.

Cumulative Review
1. The length of a rectangle is 4 more than 3 times the width. The perimeter is 24. Find the length and the width.
2. Simplify $\dfrac{4x^2 - 36}{x^2 + x - 6}$.
1. *10; 2*   2. $\dfrac{4(x - 3)}{x - 2}$

GROUPS [227]

As an extension you may wish to discuss modular arithmetic. Ask students to determine whether mod 5 arithmetic forms a group under addition. This demonstrates beautifully that an additive inverse need *not* be negative.

CHAPTER 9 *Algebra in a Plane*

The basic goals of the chapter are to compute the slope of a line, given two points, and to describe the slant of a line from its slope. After introducing the concept of absolute value, we develop the idea of directed distance between points on vertical and horizontal lines. Slope of a segment is then presented as a ratio of a vertical directed distance to a horizontal directed distance. In effect, this represents a modern interpretation of the idea that slope $= \dfrac{\text{rise}}{\text{run}}$. The slope of a line is then defined as the slope of any segment on it.

THE GREAT SWAMI [230]

This mathematical recreation serves as a change of pace and may be used at any time.

ABSOLUTE VALUE [231]

Example 7 illustrates an application of the basic definition. The only type of absolute value equation discussed is the simplest type like $|a| = 5$. Students will encounter equations like $|3x - 2| = 7$ in the next lesson.

Cumulative Review

1. Solve $3x - (4 - 5x) = 6x - 8$.
2. Find and graph the solution set of $3x - 4 \geq 5x + 8$.   3. Solve $3x + 2 = 3(x + 7)$.
1. -2.   2. $\{x \mid x \leq -6\}$ 3. ϕ

EQUATIONS WITH ABSOLUTE VALUE [234]

Students should observe that an absolute value equation generally has two solutions.

Cumulative Review

1. Factor $2a^2 + 12a - 32$ completely.
2. Solve $7x - 5 = 2x^2$.
3. Multiply $(3a - 4)(2a + 1)$.
1. $2(a + 8)(a - 2)$ 2. $1; \frac{5}{2}$ 3. $6a^2 - 5a - 4$

DIRECTED DISTANCE ON A NUMBER LINE [236]

A visual method, leading to a formula in terms of coordinates, is presented. Students frequently find this visual approach so easy to use that they avoid the formula. But, they must make the transition to the formula to enable them to work with slope and to find equations of lines.

Cumulative Review

1. Simplify $(3a^2b)(2a^3b^5)$.
2. Evaluate a^3b^2 if $a = -2$, $b = 3$.
3. Write $\dfrac{49 - a^2}{2a^2 - 11a - 21}$ in simplest form.

1. $6a^5b^6$ 2. -72 3. $-\dfrac{a + 7}{2a + 3}$

FUN FOR PHILATELISTS [239]

Students may be interested in designing stamps of their own to illustrate a mathematical concept.

LOCATING POINTS IN A PLANE [240]

To help students realize the significance of the ordered pair, you might show them several pairs of points such as $(3, 2)$ and $(2, 3)$. Students sometimes have difficulty with naming coordinates of points on the axes. They mix up zero coordinates. We cover this concept in the next lesson. For enrichment, students can experiment with three-dimensional graphing. (See p. 454.)

Cumulative Review

1. Divide $\dfrac{a^2 - 7a + 12}{a^2 - 25} \div \dfrac{2a - 8}{5 - a}$.

2. Add $\dfrac{6}{5a - 10} + \dfrac{2}{2 - a}$.

3. Add $\dfrac{y - 2}{y^2 - 3y + 2} + \dfrac{4}{2 - y}$.

1. $\dfrac{-1(a - 3)}{2(a + 5)}$ 2. $\dfrac{-4}{5(a - 2)}$ 3. $\dfrac{-3y + 2}{(y - 2)(y - 1)}$

PLOTTING POINTS IN A PLANE [242]

Points are plotted by directed movement from the origin. The bottom of page 242 provides a good summary telling students how to use the signs of coordinates to determine in which directions to move. Example 4 stresses the coordinates of points on the *x*-axis and *y*-axis.

Cumulative Review
1. One number is 5 more than another. Their sum is 11. Find the numbers.
2. Find two consecutive odd integers whose product is 35.
1. *3 and 8*   **2.** *5 and 7, and −7 and −5*

PASCAL'S TRIANGLE   [245]
You may wish to discuss the symmetry of the coefficients and the sum of the exponents of any term in the expansion of $(a + b)^n$.

   If you assigned research on permutations and combinations, you may wish to show that the coefficients can be found by using combinations.

LINES PARALLEL TO THE AXES   [246]
Some students may forget which coordinates are the *same* if a line is parallel to the *x*- or *y*-axis. There is no real harm done if students wish to draw a rough sketch each time.

Cumulative Review
1. Solve $5a - (4 - 3a) = 9a + 5$.
2. Solve $4(a + 2) - 1 = 4a + 7$.
3. Find the solution set of $|2a + 5| = 9$.
1. *−9*   **2.** *all numbers*   **3.** *{2, −7}*

DIRECTED DISTANCES   [248]
As with directed distance on a number line, students should learn to use the definition and not rely on a drawing.

Cumulative Review
1. Factor $x^2 - 25$.
2. Find the solution set of $x^2 = 15 - 2x$.
3. Multiply $(2m + 5)(2m - 3)$.
1. *$(x - 5)(x + 5)$*   **2.** *{−5, 3}*
3. *$4m^2 + 4m - 15$*

SLOPES OF LINE SEGMENTS   [251]
We sketch the right triangle above the line to emphasize vertical movement first, followed by horizontal movement. A slope of $\frac{2}{3}$ is interpreted as moving up 2 then right 3.

   In developing the formula for slope, we provide the coordinates of the vertex of the right angle in the triangle since students with little geometry background will have difficulty obtaining this for themselves. Emphasize that although the slope

of $\overline{PQ}$ for $P(a, b)$ and $Q(c, d)$ is $\dfrac{d - b}{c - a}$ or $\dfrac{b - d}{a - c}$, we cannot write $\dfrac{d - b}{a - c}$.

Cumulative Review
1. Simplify $(4ab^3)^2$.
2. Evaluate $3a^3b$ if $a = -2$, $b = -1$.
3. Write $\dfrac{12m^3n^6(t^2 - 13t + 42)}{8mn^{10}(7 - t)}$ in simplest form.

1. *$16a^2b^6$*   **2.** *24*   **3.** *$\dfrac{3m^2(t - 6)}{-2n^4}$*

SLOPE OF LINES   [255]
The concept that the slope of a line is the same for any two points on the line is critical to the development of the equation of a line in the next chapter. Students tend to confuse $\frac{0}{5}$ and $\frac{5}{0}$. It might be advantageous to review why the denominator of a fraction cannot be zero.

Cumulative Review
1. Multiply $\dfrac{3a^2 - 4a}{2a^2 - 3a - 20} \cdot \dfrac{2a + 5}{9a^2 - 16}$.
2. Add $\dfrac{4}{y^2 + 3y} + \dfrac{2}{y + 3}$.
3. Simplify $\dfrac{2}{x^2 - 7x + 12} - \dfrac{x + 2}{x - 4}$.

1. $\dfrac{a}{(a - 4)(3a + 4)}$ **2.** $\dfrac{2y + 4}{y^2 + 3y}$
3. $\dfrac{-x^2 + x + 8}{(x - 4)(x - 3)}$

CHAPTER 10   *Linear Sentences*

Writing an equation of a line and graphing a line from its equation are the two major concepts covered. The approach differs from the traditional one which automatically assumes that an equation of the form $ax + by = c$ represents a line. The property that the slope of a line is the same for any two points on it is the foundation of the development. Thus, to find an equation of a line, students see that all they are doing is setting two slopes equal. Experiment leads to the discovery of the significance of the $y = mx + b$ form. The chapter concludes with graphing linear inequalities in two variables.

MATHEMATICS IN CONSTRUCTION [260]

You may wish to ask students to research this career. They should find answers to questions such as the following: How much math is required for acceptance into construction apprenticeships and/or vocational schools? Which states require a math test for entrance into an apprenticeship?

RATIO AND PROPORTION [261]

Writing the equation of a line hinges on solving a proportion. Thus, students are taught to work with the special type of fractional equation. The more formal methods for fractional equations are covered in Chapter 13.

Cumulative Review

1. Multiply $\dfrac{a^2 - 4}{a^2 - a - 6} \cdot \dfrac{a - 3}{a^2 - 2a}$.
2. Find the solution set of $|x - 3| = -2$.
3. Find the slope of $\overleftrightarrow{AB}$ for $A(-3, -1)$ and $B(5, -2)$.

1. $\dfrac{1}{a}$ 2. ϕ 3. $-\dfrac{1}{8}$

EQUATION OF A LINE [265]

All lines in this lesson have integral slopes to facilitate solving for y. In the next lesson, students learn to solve equations like $3y = 2x + 9$ for y. In Example 1, it might be helpful to show students that using either R or S with G produces the same equation. For Example 5, students can plot the original two points, draw the line, and see that the point $R(5, -14)$ is on it.

Cumulative Review

1. Find the solution set of $2b^2 - 9b - 5 = 0$.
2. Multiply $(x + 5)(2x - 7)$.
3. Factor $16a^3 - 25a$ completely.

1. $\left\{-\dfrac{1}{2}, 5\right\}$ 2. $2x^2 + 3x - 35$
3. $a(4a - 5)(4a + 5)$

MORE DIFFICULT EQUATIONS [268]

In this lesson, students learn to write equations of lines with nonintegral slopes. An important Part B extension is the ability to write a table of values for x and y given an equation. A table of values is useful when graphing nonlinear functions and provides a good alternate method for graphing a line.

T–38

Cumulative Review

1. Simplify $2a^3(3a^2 - 5a + 2)$.
2. Simplify $(3x^2y^3)^2$.   3. Find and graph the solution set of $6 - 9x < -21$.

1. $6a^5 - 10a^4 + 4a^3$ 2. $9x^4y^6$
3. $\{x | x > 3\}$

RATIO AND PROPORTION APPLIED TO TRAVEL [271]

This topic may be extended to reading maps.

y = mx + b [272]

The discovery approach is used to lead students to recognize the significance of the $y = mx + b$ form. The pattern is applied in graphing a line from its slope and y-intercept. Students seem to have difficulty with x coefficients that are integral or zero. These are handled in the next lesson. Rewriting an equation like $3y - 2x = 4$ in $y = mx + b$ form is also deferred.

Cumulative Review

1. Find the solution set of $3x + 4 = 3x + 2$.
2. Solve $2x - (3 - 4x) = 7x - 1$.
3. Find $\{3, 4, 5\} \cap \{2, 3, 7, 8\}$.

1. ϕ 2. -2 3. $\{3\}$

GRAPHING A LINE [276]

Students rewrite equations in the form $y = mx + b$ in order to identify easily the slope and y-intercept and then graph the line. This technique of solving an equation for one of its variables will again be useful in the process of solving systems of equations by substitution.

Emphasize that the equation of a horizontal line is just a special case of $y = mx + b$; namely, $y = 0x + b$.

Cumulative Review

1. Simplify $\dfrac{5b - 45}{3b - 27}$.

2. Divide $\dfrac{r^2 - 7r + 12}{r^2 - 25} \div \dfrac{2r - 8}{5 - r}$.

3. Simplify $\dfrac{2}{a + 6} + \dfrac{3a + 4}{a^2 + 3a - 18} + \dfrac{7}{a - 3}$.

1. $\dfrac{5}{3}$ 2. $\dfrac{-(r - 3)}{2(r + 5)}$ 3. $\dfrac{4(3a + 10)}{(a + 6)(a - 3)}$

VERTICAL LINES [279]

Again, students may have difficulty seeing the difference between $\frac{0}{5}$ and $\frac{5}{0}$.

Cumulative Review

1. One number is 7 more than another. Find the numbers if their sum is 17. **2.** Find three consecutive odd integers whose sum is 63. **3.** Find two consecutive integers whose product is 42.

1. *5; 12* **2.** *19; 21; 23* **3.** *6, 7 or* $-7, -6$

GRAPHING INEQUALITIES IN
TWO VARIABLES [281]

Review graphing linear inequalities in one variable and show the analogy to this new concept.

For Example 3, you may want to have students test several more points in order to convince them that the coordinates of the points *above* the line satisfy $y > 2x - 1$, while the coordinates of the points *below* the line satisfy $y < 2x - 1$.

Cumulative Review

1. Simplify $\dfrac{x^2 - 2x - 15}{30 - x - x^2}$.

2. Graph $\{x | x < -3\} \cup \{x | x > -2\}$.

3. Solve $9 - 4(2 - y) = 7y - (3 + y)$.

1. $-\dfrac{x + 3}{x + 6}$ **2.** *{x|x < −3 or x > −2}* **3.** *2*

DIOPHANTUS [285]

You may wish to refer back to this page after students have studied algebraic solutions of systems of equations. At that time you may wish to assign a project on Diophantine equations.

CHAPTER 11 *Linear Systems*

This chapter develops three methods of solving linear systems: graphing, substitution, and addition. The graphic method, which depends on eyesight and the thickness of the student's pencil, is limited. The chapter culminates in applications to mixture and number relation problems.

LINEAR PROGRAMMING [288]

As an additional project, students may investigate careers in which linear programming is used.

A course in linear programming is required in fields such as hotel management, business administration, and sociology.

SYSTEMS OF EQUATIONS:
GRAPHING [289]

It might be helpful to precede the lesson with oral practice on graphing lines. For example, to graph $y = \frac{2}{3}x + 5$: begin at $A(0, 5)$; move up 2 and right 3 to B; join A and B.

If time permits, you might wish to discuss dependent equations such as $3x + 2y = 4$ and $6x + 4y = 8$.

Cumulative Review

1. Simplify $\dfrac{4}{x^2 - 36} - \dfrac{5}{6 - x}$. **2.** Write an equation of the line $\overleftrightarrow{PQ}$ for $P(2, 9)$ and $Q(0, 5)$.
3. Graph $3x - 2y < 12$.

1. $\dfrac{5x + 34}{(x + 6)(x - 6)}$ **2.** *y = 2x + 5* **3.** *The shaded region above the line for* $y = \frac{3}{2}x - 6$

SYSTEMS OF INEQUALITIES:
GRAPHING [292]

You may wish to assign all or part of this optional lesson to all students.

SYSTEMS OF EQUATIONS:
SUBSTITUTION [294]

The substitution method for solving systems of equations is most advantageous in solving a system in which either *one* of the equations is already solved for a variable or in which the coefficient of one of the variables is -1 or 1.

Cumulative Review

1. Find the slope of $\overleftrightarrow{PQ}$ for $P(3, 4)$ and $Q(7, 6)$.
2. Describe the position of a line with slope $-\frac{2}{7}$.
3. Simplify $(2x^3 y)^2$.

1. $\frac{1}{2}$ **2.** *down to the right* **3.** $4x^6 y^2$

SYSTEMS OF EQUATIONS:
ax + by = c
dx − by = e [297]

Applications are restricted to systems involving x and y such that the coefficients in one pair of terms are already additive inverses of each other.

Emphasize the idea that once students have solved for one variable they may find the other by using either of the two original equations.

Cumulative Review
1. Multiply $(3x + 2)(x - 4)$.
2. Solve $7a - 2(3 - a) = 5a + 4$.
3. Give the slope and y-intercept of the line with equation $3x - 2y = 6$.
1. $3x^2 - 10x - 8$ 2. $\frac{5}{2}$ 3. $\frac{3}{2}; -3$

SYSTEMS OF EQUATIONS:
$ax + by = c$
$dx + ey = f$ [300]
The procedures in the previous lesson motivated students to rewrite the equations so that the coefficients in one pair of terms became additive inverses of each other. The fundamental technique is to select the appropriate multipliers such that the sum of the resulting equations produces an equation in only one variable. Students should be careful to multiply each side of the equation. Example 3 shows students that it is not always necessary to find a multiplier for both equations.

Cumulative Review
1. One number is twice another. If 3 more than the smaller is increased by the larger, the result is 15. Find the numbers.   2. Find three consecutive integers whose sum is 42.
1. $4; 8$ 2. $13; 14; 15$

MATHEMATICS IN PHARMACY   [303]
You may wish to ask students to research this career. They may look through college catalogs for descriptions of required courses for one majoring in pharmacy. Students may be interested in finding out how many college math courses are required.

DRY MIXTURES: REPRESENTING
COSTS   [304]
Learning to display information in a chart is valuable in solving the dry mixture problems appearing in the next lesson. Costs are represented in cents to avoid equations with decimal coefficients. In setting up mixture problems, students should be clear on the difference between total number of kilograms and total cost.

Cumulative Review
1. Write $\frac{4 - x^2}{x^2 + 3x - 10}$ in simplest form.
2. Multiply $\frac{a^2 - 3ab + 2b^2}{a^2 - ab} \cdot \frac{a^3}{2b - a}$.
3. Simplify $\frac{5}{a^2 - 4} - \frac{3}{2 - a}$.
1. $\frac{-(x + 2)}{x + 5}$ 2. $-a^2$ 3. $\frac{3a + 11}{(a + 2)(a - 2)}$

SOLVING DRY MIXTURE
PROBLEMS   [306]
Students go from just displaying the information in a table to writing a system of equations and solving the mixture problem.

Cumulative Review
1. Simplify $\frac{2}{x^2 - 7x + 12} - \frac{x + 2}{x - 4}$.
2. Solve $\frac{3}{m + 1} = \frac{2}{m - 6}$.
3. Write an equation of $\overleftrightarrow{PQ}$ for $P(3, -3)$ and $Q(6, -1)$.
1. $\frac{-x^2 + x + 8}{(x - 3)(x - 4)}$ 2. 20 3. $2x - 3y = 15$

SOLVING NUMBER RELATION
PROBLEMS   [310]
Again, the Review Capsule is an important element in the development. The ability to interpret phrases like *increased by, decreased by, more than,* and *less than* is critical in writing equations to solve problems.

Cumulative Review
1. Simplify $(4a^2b^3)^2$.
2. Graph $\{(x, y) \mid 3x - 4y = 8\}$.
3. Graph $\{(x, y) \mid y = -2\}$.
1. $16a^4b^6$ 2. *line through* $(0, -2)$ *and* $(4, 1)$ 3. *horizontal line through* $(0, -2)$

CHAPTER 12   *Relations and Functions*

A function is defined as a special kind of relation, and the vertical line test is introduced as a means for determining if a relation is a function by examining its graph. Linear functions, constant functions, functional notation, direct variation, and inverse variation are also presented.

GALILEO AND FREE FALL [316]
With your more able students, you may wish to include a discussion on projectiles. Discuss the formula $s = -4.9t^2 + v_0 t + h$, where s is the height reached after t seconds by an object thrown straight up from an initial height (h) and initial velocity (v_0) expressed in m/sec.

RELATIONS AND FUNCTIONS [317]
Students often have difficulty understanding the definition of a function. Point out that in a function the second elements of the ordered pairs may be the same, but the first elements may *not* be the same. The inverse of a relation is introduced in Part B of the exercise set.

Cumulative Review
1. Graph $\{x|x \geq -1\} \cap \{x|x < 3\}$.
2. Factor $5x^3 - 5x$ completely.
3. Multiply $(2x + 3)(x - 1)$.
1. *-1 and all points between -1 and 3*
2. $5x(x + 1)(x - 1)$ 3. $2x^2 + x - 3$

TYPES OF FUNCTIONS [320]
Since no two ordered pairs of a function may have the same first element, it follows that no two points of the graph may lie on the same vertical line. Thus, we have the vertical line test as a means for determining if a graph is the graph of a function and ultimately whether a linear function or constant function exists.

In Part B of the exercise set, students graph parabolas using a table of values.

Cumulative Review
1. Solve $2x - 8(x + 1) = 6x + (3x - 4)$.
2. Factor $2y^2 + 5y + 2$.
3. Simplify $\dfrac{3 - x}{x^2 - 5x + 6}$.
1. $-\frac{4}{15}$ 2. $(2y + 1)(y + 2)$ 3. $-\dfrac{1}{x - 2}$

f(x) NOTATION [323]
Example 1 leads to the definition of the value of f at x. When given a function and its domain, students determine the range.

Cumulative Review
1. Simplify $-6x - (3x + 2) + 4x$. Then evaluate if $x = -4$.   2. Add $\dfrac{4y - 3}{y^2 - 3y - 10} + \dfrac{4}{y + 2}$.
3. Factor $3x^2 + 5xy - 2y^2$.

1. $-5x - 2;\ 18$ 2. $\dfrac{8y - 23}{(y + 2)(y - 5)}$
3. $(3x - y)(x + 2y)$

THE GREATEST INTEGER FUNCTION [325]
You may wish to explore this concept further with some students. For example, you might explore the idea of translations by assigning graphs such as the following:
$$y = [x - 4]$$
$$y = [x - 4] + 2$$
$$y = 3[x - 4] + 2$$

DIGIT PROBLEMS [326]
Examples 1–4 involve representing the digits of two-digit numbers in preparation for solving problems about two-digit numbers.

You may wish to assign part of the exercises to all students.

DIRECT VARIATION [330]
The formula for the perimeter of an equilateral triangle, $p = 3s$, serves as an introduction to the concept of direct variation. Verbal problems that apply the concept are given in Parts B and C of the exercise set. For enrichment, students can try to determine the graph of a direct variation. Experiments of graphing several direct variations on the same set of axes should lead students to the conclusion that the graph is a line with slope k and y-intercept 0. In Exercises 1–5, the constant of proportionality can be found by using the ratio y to x or x to y. Thus, the answer to Exercise 1 can be 6, or $\frac{1}{6}$.

Cumulative Review
1. Simplify $\dfrac{2x^9 y^{12} z}{4x^7 yz^3}$.   2. Solve $x^3 - 64x = 0$.

3. Multiply $\left(\dfrac{x^2 - 16}{x^2 + 5x + 4}\right)\left(\dfrac{x + 4}{2x - 8}\right)$.

1. $\dfrac{x^2 y^{11}}{2z^2}$ 2. *0; 8; -8*   3. $\dfrac{x + 4}{2(x + 1)}$

T–41

INVERSE VARIATION [334]

The formula $l \cdot w = 12$ serves as an introduction to the concept of inverse variation. Verbal problems that apply the concept are given in Parts B and C of the exercise set.

Cumulative Review

1. Divide $\dfrac{x-8}{4} \div \dfrac{2x-16}{12}$.
2. Solve $6x^2 - 31x + 35 = 0$.
3. Find and graph the solution set of $7x - 8x < 12 + 3x$.

1. $\frac{3}{2}$ 2. $\frac{7}{2}; \frac{5}{3}$ 3. $\{x \mid x > -3\}$

CHAPTER 13 *Fractional Equations*

Solving fractional equations and simplifying complex fractions are treated. Applications of solving fractional equations are illustrated in lessons on work problems, decimal equations, and formulas. In turn, decimal equations are used in studying the relationship between rational numbers and repeating decimals. If you wish to have students check solutions, we suggest that you take care in choosing those for which the arithmetic is feasible.

MATHEMATICS AND ELECTRICIANS [340]

You may wish to tie in this page with the one on parallel series circuits. (See p. 377.)

Some students may make a drawing of a simple electrical circuit. A simple analogy of this is a battery operated portable radio. The battery is the power; the flow of current delivers sound. The volume control is like a resistor: volume is turned down by means of a "variable resistor" which slows the flow of current.

SOLVING FRACTIONAL EQUATIONS [341]

Students have worked with a special type of fractional equation, the proportion. Now, they learn to solve any fractional equation by the method of multiplying each side by the LCD. In Example 6, we tie in the new knowledge with the old by showing that proportions can be solved in two ways. It might be helpful to show an exercise in adding fractions alongside one on solving fractional equations. Students should see why the LCD remains in the first case but disappears in the second.

Cumulative Review

1. Solve $\begin{array}{l} 3x + 2y = 7 \\ 2x + 3y = 8 \end{array}$.
2. Multiply $(2x - 3)(x + 5)$.   3. Find the solution set of $2x^2 = -9x + 5$.

1. $(1, 2)$ 2. $2x^2 + 7x - 15$ 3. $\left\{-5, \frac{1}{2}\right\}$

PERCENT OF A NUMBER [345]

Usually in business, any fraction of a cent is rounded to the next higher penny. However, some merchants round down to the next lower penny when selling articles at a discount.

Encourage students to find a shortcut for solving the following problem: Find the selling price of a $500 TV advertised at 25% off. Someone should come up with "Find 75% of $500."

MORE FRACTIONAL EQUATIONS [346]

Fractional equations in this lesson include polynomial denominators. The concept of extraneous solutions, presented in Part B, will be especially useful for students when they study Algebra 2. Although the equations are easy to solve, the checks involve tedious arithmetic.

Cumulative Review

1. $f(x) = x^2 - 7x + 2$. Find $f(3)$.   2. y varies directly as x. If $x = 4$ and $y = 6$, find y if $x = 8$.
3. Graph $\{(x, y) \mid 3x - 2y = 8\}$.

1. -10 2. 12 3. *line through* $(0, -4)$ and $(2, -1)$

REPRESENTING AMOUNTS OF WORK [350]

Students must be able to express the time spent on a job in comparison with the total time needed to complete the job as a ratio. The last example suggests that the sum of the fractional parts of work done by several people working together is 1, a property which is critical to solving the work problems in the next lesson.

Cumulative Review

1. Simplify $(3a^2 b^3)^2$.
2. Divide $\dfrac{2x-1}{3x+2} \div \dfrac{2x^2-x}{4-9x^2}$.   3. Write the equation of the line $\overleftrightarrow{PQ}$ for $P(3, 4)$ and $Q(6, 6)$.

1. $9a^4 b^6$ 2. $-\dfrac{3x-2}{x}$ 3. $-2x + 3y = 6$

WORK PROBLEMS [353]

Setting up a chart, as indicated, helps many students. Example 2 illustrates the case where students are asked to find the amount of time needed for each person to complete the job. Students should be careful that their final result answers the question posed by the problem.

Cumulative Review
1. Solve $4 - (3 - 2x) = 5x + 7$.
2. Simplify $\dfrac{5}{x^2 - 49} - \dfrac{2}{7 - x} + \dfrac{3}{x + 7}$.
3. Find and graph the solution set of $7x - 2 < 9x + 12$.

1. -2 2. $\dfrac{5x - 2}{(x + 7)(x - 7)}$ 3. $\{x|x > -7\}$

APPLYING PERCENT [356]

You may wish to include additional applications such as the following:

At a 10% off sale a radio sold for $27. What was the original price of the radio?

If the diagonal measurement of a TV screen is increased 50%, how much will its area increase?

EQUATIONS WITH DECIMALS [358]

The technique is easy, once students are reminded that multiplying a decimal by a power of ten just shifts the decimal point. The motivation for choosing the LCD is first suggested by rewriting the decimals in fractional form. Do not require checks.

Cumulative Review
1. Solve $\begin{array}{l} 3x - 4y = 7 \\ 2x + 3y = 16 \end{array}$.
2. Solve $\begin{array}{l} x = 4y - 2 \\ 3x + 2y = 8 \end{array}$.
3. Factor $2a^2 + 5ab - 12b^2$.

1. $(5, 2)$ 2. $(2, 1)$ 3. $(2a - 3b)(a + 4b)$

RATIONAL NUMBERS [361]

Students are led to see that repeating decimals are rational numbers that can be expressed in the form $\dfrac{a}{b}$, where a and b are integers $[b \neq 0]$.

As a challenge, ask students to invent a nonrepeating, nonterminating decimal. For example,

.343443444 . . . . The next chapter discusses such irrational numbers.

Cumulative Review
1. Find and graph the solution set of $6 - (2 - 3x) \geq 5 - 4x$.
2. Solve $\dfrac{a + 4}{6} - \dfrac{a + 2}{2} = 4$.
3. Simplify $\dfrac{c - 3}{c + 1} - \dfrac{c - 7}{1 - c^2}$.

1. $\left\{x|x \geq \frac{1}{7}\right\}$ 2. -13 3. $\dfrac{c - 4}{c - 1}$

INVESTMENT AND LOAN PROBLEMS [364]

Students apply percent to solving problems, using the interest formula $i = prt$.

COMPLEX FRACTIONS [368]

The first step in simplifying complex fractions is the same as that for adding fractions: factor all denominators and find the LCD. For students who have difficulty, you might wish to illustrate several examples without variables like $\dfrac{\frac{2}{3} + \frac{1}{2}}{\frac{5}{6} + \frac{1}{3}}$.

Cumulative Review
1. For what value(s) of m is $\dfrac{m^2 - 5m + 2}{m^2 - 4}$ undefined?   2. y varies inversely as x. If $y = 16$ when $x = 2$, find y when $x = 4$.   3. Find the slope of $\overleftrightarrow{PQ}$ for $P(3, 7)$ and $Q(3, 12)$.

1. $-2, 2$ 2. 8 3. undefined

MORE COMPLEX FRACTIONS [371]

The denominators are no longer restricted to being monomials. Example 2 emphasizes the step of showing $a(a + 6)$ multiplied by each fraction of the numerator and each fraction of the denominator. In an exercise like Example 3, students should be warned to check to be sure that their final result is in simplest form.

Cumulative Review
1. Is $\{(x, y)|y = 6\}$ a function?   2. Find the slope and the y-intercept for the line with equation $2x - 5y = 20$.   3. Solve $\begin{array}{l} 3x - 2y = 11 \\ y = x - 3 \end{array}$.

1. yes   2. $\frac{2}{5}$; -4 3. $(5, 2)$

FORMULAS [374]

Solving for one variable in terms of several others is tied to previous knowledge of solving an equation. Show the analogy between solving $3x = 19$ and $ax = b$. This and similar comparisons will help students solve literal equations.

Cumulative Review

1. Solve $x^2 - 64 = 0$.　**2.** For what value(s) of x is $\dfrac{5x + 2}{x^2 - 7x + 12}$ undefined?　**3.** One number is 4 more than twice another. Their sum is 13. Find the numbers.

1. $-8, 8$　**2.** $3, 4$　**3.** $3, 10$

PARALLEL SERIES CIRCUITS [377]

You may wish to assign this application of complex fractions to Level C students only.

CHAPTER 14　*Real Numbers*

The set of real numbers is introduced as the union of the set of rational numbers and the set of irrational numbers. Then the concept of square root is introduced, and it is shown that the square roots of many whole numbers are irrational numbers. Most of the chapter is devoted to operations with radical expressions.

THE NORMAL CURVE [380]

If possible, arrange to get a printout of the SAT scores from the guidance department. Using $\{300, 350, 400, \ldots, 800\}$ as the domain and {number of students in each category} as the range, have the class plot the information. Hopefully, the graph will approximate the normal curve. You may use the following scheme for intermediary domain values:

　　　If $300 \le x < 325$, use 300 for x.
　　　If $325 < x \le 350$, use 350 for x.
　　　If $x = 325$, use 300 for x.
　　　But, if $x = 375$, use 400 for x.

THE SET OF REAL NUMBERS [382]

In a decimal like $.313113111311113\ldots$, no period of digits repeats, although the 3's and 1's repeat. Thus, $.313113111311113\ldots$ names an *irrational* number. If a period of digits repeats, such as $311311311\ldots$, then the number is a rational number.

Cumulative Review

1. Simplify $\dfrac{7x}{x^2 - 7x + 10} - \dfrac{3}{5 - x}$.
2. Find $d(\overrightarrow{MN})$ for $M(-4, 3)$ and $N(7, 3)$.
3. Find $\{5, 10, 15\} \cap \{-5, 0, 5\}$.

1. $\dfrac{2(5x - 3)}{(x - 5)(x - 2)}$　**2.** 11　**3.** $\{5\}$

SQUARE ROOTS [384]

You may want to ask students to memorize the perfect squares from 1 to 400. This knowledge will increase their ability to estimate the decimal values of numbers like $\sqrt{156}$, $\sqrt{230}$, etc. It will also help them to simplify radicals.

Cumulative Review

1. Solve　$2x^2 - 11x + 5 = 0$.　**2.** Find　the slope of $\overleftrightarrow{AB}$ for $A(2, -6)$ and $B(-3, 1)$.

3. Multiply $\dfrac{2x^2 - 13x - 7}{x} \cdot \dfrac{6x}{3x - 21}$.

1. $\frac{1}{2}; 5$　**2.** $-\frac{7}{5}$　**3.** $2(2x + 1)$

THE GALTON BOARD [387]

Interested students may make a model of the Galton board. You may wish to have some students report on career opportunities and requirements in the field of statistics.

APPROXIMATING SQUARE ROOTS [388]

It doesn't matter what a student's first guess is in approximating a square root like $\sqrt{34}$. When students average the guess and the first quotient, they will begin to "move in on" the actual value of $\sqrt{34}$.

Cumulative Review

1. Divide $\dfrac{x^2 - 7x + 12}{x^2 - 25} \div \dfrac{2x - 8}{5 - x}$.
2. Factor $2x^2 + 7x - 15$.

3. Simplify $\dfrac{\dfrac{6}{x^2} + \dfrac{1}{2}}{\dfrac{3}{x} + \dfrac{1}{2}}$.

1. $-\dfrac{x - 3}{2(x + 5)}$　**2.** $(2x - 3)(x + 5)$

3. $\dfrac{12 + x^2}{6x + x^2}$

SIMPLIFYING RADICALS [391]

For Example 5, students can use either of the two methods for simplifying radicals. The second way is less tedious, but it requires a knowledge of perfect squares.

Cumulative Review

1. Graph $\{(x, y) \mid y = 3x - 1\}$.
2. Solve $\begin{array}{l} 7x + 2y = 9 \\ 3x + 8y = 11 \end{array}$.
3. Simplify $\dfrac{2}{x^2} + \dfrac{3}{2x} - \dfrac{4}{3x^2}$.

1. *line through* $(0, -1)$ *and* $(1, 2)$ 2. $(1, 1)$
3. $\dfrac{9x + 4}{6x^2}$

EVEN EXPONENTS [394]

Examples 3 and 4 make it clear that we must restrict the values of the variables under a radical sign so that they represent only positive numbers or zero. Stress this restriction.

Cumulative Review

1. Graph $\{(x, y) \mid y > -2x + 3\}$.
2. Solve $\dfrac{4}{5} + \dfrac{3}{x} = 2$.   3. Find the slope of $\overleftrightarrow{PQ}$ for $P(-3, -2)$ and $Q(4, -5)$.

1. *region above the line through* $(0, 3)$ *and* $(1, 1)$
2. $\dfrac{5}{2}$ 3. $-\dfrac{3}{7}$

ODD EXPONENTS [396]

When nonperfect squares and odd exponents occur in a radical expression, students should look for the greatest perfect square factor in the expression. Cube roots, fourth roots, etc., are introduced in Parts B and C of the exercise set.

Cumulative Review

1. Solve $\begin{array}{l} 5x + 2y = 21 \\ 2x - y = 3 \end{array}$.
2. Is $\{(x, y) \mid y = -4\}$ a function?
3. $f(x) = x^2 - 4$. Find $f(-2)$.

1. $(3, 3)$ 2. *yes*   3. 0

FLOW CHART: FINDING SQUARE ROOTS [398]

If only pencil and paper are to be used to approximate square roots, the method discussed here is excellent. It is relatively accurate to the nearest tenth after the third application.

THE PYTHAGOREAN THEOREM [399]

In discussing the converse of the Pythagorean theorem, you might want to give some simple examples to illustrate the meaning of *converse.* Examples to illustrate the fact that if a statement is true its converse is not necessarily true should be used also. Much has been written about Pythagoras and the Pythagorean theorem. Students might want to do some supplementary reading.

Cumulative Review

1. Write an equation of PQ for $P(1, 3)$ and $Q(-2, 4)$.
2. Simplify $\dfrac{\dfrac{6}{x-1} + \dfrac{2}{x}}{\dfrac{5}{x^2 - x}}$.
3. Find the slope and the y-intercept for the line with equation $3x - 4y = 8$.

1. $x + 3y = 10$ 2. $\dfrac{2(4x - 1)}{5}$ 3. $\dfrac{3}{4}, -2$

COMBINING RADICALS [402]

Combining like radicals is similar to combining like terms. The number line illustrating $5\sqrt{2} + 2\sqrt{2}$ is helpful in making this clear.

Cumulative Review

1. Solve $4(x - 2) = 8 + 3(x - 1)$.
2. $A = \{-3, 2, 3\}$ and $B = \{-3, -2, 0\}$. Find $A \cup B$.   3. Factor $2x^2 - 10x + 12$ completely.

1. 13 2. $\{-3, -2, 0, 2, 3\}$
3. $2(x - 2)(x - 3)$

PRODUCTS OF RADICALS [404]

Example 6 is an application of $(a + b)(a - b) = a^2 - b^2$. Products like the one in Example 6 name *rational* numbers since the middle term drops out. Example 7 is an application of $(a + b)^2 = a^2 + 2ab + b^2$.

Cumulative Review

1. Solve $2x^2 + 3x = 20$.
2. Simplify $2\sqrt{5} + \sqrt{6} - 4\sqrt{5} + 3\sqrt{6}$.
3. $f(x) = 2x^2 - 5$. Find $f(-3)$.

1. $\dfrac{5}{2}, -4$ 2. $-2\sqrt{5} + 4\sqrt{6}$ 3. 13

POINTS FOR IRRATIONAL NUMBERS [407]

With some students, you may wish to show how to generate the square roots in a spiral fashion. Start with a drawing similar to the one at the top of the page. The sides of the first triangle are $1, 1, \sqrt{2}$; of the second, $\sqrt{2}, 1, \sqrt{3}$; of the third, $\sqrt{3}, 1, 2$, etc.

RATIONALIZING DENOMINATORS [408]

For Example 6, it is sufficient to multiply the numerator and the denominator by $\sqrt{3y}$ in order to produce a perfect square denominator. Multiplying by $\sqrt{12y}$ would produce common factors which would have to be removed from the numerator and the denominator.

Cumulative Review

1. Find $\overrightarrow{d}(AB)$ for $A(5, -2)$ and $B(-1, -2)$.

2. Add $\dfrac{5}{x-1} + \dfrac{3}{x+2}$. 3. Simplify $\dfrac{3a^6b^3}{12ab^4}$.

1. -6 2. $\dfrac{8x+7}{(x-1)(x+2)}$ 3. $\dfrac{a^5}{4b}$

FRACTIONAL RADICANDS [411]

To simplify a radical means to rewrite the expression so that the radicand is *not* a fraction and the denominator is a rational number.

Cumulative Review

1. Can the sides of a right triangle have measures 1, 2, and $\sqrt{5}$? 2. Multiply $(2\sqrt{3}+1)(2\sqrt{3}-1)$.

3. Solve $\dfrac{5}{2x} + \dfrac{2x}{x+1} = 2$.

1. *yes*   2. *11*   3. -5

MATHEMATICS IN BANKING [413]

All students will benefit by this practical application.

CHAPTER 15 *Equations with Real Solutions*

The first topic is radical equations. Then the fact that the solution set of $x^2 = a$ is $\{\sqrt{a}, -\sqrt{a}\}$ is used to develop the method of completing the square for solving quadratic equations. The quadratic formula is derived. Applications are given in the form of area problems.

PYTHAGOREAN TRIPLES [416]

Early Greek mathematicians were intrigued by number relationships that had an almost mystical power. Some students may wish to research the Pythagoreans and other number relationships such as amicable numbers. One suggested reference is *History of Mathematics* by Howard Eves.

RADICAL EQUATIONS [417]

The Review Capsule and the first display explain why students must always check their solutions when they solve radical equations. Squaring each side of an equation does not necessarily produce an equation that has the same solution as the original equation.

Cumulative Review

1. Find and graph the solution set of $6x - 9 \geq -12 + 5x$.   2. For $P(-3, 3)$ and $Q(-3, 1)$ is $\overleftrightarrow{PQ}$ vertical or horizontal?

3. Simplify $\dfrac{x^3(x-8)}{x^4(x^2-7x-8)}$.

1. $\{x \mid x \geq -3\}$ 2. *vertical*   3. $\dfrac{1}{x(x+1)}$

THE SOLUTION SET OF $x^2 = a$ [420]

The fact that the solution set of $x^2 = a$ is $\{\sqrt{a}, -\sqrt{a}\}$ is the key to finding the solution sets of the equations in this lesson and the next one.

Cumulative Review

1. Find the slope of $\overleftrightarrow{AB}$ for $A(4, -1)$ and $B(-2, 3)$.   2. Rationalize the denominator of $\dfrac{2}{1-\sqrt{7}}$.   3. Multiply $(\sqrt{3}+1)(\sqrt{3}+1)$.

1. $-\frac{2}{3}$ 2. $-\dfrac{(1+\sqrt{7})}{3}$ 3. $4 + 2\sqrt{3}$

COMPLETING THE SQUARE [423]

In Part A of the exercise set, the coefficient of the x term is even to facilitate completing the square. In Part B the coefficient of the x term is odd, so students need to work with fractions. Some of the solution sets in Part C are empty (the solutions are not real numbers).

Cumulative Review
1. *y* varies directly as *x*, and *y* is 12 when *x* is 10.
Find *x* when *y* is 32.   **2.** Solve $\begin{aligned} 8x + 2y &= 14 \\ -7x + 4y &= 5 \end{aligned}$.
3. $A = \{-5, -4, 0, 4\}$ and $B = \{-4, -3, -2, -1\}$.
Find $A \cap B$.
1. $26\frac{2}{3}$ **2.** $(1, 3)$ **3.** $\{-4\}$

THE QUADRATIC FORMULA   [427]
All of the equations in the exercise set have integral solutions. Quadratics with nonintegral solutions will be treated in the next lesson. This lesson emphasizes putting a quadratic equation in standard form and identifying the coefficients *a*, *b*, and *c*.

Cumulative Review
1. Solve $(x - 8)^2 = 64$.   **2.** Solve $\frac{5}{x} + 2 = 15$.
3. Simplify $(2\sqrt{5} - \sqrt{3})^2$.
1. $16, 0$ **2.** $\frac{5}{13}$ **3.** $23 - 4\sqrt{15}$

WET MIXTURE PROBLEMS   [430]
You may wish to assign all or part of this optional lesson to the entire class.

APPLYING THE QUADRATIC FORMULA   [434]
Quadratic equations whose solution sets contain rational and real solutions are treated. Some solution sets are empty.

For enrichment, some students might enjoy exploring the properties of the *discriminant* of a quadratic equation.

Cumulative Review
1. Find *a* so that $\overleftrightarrow{PQ}$ is vertical: $P(-2, -1)$, $Q(a, 2)$.   **2.** Solve $\sqrt{4x + 6} = \sqrt{27 + 3x}$.
3. Simplify $\frac{12xy}{\sqrt{x^2 y}}$.
1. -2 **2.** 21 **3.** $12\sqrt{y}$

AREA PROBLEMS   [437]
The solutions of area problems result in quadratic equations. The quadratic formula is applied. Students are expected to give answers to the nearest tenth when the solutions are not rational.

Cumulative Review
1. *D* is the domain of function *f*. Determine the range of $f(x) = 5x - 6$ if $D = \{-1, 0, 1\}$.
2. Rational or irrational? .123; 0; .2626; .141141114. . . .   **3.** Solve $x^2 + 3x - 5 = 0$ using the quadratic formula.
1. $\{-11, -6, -1\}$ **2.** *Rational: .123, 0, .2626*
Irrational: .141141114. . .   **3.** $\frac{-3 \pm \sqrt{29}}{2}$

ZELLER'S CONGRUENCE   [440]
This topic may be used at any time during the course. All students will find this topic enjoyable.

CHAPTER 16   *Trigonometry*

The basic properties of angles and triangles are covered in the first lesson. Then similar triangles are used as the basis for defining the three trigonometric ratios: *sine, cosine,* and *tangent.* Students use trigonometry to solve applied problems.

APPROXIMATING CUBE ROOTS   [444]
You may wish to have students check their answers by using a mini-calculator. If their calculators do not have a cube root key, they can check in reverse by cubing the answers.

ANGLES AND TRIANGLES   [445]
The properties of angles and triangles treated in this lesson are the properties that are essential to developing and applying the definitions of the trigonometric ratios.

Cumulative Review
1. Simplify $-(-6x + 2) - 8x + 1$. Then evaluate if $x = -2$.   **2.** Solve $2y - 15 = -3y - 22$.
3. Factor $7x^3 - 63x$.
1. $-2x - 1; 3$ **2.** $-\frac{7}{5}$
3. $7x(x - 3)(x + 3)$

SIMILAR TRIANGLES   [448]
In stating the similarity of two triangles, corresponding vertices must be listed in the same order.

$$\triangle\ A\ B\ C \sim \triangle\ D\ E\ F$$

For enrichment, some students may want to learn the method of *interpolation* for finding trigonometric ratios of angle measures given to minutes.

Cumulative Review

1. Solve $13a - 4a = -14 + 2a$.
2. Which are finite sets? Which are infinite sets? $\{0\}$; $\{0, 1, 2, 3, \ldots\}$; {all negative integers greater than -8}. **3.** Graph the solution set of $2x + 18 = 25 + 2 + x$.
1. -2 **2.** *Finite: $\{0\}$, {all negative integers greater than -8} Infinite: $\{0, 1, 2, 3, \ldots\}$* **3.** *$\{9\}$*

TRIGONOMETRIC RATIOS [451]

Right triangle trigonometry is only a small branch of the subject of trigonometry. If students study trigonometry on a more advanced level, the tangent, sine, and cosine will be defined in a broader sense. In Exercise 13, point out that $(\sin A)^2 + (\cos A)^2 = 1$ may also be written $(\sin^2 A) + (\cos^2 A) = 1$.

Cumulative Review

1. Graph the solution set of $4x + 1 > 3x + 9$.
2. Simplify $-(7 + 3x) - 5(2x - 6)$. Then evaluate if $x = -3$. **3.** List all the subsets of $\{0, 1, 2\}$.
1. $\{x | x > 8\}$ **2.** $-13x + 23$; 62
3. ϕ, $\{0\}$, $\{1\}$, $\{2\}$, $\{0, 1\}$, $\{0, 2\}$, $\{1, 2\}$, $\{0, 1, 2\}$

GRAPHING IN SPACE [454]

You may wish to use the following game: Beginning with $A(0, 0, 0)$, name the coordinates of B, C, D, E, F, G, and H so that the figure formed is a cube with each side 4 units long.

TABLES OF TRIGONOMETRIC RATIOS [456]

In the preceding lesson, students computed the values of the sine, cosine, and tangent for certain special measures such as $30°$, $45°$, and $60°$. More advanced mathematical techniques are needed to derive values for other measures.

Cumulative Review

1. Find $\{1, 2, 3\} \cap \{0, 1, 2\}$.
2. Evaluate $(-2y)^3$ if $y = -3$.
3. Multiply $(3x^4 y)(-xy^5)$.
1. $\{1, 2\}$ **2.** 216 **3.** $-3x^5 y^6$

SOLVING RIGHT TRIANGLES [458]

For Example 3, the second way is easier from the standpoint of computation. It is easier to multiply 1.963 by 18 than it is to divide 18 by .5095.

Cumulative Review

1. Solve $7(2x - 2) - 5x = 4x + 1$.
2. Which are prime numbers? 0; 31; 2; 49; 1; 51.
3. Multiply $-4a^2(3a^2 - 2a - 5)$.
1. 3 **2.** $31, 2$ **3.** $-12a^4 + 8a^3 + 20a^2$

APPLICATIONS OF TRIGONOMETRY [461]

Drawing the proper figure is of great importance in solving problems that are applications of trigonometry.

Cumulative Review

1. Graph the solution set of $8y - 9 \le 6 - 7y$.
2. Factor $7x^3 - 21x^2 + 42x$.
3. Find $\{-3, 0, 3\} \cap \{-2, 0, 2\}$.
1. $\{y | y \le 1\}$ **2.** $7x(x^2 - 3x + 6)$ **3.** $\{0\}$

DISTANCE FORMULA [466]

As an extension of this topic, you may wish to have your Level C students apply the distance formula to graphing in space. (See p. 454.) Ask them to find the distance between $P(1, 2, 3)$ and $Q(4, 6, 8)$.

PACING CHART

The Pacing Chart is designed as an aid to help you plan differentiated assignments for your class over the course of 170 days. The entries under the DAY heading indicate the day of the regular school year. The entries under each LEVEL heading give the daily assignments: first the page and then the exercises of the assignment. The column in color gives a minimum course, the middle column an average course, and the grey column an above average course.

The Pacing Chart is meant only as a guide and may be adapted by you to better meet the needs of your students.

DAY	LEVEL A	LEVEL B	LEVEL C
1	1–2 Ex 1–30	1–2 Ex 8–36	1–2 Ex 11–39
2	4–5 Orals All Ex 1–15	4–5 Orals All Ex 4–6; 10–23	4–5 Ex 7–15; 18–26
3	6–8 Ex 1–24	6–8 Ex 4–9; 13–30	6–8 Ex 4–9; 19–32
4	9–11 Ex 1–26; 29–31	9–11 Ex 1–12; 23–39	9–11 Ex 1, 4, 10, 13; 19–43
5	14–15 Orals All Ex 1–16; 19, 22, 25, 28; 31–34	14–15 Orals All Ex 1, 4, 7, 10; 20–36	14–15 Ex 4, 7, 13, 17, 18; 22–38
6	16–17 Orals All Ex 1–18; 23, 24	16–17 Orals All Ex 3, 4; 17–24	16–17 Ex Odd 11–27; 28–30
7	18 Chapter Review	18 Chapter Review	18 Chapter Review
8	19 Chapter Test	19 Chapter Test	19 Chapter Test
9	21–23 Ex 1–32; 37–40; 49–52; 57–64	21–23 Ex 9–36; 41–44; 53–56; 65–72	20 21–23 Ex 25–32; 45–48; 55, 56; 71–92
10	24–26 Orals All Ex 1–20	24–26 Orals All Ex 4; 7–26	24–26 Ex 3; 9–11; 13; 15–32
11	28–30 Orals All Ex 1–30; 53–56	28–30 Orals All Ex 25–60	28–30 Ex 29–63
12	31–33 Orals All Ex 1–24; 31–34; 39–48	31–33 Orals All Ex 19–54	31–33 Ex 19–52; 55–58

DAY	LEVEL A	LEVEL B	LEVEL C
13	36–38 Orals All Ex 1–20; 25–27	36–38 Orals All Ex 9–33	34–35
14	40–41 Ex 1–19	40–41 Ex 5–23	36–38 Ex 13–36
15	42–43 Ex Odd 1–29	42–43 Ex 7–36	40–41 Ex 9–27
16	44–45 Orals All Ex 1–26	44–45 Orals All Ex 7–32	42–43 Ex 10–38
17	46–47 Ex 1–28	46–47 Ex 13–36	44–45 Ex 11–34
18	48–49 Ex 1–16; 21–28	48–49 Ex 11–22; 29–36	46–47 Ex 17–40
19	50–51 Ex Odd 1–9; Ex 10–19	50–51 Ex 6–9; 12; 14–17; 20–25	48–49 Ex 17–22; 27–40
20	52 Chapter Review	52 Chapter Review	50–51 Ex Even
21	53 Chapter Test	53 Chapter Test	52 Chapter Review
22	56–58 Orals All Ex 1–16; 19–26	56–58 Orals All Ex 15–22; 25–34	53 Chapter Test
23	59–60 Examples 1–2	59–60 Examples 1–2	56–58 Ex 9, 10; 21–38
24	60–62 Orals All Ex 1–21; 31–33	60–62 Orals All Ex 4, 6; 13–33	59–62 Ex 9, 10; 23–39
25	64–66 Ex 1–10; 22–27; 37, 38	64–66 Ex 11–21; 28–42	64–66 Ex 28–36; 43–57
26	68–69 Ex 1–18; 41, 42	68–69 Ex 19–36; 43–46	68–69 Ex 37–58
27	70–71 Ex 1–22	70–71 Ex 11–30	70–71 Ex 15–34
28	72–74 Orals All Ex 1–10	72–75 Orals All Ex 7–15; 25, 28	72–75 Ex 9, 12; 23–32
29	74–75 Ex 11–22	76–79 Ex 5–10; 13, 14	76–79 Ex 5, 6; 11–16
30	76–78 Ex 1–4	80–82 Ex 3–12	80–82 Ex 5–14

DAY	LEVEL A	LEVEL B	LEVEL C
31	78–79 Ex 5–12	84–86 Ex 3–14	84–86 Ex 9–16
32	80–82 Ex 1–8	88 Chapter Review	88 Chapter Review
33	84–86 Ex 1–10	89 Chapter Test	89 Chapter Test
34	88 Chapter Review	91–93 Ex 7-31	91–93 Ex 17–33
35	89 Chapter Test	94–96 Orals All Ex 25–44	94–96 Ex 29–48
36	91–93 Ex 1–28	98–101 Orals All Ex 11–32	98–101 Ex 15–36
37	94–96 Orals All Ex 1–24; 37, 42	102–104 Ex 11–26	102–104 Ex 13–28
38	98–101 Orals All	105–107 Ex 7–16; 20–23; 33–42	105–107 Ex 11–16; 20–22; 24; 33–50
39	101 Ex 1–20; 27–30	108–111 Ex 1–4	108–111 Ex 1–4
40	102–104 Ex 1–16	112–114 Ex 21–38	111 Ex 5–10
41	105–107 Ex 1–19; 25–32	116 Chapter Review	112–114 Ex 25–42
42	112–114 Ex 1–20; 31, 32	117 Chapter Test	115; 116 Chapter Review
43	116 Chapter Review	119–120 Ex 9–29	117 Chapter Test
44	117 Chapter Test	121–123 Orals All Ex Odd 9–23; 33–55	119–120 Ex 15–31
45	119–120 Ex 1–20	124–125 Orals All Ex 7–22	121–123 Ex 21–28; 41–45; 54–65
46	121–123 Orals All Ex Odd 1–11; Ex 21–32; 39–43	128–130 Orals All Ex 4–6; 13–24; 27–30; 35–38; 41–44	124–125 Ex 9–25

DAY	LEVEL A	LEVEL B	LEVEL C
47	124–125 Orals All Ex 1–14	132–134 Orals All Ex 9–16; 21–36	126–127
48	128–130 Orals All Ex 1–12; 25–28; 31–34; 39, 40	135–137 Ex 9–27	128–130 Ex 25–30; 37–40; 41–52
49	132–134 Orals All Ex 1–8; 17–30	138 Chapter Review	132–134 Ex 23–43
50	135–137 Ex 1–20	139 Chapter Test	135–137 Ex Even 14–30
51	138 Chapter Review	141–143 Ex 16–34	138 Chapter Review
52	139 Chapter Test	145–147 Ex 1–18	139 Chapter Test
53	141–143 Ex 1–21	148 Ex 19–21; 25–45	141–143 Ex 19–38
54	145–147 Ex 1–12	150–152 Orals All Ex 10–33	145–148 Ex 22–24; 31–39; 46–57
55	147–148 Ex 13–27	153–155 Ex 7–9; 16–30	150–152 Ex 13–16; 31–45
56	150–152 Orals All Ex 1–21	156–157 Ex 7–24	153–155 Ex 8; 19–36
57	153–155 Ex 1–18	158–160 Orals All Ex 4–6; 13–27	156–157 Ex 16–33
58	156–157 Ex 1–18	162–164 Ex 16–21; 28–39	158–160 Ex 5; 19–36
59	158–160 Orals All Ex 1–17; 20, 21	165–167 Orals All Ex 3–14	162–164 Ex 22-27; 31–41
60	162–164 Ex 1–15; 22–24	168–170 Ex 10–23	165–167 Ex 7–18
61	165–167 Orals All Ex 1–10	172 Chapter Review	168–170 Ex Even 14–24
62	168–170 Ex 1–13	173 Chapter Test	172 Chapter Review
63	172 Chapter Review	175–177	173 Chapter Test
64	173 Chapter Test	178 Ex 3–5; 8–22	175–178 Ex 3–5; 8, 10, 12; 14–25

DAY	LEVEL A	LEVEL B	LEVEL C
65	175–177	180–183 Orals All	180–183; 25–36
66	178 Ex 1–17	183 Ex 7, 11, 12, 14, 15, 17, 18; 20–28	184–186 Ex 17–34
67	180–183 Orals All	184–186 Ex 11–28	188–190 Ex 19–32
68	183 Ex 1–10	188–190 Ex 13–26	191–193 Ex 6, 9, 12, 15; 17–24
69	184–186 Ex 1–15; 17, 22	191–193 Orals All Ex 6, 8, 9, 11, 12; 14–21	194–196 Ex 23–37
70	188–190 Ex 1–14; 17, 18	194–196 Orals All Ex 14, 15, 17, 18, 20; 22–30	198–199 Ex 9–21
71	191–193 Orals All Ex 1–10; 13, 16	198–199 Ex 6–19	200 Chapter Review
72	194–196 Orals All Ex 1–13; 19, 21	200 Chapter Review	201 Chapter Test
73	198–199 Ex 1–13; 16	201 Chapter Test	203–205 Ex 15–28
74	200 Chapter Review	203–205 Orals All Ex 11–23	206–209 Ex 1–5
75	201 Chapter Test	206–209 Ex 1–6	209 Ex 7–16
76	203–205 Orals All Ex 1–16	210–213 Orals All Ex 5–19	210–213 Ex 11–23
77	206–208 Examples Only	214–216 Ex 5–15	214–216 Ex 7–17
78	210–213 Orals All	218–220 Orals All Ex 6, 9; 11–23	217 218–220 Ex 8, 10; 15–27
79	213 Ex 1–15	221–223 Ex 3, 6, 9, 12; 14–22	221–223 Ex 16–28
80	214–216 Ex 1–9; 11, 13	224–226 Ex 5, 7, 9, 10; 12–19	224–226 Ex 14–24
81	218–220 Orals All Ex 1–11; 13, 14, 16, 18	228 Chapter Review	227; 228 Chapter Review

DAY	LEVEL A	LEVEL B	LEVEL C
82	221–223 Ex 1–13	229 Chapter Test	229 Chapter Test
83	224–226 Ex 1–9; 11, 13, 15	231–233 Orals All Ex 7–20	231–233 Ex 10–12; 16–26
84	228 Chapter Review	234–235 Ex 5; 7–18	234–235 Ex 8–20
85	229 Chapter Test	236–238 Orals All Ex 4–12	236–238 Ex 6–15
86	231–233 Orals All Ex 1–16	240–241 Ex 6–18	240–241 Ex 9–22
87	234–235 Ex 1–15	242–244 Orals All Ex 6–19	242–244 Ex 9–21
88	236–238 Orals All Ex 1–9	246–247 Ex 4–13	245; 246–247 Ex Even 6–16; 15, 17
89	240–241 Ex 1–13	248–250 Ex 13–25	248–250 Ex 22–34
90	242–244 Orals All Ex Odd 1–15	251–252 Examples 1–3	251–254 Ex 5–13
91	246–247 Ex 1–9	253–254 Ex 3–11	255–257 Ex 7–20
92	248–250 Ex 1–15	255–257 Orals All Ex 4–16	258 Chapter Review
93	251–252 Examples 1–3	258 Chapter Review	259 Chapter Test
94	253–254 Ex 1–9	259 Chapter Test	261–263 Orals All
95	255–257 Orals All Ex 1–12	261–263 Orals All	264 Ex 9–21
96	258 Chapter Review	264 Ex 4; 7–19	265–267 Ex 14–26
97	259 Chapter Test	265–267 Orals All Ex 10–22	268–270 Ex 12, 13, 18, 19; 22–29
98	261–263 Orals All	268–270 Orals All Ex 10–22	272–275 Ex 1–6
99	264 Ex 1–14	272–273 Ex 1–4	274–275 Ex 7; 11–23

DAY	LEVEL A	LEVEL B	LEVEL C
100	265–267 Orals All Ex Odd 1–11; 16, 17	274–275 Ex 5–13; 17–21	276–278 Ex Even 6–18
101	268–270 Orals All Ex 1–13	276–278 Ex 4–15	279–280 Ex 3–11
102	272–273 Ex 1–3	279–280 Ex 2–9	281–284 Ex 30–50
103	274–275 Ex 4–16	281–284 Orals All Ex 17–24; 27–38	286 Chapter Review
104	276–278 Ex 1–12	286 Chapter Review	287 Chapter Test
105	279–280 Ex 1–8	287 Chapter Test	289–291 Ex 5–16
106	281–284 Orals All Ex 1–16; 25, 26	289–291 Ex 2–12	292–293 Ex 2; 4–10
107	286 Chapter Review	292–293 Ex 2–8	294–296 Ex 9–16
108	287 Chapter Test	294–296 Orals All Ex 5–12	297–299 Ex 9–15
109	289–291 Ex 1–10	297–299 Ex 5–12	300–302 Ex 15–23
110	292–293 Ex 1–6	300–302 Orals All Ex 10–14; 17–20	304–305 Ex 4–9
111	294–296 Orals All Ex 1–8	304–305 Orals All Ex 2–7	306–309 Ex 8–18
112	297–299 Ex 1–8	306–309 Ex 6–16	310–313 Ex 3–6
113	300–302 Orals All Ex 1–8; 9, 13	310–313 Ex 1–4	313 Ex 8; 10–14
114	304–305 Orals All Ex 1–6	313 Ex 5, 7, 9, 11, 12	314 Chapter Review
115	306–309 Ex 1–12	314 Chapter Review	315 Chapter Test
116	310–313 Ex 1–4	315 Chapter Test	317–319 Ex 2, 3; 7–15
117	313 Ex 5–10	317–319 Ex 3–13	320–322 Ex 18, 21, 24, 27, 30; 39–48

DAY	LEVEL A	LEVEL B	LEVEL C
118	314 Chapter Review	320–322 Orals All Ex 17, 20, 23, 26, 29; 31–39	323–324 Ex 5, 10, 15; 24–37
119	315 Chapter Test	323–324 Ex 5, 10, 15; 16–29	326–328 Ex 5–7
120	317–319 Ex 1–10	326–328 Ex 1, 2	329 Ex 8–12
121	320–322 Orals All Ex 1–16; 19, 22, 25, 28	329 Ex 3–7	330–333 Ex 4, 5, 8, 9; 16–21
122	323–324 Ex 1–23	330–333 Ex 3–11	334–337 Ex 4–8; 16–24
123	326–328 Examples Only	333 Ex 12–17	338 Chapter Review
124	329 Ex 1, 2	334–336 Orals All Ex 1–10	339 Chapter Test
125	329 Ex 3, 4	337 Ex 11–20	341–344 Ex 6, 9; 12–16
126	330–332 Ex 1–5	338 Chapter Review	346–349 Ex 10, 12; 14–18
127	332–333 Ex 6–13	339 Chapter Test	350–352 Ex 5–14
128	334–336 Orals All Ex 1–5	341–342; 344 Ex 2–6	353–355 Ex 7–14
129	336–337 Ex 6–12	343–344 Ex 7–14	358–360 Ex 13–20
130	338 Chapter Review	346–349 Ex 3–8	361–363 Ex 11–22
131	339 Chapter Test	348–349 Ex 8, 10, 11; 14–16	364–367 Ex 2–6
132	341–342 Examples 1–3 344 Ex 1–3	350–352 Orals All Ex 2–12	367 Ex 7–12
133	343–344 Ex 4–12	353–355 Ex 2; 4–10	368–370 Ex 6–15
134	346–349 Ex 1–6	358–360 Ex 10–18	371–373 Ex 13–21

DAY	LEVEL A	LEVEL B	LEVEL C
135	348–349 Ex 7–14	361–363 Ex 8–19	374–376 Ex 27–43
136	350–352 Orals All Ex 1–11	364–367 Ex 1, 2	378 Chapter Review
137	353–355 Ex 1–8	367 Ex 3–7	379 Chapter Test
138	358–360 Ex 1–12	368–370 Ex 5–14	382–383 Ex 16–34
139	361–363 Ex 1–14	371–373 Ex 8, 9, 11, 12; 14–18	384–386 Ex 3–12
140	364–366 Examples Only	374–376 Ex 18–20; 24–37	388–390 Ex 17–26
141	367 Ex 1, 2	378 Chapter Review	391–393 Ex 13–31
142	368–370 Ex 1–9; 11	379 Chapter Test	394–395 Ex 28–45
143	371–373 Ex 1–7; 10, 13	382–383 Ex 10–28	396–397 Ex 41–64
144	374–376 Ex 1–17; 21–23	384–386 Orals All Ex Odd 1–11	399–401 Ex 12–23
145	378 Chapter Review	388–390 Ex 10–19	402–403 Ex 25–42
146	379 Chapter Test	391–393 Ex 6–26	404–406 Ex 20–37
147	382–383 Ex 1–17	394–395 Orals All Ex 20, 21, 23, 24; 26–39	408–410 Ex 18–35
148	384–386 Orals All Ex 1–10	396–397 Ex 26–46	411–412 Ex 25–40
149	388–390 Ex 1–9	399–401 Ex 9–21	414 Chapter Review
150	391–393 Ex 1–20	402–403 Ex 13–34	415 Chapter Test
151	394–395 Orals All Ex 1–19; 22, 25	404–406 Ex 14–33	417–419 Ex 14–31
152	396–397 Ex 1–25; 29, 35	408–410 Ex 14–30	420–422 Ex 20–39
153	399–401 Ex 1–17	411–412 Ex 5, 10, 15, 20; 22–38	423–426 Ex 35–51

DAY	LEVEL A	LEVEL B	LEVEL C
154	402–403 Ex 1–9; 21, 23, 25, 27	414 Chapter Review	423–426 52–66
155	404–406 Orals All Ex 1–12; Ex Odd 13–27	415 Chapter Test	427–429 Ex 15–33
156	408–410 Ex 1–16	416	430–433 Ex 5–14
157	411–412 Ex 7–21; 26, 31	417–419 Ex 11–28	434–436 Ex 23–39
158	414 Chapter Review	420–422 Ex 17–36	437–439 Ex 11–22
159	415 Chapter Test	423–426 Orals All Ex 28–40	442 Chapter Review
160	417–419 Ex 1–17; 19, 21	426 Ex 41–54	443 Chapter Test
161	420–422 Ex 1–16; 19, 22 25, 28	427–429 Ex 12–30	445–447 Examples 1, 2 Orals All
162	423–425 Orals All Ex 1–15	430–432 Examples Only	446–447 Ex 3–12
163	425 Ex 16–27	433 Ex 1–4	448–450 Ex 3–14
164	427–429 Ex 1–19; 22, 25	434–436 Ex 20–36	451–453 Orals All Ex Odd 1–17
165	430–432 Examples Only	437–439 Orals All Ex 9–20	454–455
166	433 Ex 1, 2	442 Chapter Review	456–457 Orals All Ex Odd 1–31
167	434–436 Ex 1–19; 22, 25, 28	443 Chapter Test	458–460 Ex Odd 1–19
168	437–439 Orals All Ex 1–12	445–447 Examples 1, 2 Orals All	461–463 Ex 1–18
169	442 Chapter Review	446–447 Ex 1–12	464 Chapter Review
170	443 Chapter Test	448–450 Ex 1–13	465 Chapter Test

ANSWERS

This section contains a complete set of answers for the Exercise sets (including Oral Exercises), the Special Topics, the Chapter Reviews, and the Chapter Tests.

Page x

Puzzle　**2.** (9, 2, 4), (8, 6, 1), (7, 5, 3) or (9, 5, 1), (8, 3, 4), (7, 6, 2)

Puzzle　**3.** Turn both hourglasses over and start the egg when the 3-minute hourglass runs out. When the 8-minute hourglass runs out (5 minutes later), turn it over again to get 8 more minutes.

Page 2

1. 25　**2.** 43　**3.** 30　**4.** 47　**5.** 29　**6.** 50　**7.** 35
8. 21　**9.** 18　**10.** 40　**11.** 68　**12.** 35　**13.** 26　**14.** 0
15. 10　**16.** 54　**17.** 73　**18.** 12　**19.** 32　**20.** 52
21. 76　**22.** 71　**23.** 69　**24.** 5　**25.** 19　**26.** 70
27. 79　**28.** 59　**29.** 73　**30.** 63　**31.** 53　**32.** 23
33. 57　**34.** 89　**35.** 220　**36.** 245　**37.** 1.1835
38. .15872　**39.** .1017

Page 5

ORALS　**1.** 6x, 1; x; 6　**2.** 4, 3c; c; 3　**3.** 2y,
5; y; 2　**4.** 5a, 6, 4b; a, b; 5, 4　**5.** 7, 3x, 8y; x,
y; 3, 8　**6.** 9m, 1, 2n; m, n; 9, 2　**7.** 3c, 2d, 6; c,
d; 3, 2　**8.** 7g, 3h, 12k; g, h, k; 7, 3, 12　**9.** 4y,
12z, 5w; y, z, w; 4, 12, 5

EXERCISES　**1.** 13　**2.** 17　**3.** 49　**4.** 17　**5.** 55
6. 11　**7.** 18　**8.** 39　**9.** 14　**10.** 22　**11.** 46　**12.** 39
13. 31　**14.** 70　**15.** 78　**16.** 51　**17.** 73　**18.** 45
19. 93　**20.** 100　**21.** 95　**22.** 160　**23.** 416
24. 265　**25.** 222　**26.** 298

Page 8

1. 77　**2.** 66　**3.** 96　**4.** 127　**5.** 105　**6.** 77
7. 1,700　**8.** 2,300　**9.** 1,640　**10.** 3,900
11. 49,000　**12.** 7,800　**13.** Comm. Prop. Add.
14. Assoc. Prop. Mult.　**15.** Assoc. Prop. Add.
16. Comm. Prop. Mult.　**17.** Assoc. Prop. Mult.
18. Assoc. Prop. Add.　**19.** Comm. Prop. Add.
20. Assoc. Prop. Mult.　**21.** Comm. Prop. Mult.

22. 80　**23.** 210　**24.** 270　**25.** 600　**26.** 1,000
27. 390　**28.** 56,000　**29.** 18,700　**30.** 7,200
31. no; no　**32.** no

Page 11

1. $4 \cdot 6 + 4 \cdot 2$; 32　**2.** $5 \cdot 3 + 5 \cdot 8$; 55
3. $2 \cdot 9 + 2 \cdot 4$; 26　**4.** $1 \cdot 9 + 1 \cdot 7$; 16
5. $2 \cdot 6 + 9 \cdot 6$; 66　**6.** $3 \cdot 5 + 7 \cdot 5$; 50
7. 98 = 98　**8.** 84 = 84　**9.** 6(3) + 6(5)
10. 8(4) + 8(9)　**11.** 3(8) + 3(1)
12. (8)5 + (1)5 + (9)5　**13.** 4(2) + 4(7) + 4(6)
14. (5)3 + (4)3 + 9(3)　**15.** 4(6 + 2)　**16.** 7(3 + 9)
17. (5 + 9)6　**18.** (1 + 9)5　**19.** (3 + 7)8
20. 9(2 + 4)　**21.** 5(4 + 2 + 7)　**22.** (1 + 2 + 8)3
23. (6 + 4 + 7)8　**24.** 2(9 + 4 + 6)　**25.** 4(3 +
7 + 1)　**26.** (5 + 4 + 9)6　**27.** 7(8 + 4 + 2)
28. (1 + 5 + 3)9　**29.** 7(5) + 7(1) + 7(9) + 7(2)
30. (6)5 + (8)5 + (4)5 + (3)5　**31.** 4(1) + 4(9) +
4(7) + 4(2)　**32.** $3 \cdot 2 + 3 \cdot 6 + 3 \cdot 4 + 3 \cdot 8$
33. 7(8) + 7(4) + 7(3) + 7(5)　**34.** 5(5) + 5(2) +
5(6) + 5(5)　**35.** $4 \cdot 8 + 4 \cdot 1 + 4 \cdot 3 + 4 \cdot 5 +$
$4 \cdot 9$　**36.** (2)7 + (7)7 + (1)7 + (6)7 + (3)7
37. 3(8) + 3(9) + 3(1) + 3(4) + 3(6)　**38.** 6(3 +
4 + 1 + 2)　**39.** 4(7 + 7 + 2 + 7)　**40.** yes　**41.** no
42. no　**43.** yes

Page 12

1. 3,000 mm　**2.** 60,000 cm　**3.** 70,000 dm
4. .005 km　**5.** .08 m　**6.** .000004 km　**7.** 300 cL
8. 5,000 cL　**9.** 6,000,000 mL　**10.** .007 hL
11. .008 kL　**12.** .000009 kL　**13.** 5,000 mg
14. 3,000 cg　**15.** 8,000,000 mg　**16.** .02 dag
17. .007 kg　**18.** .000006 kg

Page 15

ORALS　(3, 6, 8, 11, 13, 16, 18, 20 cannot
be simplified.)　**1.** 5x　**2.** 11p　**4.** 13b　**5.** 11y
7. 15r　**9.** 10m　**10.** 16x　**12.** 13c　**14.** 7x
15. 13w　**17.** 8z　**19.** 10g

EXERCISES **1.** $10x + 3$ **2.** $8x + 13$
3. $7y + 9$ **4.** $8m + 2$ **5.** $11a + 9$ **6.** $8r + 8$
7. $6z + 12$ **8.** $13z + 9$ **9.** $9b + 7$ **10.** $6x + 11$
11. $9k + 7$ **12.** $6x + 17$ **13.** $5y + 1$ **14.** $2a + 12$
15. $11z + 4$ **16.** $5m + 9$ **17.** $10t + 16$
18. $10y + 10$ **19.** $8z + 13$ **20.** $12x + 8$
21. $9x + 9y$ **22.** $8a + 15b$ **23.** $7m + 9q$
24. $12c + 9d$ **25.** $11x + 8y + 1$ **26.** $4y +$
$3z + 7$ **27.** $16a + 8b + 6$ **28.** $10a + 4b + 9c$
29. $7x + 2y + 5z + 1$ **30.** $15g + 5h + 4$ **31.** 25
32. 45 **33.** 64 **34.** 51 **35.** 54 **36.** 40 **37.** 86
38. 97

Page 17

ORALS **1.** $24x$ **2.** $63r$ **3.** $20y$ **4.** $27z$ **5.** $28a$
6. $56x$ **7.** $6a + 15$ **8.** $12x + 8$ **9.** $35c + 28$
10. $5 + 45a$

EXERCISES **1.** $43y + 7$ **2.** $10z + 15$
3. $29m + 36$ **4.** $6m + 33$ **5.** $36c + 14$
6. $55b + 6$ **7.** $29x + 12$ **8.** $8d + 29$ **9.** $42r + 56$
10. $14n + 20$ **11.** $27y + 30$ **12.** $23d + 56$
13. $39c + 5$ **14.** $51z + 24$ **15.** $8x + 11$
16. $47a + 12$ **17.** $13x + 24$ **18.** $33y + 26$
19. $18c + 11$ **20.** $23g + 43$ **21.** $14x + 26$
22. $28z + 61$ **23.** $22r + 29$ **24.** $53y + 24$
25. $38e + 38$ **26.** $52a + 41$ **27.** $170c + 70$
28. $77a + 80$ **29.** $87x + 120$ **30.** $72y + 93$

Page 18
1. 22 **2.** 21 **3.** 4 **4.** 14 **5.** 25 **6.** 43 **7.** 65
8. 27 **9.** 44 **10.** 60 **11.** 85 **12.** 72 **13.** 5, $9x$; x;
9 **14.** $5y$, 1, $4z$; y, z; 5, 4 **15.** $8a$, $7b$, $2c$; a, b,
c; 8, 7, 2 **16.** 87 **17.** 80 **18.** 520 **19.** 4,700
20. 97,000 **21.** 8,200 **22.** Comm. Prop. Add.
23. Assoc. Prop. Mult. **24.** Assoc. Prop. Add.
25. Comm. Prop. Mult. **26.** $7 \cdot 4 + 7 \cdot 9$
27. $6 \cdot 3 + 8 \cdot 3$ **28.** $5 \cdot 9 + 2 \cdot 9 + 6 \cdot 9$
29. $8 \cdot 3 + 8 \cdot 7 + 8 \cdot 5$ **30.** $5(6 + 3)$
31. $9(8 + 2)$ **32.** $(6 + 1 + 6)7$ **33.** $4(5 + 8 +$
$3 + 1)$ **34.** $45 = 45$ **35.** $45 = 45$ **36.** $10x + 8$
37. $12y + 9$ **38.** $8t + 16$ **39.** $11p + 14q + 3$
40. $23r + 6$ **41.** $20y + 24$ **42.** $49p + 18$
43. $14z + 14$ **44.** $60x + 62$ **45** $57y + 101$
46. $10x + 9$; 89 **47.** $13 + 9y$; 31 **48.** $10a + 10b$;
30 **49.** $4 + 12x + 11y$; 166

Page 19
1. 38 **2.** 37 **3.** 39 **4.** 63 **5.** 67 **6.** 26 **7.** 38
8. 4, $7x$, $9y$; x, y; 7, 9 **9.** 87 **10.** 5,800

11. 110 **12.** 18,600 **13.** Assoc. Prop. Add.
14. Comm. Prop. Add. **15.** Comm. Prop. Mult.
16. Assoc. Prop. Mult. **17.** $6(4) + 6(9)$
18. $8 \cdot 3 + 1 \cdot 3 + 7 \cdot 3$ **19.** $9(7 + 2)$ **20.** $(4 +$
$6 + 7)5$ **21.** $45 = 45$ **22.** $77 = 77$ **23.** $9x + 7$
24. $12y + 7z + 8$ **25.** $22a + 28$ **26.** $13r + 27$
27. $47x + 33$ **28.** $46y + 47$ **29.** 55 **30.** 82

Page 20
1. $15°C$ **2.** $30°C$ **3.** $0°C$ **4.** $180°C$

Page 23
1. $+10$ **2.** $+13$ **3.** -14 **4.** $+2$ **5.** -10 **6.** $+6$
7. $+7$ **8.** -8 **9.** $+5$ **10.** $+8$ **11.** -3 **12.** -10
13. -1 **14.** $+4$ **15.** -9 **16.** $+7$ **17.** -10
18. -4 **19.** -4 **20.** $+9$ **21.** -13 **22.** $+16$
23. $+3$ **24.** $+12$ **25.** $+5$ **26.** -19 **27.** -11
28. -11 **29.** -23 **30.** $+11$ **31.** $+20$ **32.** -26
33. $+9$ **34.** $+9$ **35.** -7 **36.** -7 **37.** $+5$
38. $+5$ **39.** -4 **40.** -4 **41.** $+6$ **42.** $+6$
43. -10 **44.** -10 **45.** -2 **46.** -2 **47.** $+8$
48. $+8$ **49.** 0 **50.** 0 **51.** 0 **52.** 0 **53.** 0 **54.** 0
55. 0 **56.** 0 **57.** -22 **58.** -58 **59.** $+24$
60. -10 **61.** $+67$ **62.** $+19$ **63.** -81 **64.** 0
65. $+8$ **66.** -4 **67.** -75 **68.** -79 **69.** -131
70. $+11$ **71.** 0 **72.** $+4$ **73.** $+22$ **74.** $+625$
75. -787 **76.** -230 **77.** -132 **78.** $-1,017$
79. $+994$ **80.** -227 **81.** Drop the signs; add
the numbers; give a positive sign to the result.
82. Drop the signs; add the numbers; give a
negative sign to the result. **83.** Drop the signs;
subtract the smaller number from the larger;
give the result the same sign as the larger.
84. Same as **83**. **85.** $-.83$ **86.** $-.24$
87. -1.074 **88.** $-.61$ **89.** $+1.87$ **90.** -3.98
91. $+85.63$ **92.** $+1.7026$

Page 25

ORALS **1.** -2 **2.** $+6$ **3.** -10 **4.** 0 **5.** $+1$
6. $+9$ **7.** -7 **8.** $+5$ **9.** -18 **10.** $+93$ **11.** -87
12. $+125$ **13.** $+50$ **14.** -233 **15.** $+424$
16. $-a$ **17.** x **18.** n **19.** the opposite of x
20. $-a$ is positive if a is negative.

EXERCISES **1.** $+1 = +1$ **2.** $+5 = +5$
3. $-13 = -13$ **4.** $-8 = -8$ **5.** Comm. **6.** Add.
Inv. **7.** Add. Iden. **8.** Assoc. **9.** Add. Iden.
10. Add. Inv. **11.** Comm. **12.** Comm.
13. Assoc. **14.** Add. Inv. **15.** Add. Inv. **16.** Add.

Iden. **17.** Comm. **18.** Assoc. **19.** −3 **20.** +5
21. +2 **22.** −8 **23.** −7 **24.** 0 **25.–26.** opposite
of neg. is pos.

27.

Expression	Reason
$(-9 + +4) + -8$	Given
$-8 + (-9 + +4)$	Comm.
$-8 + (+4 + -9)$	Comm.
$(-8 + +4) + -9$	Assoc.

28.

Expression	Reason
$(-6 + +7) + -5$	Given
$(+7 + -6) + -5$	Comm.
$+7 + (-6 + -5)$	Assoc.
$+7 + (-5 + -6)$	Comm.
$(+7 + -5) + -6$	Assoc.
$(-5 + +7) + -6$	Comm.

29.

Expression	Reason
$(-3 + +5) + +3$	Given
$(+5 + -3) + +3$	Comm.
$+5 + (-3 + +3)$	Assoc.
$+5 + 0$	Add. Inv.
$+5$	Add. Iden.

30.

Expression	Reason
$(-8 + -3) + +8$	Given
$(-3 + -8) + +8$	Comm.
$-3 + (-8 + +8)$	Assoc.
$-3 + 0$	Add. Inv.
-3	Add. Iden.

31.

Expression	Reason
$(x + y) + z$	Given
$(y + x) + z$	Comm.
$y + (x + z)$	Assoc.
$y + (z + x)$	Comm.
$(y + z) + x$	Assoc.
$(z + y) + x$	Comm.

32.

Expression	Reason
$(-x + -y) + x$	Given
$(-y + -x) + x$	Comm.
$-y + (-x + x)$	Assoc.
$-y + 0$	Add. Inv.
$-y$	Add. Iden.

Page 27

1. $\{H1, H2, H3, H4, H5, H6, T1, T2, T3, T4, T5, T6\}$ **2.** $\{1, 2, 3, 4, 5, 6\}$; $\frac{1}{2}$ **3.** $\frac{5}{36}$; $\frac{1}{2}$ **4.** $\frac{1}{6}$; 0

Page 30

ORALS **1.** neg. **2.** pos. **3.** pos. **4.** neg.

EXERCISES **1.** +21 **2.** −8 **3.** −48 **4.** +3
5. −45 **6.** 0 **7.** −28 **8.** 0 **9.** −7 **10.** +30
11. −16 **12.** 0 **13.** +27 **14.** −42 **15.** 0 **16.** +6
17. −8 **18.** +27 **19.** +60 **20.** −60 **21.** +72
22. 0 **23.** −18 **24.** +130 **25.** 0 **26.** −70
27. +100 **28.** +77 **29.** 0 **30.** −36 **31.** −100
32. −96 **33.** −39 **34.** −48 **35.** −120 **36.** 0
37. −32 **38.** −75 **39.** +72 **40.** 0 **41.** +250
42. +120 **43.** −480 **44.** +130 **45.** −720
46. +41 **47.** −1,600 **48.** +89 **49.** +900
50. −546 **51.** 0 **52.** −3,969 **53.** +90
54. +48 **55.** +144 **56.** +945 **57.** +1,512
58. 0 **59.** −5,040 **60.** +1,080 **61.** $(-4)(+2) = (+2)(-4)$; $(-6)(-5) = (-5)(-6)$ **62.** $(-2 \cdot +3) \cdot -8 = -2 \cdot (+3 \cdot -8)$; $(+6 \cdot -9) \cdot -4 = +6 \cdot (-9 \cdot -4)$ **63.** $-8(-6 + +3) = (-8)(-6) + (-8)(+3)$; $+2(-7 + -9) = (+2)(-7) + (+2)(-9)$

Page 32

ORALS **1.** pos. **2.** pos. **3.** neg. **4.** neg.
5. pos. **6.** neg. **7.** pos. **8.** neg. **9.** pos.
10. pos.

EXERCISES **1.** +2 **2.** −4 **3.** −5 **4.** +8
5. +7 **6.** −23 **7.** +9 **8.** −1 **9.** −9 **10.** −4
11. 0 **12.** +17 **13.** +6 **14.** −7 **15.** +3 **16.** +5
17. +4 **18.** −5 **19.** −3 **20.** −5 **21.** +1 **22.** −6
23. +5 **24.** +4 **25.** −42 **26.** −6 **27.** −4
28. +8 **29.** +7 **30.** −2 **31.** −9 **32.** −4 **33.** −8
34. +8 **35.** +15 **36.** −10 **37.** +5 **38.** −7
39. +6 **40.** −8 **41.** −32 **42.** +46 **43.** +1
44. +1 **45.** +1 **46.** +1 **47.** +9 **48.** +8 **49.** +1
50. +5 **51.** −3 **52.** −18 **53.** −5 **54.** −3
55. −2 **56.** −8 **57.** +.0002 **58.** −30,000

Page 34

1. 60 m above sea level **2.** 0 **3.** yes **4.** 0
5. $.62 **6.** 10,000 m

ORALS **1.** pos. 3 plus neg. 8 **2.** neg. 7 plus pos. 6 **3.** neg. 5 plus neg. 9 **4.** pos. 2 plus pos. 8 **5.** pos. 4 plus neg. 3 plus pos. 10 **6.** neg. 8 plus pos. 12 plus neg. 7 **7.** neg. 3 plus neg. 1 plus pos. 6 **8.** pos. 3 plus neg. 7 plus pos. 9 **9.** neg. 8 plus pos. 3 times z plus neg. 1 **10.** neg. 4 times x plus neg. 3 **11.** pos. 6 times x plus neg. 5 times y plus pos. 1 **12.** pos. 7 times x plus neg. 5 times y plus neg. 3

EXERCISES **1.** -6 **2.** -6 **3.** 13 **4.** -12 **5.** 0 **6.** -6 **7.** -44 **8.** 17 **9.** 12 **10.** -9 **11.** 7 **12.** -19 **13.** 19 **14.** -30 **15.** 10 **16.** -9 **17.** 17 **18.** -41 **19.** -21 **20.** -11 **21.** 5 **22.** 33 **23.** 34 **24.** -1 **25.** -126 **26.** -54 **27.** -83 **28.** -17 **29.** 16 **30.** -127 **31.** -102 **32.** 90 **33.** -94 **34.** -5 **35.** 0 **36.** -7

Page 39

1.

1	12	7	14
8	13	2	11
10	3	16	5
15	6	9	4

2.

16	2	3	13
5	11	10	8
9	7	6	12
4	14	15	1

Page 41
1. 14 **2.** 44 **3.** -2 **4.** 1 **5.** 11 **6.** 7 **7.** 12 **8.** 38 **9.** 63 **10.** 28 **11.** 3 **12.** 94 **13.** -32 **14.** 40 **15.** -68 **16.** 95 **17.** -74 **18.** -132 **19.** -41 **20.** -36 **21.** 94 **22.** -117 **23.** 71 **24.** -26 **25.** -211 **26.** $6x + 36y + 96$; 192 **27.** $13x + 36y + 8$; 90

Page 43
1. $5y$ **2.** $-3a$ **3.** $2b$ **4.** $-11x$ **5.** $-2z$ **6.** $-11c$ **7.** $-5r$ **8.** $-10y$ **9.** $-7r$ **10.** $2x - 5$ **11.** $-4z - 8$ **12.** $-12c - 8$ **13.** $-2q - 9$ **14.** $5x - 4$ **15.** $-9y - 4$ **16.** $2t + 16$ **17.** $-12x + 1$ **18.** $-13y + 11$ **19.** $2x + 6y + 3$ **20.** $-2a - 3b - 4$ **21.** $4r - 6s - 6$ **22.** $-4p + 2q - 5$ **23.** $-14x + 4y + 8$ **24.** $-4d + 3e - 11$ **25.** $-10x + 3y - 4$ **26.** $-5j - 7k - 6$ **27.** $13a - 4c - 16$ **28.** $-2q + 5s - 2$ **29.** $-6a + 3b + 1$ **30.** $-8a + 4b + 4$ **31.** $2x + 6y - 3$; -25 **32.** $-13z + 6x + 8$; -108 **33.** $6x + 4y - 4z$; -56 **34.** $-2z - 12y - 3x$; 26 **35.** $-11x + 6y - 6$; -2 **36.** $-8y - 5z - 7$; -23

37. $1.2x - 1.193y - 4$; -7.3425 **38.** $-.78x + .3y + 3.02z + 2.3$; 3.29608

Page 45

ORALS **1.** Mult. Prop. -1 **2.** Mult. Iden. **3.** Mult. Iden. **4.** Mult. Prop. -1

EXERCISES **1.** 0 **2.** $-2a$ **3.** $3b$ **4.** $5c$ **5.** $12r$ **6.** $-y$ **7.** $-a + 2$ **8.** $-4z + 11$ **9.** $c - 1$ **10.** $8d + 4$ **11.** $-e - 3$ **12.** $x - 5$ **13.** $-9q + 15$ **14.** $s - 4$ **15.** $2p - 7$ **16.** $6a + 1$ **17.** $-5d - 10$ **18.** -14 **19.** $-3a + 2$ **20.** $-3r - 13$ **21.** $-7z + 16$ **22.** $-3y + 10$ **23.** $14b - 14$ **24.** $-6f + 2$ **25.** $2x - 4y - 8$; -36 **26.** $-y + z - 5$; -14 **27.** $-x - y + 8z$; -28 **28.** $-x + 3y + z$; 17 **29.** $x - 8y - z$; -47 **30.** $6x - y - z$; -15 **31.** $x - 9y - 6z + 1$; -37 **32.** $-15x + 2z + 3$; 27 **33.** $.7x + .002y - z$; -1.98692 **34.** $2.1x + 1.99y - z$; .1226

Page 47
1. $29x - 16$ **2.** $27z - 17$ **3.** $14y - 14$ **4.** $-18b - 56$ **5.** $-8a + 38$ **6.** $29c - 48$ **7.** $2x - 27$ **8.** $22x - 21$ **9.** $-39a - 63$ **10.** $32d + 48$ **11.** $-29a - 21$ **12.** $c + 10$ **13.** $-6x - 11$ **14.** $-53y - 32$ **15.** $25c - 27$ **16.** $-19r + 12$ **17.** $17x$ **18.** $9z - 22$ **19.** $-38y - 74$ **20.** $-11x + 37$ **21.** $17y - 32$; 104 **22.** $15c - 12$; -87 **23.** $-37x - 6$; 142 **24.** $-x + 12$; 6 **25.** $10x - 7$; -97 **26.** $31y - 32$; -218 **27.** $31d - 26$; 67 **28.** $-12r + 8$; 92 **29.** $-17x - 1$; 16 **30.** $-14g - 5$; 37 **31.** $-33x + 14$ **32.** $-23y + 23$ **33.** $-29y + 33$ **34.** $-39x + 28$ **35.** $87z + 19$ **36.** $44d - 38$ **37.** $-20x - 48$ **38.** $54z - 60$ **39.** $-20x + 2$ **40.** $-27x + 36$

Page 49
1. $-11y - 2$ **2.** $-6x + 12$ **3.** $-5z - 12$ **4.** $-11x - 3$ **5.** $-2c + 8$ **6.** $-2x + 3$ **7.** $3f - 8$ **8.** $-16z - 8$ **9.** $9y - 9$ **10.** $-13p - 1$ **11.** $8y - 17$ **12.** $11r + 21$ **13.** $-6e - 13$ **14.** $-9c - 2$ **15.** $-6d - 1$ **16.** $2x - 14$ **17.** $4y - 4$ **18.** $6q + 24$ **19.** $-11z + 6$ **20.** $17x - 9$ **21.** $-19b - 10$ **22.** $-5c + 14$ **23.** -12 **24.** 62 **25.** -23 **26.** -3 **27.** 39 **28.** -12 **29.** -7 **30.** 84 **31.** -7 **32.** -60 **33.** $-23y + 33$ **34.** $-41x + 26$ **35.** $-4z - 2$

36. $2a - 25$ **37.** $9r - 2$ **38.** 13 **39.** $-8x + 10$
40. $-19a + 7$

Page 51
1. 3 **2.** 7 **3.** -2 **4.** -13 **5.** -14 **6.** 7 **7.** 9
8. 20 **9.** -18 **10.** $2x - 1$ **11.** $3b + 8$
12. $5y + 8$ **13.** $-x - 12$ **14.** $3x + 9$ **15.** $2y +$
17 **16.** $8x + 17$ **17.** $-5x + 3$ **18.** $-20y - 3$
19. $20z + 10$ **20.** $3a + 3$ **21.** $3y - 27$
22. $4x - 4$ **23.** $18z - 6$ **24.** $-3y + 27$
25. $-3x - 11$
26. $a - b = a + -b$ (meaning of $a - b$)
$\quad\quad = a + (-1)b$ (Mult. Prop. -1)

Page 52
1. $+10$ **2.** $+4$ **3.** $+3$ **4.** -5 **5.** -18 **6.** -7
7. -5 **8.** 9 **9.** -9 **10.** -23 **11.** 8 **12.** 11
13. 6 **14.** -28 **15.** -9 **16.** -63 **17.** -16
18. 24 **19.** 105 **20.** 0 **21.** -75 **22.** 84
23. -120 **24.** 320 **25.** 7 **26.** -7 **27.** -6
28. 13 **29.** -5 **30.** 3 **31.** -27 **32.** 55 **33.** 49
34. y **35.** $-3x$ **36.** $4d - 2$ **37.** $-5p + 20$
38. $8c - 6$ **39.** $5a + 16$ **40.** $-3x + 1$
41. $-9z - 5$ **42.** $27x - 35$; 73 **43.** $-30k + 16$;
166 **44.** -13 **45.** 15 **46.** 3 **47.** $4x + 12$
48. $11a - 10$ **49.** $2a - 8$ **50.** $-a - 9$
51. Comm. **52.** Add. Iden.

Page 53
1. $+5$ **2.** -13 **3.** -5 **4.** -14 **5.** -74 **6.** 7
7. $+16$ **8.** -21 **9.** -54 **10.** 0 **11.** $+45$
12. -112 **13.** -4 **14.** $+6$ **15.** -14 **16.** $+9$
17. $+4$ **18.** $+36$ **19.** -22 **20.** -59 **21.** $-6x$
22. $6c + 6$ **23.** $2a - 5b - 9$ **24.** $3z + 5$
25. $-8y - 1$ **26.** $-20x + 10$ **27.** $20a - 25$
28. $6y - 7$ **29.** $-13b - 10$ **30.** $4p - 3$ **31.** 21
32. 119 **33.** 5 **34.** -13 **35.** $13y - 8$
36. $2a - 3$ **37.** Assoc. Prop. Add. **38.** Comm.
Prop. Add.

Page 54
1. Start. Insert first key. Does it work? No:
Insert second key. Yes: Stop. Does second key
work? No: Insert third key. Yes: Stop. **2.** Start.
Select unused bulb. Remove old bulb. Insert
unused bulb. Turn on light. Does bulb work?
Yes: Stop. No: Select another unused bulb.
(Return to step 4.)

Page 58
ORALS **1.** O **2.** T **3.** O **4.** O **5.** O **6.** T
7. F **8.** O **9.** F **10.** O **11.** T **12.** O **13.** O
14. F **15.** O

EXERCISES **1.** 5 **2.** 8 **3.** 9 **4.** 7 **5.** 5 **6.** 2
7. 9 **8.** 3 **9.** 7 **10.** 8 **11.** 4 **12.** 9 **13.** 5
14. 17 **15.** 7 **16.** 9 **17.** 4 **18.** 7 **19.** 3 **20.** 2
21. 4 **22.** 9 **23.** 2 **24.** 3 **25.** 6 **26.** 5 **27.** 3
28. 4 **29.** 0 **30.** -1 **31.** $\frac{1}{4}$ **32.** $\frac{4}{3}$ **33.** -3 **34.** 0
35. none **36.** -3 **37.** $\frac{1}{2}$ **38.** none

Page 62
ORALS **1.** -9; 2 **2.** -2; 5 **3.** -30; -6
4. -14; -3 **5.** 7; 4 **6.** -40; -8 **7.** -19; 4
8. 7; 3 **9.** -20; 7 **10.** 32; 10 **11.** 58; -9
12. -20; 7 **13.** 5; 4 **14.** 42; 8 **15.** -14; 10
16. -2; 11 **17.** 5; 12 **18.** -8; 9 **19.** 17; 10
20. -62; 13 **21.** 7; 15 **22.** -73; -20 **23.** 9; 10
24. -51; -9

EXERCISES **1.** 4 **2.** -2 **3.** 6 **4.** 9 **5.** -1
6. 7 **7.** -3 **8.** 5 **9.** -2 **10.** 4 **11.** -8
12. 6 **13.** -1 **14.** 10 **15.** -5 **16.** 2 **17.** -3
18. 0 **19.** 1 **20.** -6 **21.** -2 **22.** 5 **23.** 0
24. -4 **25.** $\frac{1}{5}$ **26.** $\frac{3}{4}$ **27.** $\frac{1}{6}$ **28.** $\frac{1}{3}$ **29.** $\frac{1}{8}$ **30.** $\frac{3}{4}$
31. $\frac{2}{5}$ **32.** $\frac{2}{3}$ **33.** $\frac{1}{4}$ **34.** $\frac{5}{6}$ **35.** $\frac{3}{8}$ **36.** $\frac{4}{7}$ **37.** $-.176$
38. 1.4 **39.** .406

Page 63
1. 7 **2.** 8

Page 66
1. 3 **2.** 7 **3.** 3 **4.** 4 **5.** 8 **6.** 1 **7.** 15 **8.** 6 **9.** 4
10. 5 **11.** 7 **12.** -4 **13.** -11 **14.** 1 **15.** 6
16. 5 **17.** 1 **18.** -7 **19.** 4 **20.** -6 **21.** 5
22. 4 **23.** 2 **24.** 21 **25.** 6 **26.** 6 **27.** 7 **28.** 9
29. -4 **30.** 6 **31.** 1 **32.** 7 **33.** 3 **34.** -6
35. 4 **36.** -2 **37.** -3 **38.** $-\frac{2}{5}$ **39.** $\frac{1}{4}$ **40.** $-\frac{2}{3}$
41. $\frac{3}{5}$ **42.** $-\frac{4}{7}$ **43.** $\frac{5}{6}$ **44.** $-\frac{2}{7}$ **45.** $\frac{5}{4}$ **46.** $\frac{9}{5}$ **47.** $-\frac{7}{5}$
48. $-\frac{4}{3}$ **49.** $\frac{3}{2}$ **50.** $-\frac{7}{4}$ **51.** $\frac{3}{2}$ **52.** $-\frac{7}{3}$ **53.** $\frac{5}{2}$
54. $-\frac{5}{7}$ **55.** .3 **56.** $-.021$ **57.** .64

Page 67
1. x; $2x$; $2x + 6$; $3x + 6$; $x + 2$; $x + 2$
2. Answers may vary.

Page 69

1. 7 **2.** 6 **3.** −7 **4.** 12 **5.** 8 **6.** −5 **7.** −6
8. −5 **9.** 20 **10.** 12 **11.** −8 **12.** 2 **13.** 9 **14.** 4
15. −1 **16.** 4 **17.** 10 **18.** −1 **19.** 5 **20.** −3
21. −3 **22.** 2 **23.** −4 **24.** 1 **25.** 2 **26.** −1
27. 2 **28.** 2 **29.** −1 **30.** 3 **31.** 1 **32.** 8 **33.** 11
34. 1 **35.** 3 **36.** −1 **37.** −2 **38.** 2 **39.** 1
40. −2 **41.** $\frac{16}{5}$ **42.** $-\frac{10}{9}$ **43.** $\frac{1}{13}$ **44.** 11 **45.** $-\frac{1}{6}$
46. $\frac{13}{9}$ **47.** $-\frac{3}{19}$ **48.** $-\frac{4}{15}$ **49.** 2 **50.** $-\frac{7}{9}$ **51.** 9
52. $\frac{13}{6}$ **53.** $\frac{42}{11}$ **54.** $-\frac{1}{4}$ **55.** $-\frac{3}{8}$ **56.** $\frac{9}{2}$ **57.** $-\frac{4}{9}$
58. $-\frac{8}{7}$

Page 71

1. $8 - 5$ **2.** $9 + 7$ **3.** $12 + 6$ **4.** $15 - 8$
5. $23 + 2$ **6.** $15 - x$ **7.** $y + 4$ **8.** $x + 7$ **9.** $n - 8$
10. $8 - 2x$ **11.** $5y + 3$ **12.** $7n - 2$ **13.** $3n - 6$
14. $5 - 2n$ **15.** $25 - 4n$ **16.** $7n + 8$ **17.** $4x + 8$
18. $3n - 12$ **19.** $14 + 2n$ **20.** $2n - 4$
21. $9n - 7$ **22.** $2n + 1$ **23.** $x + y$ **24.** $y + x$
25. $7x - 2y$ **26.** $3n - m$ **27.** $xy + 9$
28. $20 - mn$ **29.** $y - 5x$ **30.** $6x + 5y$
31. $5 + 7y + 8$, or $7y + 13$ **32.** $2x + 7 + 6$, or
$2x + 13$ **33.** $5n - 2 + 9$, or $5n + 7$ **34.** $8y +$
$x - 2x$, or $8y - x$

Page 74

ORALS **1.** $2x + 5 = 14$ **2.** $6 - 4n = 18$
3. $7n = n + 3$ **4.** $n - 2 = 20$ **5.** $2n + 8 = 2$
6. $x + 6 = 8x$ **7.** $2 - 4x = 15$ **8.** $12 = 6x + 5$
9. $2x - 16 = 32$ **10.** $9 + 5n = 18$

EXERCISES **1.** 4 **2.** 26 **3.** 3 **4.** 6 **5.** 1
6. −4 **7.** 3 **8.** −1 **9.** −2 **10.** −4 **11.** −3
12. −1 **13.** 1 **14.** −10 **15.** −36 **16.** 4
17. 5 **18.** −9 **19.** 7 **20.** 17 **21.** −8 **22.** −5
23. −10 **24.** −2 **25.** 7 **26.** 9 **27.** −9 **28.** 3
29. 1 **30.** −14 **31.** −3 **32.** −2

Page 78

1. 7, 35 **2.** 7, 17 **3.** 39, 11 **4.** 8, 47 **5.** 37, 46
6. 9, 10 **7.** 51, 17 **8.** $51.50, $63.50 **9.** $31,
$58 **10.** 31, 12 **11.** 8, 11, 15 **12.** 4, 8, 14
13. 9, 12 **14.** 5, 9 **15.** 26, 13 **16.** 14, 17

Page 82

1. 3 dimes, 12 nickels **2.** 15 nickels **3.** 1 dime,
3 quarters **4.** 28 dimes **5.** 7 dimes, 4 quarters

6. 21 dimes **7.** 14 pennies, 21 nickels
8. 3 dimes **9.** 502 tickets **10.** 35 dimes, 11
quarters **11.** 3 nickels, 18 dimes, 20 pennies
12. 21 pennies **13.** 44 dimes **14.** 9 nickels,
18 dimes, 11 quarters

Page 83

1. 326 km **2.** 889 km **3.** Bus tour is more
economical by $6. **4.** 960 km

Page 86

1. 13 m; 7 m **2.** 14 cm; 7 cm **3.** 19 km; 8 km
4. 25 m; 9 m **5.** 15 cm; 13 cm; 21 cm **6.** 7 m;
14 m; 19 m **7.** 9 cm; 12 cm; 17 cm **8.** 17 km;
11 km; 19 km **9.** 11 m; 11 m **10.** 10 cm
11. 16 m **12.** 15 cm **13.** 18 cm; 9 cm **14.** 8 m
15. 6 cm; 9 cm **16.** 8 m; 32 m

Page 88

1. 7 **2.** none **3.** 3 **4.** 6 **5.** none **6.** 3 **7.** −11
8. 2 **9.** $-\frac{8}{5}$ **10.** 10 **11.** 5 **12.** −3 **13.** 1 **14.** 0
15. $\frac{23}{2}$ **16.** 7 **17.** 3 **18.** 6 **19.** 22 **20.** 9
21. −4 **22.** 4 **23.** −13 **24.** 3 **25.** −5 **26.** $\frac{2}{3}$
27. −3 **28.** −1 **29.** 8 **30.** −1 **31.** −2 **32.** 1
33. $6 + x$ **34.** $y - 12$ **35.** $n - 3$ **36.** $3x + 6$
37. $2y - 5$ **38.** $9x - 7$ **39.** 4 **40.** 7, 19 **41.** 5,
22 **42.** 3 quarters **43.** 26 cm; 8 cm **44.** 7 m;
4 m; 6 m

Page 89

1. 3 **2.** 9 **3.** 4 **4.** 3 **5.** −5 **6.** 4 **7.** 7 **8.** 0
9. −2 **10.** 0 **11.** $\frac{31}{10}$ **12.** 6 **13.** 3 **14.** 12 **15.** 1
16. −1 **17.** 2 **18.** 10 **19.** $7 - 2$ **20.** $5 + x$
21. $2y - x$ **22.** $3n + 8$ **23.** 5 **24.** 11, 25
25. 8 dimes, 17 quarters **26.** 24 m; 9 m

Page 90

1. −11, −12, −13 **2.** 243, 729, 2,187 **3.** −3,
−3, −3 **4.** −2, 2, −2 **5.** .00001, .000001,
.0000001 **6.** 48, −96, 192 **7.** 13, 14, 16
8. 36, 49, 64 **9.** 125, 216, 343 **10.** 14, 18, 22
11. $\frac{5}{6}$, $\frac{6}{7}$, $\frac{7}{8}$ **12.** 128, 512, 2,048 **13.** 24, 35, 48
14. $\frac{25}{6}$, $\frac{36}{7}$, $\frac{49}{8}$ **15.** 124, 215, 342 **16.** 21, 34, 55

Page 93

1. equal **2.** not equal **3.** not equal **4.** equal
5. equal **6.** not equal **7.** finite **8.** infinite

9. infinite **10.** finite **11.** finite **12.** infinite
13. {1, 2, 3, 4, 5} **14.** {9, 10, 11, . . .}
15. {−3, −2} **16.** ϕ **17.** {7} **18.** ϕ **19.** {7}
20. ϕ **21.** {4} **22.** {6} **23.** {4} **24.** {4} **25.** {9}
26. ϕ **27.** {−1} **28.** ϕ **29.** {all numbers}
30. ϕ **31.** {all numbers} **32.** ϕ **33.** {all numbers}

Page 96

ORALS **1.** < **2.** > **3.** < **4.** > **5.** < **6.** >
7. < **8.** < **9.** > **10.** > **11.** {−4, −3, −2, . . .}
12. {−8, −7, −6, . . .} **13.** {+2, +1, 0, . . .}
14. {−6, −7, −8, . . .} **15.** {−3, −2, −1, . . .}
16. {−8, −9, −10, . . .}

EXERCISES **1.** all points to the left of 3
2. all points to the right of 1 **3.** 5 and all points to the left **4.** −5 and all points to the right **5.** −2 and all points to the left **6.** all points to the right of −4 **7.** all points to the right of 2 **8.** all points to the left of 4 **9.** −6 and all points to the right **10.** all points to the right of −5 **11.** all points to the left of 2 **12.** 0 and all points to the left **13.** all points to the right of 4 **14.** 4 and all points to the right **15.** 4 and all points to the right **16.** all points to the left of −1 **17.** all points to the left of −3 **18.** all points to the right of 0 **19.** 1 and all points to the right **20.** 3 and all points to the left **21.** −3 and all points to the left **22.** all points to the left of 1 **23.** all points to the left of −2 **24.** 3 and all points to the right **25.** −1 and all points to the right **26.** −2 and all points to the left **27.** −4 and all points to the left **28.** all points to the left of −5 **29.** all points to the right of −2 **30.** all points to the right of −1 **31.** 2 and all points to the right **32.** 2 and all points to the left **33.** 1 and all points to the right **34.** all points to the left of −3 **35.** 5 and all points to the left **36.** all points to the left of −4 **37.** all points to the right and left of $2\frac{1}{2}$ **38.** all points to the left of $-\frac{1}{4}$ **39.** all points to the left of $\frac{5}{4}$ **40.** $-\frac{3}{2}$ and all points to the right **41.** $\frac{1}{2}$ and all points to the left **42.** all points to the right and left of 0 **43.** $-\frac{2}{3}$ and all points to the right **44.** 0 and all points to the left **45.** all points to the right of 5 **46.** −8 and all points to the right **47.** all points to the right of −2.5 **48.** −8.1 and all points to the right

Page 97

1. −6 **2.** 27 **3.** 6 **4.** Start. Read: *a, b, c.* Add: $a + b + c$. Store as *X*. Divide *X* by 3. Store as *Z*. Print *Z*. Stop.

Page 101

ORALS **1.** no **2.** yes **3.** yes **4.** no **5.** no
6. no **7.** no **8.** no **9.** yes **10.** yes **11.** no
12. no **13.** yes **14.** yes **15.** no **16.** no **17.** no
18. yes **19.** no **20.** no **21.** no **22.** yes **23.** no
24. yes **25.** no **26.** no

EXERCISES **1.** 10 > 9 **2.** 3 > 1 **3.** −24 < 4
4. 2 > −1 **5.** −4 < −1 **6.** 4 > −7 **7.** −21 < 14
8. 20 > 0 **9.** 0 > −15 **10.** 3 ≥ 1 **11.** −8 < 4
12. −1 < 8 **13.** −42 < 6 **14.** 3 ≥ −1 **15.** 2 ≤ 3
16. −9 ≤ −4 **17.** 2 > −2 **18.** −2 ≤ −1 **19.** 3 ≥ −10 **20.** 0 < 48 **21.** 0 ≤ 15 **22.** 20 > 0
23. 7 ≤ 11 **24.** 8 > −6 **25.** 6 > 5 **26.** −24 > −28 **27.** Add −3. **28.** Multiply by 2.
29. Multiply by −3. **30.** Divide by 4. **31.** Add 5.
32. Multiply by 4. **33.** Divide by −3. **34.** Add 3.
35. Multiply by −3. **36.** Divide by −7.

Page 104

1. {x|x > −2} **2.** {x|x ≥ −5} **3.** {y|y > −1}
4. {x|x < 5} **5.** {x|x > 7} **6.** {y|y > 1}
7. {a|a ≤ 8} **8.** {x|x ≥ 6} **9.** {d|d < −3}
10. {y|y < 5} **11.** {r|r ≥ 4} **12.** {x|x > 4}
13. {x|x ≤ 3} **14.** {y|y > 0} **15.** {x|x < 4}
16. {x|x < −1} **17.** {x|x ≤ 6} **18.** {y|y ≤ −3}
19. {y|y > 3} **20.** {x|x ≤ 4} **21.** {x|x ≥ 8}
22. {y|y < 4} **23.** {y|y > 9} **24.** {x|x < 17}
25. {x|x > 5} **26.** {y|y > 2} **27.** {all numbers}
28. ϕ

Page 107

1. *A* ⊄ *B*; *B* ⊆ *A* **2.** *A* ⊄ *B*; *B* ⊄ *A* **3.** *A* ⊆ *B*; *B* ⊄ *A* **4.** *A* ⊆ *B*; *B* ⊆ *A* **5.** *A* ⊆ *B*; *B* ⊄ *A* **6.** *A* ⊄ *B*; *B* ⊄ *A* **7.** *A* ⊆ *B*; *B* ⊄ *A* **8.** *A* ⊄ *B*; *B* ⊆ *A* **9.** *A* ⊆ *B*; *B* ⊆ *A* **10.** *A* ⊆ *B*; *B* ⊄ *A* **11.** *A* ⊄ *B*; *B* ⊄ *A* **12.** *A* ⊄ *B*; *B* ⊆ *A* **13.** *A* ⊄ *B*; *B* ⊆ *A* **14.** *A* ⊆ *B*; *B* ⊄ *A* **15.** *A* ⊆ *B*; *B* ⊄ *A* **16.** *A* ⊄ *B*; *B* ⊄ *A* **17.** {1, 2}, {1}, {2}, ϕ; 4 **18.** {2, 4, 6}, {2, 4}, {4, 6}, {2, 6}, {2}, {4}, {6}, ϕ; 8 **19.** {8}, ϕ; 2

20. ϕ; 1 **21.** $\{-1, 0\}$, $\{-1\}$, $\{0\}$, ϕ; 4
22. $\{1, 3, 5, 7\}$, $\{1, 3, 5\}$, $\{1, 5, 7\}$, $\{3, 5, 7\}$, $\{1, 3, 7\}$
$\{1, 3\}$, $\{1, 5\}$, $\{1, 7\}$, $\{3, 5\}$, $\{3, 7\}$, $\{5, 7\}$, $\{1\}$, $\{3\}$,
$\{5\}$, $\{7\}$, ϕ; 16 **23.** $\{3, 5\}$; $\{1, 3, 5\}$ **24.** $\{2, 4, 6\}$;
$\{2, 4, 6\}$ **25.** ϕ; $\{4, 5, 6, 7\}$ **26.** $\{1, 5\}$;
$\{1, 2, 4, 5, 9\}$ **27.** ϕ; $\{0, 2, 4\}$ **28.** $\{0\}$;
$\{-8, -4, 0, 4, 8\}$ **29.** ϕ; $\{-3, -2, -1, 1, 2, 3\}$
30. $\{-1, -2\}$; $\{-2, -1, 0, 1, 2\}$ **31.** $\{1, 4, 5\}$;
$\{1, 2, 3, 4, 5\}$ **32.** ϕ; $\{0\}$ **33.** $\{6\}$; $\{2, 4, 6, 8, 10\}$
34. ϕ; $\{1, 2, 3, 4, 5, 6, 7, 8\}$ **35.** $\{2, 5, 8, 9\}$;
$\{2, 5, 8, 9\}$ **36.** $\{0, 6\}$; $\{0, 2, 3, 4, 6, 9\}$
37. ϕ; $\{0, 1, 2, 3, \ldots\}$ **38.** $\{0\}$;
$\{\ldots, -3, -2, -1, 0, 1, 2, 3, \ldots\}$
39. $\{0, 6, 12, 18, \ldots\}$;
$\{0, 2, 3, 4, 6, 8, 9, 10, 12, \ldots\}$
40. $\{0, -4, -8, -12, \ldots\}$; $\{0, -2, -4, -6, \ldots\}$
41. $\{0\}$; $\{$integers$\}$ **42.** ϕ;
$\{\ldots, -3, -2, -1, 1, 2, 3, \ldots\}$
43. $\{$positive integers$\}$; $\{$whole numbers$\}$
44. $\{$negative integers$\}$; $\{$integers$\}$
45. $\{0, 1, 2, 3, 4, 5, 6\}$ **46.** $\{0, 1, 2, 3, 4, 5, 6\}$
47. ϕ **48.** ϕ **49.** $\{0, 2, 4\}$ **50.** $\{0, 1, 2, 3, 4, 6\}$

Page 111
1. 4 hr **2.** 3 hr **3.** 3 hr **4.** 3 hr **5.** 3 hr **6.** 22 hr
7. 48 km **8.** 15 km **9.** 5 hr **10.** 2 hr

Page 114
1. $\{x|x > -2 \text{ and } x < 5\}$; $\{$all numbers$\}$ **2.** ϕ;
$\{x|x > 3 \text{ or } x < -1\}$ **3.** $\{x|x \geq -4 \text{ and } x < 2\}$;
$\{$all numbers$\}$ **4.** ϕ; $\{x|x > 4 \text{ or } x \leq 0\}$
5. $\{x|x \geq -1\}$; $\{x|x > -3\}$ **6.** $\{x|x < 3\}$; $\{x|x \leq 5\}$
7. $\{x|x \geq -1 \text{ and } x \leq 3\}$; $\{$all numbers$\}$ **8.** ϕ;
$\{x|x \leq 1 \text{ or } x \geq 4\}$ **9.** $\{x|x < 0\}$; $\{x|x < 4\}$
10. $\{x|x > -1\}$; $\{x|x > -7\}$ **11.** $\{1\}$;
$\{$all numbers$\}$ **12.** ϕ; $\{$all numbers$\}$
13. $\{x|x > -4\}$; $\{x|x > -5\}$
14. $\{x|x > -1 \text{ and } x \leq 0\}$; $\{$all numbers$\}$
15. $\{x|x \leq 2 \text{ and } x > -1\}$; $\{$all numbers$\}$
16. ϕ; $\{x|x < -3 \text{ or } x > -3\}$ **17.** $\{x|x > 3\}$;
$\{x|x \geq 3\}$ **18.** ϕ; $\{x|x > 2 \text{ or } x < -2\}$ **19.** ϕ;
$\{$all numbers$\}$ **20.** $\{x|x < -2\}$; $\{x \leq -2\}$ **21.** ϕ;
$\{x|x \geq 5\}$ **22.** ϕ; $\{x|x \geq 3 \text{ or } x \leq -3\}$
23. $\{x|x \geq -3 \text{ and } x \leq 3\}$; $\{$all numbers$\}$
24. $\{0\}$; $\{x|x \geq 0\}$ **25.** $\{-3\}$; $\{x|x \leq -3\}$ **26.** ϕ;
$\{x|x \geq 0\}$ **27.** $\{x|x > 3 \text{ and } x \leq 4\}$; $\{$all numbers$\}$
28. ϕ; $\{x|x \leq 1 \text{ or } x > 2\}$ **29.** $\{x|x > 2\}$;
$\{$all numbers$\}$ **30.** $\{-1\}$; $\{$all numbers$\}$

31. $\{x|x \geq 1 \text{ and } x \leq 4\}$ **32.** $\{x|x \leq -1 \text{ or } x > 3\}$
33. $\{x|x > -4 \text{ and } x < 3\}$ **34.** $\{x|x < 0\}$
35. $\{x|x \leq -2 \text{ or } x \geq 0\}$ **36.** $\{x|x < -4 \text{ or } x > -3\}$
37. $\{x|x > 2 \text{ and } x \leq 3\}$
38. $\{x|x < -2 \text{ or } x > -2\}$ **39.** segment with
endpoints 0 and 5 **40.** all points **41.** all points
to the right of -4 **42.** 0 and all points to the
right

Page 116
1. equal **2.** not equal **3.** not equal **4.** equal
5. infinite; the set of all positive odd integers
6. finite; the set of all positive even integers
less than 10 **7.** infinite; the set of all negative
integers **8.** $\{-4, -3, -2, -1\}$ **9.** ϕ **10.** ϕ
11. $\{-13\}$ **12.** $\{$all numbers$\}$ **13.** all points
to the right of -2 **14.** 5 and all points to the
left **15.** all points to the right and left of $-\frac{1}{2}$
16. all points to the left of -4 **17.** all points to
the right of 2 **18.** -3 and all points to the left
19. $1 \geq -3$ **20.** $56 \leq 64$ **21.** $3 > -6$ **22.** Divide
by -3. **23.** Add -2. **24.** Multiply by -2.
25. $\{x|x \leq -2\}$ **26.** $\{x|x \leq 5\}$ **27.** $\{x|x < 1\}$
28. $A \subseteq B$; $B \not\subseteq A$ **29.** $A \subseteq B$; $B \not\subseteq A$
30. $A \subseteq B$; $B \subseteq A$ **31.** $\{3\}$, ϕ; 2 **32.** $\{4\}$, $\{1\}$,
$\{4, 1\}$, ϕ; 4 **33.** $\{9\}$, $\{8\}$, $\{7\}$, $\{9, 8\}$, $\{9, 7\}$, $\{8, 7\}$,
$\{9, 8, 7\}$, ϕ; 8 **34.** $\{9, 5\}$; $\{4, 5, 9\}$ **35.** ϕ;
$\{1, 2, 3, 4, 5, 6\}$ **36.** $\{0\}$; $\{-2, -1, 0, 1, 2\}$
37. $\{x|x > 3 \text{ and } x \leq 4\}$; $\{$all numbers$\}$
38. $\{x|x \geq -4 \text{ and } x < 1\}$; $\{$all numbers$\}$
39. $\{x|-4 \leq x \leq 2\}$ **40.** $\{x|x < -3 \text{ or } x \geq 5\}$

Page 117
1. equal **2.** not equal **3.** equal **4.** infinite; the
set of all integers greater than 4 **5.** finite; the
set of all positive odd integers less than 9
6. infinite; the set of all negative even integers
7. $\{-2, -1, 0, 1\}$ **8.** $\{1, 2, 3\}$ **9.** ϕ
10. $\{-4\}$ **11.** ϕ **12.** -3 and all points to
the right **13.** all points to the right of 4 **14.** all
points to the right and left of 5 **15.** $-2 > -13$
16. $3 \geq 2$ **17.** Multiply by -4. **18.** Add -3.
19. all points to the right of 3 **20.** -6 and all
points to the left **21.** all points to the right of -4
22. $A \not\subseteq B$; $B \subseteq A$ **23.** $A \subseteq B$; $B \subseteq A$ **24.** $\{7\}$, ϕ;
2 **25.** $\{1\}$, $\{3\}$, $\{5\}$, $\{1, 3\}$, $\{3, 5\}$, $\{1, 5\}$,
$\{1, 3, 5\}$, ϕ; 8 **26.** $\{0\}$; $\{-5, -4, 0, 4, 5\}$ **27.** ϕ;
$\{0, 1, 2, 3, 4, 5\}$ **28.** $\{x|x \geq -3 \text{ and } x < 1\}$;

Page 120

1. $x \cdot x \cdot x \cdot x \cdot x$ **2.** $x \cdot x \cdot x$ **3.** $a \cdot a \cdot a \cdot a$
4. $a \cdot a$ **5.** $4 \cdot n \cdot n \cdot n$ **6.** $m \cdot m \cdot m \cdot m \cdot m \cdot m$
7. $-3 \cdot a \cdot a$ **8.** $a \cdot a \cdot a \cdot b \cdot b$ **9.** -27 **10.** -32
11. 16 **12.** -18 **13.** -24 **14.** -64 **15.** 64
16. -25 **17.** 243 **18.** -32 **19.** 24 **20.** -64
21. -27 **22.** -256 **23.** -4 **24.** -64 **25.** 64
26. 64 **27.** 11,664 **28.** $-4,096$ **29.** 1,048,576
30. 200 **31.** -216

Page 123

ORALS **1.** m^5 **2.** b^{10} **3.** b^7 **4.** c^{11} **5.** b^6
6. m^5 **7.** b^2 **8.** a^7 **9.** x^4 **10.** m^{10} **11.** c^6 **12.** a^{20}
13. x^{16} **14.** y^{12} **15.** x^{18}

EXERCISES **1.** $12a^8$ **2.** $15a^{11}$ **3.** $6m^{11}$
4. $6b^7$ **5.** $28x^{12}$ **6.** $8n^7$ **7.** $15a^9$ **8.** $10y^7$ **9.** $4a^5$
10. $3b^7$ **11.** $6a^{11}$ **12.** $3m^{10}$ **13.** $-8a^8$ **14.** $12b^{12}$
15. $-8m^8$ **16.** $-3a^{15}$ **17.** $8a^4$ **18.** $-20b^3$
19. $-15b^8$ **20.** $-12b^5$ **21.** $12a^5b^6$ **22.** $8x^5y^7$
23. $-20m^4n^7$ **24.** $-8a^3b^8$ **25.** $6a^5b^4$ **26.** a^2b^2
27. a^6 **28.** b^{12} **29.** x^{12} **30.** y^{15} **31.** z^{30} **32.** c^{27}
33. r^{30} **34.** f^{49} **35.** g^{45} **36.** d^{100} **37.** c^{28} **38.** h^{200}
39. $16x^8$ **40.** $9y^6$ **41.** $-8z^{12}$ **42.** $125a^{15}$
43. $256x^{12}$ **44.** $16a^6m^4$ **45.** $9a^4x^6$ **46.** $4x^4y^6$
47. $8m^9n^{12}$ **48.** $125a^6b^9$ **49.** $-64a^9m^{12}$
50. $81x^8y^{16}$ **51.** $8x^3a^6$ **52.** $-27a^6b^9$
53. $-243x^5y^{10}m^5$ **54.** $x^9y^6z^{12}$ **55.** $a^{10}b^{20}c^{15}$
56. $x^{14}y^{21}z^{28}$ **57.** $27a^9b^6$ **58.** $8x^{18}y^{12}$
59. $-27x^9y^{12}z^6$ **60.** x^{4a} **61.** y^{4b} **62.** $6x^{a+3}$
63. x^{6a} **64.** y^{15b} **65.** $2^a x^{5a^2}$

Page 125

ORALS **1.** B **2.** M **3.** T **4.** M **5.** $-5x^3 +$
$3x^2 + 7x - 4$ **6.** $-4x^2 + 5x - 3$ **7.** $-5a^3 +$
$4a^2 + 2a + 1$ **8.** $x^4 - 7x^3 - 4x^2 + 5x + 1$
9. $-4x^3 + 7x^2 + 5x + 2$ **10.** $x^4 - 5x^3 + 3x^2 +$
$2x + 6$ **11.** $6x^4 + 2x^3 - 3x^2 + x - 5$

EXERCISES **1.** $3x^2 - 3x - 8$ **2.** $5x^2 - 5x + 4$
3. $9x^2 + 4x + 5$ **4.** $14x^2 - 6x - 2$ **5.** $5x^2 -$
$11x + 3$ **6.** $3x^2 + 13x - 7$ **7.** $m^2 - 9$
8. $-2m^2 + 4$ **9.** $7x^3 - 9x^2 + 9x$ **10.** $x^3 + 7x^2 +$
$2x$ **11.** $-m^3 + 5m$ **12.** $6m^3 - m^2$ **13.** $8a^4 + a^2$
14. $-a^4 + 12a$ **15.** $2a^2 + a - 1$ **16.** $-3a^2 +$

$12a - 7$ **17.** $7b^3 - 2b^2 - b + 8$ **18.** $-9b^3 +$
$2b^2 + 9b - 11$ **19.** $10a^3 + 2a^2 - 12a - 4$
20. $3a^3 + 3a^2 + 3a + 2$ **21.** $3a^4 - 7a^3 + 2a^2 +$
$a - 6$ **22.** $-9b^4 - b^3 + 9b^2 - 6b - 3$
23. $-22m^9 - m^6 - 3$ **24.** $-7b^7 + 4b^5 +$
$4b^4 - 2b^2$ **25.** $a^4 + 12a^3 - 10a^2 + 13a - 19$

Page 126

1. 6, 8, 10 **2.** 2, 7, 14, 38 **3.** -8, -2, 6, 20
4. -3, 3, 18, 26, 59 **5.** Follow the flow chart on
page 126, but change $x > y$ to $y > x$; or after
the question, "Is $x > y$?", exchange Yes and No
branches; so Yes branch becomes No branch,
No branch becomes Yes branch.

Page 129

ORALS **1.** $6a^2 - 18a - 12$ **2.** $10a^2 -$
$20a + 15$ **3.** $6a^2 - 10a + 12$ **4.** $20a^3 - 10a^2 +$
$25a - 10$ **5.** $6a^3 - 4a^2 + 10a - 4$ **6.** $16a^3 -$
$8a^2 + 28a - 12$ **7.** $a^5 + a^4$ **8.** $b^7 + b^5$
9. $b^8 + b^7$ **10.** $m^4 + m^3$ **11.** $m^7 + m^4$ **12.** $a^4 +$
a^3 **13.** $a^6 + a^5$ **14.** $a^4 + a^3 + 5a^2$ **15.** $a^5 +$
$a^4 + a^3$

EXERCISES **1.** $3f^4 - 5f^3 + 4f^2$ **2.** $3t^4 -$
$5t^3 + 6t^2$ **3.** $2a^3 - 5a^2 + 4a$ **4.** $15b^3 -$
$20b^2 + 15b$ **5.** $6x^5 - 14x^4$ **6.** $15a^5 - 35a^4$
7. $24b^3 - 30b^2$ **8.** $6m^3 - 15m^2$ **9.** $20c^4 - 25c^3$
10. $-2b^2 + 5b$ **11.** $-4x^2 + 5x$ **12.** $-3x^2 +$
$4x - 2$ **13.** $-2x^2 - 5x + 7$ **14.** $b^2 + 5b$
15. $b^2 - 2b$ **16.** $x^2 + x + 2$ **17.** $-a^2 + a + 4$
18. $c^3 - c + 5$ **19.** $9a^3 + 15a^2 - 6a$ **20.** $10b^3 +$
$15b^2 + 20b$ **21.** $-4a^4 + 12a^3 + 16a^2$
22. $-2a^3 + a^2 + 3a$ **23.** $m^3 + m^2 + 5m$
24. $g^3 + 2g^2 - 5g$ **25.** $x^3 + 8x^2 - 12x + 9$
26. $x^3 + 6x^2 - 8x + 8$ **27.** $2x^3 + x - 9$
28. $-c^2 - 2c + 6$ **29.** $x^5 + x^3 - 8x + 7$
30. $a^4 + a^2 - 3a + 5$ **31.** $3a^2 - 2a - 7$
32. $-5b^2 - 8b - 2$ **33.** $4x^2 - 9x + 17$
34. $5y^2 - 17$ **35.** $6a^2 - 11a$ **36.** $6c^2 - 10c - 9$
37. $5x^4 - 2x^3 + 4x^2 - 3$ **38.** $5a^3 - 8a^2 +$
$10a - 3$ **39.** $x^4 + x^3 + 3x^2 - 3x + 3$ **40.** $3c^3 -$
$c^2 + c - 10$ **41.** $2m^5n^2 - 3m^4n^3 + m^3n^4$
42. $a^3b - 5a^2b^2 + 7ab^3$ **43.** $2a^3b - 6a^2b^2 +$
$10ab^3$ **44.** $3m^5n^2 - 9m^4n^3 + 3m^3n^4 + 3m^2n^5$
45. $-2x^3y^2 + x^2y^3 - xy^4$ **46.** $-p^3q + p^2q^2 -$
pq^3 **47.** $-2a^4c + 2a^3c^2 - 2a^2c^3 + 2ac^4$
48. $3x^4y + 6x^3y^2 + 3x^2y^3$ **49.** $3m^5n^2 - 5m^4n^3 +$

$4m^3n^4$ **50.** $-7a^3b + 15a^2b^2 + 37ab^3$
51. $-2x^3y^2 + x^2y^3 - 6xy^4$ **52.** $a^4b^2 - a^2b^4 - ab^5$

Page 131
1. no **2.** 6 **3.** no **4.** 496 **5.** 8,128 **6.** no

Page 133
ORALS **1.** no **2.** yes **3.** no **4.** yes **5.** yes
6. no **7.** no **8.** yes **9.** no **10.** yes **11.** no
12. yes **13.** no **14.** yes **15.** yes **16.** no
17. $(12)(1); (3)(4); (6)(2)$ **18.** $(60)(1); (3)(20);$
$(4)(15); (2)(30); (6)(10); (12)(5)$
19. $(28)(1); (7)(4); (14)(2)$ **20.** $(30)(1); (15)(2);$
$(10)(3); (6)(5)$ **21.** $(36)(1); (18)(2); (12)(3);$
$(9)(4); (6)(6)$ **22.** $(52)(1); (2)(26); (4)(13)$
23. $(42)(1); (7)(6); (3)(14)$ **24.** $(20)(1); (4)(5);$
$(2)(10)$ **25.** $(3)(6); (2)(9); (1)(18)$ **26.** $(24)(2);$
$(8)(6); (1)(48); (3)(16); (12)(4)$ **27.** $(16)(2);$
$(8)(4); (32)(1)$ **28.** $(2)(22); (4)(11); (1)(44)$

EXERCISES **1.** $2 \cdot 2 \cdot 3$ **2.** $3 \cdot 2 \cdot 2 \cdot 2$
3. $3 \cdot 3 \cdot 2$ **4.** $7 \cdot 2 \cdot 2$ **5.** $3 \cdot 3 \cdot 5$ **6.** $5 \cdot 2 \cdot 2 \cdot 3$
7. $2 \cdot 13$ **8.** $5 \cdot 7$ **9.** $5 \cdot 5 \cdot 2$ **10.** $2 \cdot 2 \cdot 2 \cdot 3 \cdot 3$
11. $2 \cdot 2 \cdot 11$ **12.** $3 \cdot 2 \cdot 5$ **13.** $5 \cdot 2 \cdot 2 \cdot 2$
14. $3 \cdot 2 \cdot 7$ **15.** $3 \cdot 2 \cdot 2 \cdot 2 \cdot 2$ **16.** $3 \cdot 3 \cdot 3$
17. a^3 **18.** a^3 **19.** $6m^3$ **20.** $8a^4$ **21.** $-9x^2$
22. $-6x^3$ **23.** $7x^5$ **24.** $2m^4$ **25.** $-10x^4$
26. $-2a^5$ **27.** b^5 **28.** b^3 **29.** $-2b$ **30.** $-5b$
31. $9a^3b$ **32.** $6a^4m^4$ **33.** $-8a^2m^2$ **34.** $13a^2b^2$
35. $-ab$ **36.** $-2xy$ **37.** $-x^2y^4$ **38.** $-8ab$ **39.** x
40. $-a^4$ **41.** a^{3m} **42.** x^{5a} **43.** a^{2m+4}

Page 137
1. $3(x^2 + 9x + 3)$ **2.** $4(a^2 + 8a + 5)$
3. $6(b^2 + 3b + 5)$ **4.** $2(m^2 - 5m + 2)$
5. $7(a^2 - 3a + 7)$ **6.** $m(m^2 + m + 1)$
7. $x^3(x^2 + x - 1)$ **8.** $b^2(b^2 - 2b + 1)$
9. $a(2a^2 - a + 1)$ **10.** $y(y^2 - 7y + 1)$ **11.** $7a(a - 4)$
12. $3x(x - 3)$ **13.** $4a^2(a + 2)$ **14.** $5b(b^2 - 2)$
15. $6a(a - 4)$ **16.** $4a(a^2 - 4a + 8)$
17. $4a(a^2 - 3a + 2)$ **18.** $7b(b^2 - 2b + 7)$
19. $6x(2x^2 - x + 3)$ **20.** $4m(m^2 - 6)$
21. $4(m^2 - 5)$ **22.** $a^2(3a - 5)$ **23.** $4m^2(m - 8)$
24. $5a(a^2 - 7)$ **25.** $7a^3(a^2 - 5a + 3)$
26. $3a(2a^3 - 4a^2 + 8a + 1)$
27. $3(a^2 + 4ab + 12b^2)$ **28.** $13a(3a^2 - 4a + 2)$
29. $9m(2m^3 - 3m^2 - 5m + 4)$
30. $6y(y^2 - 3y - 2)$

Page 138
1. -8 **2.** -12 **3.** 16 **4.** -128 **5.** 36 **6.** -6
7. 64 **8.** 36 **9.** 64 **10.** x^{10} **11.** a^{16} **12.** $10a^7$
13. $15b^3$ **14.** $-12a^7$ **15.** $-21a^5b^7$ **16.** $27a^6$
17. $16b^2$ **18.** $-8m^6n^9$ **19.** binomial
20. monomial **21.** trinomial **22.** $2x^2 + 10x + 5$
23. $5a^2 - 2a + 8$ **24.** $3m^2 - 11$ **25.** $9b^3 + 5b^2 + 5b + 7$ **26.** $a^5 + a^4$ **27.** $2b^8 + 2b^7 + 2b^6$
28. $a^3 - 2a^2 + 3a$ **29.** $m^3 + 5m^2 + 2m$
30. $a^2 + a + 1$ **31.** $a^4 + 3a^3 - 3a^2 - 11a + 7$
32. $3x^5 - 2x^4 + 6x^3 - 3x^2 + 5$ **33.** $3c^2 + 2c - 1$
34. $3a^3b - 15a^2b^2 + 12ab^3$ **35.** $-3a^4c^2 + 6a^3c^3 - 3a^2c^4 + 3ac^5$ **36.** $x^4 - 2x^3 - x^2 + 9$
37. $-3a^2 - 6a + 5$ **38.** $2x^3 - 6x^2 + 8x - 2$
39. $2y^3 + 2y^2 - 2y + 4$ **40.** $3 \cdot 3 \cdot 2$
41. $2 \cdot 2 \cdot 2 \cdot 2 \cdot 2$ **42.** $7 \cdot 2 \cdot 2$ **43.** a^5 **44.** x^5
45. a **46.** $5a$ **47.** $-9ab^4$ **48.** $-x^2y^4$
49. $2(2a^2 - 4a + 3)$ **50.** $2(3x - 1)$ **51.** $x(4x - 7)$
52. $a(a^2 - 7a + 3)$ **53.** $4y(y^2 - 2y + 3)$
54. $5a(a^3 - 6a^2 + 4a - 3)$

Page 139
1. 81 **2.** -432 **3.** -64 **4.** $21b^3$ **5.** $-12a^3b^4$
6. $9x^4y^6$ **7.** binomial **8.** monomial **9.** trinomial
10. $4x^2 - 3x + 7$ **11.** $8a^2 + 2$ **12.** $-4a^2 - 7a + 6$ **13.** $8a^5 - 10a^4$ **14.** $m^5 + 7m^4 - 5m^3$
15. $e^2 + 2e + 5$ **16.** $-4a$ **17.** $4a^3 - 9a^2 - a$
18. $4c^2 - 4a - 7$ **19.** $-8a^4c^2 + 24a^3c^3 - 16a^2c^4 - 8ac^5$ **20.** $x^4 + 3x^3 + 2x + 2$
21. $-c^3 - 2c^2 - 4c$ **22.** $4x^3 - 7x^2 + 8x - 1$
23. $2y^3 + 3y^2 - 2y + 2$ **24.** $2 \cdot 2 \cdot 3$ **25.** $5 \cdot 5 \cdot 2$
26. x^6 **27.** x **28.** $8m^7$ **29.** $-6a^3$ **30.** $-7a$
31. $-4ab^4$ **32.** $3(a^2 - 6)$ **33.** $5a(a - 2)$
34. $8(a^2 - 2a + 5)$ **35.** $a(a^2 - a - 7)$
36. $m(m^2 - m - 1)$ **37.** $6x(x^2 - 2x + 3)$
38. $3a^2 - 7a - 25$ cannot be factored
39. $4a(a^3 - 6a^2 + 3a - 7)$

Page 140
1. 400 **2.** 5,800,000 **3.** 26,300,000 **4.** 4×10^8
5. 6.3×10^4 **6.** 2.32×10^{10} **7.** 1.75×10^6, or
1,750,000 **8.** 2.79×10^5, or 279,000
9. 4.3902×10^8, or 439,020,000

Page 143
1. $6x^2 + 25x + 14$ **2.** $20x^2 + 37x + 15$
3. $6m^2 + 13m + 5$ **4.** $6x^2 - x - 1$
5. $8a^2 + 10a - 7$ **6.** $6b^2 - 5b - 25$ **7.** $m^2 - 25$
8. $y^2 - 16$ **9.** $4r^2 - 9$ **10.** $3x^2 + 5x - 2$

11. $3a^2 - 5a + 2$ **12.** $4m^2 - 24m + 36$
13. $2y^2 + 3y - 20$ **14.** $9t^2 - 1$ **15.** $2b^2 - b - 10$
16. $4d^2 + 7d - 2$ **17.** $3x^2 - 16x - 35$
18. $2n^2 + 15n - 8$ **19.** $9y^2 - 1$ **20.** $14a^2 + 19a - 3$ **21.** $6a^2 + 7a - 10$ **22.** $3a^2 - 23ab + 40b^2$ **23.** $4y^2 + 16my - 9m^2$
24. $6p^2 + 11pq + 3q^2$ **25.** $9y^2 - 30y + 25$
26. $16x^2 - 8x + 1$ **27.** $4x^2 + 12x + 9$
28. $25n^2 + 10n + 1$ **29.** $6x^3 + 10x^2 + 5x - 3$
30. $8x^3 + 22x^2 - 17x + 14$ **31.** $3x^3 + 20x^2 - 2x + 35$ **32.** $x^3 - 12x^2 + 36x - 5$
33. $3x^4 - 19x^3 - 5x^2 + 6x$ **34.** $2x^4 - x^3 - 4x^2 - 3x - 9$ **35.** $x^2 - 14x + 49$ **36.** $4x^2 + 12x + 9$
37. $4m^2 - 4m + 1$ **38.** $9a^2 - 24ab + 16b^2$

Page 144

1. $a^2 + 5a + 6$ **2.** $x^2 + 13x + 40$ **3.** $x^2 + 7x + 10$

Page 147

1. $(2x + 5)(x + 1)$ **2.** $(3x + 7)(x + 1)$
3. $(5x + 2)(x + 1)$ **4.** $(4x - 3)(2x - 1)$
5. $(3x - 1)(2x - 5)$ **6.** $(5x - 7)(2x - 1)$
7. $(x + 3)(x - 2)$ **8.** $(x + 4)(x - 3)$
9. $(x + 6)(x - 5)$ **10.** $(2a + 1)(a - 4)$
11. $(3x + 5)(x - 5)$ **12.** $(2x - 3)(x + 1)$
13. $(x + 5)(x + 2)$ **14.** $(b + 3)(b + 2)$
15. $(a + 3)(a + 1)$ **16.** $(y - 8)(y - 2)$
17. $(m - 5)(m - 4)$ **18.** $(d - 6)(d - 5)$
19. $(a - 5)(a + 4)$ **20.** $(y - 5)(y + 3)$
21. $(a - 9)(a + 2)$ **22.** $(x + 1)(x + 1)$
23. $(b - 3)(b - 3)$ **24.** $(k + 6)(k + 6)$
25. $(2a - 3)(a - 2)$ **26.** $(2x - 1)(x + 3)$
27. $(2a + 1)(a - 4)$ **28.** $(2m - 1)(m + 5)$
29. $(2a + 3)(a + 5)$ **30.** $(3b - 2)(b - 3)$
31. $(3x - 5)(x + 5)$ **32.** $(2m + 5)(m + 3)$
33. $(2m - 5)(m - 1)$ **34.** $(3a - 1)(2a + 1)$
35. $(3y - 5)(y + 4)$ **36.** $(2p - 5)(p - 5)$
37. $(2b + 5)(b + 6)$ **38.** $(2x + 1)(x + 2)$
39. $(4y + 1)(3y + 1)$ **40.** $(2x + 5)(x - 8)$
41. $(2x + 5)(x + 9)$ **42.** $(3x - 8)(x + 6)$
43. $(2a - 5)(a - 10)$ **44.** $(3a - 7)(a + 5)$
45. $(2b - 5)(b - 12)$ **46.** $(3m + 5)(m + 8)$
47. $(5x + 3)(x - 9)$ **48.** $(3y - 7)(y - 8)$
49. $(5d - 3)(3d - 2)$ **50.** $(5y + 9)(3y - 2)$
51. $(7b + 3)(2b - 3)$ **52.** $(2a - 5)(2a - 5)$
53. $(3a - 2)(3a - 2)$ **54.** $(3a - 5)(2a + 3)$
55. $(5x - 3)(3x - 4)$ **56.** $(8y - 5)(2y + 3)$
57. $(6a + 7)(3a - 5)$

Page 149

1. $x = 3$ **2.** Start. Read: a, b, c, d. Subtract $d - b$. Store as S. Subtract $a - c$. Store as T. Is $T = 0$? Yes: Print "No solution". Stop. No: Divide $\dfrac{S}{T}$. Store as R. Print R. Stop. $x = 5$

Page 152

ORALS **1.** 3^2 **2.** 8^2 **3.** 6^2 **4.** 10^2 **5.** 4^2
6. 12^2 **7.** $(4b)^2$ **8.** $(9x)^2$ **9.** $(11x)^2$ **10.** $(7m)^2$
11. c^2 **12.** $(10x)^2$ **13.** $(3t)^2$ **14.** $(5b)^2$ **15.** $(15k)^2$
16. yes **17.** no **18.** no **19.** yes **20.** no **21.** yes
22. no **23.** no **24.** no

EXERCISES **1.** $(x - 4)(x + 4)$
2. $(m - 7)(m + 7)$ **3.** $(b - 5)(b + 5)$
4. $(a + 9)(a - 9)$ **5.** $(b - 1)(b + 1)$
6. $(m - 10)(m + 10)$ **7.** $(m + 8)(m - 8)$
8. $(x - 6)(x + 6)$ **9.** $(2b - 7)(2b + 7)$
10. $(3a + 5)(3a - 5)$ **11.** $(5a + 6)(5a - 6)$
12. $(4x - 5)(4x + 5)$ **13.** $(7y - 2)(7y + 2)$
14. $(4m - 1)(4m + 1)$ **15.** $(5m - 2)(5m + 2)$
16. $(6a + 5)(6a - 5)$ **17.** $(2t - 5)(2t + 5)$
18. $(2b - 1)(2b + 1)$ **19.** $(5 + x)(5 - x)$
20. $(8 - y)(8 + y)$ **21.** $(9 - t)(9 + t)$
22. $(6 - a)(6 + a)$ **23.** $(7 + b)(7 - b)$
24. $(10 - c)(10 + c)$ **25.** $(1 - y)(1 + y)$
26. $(10 - 7x)(10 + 7x)$ **27.** $(8 - 9c)(8 + 9c)$
28. $(1 - 3x)(1 + 3x)$ **29.** $(4 - 9y)(4 + 9y)$
30. $(8 - 7b)(8 + 7b)$ **31.** $(12a - 9)(12a + 9)$
32. $(10x - 7)(10x + 7)$ **33.** $(5m - 12)(5m + 12)$
34. $(2m - 13)(2m + 13)$ **35.** $(6x + 5)(6x - 5)$
36. $(5 - 12b)(5 + 12b)$ **37.** $(13p - 4)(13p + 4)$
38. $(x + 14)(x - 14)$ **39.** $(7 + 15x)(7 - 15x)$
40. $(11 - 4b)(11 + 4b)$ **41.** $(4t - 15)(4t + 15)$
42. $(10a - 7)(10a + 7)$ **43.** $(15a - 13)(15a + 13)$
44. $(6a - 13)(6a + 13)$
45. $(11m - 15)(11m + 15)$

Page 155

1. $2(a - 4)(a - 1)$ **2.** $2(b - 2)(b - 1)$
3. $2(a + 7)(a - 5)$ **4.** $m(2m - 3)(m - 1)$
5. $x(3x - 2)(x + 2)$ **6.** $m(m + 3)(m - 3)$
7. $2x(x + 1)(x - 1)$ **8.** $3a(a + 3)(a - 3)$
9. $2m(2m + 5)(2m - 5)$ **10.** $2x(x - 3)(x - 4)$
11. $2m(m - 9)(m - 1)$ **12.** $3x(x - 6)(x - 2)$
13. $4a(a - 5)(a + 2)$ **14.** $2x(3x + 1)(x - 5)$
15. $3b(2b - 5)(b + 2)$ **16.** $4(a - 5)(a - 1)$

17. $2a(a + 3)(a + 5)$ **18.** $3(4m - 1)(m + 3)$
19. $(2a - 1)(a + 7)$ **20.** $(4y - 1)(y + 2)$
21. $(2a + 1)(a + 1)$ **22.** $2(3x - 7)(3x + 7)$
23. $3(2x - 7)(x + 5)$ **24.** $a(13 - 5a)(13 + 5a)$
25. $y^2(3y + 5)(y - 4)$ **26.** $2e(5e - 7)(3e + 1)$
27. $3a(2a - 1)(2a - 11)$ **28.** $3(5a - 9)(a - 2)$
29. $3a(3a - 2)(a + 8)$
30. $2m(3m + 16)(3m - 16)$ **31.** $(x - a)(m + n)$
32. $(x + y)(4 + b)$ **33.** $(r + t)(p - 2)$
34. $(x + 4)(x - 4)(a + b)$
35. $(y + 1)(p + 5)(p - 5)$
36. $(4 - y)(4 + y)(a + 1)$

Page 157

1. $(a + b)(a + 3b)$ **2.** $(x + 4y)(x + y)$
3. $(c + 6d)(c + d)$ **4.** $4(a + 3b)(a - 3b)$
5. $5(x - 3y)(x + 3y)$ **6.** $4(a + 5b)(a - 5b)$
7. $(2m - 5b)(m + 2b)$ **8.** $(2a + b)(a - 3b)$
9. $(2a + b)(a - 5b)$ **10.** $(a - 7b)(a + 6b)$
11. $(a - 2b)(a - b)$ **12.** $(x - 7y)(x - 6y)$
13. $2(a + 7b)(a + 3b)$ **14.** $2(2x + 3y)(2x + 3y)$
15. $2(y + z)(y + 9z)$ **16.** $2(m - 5n)(m + 4n)$
17. $2(3x + 2y)(x - 5y)$ **18.** $3(x - 5y)(x + 2y)$
19. $b(ab - 5)(ab + 5)$ **20.** $x(x - y)(x - 2y)$
21. $ab(a + b)(a - b)$ **22.** $(7x - 2y)(x + 3y)$
23. $3(2x - 5y)(x - 7y)$ **24.** $(2m + 5n)(m + 6n)$
25. $2(2k - 5r)(k - 8r)$ **26.** $3(2m + 5y)(2m - 5y)$
27. $(3a - 5b)(a + 6b)$ **28.** $5(2m + 3n)(2m + 3n)$
29. $(3a + 7b)(2a - 3b)$ **30.** $(4x + 3y)(3x - 2y)$
31. $(5x + 3y)(2x + 3y)$ **32.** $ab(2a - 3b)(a + 7b)$
33. $xy(3x - 4y)(2x + 5y)$

Page 160

ORALS **1.** $2, -3$ **2.** $0, -5$ **3.** $0, 7$ **4.** $\frac{1}{3}, 2$
5. 3 **6.** $5, -5$

EXERCISES **1.** $2, 3$ **2.** $2, 5$ **3.** $1, 8$ **4.** $0, 6$
5. $6, -6$ **6.** $-2, -6,$ **7.** $\left\{\frac{1}{2}, -5\right\}$ **8.** $\left\{\frac{1}{3}, -3\right\}$
9. $\left\{\frac{1}{2}, -3\right\}$ **10.** $\left\{\frac{1}{3}, -5\right\}$ **11.** $\left\{\frac{3}{2}, -5\right\}$ **12.** $\left\{\frac{3}{2}, -3\right\}$
13. $\left\{\frac{1}{3}, 7\right\}$ **14.** $\{2, 8\}$ **15.** $\left\{\frac{1}{2}, 5\right\}$ **16.** $\left\{8, -\frac{1}{2}\right\}$
17. $\left\{\frac{5}{2}, -\frac{5}{2}\right\}$ **18.** $\{8, -8\}$ **19.** $\left\{\frac{3}{2}, 5\right\}$ **20.** $\{0, -17\}$
21. $\left\{0, \frac{5}{3}\right\}$ **22.** $\frac{3}{2}, -8$ **23.** $\frac{5}{3}, -7$ **24.** $\frac{1}{5}, -7$
25. $\frac{7}{2}, -6$ **26.** $\frac{7}{5}, 3$ **27.** $-\frac{7}{2}, -8$ **28.** $\frac{4}{3}, 9$ **29.** 10
30. -9 **31.** $0, 3, -3$ **32.** $0, 2, -2$ **33.** $0, 2, -2$
34. $0, 2$ **35.** $0, 7, -7$ **36.** $0, 5, -5$

Page 161

1. $5,625$ **2.** $4,225$ **3.** $9,025$ **4.** $18,225$
5. $42,025$

Page 164

1. $-3, -5$ **2.** $-4, -5$ **3.** $-4, -8$ **4.** $2, -9$
5. $2, -6$ **6.** $1, -6$ **7.** $0, -9$ **8.** $0, -10$ **9.** $0, -7$
10. $\{1, -5\}$ **11.** $\left\{\frac{2}{3}, -\frac{2}{3}\right\}$ **12.** $\{5, -2\}$
13. $\{0, -13\}$ **14.** $\left\{-\frac{5}{2}, 2\right\}$ **15.** $\{7, -7\}$
16. $\left\{-\frac{1}{2}, -1\right\}$ **17.** $\left\{\frac{2}{3}, 1\right\}$ **18.** $\{9, -2\}$
19. $\left\{\frac{1}{2}, -1\right\}$ **20.** $\left\{\frac{1}{2}, 7\right\}$ **21.** $\left\{\frac{1}{3}, -1\right\}$ **22.** $\left\{\frac{1}{2}, -\frac{1}{2}\right\}$
23. $\left\{-\frac{3}{2}, 7\right\}$ **24.** $\left\{-\frac{2}{3}, 8\right\}$ **25.** $\left\{\frac{1}{2}, -6\right\}$
26. $\left\{\frac{5}{2}, -4\right\}$ **27.** $\left\{\frac{5}{2}, -\frac{5}{2}\right\}$ **28.** $-\frac{7}{4}, \frac{5}{3}$ **29.** $\frac{3}{5}, \frac{2}{3}$
30. $-\frac{7}{4}, 6$ **31.** $\frac{2}{3}, -\frac{5}{3}$ **32.** $\frac{3}{4}, \frac{5}{3}$ **33.** $\frac{5}{3}, -\frac{7}{2}$
34. $\frac{15}{2}, -\frac{15}{2}$ **35.** $\frac{7}{2}, -\frac{5}{2}$ **36.** $\frac{4}{3}, -\frac{7}{2}$ **37.** $0, -8$
38. $\frac{2}{3}, -\frac{7}{2}$ **39.** $\frac{2}{5}, \frac{5}{2}$ **40.** $-2, -4$ **41.** $3, -3$

Page 167

ORALS **1.** $7, 8, 9$ **2.** $11, 12, 13$ **3.** $26, 27,$
$28,$ **4.** $-2, -1, 0$ **5.** $-6, -5, -4$ **6.** $-40, -39,$
-38 **7.** $a, a + 1, a + 2$ **8.** $8, 10, 12, 14$ **9.** $6, 8,$
$10, 12$ **10.** $38, 40, 42, 44$ **11.** $-4, -2, 0, 2$
12. $-10, -8, -6, -4$ **13.** $n, n + 2, n + 4,$
$n + 6$ **14.** $n + 8, n + 10, n + 12, n + 14$
15. $7, 9, 11, 13, 15$ **16.** $19, 21, 23, 25, 27$
17. $53, 55, 57, 59, 61$ **18.** $-5, -3, -1, 1, 3$
19. $-23, -21, -19, -17, -15$ **20.** $b, b + 2,$
$b + 4, b + 6, b + 8$ **21.** $b + 6, b + 8, b + 10,$
$b + 12, b + 14$

EXERCISES **1.** $x + (x + 1) + (x + 2) = 27$
2. $x + (x + 1) + (x + 2) = 33$ **3.** $x + (x + 1) +$
$(x + 2) = -15$ **4.** $x + (x + 1) + (x + 2) = -21$
5. $x(x + 2) = 35$ **6.** $x(x + 2) = 99$
7. $x(x + 2)(x + 4) = 48$
8. $x(x + 2)(x + 4) = 192$ **9.** $x + (x + 2) +$
$(x + 4) + (x + 6) = 40$ **10.** $x + (x + 2) +$
$(x + 4) + (x + 6) = 36$ **11.** $2(x + 1) + x = 35$
12. $2(x + 2) - x = 10$ **13.** $2(x + 2) + x = 19$
14. $3(x + 1) - 3x = 3$ **15.** $3(x + 2) + 2x = 46$
16. $3x - 2(x + 2) = 21$ **17.** $x(x + 1)(x + 2) =$
$8[x + (x + 1) + (x + 2)]$ **18.** $x(x + 2)(x + 4) =$
$4[x + (x + 2) + (x + 4)]$

Page 170

1. 22, 23 **2.** 19, 21, 23 **3.** 29, 30, 31, 32, 33
4. 38, 40, 42 **5.** 7, 8, 9 **6.** 5, 7, 9, 11 **7.** 37, 39,
41 **8.** 19, 20, 21 **9.** -4, -3 or 3, 4 **10.** 5, 6 or
-6, -5 **11.** 4, 6 or -6, -4 **12.** 5, 7 or -7, -5
13. 7, 9 or -9, -7 **14.** 4, 6 or -6, -4
15. -3, -2, -1 or 2, 3, 4 **16.** 5, 6, 7 or -4,
-3, -2 **17.** 5, 6, 7 or -4, -3, -2 **18.** 2, 3, 4
or -1, 0, 1 **19.** -5, -3 **20.** 4, 6 or -10, -8
21. -2, -1, 0, 1 **22.** 2, 4, 6, 8 **23.** -7, -6,
-5, -4 or 4, 5, 6, 7 **24.** 3, 4, 5, 6, 7

Page 171

1. 38.4 m **2.** yes

Page 172

1. $x^2 + 8x + 15$ **2.** $x^2 + 2x - 63$ **3.** $2x^2 +$
$13x + 15$ **4.** $3x^2 + 17x - 6$ **5.** $2b^2 + 5b - 12$
6. $m^2 - 1$ **7.** $12z^2 - 11z + 2$ **8.** $3x^2 +$
$10x - 25$ **9.** $15x^2 + 7x - 4$ **10.** $x^3 + 2x^2 -$
$32x - 15$ **11.** $2x^3 + 3x^2 - 17x + 12$
12. $3x^3 + 5x^2 - 14x + 4$ **13.** $9a^2 - 30a + 25$
14. $16x^2 - 8x + 1$ **15.** $4x^2 + 12x + 9$
16. $49x^2 + 14x + 1$ **17.** $(x - 3)(x - 4)$
18. $(p + 2)(p + 5)$ **19.** $(2a - 1)(a + 5)$
20. $(x - 3)(x - 2)$ **21.** $(3y + 2)(y + 5)$
22. $(3x - 2)(x + 6)$ **23.** $(2m - 5)(m + 4)$
24. $(2m + 3)(m + 2)$ **25.** $(2x - 3)(x - 3)$
26. $2(2a - 1)(a + 1)$ **27.** $(3x + 1)(2x - 1)$
28. $(4b - 1)(3b + 2)$ **29.** $(a - 2)(a + 2)$
30. $(x - 6)(x + 6)$ **31.** $(2a + 5)(2a - 5)$
32. $(7x - 6y)(7x + 6y)$ **33.** $3(x + 3)(x + 4)$
34. $2(a - 3)(a - 1)$ **35.** $2(a - 5)(a + 4)$
36. $3(b + 5)(b - 3)$ **37.** $3k(k + 6)(k - 5)$
38. $3(b - 10)(b + 3)$ **39.** $6x(x - 3)(x - 1)$
40. $b(b + 7)(b - 7)$ **41.** $(x + y)(x + 2y)$
42. $(a + 3b)(a - 3b)$ **43.** $(a - 7b)(a + 4b)$
44. $(2p + 3q)(p + 5q)$
45. $(12x - 13y)(12x + 13y)$
46. $2(2y + 3b)(y - 5b)$ **47.** $(3x - 7y)(x - 8y)$
48. $y(x + 2y)(x - 2y)$ **49.** $3(2x + 3)(2x - 3)$
50. $3(2x - 5)(2x - 5)$ **51.** 1, 2 **52.** 2, -2
53. -3, 12 **54.** 2, -2 **55.** 4, 6 **56.** 2, 7
57. $\{0, 5\}$ **58.** $\left\{\frac{7}{3}, -\frac{7}{3}\right\}$ **59.** $\left\{\frac{1}{2}, -5\right\}$ **60.** $\left\{\frac{7}{2}, 3\right\}$
61. $\{0, 6\}$ **62.** $\left\{-\frac{7}{2}, -4\right\}$ **63.** 8, 9 or -9, -8
64. 17, 18 **65.** 7, 8, 9 or -2, -1, 0 **66.** -6,
-4, -2 or 4, 6, 8

Page 173

1. $x^2 + 13x + 40$ **2.** $6x^2 + 5x - 4$ **3.** $9x^2 - 4$
4. $2a^3 - 11a^2 - 13a + 12$ **5.** $9a^2 - 12a + 4$
6. $16x^2 + 8x + 1$ **7.** $(a - 5)(a - 2)$
8. $(x - 7)(x + 5)$ **9.** $2(2m - 3)(m + 6)$
10. $(p + 7)(p - 7)$ **11.** $2b(b - 8)(b + 4)$
12. $a(4a + 5)(4a - 5)$ **13.** $(2x - y)(x + 3y)$
14. $2(2b - 3c)(2b + c)$ **15.** 1, 4 **16.** -2, 6
17. 0, 7 **18.** 4, 6 **19.** -4, 7 **20.** 8, -8
21. $\{0, -14\}$ **22.** $\{5, -5\}$ **23.** $\left\{-\frac{3}{2}, 7\right\}$
24. $\left\{-\frac{5}{2}, -8\right\}$ **25.** $\left\{-\frac{1}{2}, 5\right\}$ **26.** $\left\{-\frac{7}{2}, 3\right\}$
27. 40, 41 **28.** -8, -7 or 7, 8 **29.** -11, -9 or
3, 5 **30.** 4, 6

Page 174

1. Answers may vary; e.g. $\dfrac{A}{E}, \dfrac{G}{E}, \dfrac{G}{C}, \dfrac{A}{B}$.

Page 178

1. $\frac{1}{7}$ **2.** $\frac{1}{q}$ **3.** $\frac{1}{x}$ **4.** $\frac{1}{13}$ **5.** $-\frac{1}{3}$; no reciprocal; 1;
-1; -5 **6.** $\frac{5}{6}$ **7.** $-\frac{2}{3}$ **8.** $-\frac{5}{4}$ **9.** $\frac{6}{1}$ **10.** $-\frac{3}{1}$ **11.** $\frac{12}{3}$
12. $-\frac{8}{2}$ **13.** $-\frac{6}{12}$ **14.** $\frac{4}{5}$ **15.** $-\frac{5}{17}$ **16.** $\frac{x + 5}{x - 4}$
17. $\frac{a - 4}{a + 2}$ **18.** 7 **19.** 5 **20.** 4 **21.** 3, -3 **22.** 3, 4
23. 0, 5, -5 **24.** 0, 3, 4 **25.** 2, -2

Page 179

1. 1 **2.** $\frac{1}{9}$ **3.** 1 **4.** $\frac{1}{125}$ **5.** $\frac{1}{6}$ **6.** 2 **7.** $\frac{1}{3}$ **8.** $\frac{1}{9}$ **9.** 1
10. $\frac{7}{10}$

Page 183

ORALS **1.** $\frac{1}{16}$ **2.** $\frac{1}{30}$ **3.** $\frac{1}{m^5}$ **4.** $\frac{1}{a^8}$ **5.** $\frac{1}{6a}$
6. $\frac{5}{2a}$ **7.** $\frac{1}{230}$ **8.** $\frac{8}{21}$ **9.** $-\frac{3}{10}$ **10.** $\frac{8}{3}$

EXERCISES **1.** $\frac{6}{48}$ **2.** $\frac{8}{75}$ **3.** $-\frac{8}{45}$ **4.** $-\frac{4}{30}$
5. $\frac{10a^5}{18b^9}$ **6.** $\frac{28x^7}{15y^6}$ **7.** $-\frac{20a^5}{9b^9}$ **8.** $-\frac{18x^8}{10y^7}$ **9.** $-\frac{x^5}{y^{11}}$
10. $\frac{a^2}{b^7}$ **11.** $\frac{x^{11}}{y^6}$ **12.** $\frac{a^6}{b^{11}}$ **13.** $-\frac{2x^2 - x - 3}{2x^2 + 7x + 6}$
14. $-\frac{3x^2 + 5x - 2}{3x^2 + 4x + 1}$ **15.** $-\frac{2x^2 + x - 15}{2x^2 + 15x + 25}$
16. $\frac{3x - 3}{x + 5}$ **17.** $\frac{10x - 5}{x + 4}$ **18.** $\frac{6x + 12}{2x - 5}$

19. $\dfrac{2x^2 - 11x - 21}{x - 4}$ **20.** $\dfrac{-2a^2 - 7a + 4}{a + 3}$

21. $\dfrac{2a^2 + 7a - 15}{3a - 7}$ **22.** $\dfrac{a^{10}}{b^6}$ **23.** $\dfrac{x^7}{m^3}$

24. $\dfrac{a - 4}{2a^2 + 5a - 3}$ **25.** $\dfrac{a^2 - b^2}{x^2 + xy - 2y^2}$

26. $\dfrac{6m^2 - mn - n^2}{2m^2 + 7mn + 3n^2}$ **27.** $\dfrac{12r^2 - rt - t^2}{r^2 + 3rt + 2t^2}$

28. $\dfrac{x^2 + xy - 2y^2}{x + y}$ **29.** $-\dfrac{a^2 - 4b^2}{x^2 - y^2}$

30. $\dfrac{4x^2 + 12xy + 9y^2}{m^2 + 2mn + n^2}$ **31.** $\dfrac{9a^2 + 6ab + b^2}{4a^2 + 4ab + b^2}$

32. $\dfrac{a^2 - b^2}{2a - 3b}$ **33.** $-\dfrac{4a^2 + 11ab - 3b^2}{2a^2 + ab - b^2}$

34. $\dfrac{4x^2 - 4xy + y^2}{x^2 + 8xy + 16y^2}$ **35.** $\dfrac{x^3 - 8x^2 + 5x + 50}{x^3 + 6x^2 - 15x - 100}$

36. $\dfrac{18a^3 - 21a^2b + 8ab^2 - b^3}{a^3 + 3a^2b + 3ab^2 + b^3}$

Page 186

1. $\frac{1}{3}$ **2.** $\frac{1}{2}$ **3.** $-\frac{5}{12}$ **4.** $-\frac{4}{15}$ **5.** $\dfrac{a - 5}{2a - 1}$ **6.** $\dfrac{m + 2}{2m + 1}$

7. $\dfrac{b + 5}{b - 2}$ **8.** $-\dfrac{x - 2}{x + 2}$ **9.** $\frac{1}{4}$ **10.** $\dfrac{1}{a}$ **11.** $\dfrac{3}{b - 2}$

12. $-\dfrac{x - 1}{2}$ **13.** $\dfrac{4}{b + 3}$ **14.** $\dfrac{a - 3}{2}$ **15.** $\dfrac{y - 4}{y}$

16. $\dfrac{m - 2}{m}$ **17.** $\dfrac{3(x + 2)}{2}$ **18.** $\dfrac{2(x + 5)}{3}$

19. $\dfrac{b}{b + 7}$ **20.** $\dfrac{x + 4}{4}$ **21.** $\dfrac{3p - 1}{5}$ **22.** $\dfrac{2n - 1}{n - 2}$

23. $\dfrac{x + 4}{x - 4}$ **24.** $\dfrac{a}{a - 7}$ **25.** $x + 4$ **26.** $z - 8$

27. $x + 5$ **28.** $a + b$ **29.** $3a - 1$ **30.** $2x + 7$

31. $-11x - 3$ **32.** $3x + 7$ **33.** $a^2 - a - 2$

34. $a^2 + 2a - 1 + \dfrac{4}{a + 1}$

Page 187

Facts | Conclusions

1 and 2 | Flight crew names: Miller, Adams, Baker

4 and 8 | Pilot not named Baker.

7 | Copilot and Miller (crewmember) live in same town.

3 and 6 | Adams (passenger) does not live next door to pilot. (14,000 is not a multiple of 3.)

4 and 5 | Baker (passenger) does not live next door to pilot.

6 | Miller (passenger) lives next door to pilot which is halfway between Cleveland and St. Louis.

4 and 8 | Adams lives in St. Louis.

8 | The pilot's name is Adams.

7 | The copilot is not named Miller. Thus, the copilot's name is Baker, and the navigator's name is Miller.

Page 190

1. $-\dfrac{1}{x + 4}$ **2.** $-\dfrac{1}{a - 5}$ **3.** $-\frac{1}{2}$ **4.** $-\frac{1}{2}$ **5.** $\dfrac{a + 5}{4}$

6. $-\dfrac{m + 4}{2}$ **7.** $-(x - 4)$ **8.** $-(p + 3)$ **9.** -2

10. $-\dfrac{2}{x + 7}$ **11.** $-\dfrac{1}{c - 2}$ **12.** $-\dfrac{2}{b - 3}$

13. $-(a + 2)$ **14.** $-\dfrac{m - 8}{m + 3}$ **15.** $-\dfrac{a + 3}{a + 8}$

16. $-\dfrac{c + 10}{8}$ **17.** $-\dfrac{y + 6}{y + 2}$ **18.** $-\dfrac{a + 5}{a - 8}$

19. $\dfrac{x + 2}{x - 4}$ **20.** $-\dfrac{m + 6}{2(m + 2)}$ **21.** $-\dfrac{n - 4}{2(n - 3)}$

22. $-\dfrac{x}{x + 4}$ **23.** $-\dfrac{a - b}{a + 2b}$ **24.** $-\dfrac{2x - y}{2}$

25. $\dfrac{a - b}{2a - b}$ **26.** $\dfrac{2(2a - 1)}{3a - 1}$ **27.** $-\dfrac{a^2 - b^2}{a}$

28. $\dfrac{a^2(a^2 + b^3)}{b^2}$ **29.** $-\dfrac{x^2 - 5}{x}$ **30.** $-a$

31. $-(b + 3)(b + 2)$ **32.** $-\dfrac{1}{(m - 1)(m + 5)}$

Page 193

ORALS **1.** $\dfrac{1}{a^3}$ **2.** m^6 **3.** $\dfrac{1}{a^2}$ **4.** b **5.** $\dfrac{1}{b}$

6. $\dfrac{1}{a^2b^4}$ **7.** x^2y **8.** m^2n^3

EXERCISES **1.** $\dfrac{2m^3}{3n^2}$ **2.** $\dfrac{2x^3}{3y^4}$ **3.** $\dfrac{a^5}{2b}$

4. $-\dfrac{x(a + 5)}{y^2}$ **5.** $-\dfrac{n^2(n - 1)}{m^5}$ **6.** $-\dfrac{a(x + 8)}{3b^2}$

7. $2a^3b^2(x - 2)$ **8.** $\dfrac{2(x + 4)}{m^3}$ **9.** $\dfrac{b - 2}{2x}$ **10.** $\dfrac{y}{a + 5}$

11. $\dfrac{1}{k(a + 4)}$ **12.** $m^3(y + 2)$ **13.** $\dfrac{a + 2}{n(a - 1)}$

14. $\dfrac{y - 3}{2c}$ **15.** $\dfrac{b^3(x + 3)}{x - 1}$ **16.** $\dfrac{c + 7}{ab^2}$

17. $\dfrac{a(2x - 1)}{b^2(2x - 3)}$ **18.** $-\dfrac{a^2}{x + 3}$ **19.** $\dfrac{y - 1}{x^4}$

20. $\dfrac{a}{b-1}$ **21.** $\dfrac{x^5}{b+y}$ **22.** $\dfrac{1}{a^2(x+3)}$ **23.** $\dfrac{x-2}{b^3}$

24. $-\dfrac{1}{m-2}$

Page 195

ORALS **1.** $\dfrac{2x+5}{3x+4}$ **2.** $\dfrac{a-5}{7}$ **3.** x

4. $\dfrac{x-2}{a^4(x+5)}$ **5.** $\dfrac{3x+2}{b^4(2x-5)}$ **6.** $\dfrac{m^2(3x+4)}{2x+5}$

7. $-\dfrac{4}{5}$ **8.** a^2 **9.** $\dfrac{1}{x^2}$ **10.** $\dfrac{4x-6}{9x+6}$ **11.** $2a-5$ **12.** $\dfrac{x^2}{y^5}$

EXERCISES **1.** $3(x-2)$ **2.** $\dfrac{a-5}{3}$ **3.** $\dfrac{3}{n+2}$

4. 3 **5.** $\dfrac{b+4}{2(b+2)}$ **6.** $\dfrac{2(m+5)}{m+4}$ **7.** $\dfrac{2b^2}{5x}$ **8.** $\dfrac{2m^2}{3n^4}$

9. $\dfrac{3x^2}{5y}$ **10.** $\dfrac{-2y^3(a-5)}{7x2}$ **11.** $\dfrac{-3a(x+6)}{2b^4}$

12. $\dfrac{-5y^2}{4x(x-2)}$ **13.** $\dfrac{2(b-4)}{b-2}$ **14.** $\dfrac{3(x-5)}{x+7}$

15. $\dfrac{b-5}{b-7}$ **16.** $\dfrac{1}{3}$ **17.** $\dfrac{a+5}{2}$ **18.** $3(a+1)$

19. $\dfrac{4x}{3y^3(2a+3)}$ **20.** $\dfrac{3(2x+5)}{x+8}$ **21.** $\dfrac{3(a+2)}{a+3}$

22. $\dfrac{a+2}{a+3}$ **23.** $\dfrac{6(2x+5)}{x+8}$ **24.** $-\dfrac{1}{x+3}$

25. $-\dfrac{2(c+1)}{c}$ **26.** $-2(2n+1)$ **27.** $\dfrac{2(a+2)}{a-4}$

28. -1 **29.** $\dfrac{c}{c+d}$ **30.** $-\dfrac{x-5}{x-3}$ **31.** $\dfrac{2(x+2y)}{a^2b}$

32. $-\dfrac{2m+n}{2m-7}$ **33.** $-\dfrac{3(a+3b)}{a-2b}$ **34.** $\dfrac{5c-d}{2(c-5d)}$

35. $-\dfrac{m+2}{2m+1}$ **36.** -1 **37.** $-\dfrac{m+1}{2}$ **38.** 1

Page 197

1.
```
        573
        219
      5 157
      5 73
    114 6
    125,487
```
2.
```
         173
   215)37,195
        21 5
        15 69
        15 05
          645
          645
```
3.
```
        384
    26)9,984
        7 8
        2 18
        2 08
          104
          104
```

Page 199

1. $\dfrac{x-2}{3(x+6)}$ **2.** $\dfrac{2(a-7)}{a+7}$ **3.** $2(a-5)$ **4.** $\dfrac{4(k+2)}{k^3}$

5. $\dfrac{5}{3a^2(a+2)}$ **6.** $\dfrac{2(x-1)}{5x^6}$ **7.** $\dfrac{-35b^4}{3a^6}$ **8.** $-\dfrac{14x}{y^2}$

9. $-\dfrac{6m(5+m)}{n}$ **10.** $\dfrac{m+1}{2}$ **11.** $\dfrac{5(b-2)}{2(b-3)}$

12. $\dfrac{m}{m+3}$ **13.** $-\dfrac{x-1}{x+1}$ **14.** $\dfrac{-2}{y^2}$ **15.** -1

16. $\dfrac{2(a+4)}{3a^3b^5}$ **17.** $\dfrac{2y(x+5)}{x^2}$ **18.** $\dfrac{2m+1}{3m(2m-3)}$

19. $-\dfrac{m^7(m+1)}{8}$ **20.** $\dfrac{b-1}{b+3}$ **21.** $\dfrac{a+3}{a+4}$

Page 200

1. $\dfrac{4}{5}$ **2.** $-\dfrac{1}{3}$ **3.** $\dfrac{3}{2}$ **4.** $\dfrac{1}{12}$ **5.** $\dfrac{1}{a+7}$ **6.** m **7.** $\dfrac{1}{4}$; no

reciprocal; $-\dfrac{1}{5}$; -3 **8.** 5 **9.** 4 **10.** $4, 6$ **11.** $\dfrac{20}{63}$

12. $\dfrac{6a^5}{35b^9}$ **13.** $\dfrac{x^2+2x-15}{2x-3}$

14. $-\dfrac{a^2-4b^2}{a^2+4ab+3b^2}$ **15.** $\dfrac{2}{5}$ **16.** $\dfrac{3}{4}$ **17.** $\dfrac{b}{2}$

18. $\dfrac{2(2p+5)}{p+4}$ **19.** $x-2$ **20.** $z+2$ **21.** -3

22. $\dfrac{y+4}{y-4}$ **23.** $-\dfrac{3a+5}{a+7}$ **24.** $\dfrac{2b^3}{5a^2}$ **25.** $\dfrac{b-1}{x}$

26. $-\dfrac{3x(a+5)}{7y(a+2)}$ **27.** $5(x-2)$

28. $\dfrac{(x-3)(3x+7)}{(x+7)(x-4)}$ **29.** $\dfrac{x^3}{y}$ **30.** $-\dfrac{2y^2(a-3)}{x^4}$

31. $\dfrac{a-9}{5(a+7)}$ **32.** $\dfrac{7(k-3)}{k^4}$ **33.** $-\dfrac{21b^5}{5a^6}$

34. $-\dfrac{2x^5(x+7)}{3}$

Page 201

1. $\dfrac{1}{5}$ **2.** $\dfrac{6}{5}$ **3.** $\dfrac{1}{3x+1}$ **4.** $2x-9$ **5.** $\dfrac{1}{3}$; $-\dfrac{1}{7}$; no

reciprocal; -9 **6.** 4 **7.** $3, 4$ **8.** $\dfrac{15}{14}$ **9.** $\dfrac{12m^{12}}{35b^{10}}$

10. $\dfrac{m^2-m-12}{2m-7}$ **11.** $\dfrac{3}{5}$ **12.** $\dfrac{5}{4}$ **13.** $\dfrac{2(3p-5)}{3p-2}$

14. $-\dfrac{y+3}{y-7}$ **15.** $\dfrac{1-a}{y^4}$ **16.** $-\dfrac{x^2(t-6)}{3y^4(t+4)}$

17. $a+2$ **18.** $m+2$ **19.** $5(m-2)$ **20.** $\dfrac{2x+5}{x+6}$

21. $-\dfrac{5(a+1)}{xy^4}$ **22.** $-\dfrac{1}{a+2}$ **23.** $-a^2$

24. $-\dfrac{6x^3(x+6)}{35}$

Page 204

ORALS 1. $\frac{4}{5}$ 2. $\frac{8}{9}$ 3. $\frac{10}{13}$ 4. $\frac{9}{14}$ 5. $\frac{5}{m}$ 6. $\frac{-4}{a}$

7. $\frac{3x+3}{5}$ 8. $\frac{-2m+5}{2}$

EXERCISES 1. $\frac{2}{3}$ 2. $\frac{1}{2}$ 3. $\frac{1}{a}$ 4. $\frac{4}{5x}$ 5. $\frac{7y}{y-3}$

6. $\frac{13x}{x-6}$ 7. $\frac{17m}{m+7}$ 8. $\frac{x+6}{3}$ 9. $\frac{1}{6}$ 10. $\frac{1}{7}$

11. $\frac{1}{m-5}$ 12. $\frac{1}{x+6}$ 13. $\frac{1}{a}$ 14. $\frac{1}{a+4}$

15. $\frac{1}{a-3}$ 16. $\frac{1}{x}$ 17. $\frac{1}{2}$ 18. $\frac{2}{3}$ 19. $\frac{3a+2b}{7}$

20. $\frac{6a+5b}{16}$ 21. $\frac{1}{x+5}$ 22. $\frac{1}{2a+3}$ 23. $\frac{a+3}{3a+5}$

24. $\frac{b+3}{2b+7}$ 25. $a+3$ 26. $\frac{b+5}{2}$

27. $4x+3y$ 28. $\frac{2x+3y}{3}$

Page 209

1. Joe 15, Tom 22 **2.** Donna 18, Beth 36
3. Louis 3, Dorothy 12 **4.** Denise 5, Steve 21
5. Sylvia 11, Martin 27 **6.** Andrew 10, Sarah 50
7. 4 yr **8.** 3 yr **9.** 6 yr **10.** 7 yr **11.** Mona 6,
Pedro 12 **12.** Phil 18, Lee 25 **13.** 13 yr
14. 25 yr **15.** 6 yr **16.** Sue and Jeff 6, Harry 11

Page 213

ORALS 1. $3 \cdot 2$ 2. $5 \cdot 2$ 3. $3 \cdot 3 \cdot 2$
4. $7 \cdot 2 \cdot 2$ 5. $5 \cdot 2 \cdot 2 \cdot 2$ 6. $7 \cdot 5 \cdot 5 \cdot 2$
7. $3 \cdot 3 \cdot 3 \cdot 2 \cdot 2$ 8. $2 \cdot 2 \cdot 2 \cdot a$ 9. $3 \cdot 3 \cdot 3 \cdot m$

EXERCISES 1. $\frac{3}{2}$ 2. $\frac{7}{8}$ 3. $\frac{3}{2}$ 4. 2 5. $\frac{b}{2}$

6. $\frac{13m}{9}$ 7. $\frac{23a}{8}$ 8. $\frac{16k}{15}$ 9. $\frac{23a+10}{12}$

10. $\frac{35m+27}{18}$ 11. $\frac{23m+21}{28}$ 12. $\frac{15b+2}{6b}$

13. $\frac{2m-2}{3m}$ 14. $\frac{7m-3}{8m}$ 15. $\frac{5a+3}{4a}$ 16. $\frac{m+2}{2m}$

17. $\frac{7}{3}$ 18. $\frac{17a+3}{6}$ 19. $\frac{31x-11}{15}$ 20. $\frac{19t}{21}$

21. $\frac{29a-2}{6a}$ 22. $\frac{35m^2-58m+38}{28m}$

23. $\frac{23a^2+20a-33}{30a}$

Page 216

1. $\frac{9a+23}{(a-4)(a+4)}$ 2. $\frac{9b-3}{(b-5)(b+5)}$ 3. $\frac{x+2}{x}$

4. $\frac{a+2}{a}$ 5. $\frac{3x+22}{x(x+5)}$ 6. $\frac{4m-13}{m(m-4)}$

7. $\frac{2x+11}{(x-3)(x+3)}$ 8. $\frac{7m+23}{(m-4)(m+3)}$

9. $\frac{3x+11}{(x-8)(x+2)}$ 10. $\frac{7m+38}{(m-7)(m+5)}$

11. $\frac{9a+1}{(a-1)(a+1)}$ 12. $\frac{6a-21}{(a-5)(a-2)}$

13. $\frac{10a+12}{(2a-5)(a+3)}$ 14. $\frac{5k-3}{(k-5)(k+4)}$

15. $\frac{k^2+3k-5}{(k-3)(k-2)}$ 16. $\frac{a^2-a-3}{(a+2)(a+1)}$

17. $\frac{2m^2+5m-11}{m(2m+5)}$

Page 217
1. 9; 7 **2.** 12; 14 **3.** 25; 25 **4.** yes **5.** 1: comm.,
not assoc.; 2: not comm., not assoc.; 3: comm.,
not assoc.

Page 219

ORALS 1. y^3 2. a^3 3. p^5

EXERCISES 1. $\frac{2m+3}{m}$ 2. $\frac{56b+3}{7b}$

3. $\frac{3m+2}{m}$ 4. $\frac{11a+10}{(a-1)(a+2)}$ 5. $\frac{7x-10}{(x+2)(x-4)}$

6. $\frac{16a+6}{(3a-1)(2a+5)}$ 7. $\frac{17a+4}{(a-3)(2a+5)}$

8. $\frac{4b+23}{(b-7)(2b+3)}$ 9. $\frac{7x^2+8x+3}{x^3}$

10. $\frac{7y^2+10y-9}{15y^3}$ 11. $\frac{7a^2+9a+10}{6a^3}$

12. $\frac{5x^2+3x+2}{x^3}$ 13. $\frac{5m^2+3m+2}{m^2}$

14. $\frac{18k^2+5}{3k}$ 15. $\frac{a^2+2a+3}{a^2}$

16. $\frac{19a^2+9a+3}{6a^3}$ 17. $\frac{-9b^2+50b-45}{15b^3}$

18. $\frac{-10x^3-x^2+37x+3}{10x^3}$

19. $\frac{6a^3+11a^2+14a-2}{12a^3}$ 20. $\frac{a^2+3a-6}{a+5}$

21. $\frac{2m^2+9m-2}{m+5}$ 22. $\frac{3a^2-11a+1}{3a+1}$

23. $\dfrac{4x^2 - 3x - 6}{2x - 1}$ **24.** $\dfrac{2a^2 - 11}{2a + 3}$

25. $\dfrac{3x^2 - 13x - 3}{3x + 2}$ **26.** $\dfrac{2x^3 + 2x^2 - 16x - 94}{(x - 3)(x - 5)(x + 2)}$

27. $\dfrac{x^3 - 2x^2 - 14x - 1}{x - 5}$

19. $\dfrac{6n^2 - 5n + 9}{(n + 3)(n - 3)}$ **20.** $\dfrac{-5m^2 - 2m - 32}{(m + 4)(m - 4)}$

21. $\dfrac{a^2 + 2ab + 2a + 2b - 3b^2 + 7}{(a - b)(a + b)}$

22. $\dfrac{3a^2 - 2ab + 14b + 7a}{a(a - 2b)(a + 2b)}$ **23.** $\dfrac{b^2 + bc + c^2}{(b + c)(b - c)}$

24. $\dfrac{5b^2 - b + 6}{(b - 1)(b + 1)}$

Page 223

1. $\dfrac{-2}{a + 5}$ **2.** $\dfrac{-2a - 5}{a^2 - 9}$ **3.** $\dfrac{-x^2 + 3x}{x^2 + 5x + 1}$

4. $\dfrac{-2x + 1}{(x - 2)(x + 2)}$ **5.** $\dfrac{-3a + 13}{(a - 5)(a - 2)}$

6. $\dfrac{-3b + 1}{(b + 3)(b + 1)}$ **7.** $\dfrac{10x - 3}{2x}$ **8.** $\dfrac{40x - 7}{5x}$

9. $\dfrac{2a - 11}{a - 2}$ **10.** $\dfrac{4x + 32}{(x + 7)(x - 7)}$

11. $\dfrac{x - 9}{(x - 2)(x - 4)}$ **12.** $\dfrac{b - 3}{(b - 4)(b + 1)}$

13. $\dfrac{-2b + 39}{(3b - 1)(2b + 7)}$ **14.** $\dfrac{-x + 16}{(5x - 2)(3x + 4)}$

15. $\dfrac{9y - 10}{24y^3}$ **16.** $\dfrac{1}{m - 2}$ **17.** $\dfrac{6}{a - 4}$

18. $\dfrac{2(m + 5)}{m(m - 5)}$ **19.** $\dfrac{-2a^2 - 2a + 7}{(a + 3)(a + 2)}$

20. $\dfrac{-a^2 - a - 5}{(a - 2)(a + 2)}$ **21.** $\dfrac{a^2 + 15a - 25}{(2a + 3)(a - 5)}$

22. $\dfrac{y^2 + 4y + 5}{(y - 6)(y + 2)}$ **23.** $\dfrac{2a^2 - 12a - 6}{a(a - 5)}$

24. $\dfrac{-2y^2 + 13y - 12}{(y - 4)(y - 2)}$ **25.** $\dfrac{a^2 - 10a + 22}{(2a - 5)(a + 4)}$

26. $\dfrac{-3x^2 - 4x + 40}{(2x - 5)(x - 7)}$ **27.** $\dfrac{y^2 - 4y - 8}{(y - 4)(2y + 3)}$

28. $\dfrac{-17m - 2}{m(2m + 3)(2m - 3)}$

Page 227

1. not a group **2.** comm. group **3.** not a group
4. not a group

Page 228

1. $\frac{2}{3}$ **2.** $\dfrac{1}{2a + 3}$ **3.** $\frac{5}{8}$ **4.** $\frac{5}{3}$ **5.** $\dfrac{7m}{3}$ **6.** $\dfrac{9m + 7}{14}$

7. $\dfrac{2b + 5}{2b}$ **8.** $\dfrac{28x - 17}{14}$ **9.** $\dfrac{x + 6}{x}$

10. $\dfrac{5a + 19}{(a - 3)(a + 3)}$ **11.** $\dfrac{5a + 4}{(a - 6)(a + 4)}$ **12.** $\dfrac{x}{x - 5}$

13. $\dfrac{35m + 4}{5m}$ **14.** $\dfrac{11y - 9}{(y - 3)(y + 3)}$

15. $\dfrac{-6x^2 + 35x + 3}{14x^3}$ **16.** $\dfrac{28y^2 - 17y + 54}{18y^3}$

17. $\dfrac{x^2 + 2x - 11}{x - 3}$ **18.** $\dfrac{x^2 - 5x + 2}{x - 5}$

19. $\dfrac{-4x + 15}{(x - 4)(x - 3)}$ **20.** $\dfrac{13x + 7}{3x}$ **21.** $\dfrac{8}{x - 5}$

22. $\dfrac{6x + 11}{(x - 2)(x + 2)}$ **23.** $\dfrac{5}{x + 3}$ **24.** $\dfrac{6x - 7}{x(x - 1)}$

25. $\dfrac{m}{m - 9}$ **26.** $\dfrac{-2(m^2 - 4m + 1)}{(m - 2)(m - 6)}$

Page 226

1. $\dfrac{3}{x + 7}$ **2.** $\dfrac{4}{x + 5}$ **3.** $\dfrac{2}{b - 1}$ **4.** $\frac{3}{4}$

5. $\dfrac{-b - 5}{(b - 2)(b + 1)}$ **6.** $\dfrac{-11a + 30}{7(a - 3)}$ **7.** $\dfrac{a}{a - 4}$

8. $\dfrac{x}{x - 2}$ **9.** $\dfrac{a}{a + 2}$ **10.** $\dfrac{a}{a - 5}$ **11.** $\dfrac{8m + 1}{m(m - 1)}$

12. $\dfrac{10a - 27}{a(a - 4)}$ **13.** $\dfrac{-k^2 + 3k + 2}{(k - 6)(k - 2)}$

14. $\dfrac{7a - 10}{(a - 8)(a + 2)}$ **15.** $\dfrac{m}{m - 5}$ **16.** $\dfrac{x + 2}{x - 3}$

17. $\dfrac{-2m^2 + 7m - 2}{(m - 5)(m - 2)}$ **18.** $\dfrac{2a^2 + 14a + 6}{(a - 5)(a + 5)}$

Page 229

1. $\frac{13}{18}$ **2.** $\dfrac{11m + 5}{15}$ **3.** $\dfrac{3(a + 1)}{2a}$ **4.** $\dfrac{25x + 8}{21}$

5. $\dfrac{x + 7}{x}$ **6.** $\dfrac{7a + 46}{(a - 6)(a + 6)}$ **7.** $\dfrac{7a - 5}{(a - 5)(a + 2)}$

8. $\dfrac{m}{m + 2}$ **9.** $\dfrac{18m + 7}{3m}$ **10.** $\dfrac{7y - 18}{(y + 2)(y - 6)}$

11. $\dfrac{-12x^2 + 35x + 2}{21x^3}$ **12.** $\dfrac{31a^2 - 16a + 30}{20a^3}$

13. $\dfrac{x^2 - x - 10}{x + 3}$ **14.** $\dfrac{-5x + 24}{(x - 7)(x - 4)}$ **15.** $\dfrac{11x + 2}{2x}$

16. $\dfrac{6}{y - 4}$ **17.** $\dfrac{4}{x + 8}$ **18.** $\dfrac{7m - 8}{m(m - 1)}$ **19.** $\dfrac{a}{a - 8}$

20. $\dfrac{-3x^2 + 13x - 2}{(x - 9)(x - 1)}$

Page 232

ORALS **1.** 6 **2.** 5 **3.** 19 **4.** 9 **5.** 6 **6.** 1 **7.** 2
8. 2

EXERCISES **1.** 3 **2.** 11 **3.** 6 **4.** 18 **5.** 15
6. 3 **7.** 10 **8.** 1 **9.** 7 **10.** 38 **11.** 18 **12.** 14
13. 4, -4 **14.** 1, -1 **15.** 2, -2 **16.** 3, -3
17. $\frac{18}{5}$ **18.** $\frac{23}{6}$ **19.** $\frac{8}{3}$ **20.** $\frac{1}{2}$ **21.** $\{x|-2 < x < 2\}$
22. $\{x|-4 \le x \le 4\}$ **23.** $\{x|-1 < x < 1\}$
24. $\{x|x < 0 \text{ or } x > 0\}$ **25.** $\{x|x \le -2 \text{ or } x \ge 2\}$
26. $\{x|x < -5 \text{ or } x > 5\}$

Page 235

1. -1, 7 **2.** -3, 11 **3.** 3, -1 **4.** 6, -1 **5.** -3, 2
6. 4, -4 **7.** $\{1, 5\}$ **8.** $\left\{-1, \frac{11}{3}\right\}$ **9.** $\{3, -11\}$
10. $\left\{-\frac{2}{7}, \frac{8}{7}\right\}$ **11.** $\left\{-\frac{2}{3}, 4\right\}$ **12.** $\{-14, 24\}$
13. $\left\{\frac{13}{2}, \frac{15}{2}\right\}$ **14.** $\left\{\frac{11}{7}, \frac{15}{7}\right\}$ **15.** $\{1, 6\}$ **16.** 0, 6
17. 0, 7 **18.** 0, 5 **19.** 2, -2 **20.** 10, -26

Page 238

ORALS **1.** pos. **2.** neg. **3.** neg. **4.** neg.
5. neg. **6.** pos. **7.** neg. **8.** neg. **9.** pos.
10. pos. **11.** neg. **12.** pos. **13.** 3 **14.** -1
15. -21 **16.** -3 **17.** -6 **18.** 5 **19.** -5 **20.** -6

EXERCISES **1.** 4 **2.** 4 **3.** 10 **4.** 18 **5.** 6
6. 11 **7.** 18 **8.** 5 **9.** 4 **10.** $\frac{31}{4}$ **11.** $\frac{5}{6}$ **12.** $\frac{11}{9}$
13. 3 **14.** 2 **15.** -2

Page 241

1. (1, 3) **2.** (2, 2) **3.** (1, 1) **4.** (3, -2)
5. (-2, -3) **6.** (-1, 4) **7.** (-2, 2) **8.** (-2, -2)
9. (2, -1) **10.** (3, -2) **11.** (4, -3) **12.** (3, -1)
13. (3, 4) **14.** (-1, 3) **15.** (-3, 1) **16.** 3
17. 1 **18.** 4 **19.** 3 **20.** 4 **21.** 2 **22.** *x*-coord.
neg.; *y*-coord. pos.

Page 244

ORALS **1.** right 3, up 4 **2.** right 2, down 5
3. left 3, up 7 **4.** left 2, down 5 **5.** left 8, up 2
6. up 2 **7.** right 4 **8.** left 5 **9.** down 4
10. left 1, down 3

EXERCISES **1.** right 2, up 3 **2.** left 4, up 1
3. left 3, down 1 **4.** right 2, down 3 **5.** right 3
6. origin **7.** left 3 **8.** down 4 **9.** down 7
10. left 5, up 2 **11.** right 4, down 1 **12.** left 5,

up 1 **13.** up 3 **14.** right 6 **15.** left 8 **16.** right
$3\frac{1}{2}$, up $4\frac{1}{2}$ **17.** left $2\frac{1}{2}$, up $4\frac{1}{2}$ **18.** right 4.5,
down 3.5 **19.** left $1\frac{1}{4}$ **20.** (2, 5) **21.** (-4, 8)

Page 245
1. coefficients of powers of $a + b$ **2.** 1, 6, 15,
20, 15, 6, 1; 1, 7, 21, 35, 35, 21, 7, 1
3. $a^6 + 6a^5b + 15a^4b^2 + 20a^3b^3 + 15a^2b^4 +$
$6ab^5 + b^6$; $a^7 + 7a^6b + 21a^5b^2 + 35a^4b^3 +$
$35a^3b^4 + 21a^2b^5 + 7ab^6 + b^7$

Page 247
1. *x*-axis **2.** *y*-axis **3.** *x*-axis **4.** *y*-axis **5.** *y*-axis
6. *x*-axis **7.** *x*-axis **8.** *y*-axis **9.** *y*-axis **10.** -4
11. 2 **12.** 4 **13.** 4 **14.** 3 **15.** 3 **16.** none
17. 3, 4

Page 250
1. -7 **2.** -7 **3.** 1 **4.** -8 **5.** -8 **6.** -3 **7.** -3
8. 3 **9.** -11 **10.** -3 **11.** 8 **12.** -3 **13.** -6
14. 8 **15.** -23 **16.** 47 **17.** 29 **18.** 23 **19.** $-\frac{5}{4}$
20. $-\frac{3}{2}$ **21.** $\frac{13}{6}$ **22.** $\frac{7}{6}$ **23.** $\frac{19}{15}$ **24.** -5.5 **25.** .8
26. 10.2 **27.** $-\frac{23}{8}$ **28.** $\frac{13}{27}$ **29.** $-8a$ **30.** $-12n$
31. $-3k$ **32.** $-6a + 6$ **33.** $-\dfrac{5m}{6}$ **34.** $-\dfrac{2}{m^2}$

Page 254
1. $\frac{3}{4}$ **2.** $\frac{1}{4}$ **3.** $\frac{2}{3}$ **4.** $\frac{6}{11}$ **5.** $\frac{3}{10}$ **6.** $-\frac{5}{4}$ **7.** $-\frac{4}{15}$ **8.** $\frac{3}{8}$
9. 0 **10.** $\dfrac{3k}{2b}$ **11.** $-\dfrac{2t}{7i}$ **12.** $-\dfrac{11d}{7c}$ **13.** $-\dfrac{k}{b}$

Page 257

ORALS **1.** up to the right **2.** down to the
right **3.** horizontal **4.** vertical **5.** down to the
right

EXERCISES **1.** undefined; vertical **2.** $-\frac{3}{5}$;
down to the right **3.** 0; horizontal **4.** $-\frac{1}{12}$;
down to the right **5.** $\frac{5}{8}$; up to the right **6.** 0;
horizontal **7.** undefined; vertical **8.** $\frac{4}{13}$; up to the
right **9.** 0; horizontal **10.** no **11.** yes **12.** no
13. yes **14.** no **15.** no **16.** yes **17.** no **18.** no
19. yes **20.** yes

Page 258

1. 6 **2.** 2 **3.** 14 **4.** $\frac{23}{15}$ **5.** 7, -7 **6.** 2, 3 **7.** 1, $\frac{7}{3}$

8. 1, 7 **9.** 9 **10.** -9 **11.** $-\frac{3}{2}$ **12.** (2, 2)

13. (5, 1) **14.** (3, -1) **15.** (1, -3) **16.** (-2, -2)

17. (-4, -1) **18.** (-5, -3) **19.** (-3, 2)

20. (-5, 1) **21.** (-2, 0) **22.** 1; right 3, up 5

23. 2; left 3, up 2 **24.** on x-axis; left 5

25. on y-axis; up 3 **26.** x-axis **27.** y-axis

28. x-axis **29.** -5 **30.** 1 **31.** 11 **32.** 14 **33.** 5

34. 4; up to the right **35.** 0; horizontal

36. $-\frac{7}{3}$; down to the right **37.** undefined; vertical

38. yes **39.** yes **40.** no

Page 259

1. 4 **2.** 6 **3.** 17 **4.** $\frac{17}{10}$ **5.** 6, -6 **6.** -1, $\frac{11}{3}$

7. 5, -1 **8.** 7 **9.** $-\frac{7}{8}$ **10.** (-4, 2) **11.** (-2, -1)

12. (0, 0) **13.** (3, 1) **14.** (5, -2) **15.** 1; right 5,

down 2 **16.** 3; left 3, down 6 **17.** on y-axis;

down 4 **18.** x-axis **19.** y-axis **20.** -6 **21.** $\frac{5}{2}$

22. 12 **23.** $\frac{5}{4}$ **24.** $\frac{6}{5}$; up to the right **25.** 0;

horizontal **26.** 0; horizontal **27.** undefined;

vertical **28.** yes **29.** no

Page 260

70 m

Page 263

ORALS **1.** extremes 3, 10; means 5, 6

2. extremes 7, 42; means 14, 21 **3.** extremes a,

n; means b, m **4.** extremes 3, 4; means 5, x

5. extremes 2, $5a$; means 5, 7 **6.** extremes 5,

3; means 9, $2m$ **7.** extremes $3m$, $5y$; means

$2b$, $7x$ **8.** extremes x, t; means b, $2y$

EXERCISES **1.** $\frac{10}{3}$ **2.** $\frac{6}{5}$ **3.** $\frac{21}{2}$ **4.** $\frac{14}{3}$ **5.** $\frac{15}{4}$

6. $-\frac{26}{5}$ **7.** 4 **8.** -31 **9.** $\frac{15}{16}$ **10.** 42,000

11. 2,310 **12.** 10,000 **13.** 320 **14.** 6, -6 **15.** 8,

-8 **16.** 1, -4 **17.** 2, 5 **18.** 9, 15 **19.** 9, 24

20. 6, 9, 15 **21.** 49, 21

Page 267

ORALS **1.** $\frac{y-3}{x-1}$ **2.** $\frac{y-3}{x-4}$ **3.** $\frac{y-1}{x+3}$

4. $\frac{y+5}{x+3}$ **5.** $\frac{y+2}{x-1}$ **6.** $\frac{y+1}{x+1}$

EXERCISES **1.** $y = 2x - 1$ **2.** $y = 3x + 2$

3. $y = 2x - 5$ **4.** $y = x - 3$ **5.** $y = x + 4$

6. $y = 2x - 2$ **7.** $y = 4x - 2$ **8.** $y = -3x + 12$

9. $y = -2x - 2$ **10.** $y = -3x - 1$ **11.** $y = 3x + 4$

12. $y = 2x - 7$ **13.** $y = -3x + 4$ **14.** $y = -5x + 1$

15. $y = 2x - 8$ **16.** $-1 = 2(-1) + 1$

17. $-2(-3) - 5 = 1$ **18.** $-(-3) - 4 = -1$

19. $y = 4x$; $12 = 4(3)$ **20.** $y = -3x + 4$; $-5 =$

$-3(3) + 4$ **21.** $y = 3x - 5$; $4 = 3(3) - 5$

22. $y = -2x + 3$; $-3 = -2(3) + 3$ **23.** $y =$

$2x + 5$ **24.** $y = -3x + 5$ **25.** $y = x$ **26.** $y = 6$

Page 269

ORALS **1.** $\frac{3}{2}x + -\frac{5}{2}$ **2.** $-\frac{2}{7}x + \frac{5}{7}$ **3.** $\frac{4}{5}x + -\frac{8}{5}$

4. $-\frac{3}{2}x + \frac{5}{2}$

EXERCISES **1.** $y = \frac{3}{2}x + \frac{1}{2}$ **2.** $y = \frac{2}{5}x + \frac{19}{5}$

3. $y = \frac{1}{4}x + \frac{9}{2}$ **4.** $y = \frac{1}{4}x + 5$ **5.** $y = -\frac{2}{5}x + \frac{21}{5}$

6. $y = \frac{2}{5}x - \frac{11}{5}$ **7.** $y = \frac{4}{5}x + \frac{8}{5}$ **8.** $y = -\frac{8}{3}x + 8$

9. $y = \frac{5}{2}x + 5$ **10.** $y = \frac{3}{4}x + 2$; 5 **11.** $y = \frac{2}{3}x - 3$;

1 **12.** $y = \frac{2}{3}x + 1$; 3 **13.** $y = \frac{3}{2}x + 2$; -1

14. (-1, 0), (0, 1), (1, 2) **15.** (-1, -5), (0, -3),

(1, -1) **16.** (-1, 7), (0, 4), (1, 1) **17.** (-2, -3),

(0, -2), (2, -1) **18.** (-3, 1), (0, 3), (3, 5)

19. (-4, 0), (0, -1), (4, -2) **20.** $y = 3x + 1$;

(-1, -2), (0, 1), (1, 4) **21.** $y = \frac{1}{2}x + 5$; (-2, 4),

(0, 5), (2, 6) **22.** $y = \frac{2}{3}x - 5$; (-3, -7), (0, -5),

(3, -3) **23.** $y = \frac{1}{2}x - 6$; (-2, -7), (0, -6),

(2, -5) **24.** $y = -\frac{1}{4}x + 6$; (-4, 7), (0, 6), (4, 5)

25. $y = \frac{2}{3}x + 1$; (-3, -1), (0, 1), (3, 3)

26. $\frac{2}{3}$ **27.** $-\frac{1}{2}$ **28.** $\frac{2}{5}$ **29.** $-\frac{1}{8}$

Page 271

1. $20.83 **2.** $1,540

Page 275

1. $\frac{1}{2}$; -7 **2.** $\frac{2}{3}$; 4 **3.** $-\frac{4}{5}$; 7 **4.** 2; 0

5. $y = 2x + 4$ **6.** $y = -3x - 5$ **7.** $y = 5x$

8. (-3, -1), (3, 3) **9.** (-4, 5), (4, -1)

10. (-5, -2), (5, -6) **11.** (0, 1), (1, 4)

12. (1, 1), (2, 5) **13.** (1, 2), (2, 0) **14.** (0, -1),

(1, -4) **15.** (1, 1), (2, -3) **16.** (3, 8), (-3, 4)

17. (-3, 7), (3, -3) **18.** (4, 1), (-4, -5)

19. (0, 0), (2, 4) **20.** (-1, -3), (1, 3)

21. (-3, 9), (3, -9) **22.** $y = \frac{2}{3}x + 3$; (0, 3),

(3, 5) **23.** $y = -\frac{4}{5}x - 2$; (0, -2), (5, -6)

Page 278

1. $\left(2, \frac{3}{2}\right)$, $\left(4, \frac{9}{2}\right)$ **2.** $(-4, 5)$, $(4, -1)$ **3.** $(-5, 0)$, $(5, -4)$ **4.** $(-1, 0)$, $(1, 2)$ **5.** $(0, 6)$, $(2, 6)$
6. $(0, -3)$, $(-2, -3)$ **7.** $(-3, 2)$, $(3, 6)$
8. $(-1, -2)$, $(1, 2)$ **9.** $(-1, 6)$, $(1, 2)$
10. $(-1, 4)$, $(1, 4)$ **11.** $(2, 10)$, $(4, 15)$
12. $(-1, 3)$, $(1, 1)$ **13.** $(-1, 2)$, $(1, 4)$
14. $(-1, 4)$, $(1, -2)$ **15.** $(-1, 2)$, $(1, -2)$
16. $(-1, 3)$, $(1, -1)$ **17.** $\left(-3, -\frac{10}{3}\right)$, $\left(3, \frac{2}{3}\right)$
18. $(-1, -7)$, $(1, 5)$

Page 280

1. $(-2, -1)$, $(-2, 0)$, $(-2, 1)$ **2.** $(1, -1)$, $(1, 0)$, $(1, 1)$ **3.** $(-3, -1)$, $(-3, 0)$, $(-3, 1)$
4. $(9, -1)$, $(9, 0)$, $(9, 1)$ **5.** $(3, -1)$, $(3, 0)$, $(3, 1)$ **6.** $(-4, -1)$, $(-4, 0)$, $(-4, 1)$ **7.** $(7, -1)$, $(7, 0)$, $(7, 1)$ **8.** $(8, -1)$, $(8, 0)$, $(8, 1)$
9. $(3, -1)$, $(3, 0)$, $(3, 1)$ **10.** $(-4, -1)$, $(-4, 0)$, $(-4, 1)$ **11.** $(6, -1)$, $(6, 0)$, $(6, 1)$

Page 284

ORALS **1.** $y = 3x + 2$; below and including
2. $y = x + 5$; above and not including **3.** $y = 4$; below and including **4.** $y = x + 3$; below and not including **5.** $y = 2x - 1$; above and including **6.** $x = 5$; to the right and including
7. $x = 2$; to the left and not including
8. $y = 7$; above and not including **9.** $y = 4x + 1$; below and including **10.** $y = x$; above and not including **11.** $x = 3$; to the left and including
12. $y = 3$; below and not including

EXERCISES **1.** $y < -x + 3$ **2.** $y < x - 8$
3. $y > -x - 3$ **4.** $y \geq 2x - 4$ **5.** $y > -\frac{3}{2}x$
6. $y \geq -4x + 6$ **7.** $y < 3x + 4$ **8.** $y < \frac{1}{3}x$ (Two points of the boundary line are given.)
9. above; $(0, 3)$, $(2, 3)$ **10.** to the left of; $(-1, 0)$, $(-1, 2)$ **11.** below and including; $(0, -4)$, $(2, -4)$ **12.** to the right and including; $(2, 0)$, $(2, 2)$ **13.** below; $(0, 0)$, $(1, 3)$ **14.** above; $(0, 0)$, $(1, 2)$ **15.** below and including; $(0, 0)$, $(2, 2)$ **16.** above and including; $(0, 0)$, $(1, -2)$ **17.** below and including; $(0, 5)$, $(2, 7)$
18. above and including; $(0, -3)$, $(2, 1)$
19. below; $(0, -3)$, $(2, -5)$ **20.** above; $(0, -4)$, $(2, 2)$ **21.** below and including; $(0, 1)$, $(2, 5)$
22. above and including; $(0, -2)$, $(2, 4)$

23. to the left of; $(0, 0)$, $(0, 2)$ **24.** above and including; $(0, 0)$, $(2, 0)$ **25.** below; $(0, 1)$, $(3, 3)$
26. above and including; $(0, -2)$, $(5, 1)$
27. below and including; $(0, 1)$, $(2, 2)$
28. above; $(0, -2)$, $(3, 0)$ **29.** above; $(0, 1)$, $(2, 1)$; $(3, 7)$ **30.** to the left and including; $(4, 0)$, $(4, 2)$; $(-5, 3)$ **31.** above; $(0, -6)$, $(2, -4)$; $(3, 8)$ **32.** above and including; $(0, -6)$, $(2, -4)$; $(8, 2)$ **33.** below and including; $(0, 1)$, $(2, 7)$; $(3, 0)$ **34.** below; $(0, -4)$, $(2, 2)$; $(3, 2)$ **35.** below; $(0, 4)$, $(2, 4)$ **36.** to the right and including; $(-3, 0)$, $(-3, 2)$
37. below and including; $(0, 0)$, $(2, 3)$
38. below and including; $(0, -2)$, $(2, -2)$
39. above and including; $(0, -3)$, $(2, 0)$
40. below and including; $(0, -3)$, $(3, -1)$
41. below and including; $(0, -2)$, $(3, 2)$
42. below and including; $(0, -2)$, $(5, 0)$
43. above and including; $(0, -3)$, $(5, 0)$
44. above and including; $(0, -3)$, $(4, 0)$
45. above; $\left(0, \frac{1}{2}\right)$, $\left(2, -\frac{7}{2}\right)$ **46.** above; $(0, -3)$, $(2, 1)$ **47.** above and including; $(0, 3)$, $(4, 6)$
48. above; $(0, 2)$, $(1, 0)$ **49.** above $y = 6$; below and including $y = 9$ **50.** to the right of and including $x = 8$; to the left of $x = 10$

Page 285
84 years old

Page 286
1. extremes x, 3; means 4, 6; 8 **2.** extremes 2, 10; means 5, x; 4 **3.** extremes $x + 2$, 3; means 4, $x - 5$; 26 **4.** extremes 3, $x + 4$; means 4, $2x - 1$; $\frac{16}{5}$ **5.** extremes $2x + 1$, 4; means 5, x; $-\frac{4}{3}$ **6.** extremes 5, $3x + 1$; means 2, $4x - 3$; $-\frac{11}{7}$ **7.** extremes x, x; means 1, 9; 3, -3 **8.** extremes x, $x + 5$; means -1, 4; -1, -4 **9.** 6,000 **10.** 3,375
11. $y = 2x - 5$ **12.** $y = 3x + 1$ **13.** $y = -2x + 6$
14. $y = \frac{1}{2}x + \frac{1}{2}$ **15.** $y = \frac{1}{3}x + \frac{11}{3}$ **16.** $y = \frac{3}{4}x + \frac{1}{4}$
17. $y = 2x$; $8 = 2(4)$ **18.** $y = 3x - 1$;
$8 = 3(3) - 1$ **19.** $y = \frac{2}{3}x - 5$ **20.** $y = -\frac{3}{7}x + 6$
21. $y = 3x - 1$ **22.** $\frac{2}{3}$; -4; $(-3, -6)$, $(3, -2)$
23. $-\frac{4}{5}$; 2; $(-5, 6)$, $(5, -2)$ **24.** -2; 0; $(-1, 2)$, $(1, -2)$ **25.** 2; 1; $(-1, -1)$, $(1, 3)$ **26.** $\frac{1}{3}$; -2;

(−3, −3), (3, −1) **27.** 0; −6; (−1, −6), (1, −6)
28. (−1, −3), (1, 1) **29.** (−1, 3), (1, 5)
30. (−3, −7), (3, −3) **31.** (3, 0), (3, 3)
32. (−4, 0), (−4, 2) **33.** (−2, 0) (−2, 1)
34. below; (0, 5), (1, 6) **35.** below; (4, 2),
(0, −4) **36.** to the right of and including; (2, 0),
(2, 1)

Page 287

1. extremes x, 7; means 1, 14; 2 **2.** extremes
$2x + 1$, 5; means 3, $x − 4$; $−\frac{17}{7}$ **3.** extremes
$x + 2$, $x − 5$; means 6, −2; 1, 2 **4.** 8,000
5. 250 **6.** $y = 2x + 1$ **7.** $y = −2x + 1$
8. $y = −\frac{2}{3}x + \frac{13}{3}$ **9.** $y = −\frac{2}{5}x + 2$
10. $y = \frac{1}{2}x + \frac{5}{2}$; $6 = \frac{1}{2}(7) + \frac{5}{2}$ **11.** $y = \frac{7}{2}x + 3$;
$17 = \frac{7}{2}(4) + 3$ **12.** $y = \frac{3}{4}x − 7$ **13.** $y = 2x + 3$
14. $\frac{2}{3}$; −4; (−3, −6), (3, −2) **15.** $−\frac{4}{5}$; 2;
(−5, 6), (5, −2) **16.** 0; 8; (−1, 8), (1, 8)
17. −1; 5; (−1, 6), (1, 4) **18.** 3; 2; (−1, −1),
(1, 5) **19.** $\frac{2}{3}$; −2; (−3, −4), (3, 0) **20.** (−1, −9),
(1, −5) **21.** $\left(−1, \frac{15}{2}\right)$, $\left(1, \frac{17}{2}\right)$ **22.** (−2, 0),
(−2, 2) **23.** (3, 0), (3, 2) **24.** (−4, 0), (−4, 4)
25. above; (0, 2), (1, 3) **26.** above and
including; (0 − 5), (6, 3) **27.** to the left of;
(3, 0), (3, 1)

Page 288

max $k = 9$, min $k = −3$

Page 291

1. (2, −3) **2.** (2, 7) **3.** (0, 4) **4.** (3, 3) **5.** (2, 6)
6. (2, 1) **7.** (2, 5) **8.** (2, 0) **9.** (3, 6) **10.** (6, 0)
11. inconsistent **12.** consistent **13.** inconsistent
14. inconsistent **15.** 3 **16.** no value **17.** 10
18. no value

Page 293

For each of the following, the two points given
lie on the line. They are not necessarily part of
the graph. **1.** to the left of the line containing
(4, 0), (4, 1) and above and including the line
containing (0, −2), (1, −2); (3, 1) **2.** above the
line containing (0, 4), (1, 5) and below the line
containing (0, −5), (1, −7); (−5, 3) **3.** above
and including the line containing (0, 2), (1, 2)
and to the left of the line containing (−5, 0),

(−5, 1) **4.** to the left of the line containing
(4, 0), (4, 1) and above and including the line
containing (0, −5), (1, −5) **5.** above the line
containing (0, 5), (1, 6) and to the left of and
including the line containing (2, 0), (2, 1)
6. above and including the line containing (4, 0),
(5, 2) and below the line containing (0, 6), (1, 6)
7. below the line containing (1, 1) (2, 2) and
above and including the line containing (3, −3),
(0, −5) **8.** below and including the line
containing (0, −2), (1, 1) and above the line
containing (0, 4), (1, 5) **9.** above the line
containing (0, −3), (1, −1) and above the line
containing (0, −3), (9, 0) **10.** above and
including the line containing (0, −4), (2, −1)
and below the line containing (0, −4), (1, −3)

Page 296

ORALS **1.** y **2.** x **3.** x **4.** y

EXERCISES **1.** (3, 6) **2.** (5, 1) **3.** (3, 1)
4. (3, 4) **5.** (3, 0) **6.** (4, 0) **7.** (2, 0) **8.** (4, −1)
9. $\left(\frac{11}{2}, −\frac{1}{2}\right)$ **10.** $\left(\frac{2}{3}, \frac{22}{3}\right)$ **11.** $\left(\frac{5}{2}, 5\right)$ **12.** $\left(\frac{1}{2}, \frac{1}{2}\right)$
13. $\left(−1, −\frac{2}{5}\right)$ **14.** $\left(2, \frac{13}{2}\right)$ **15.** $\left(−3, −\frac{8}{5}\right)$
16. (3, 1)

Page 299

1. (6, 2) **2.** (−1, 4) **3.** (2, 2) **4.** (0, 1)
5. (2, 1) **6.** $\left(2, \frac{1}{3}\right)$ **7.** (2, 2) **8.** (4, 1) **9.** (3, 2)
10. (1, −1) **11.** (3, 2) **12.** (3, 2) **13.** (3, 6)
14. (2, 1) **15.** (15, 10)

Page 302

ORALS Answers may vary. **1.** 2; −3
2. 7; 2 **3.** 3; 2 **4.** 2; 3 **5.** 1; 2 **6.** 2; 1 **7.** −4; 1
8. 1; −2 **9.** 1; −2 **10.** −1; 1 **11.** 2; 3 **12.** 2; 1
13. −1; 1 **14.** 1; 1 **15.** −1; 1 **16.** 1; −1

EXERCISES **1.** (2, 1) **2.** (1, 1) **3.** (2, 2)
4. (1, 1) **5.** (5, 1) **6.** (2, 1) **7.** (1, 1) **8.** (3, 1)
9. (2, 1) **10.** (−5, −46) **11.** (2, 2) **12.** (3, 2)
13. (−2, 6) **14.** $\left(10, \frac{6}{7}\right)$ **15.** $\left(1, \frac{13}{2}\right)$ **16.** $\left(\frac{7}{2}, \frac{9}{2}\right)$
17. (3, 2) **18.** (−2, −1) **19.** (−18, 8)
20. $\left(−3, \frac{13}{3}\right)$ **21.** $\left(\frac{58}{27}, \frac{1}{9}\right)$ **22.** (5, −1)
23. $\left(\frac{4}{5}, −\frac{4}{25}\right)$

Page 303

1. 8.4 cm³

Page 305

ORALS 1. 225¢ 2. 1,200¢ 3. 85x¢

EXERCISES 1. 11 kg; 1,260¢ 2. 16 kg; 1,810¢ 3. $(x + y)$ kg; $(158x + 210y)$¢ 4. $(x + y)$ kg; $(215x + 335y)$¢ 5. $(x + y)$ kg; $(4x + 78y)$¢ 6. $(x + y)$ kg; $(141x + 210y)$¢ 7. $(x + y)$ kg; $(135x + my)$¢ 8. $(x + y + 3)$ kg; $(140x + 75y + 225)$¢ 9. $(x + y)$ kg; $(px + qy)$¢

Page 308

1. $x + y = 7$; $90x + 130y = 750$ 2. $x + y = 5$; $260x + 290y = 1,330$ 3. $y = x + 2$; $5x + 15y = 130$ 4. $x = 3y + 1$; $45x + 25y = 365$ 5. $x = y - 2$; $230x + 170y = 740$ 6. $x = 3y$; $140x + 180y = 600$ 7. 5 kg at \$.50, 4 kg at \$.70 8. 7 kg at \$3.00, 3 kg at \$2.70 9. 2 at \$.15, 9 at \$.35 10. 5 kg cashews, 6 kg pecans 11. 4 kg at \$1.60, 8 kg at \$1.80 12. 2 sheets at \$.25, 8 sheets at \$.30 13. 3 at \$.20, 4 at \$.15 14. 8 at \$.20, 9 at \$.30 15. 8 kg at \$.80, 5 kg at \$1.60 16. 2 pads at \$.20, 8 pads at \$.15 17. 5 kg at \$1.20, 2 kg at \$1.80 18. 1 kg at \$1.50, 4 kg at \$1.30

Page 312

1. 10, 40 2. 7, 17 3. 6, 12 4. 32, 40 5. 4, 13 6. 13, 10 7. 5, 17 8. 5, 7 9. 8, 12 10. 14, 16 11. width 7 m, length 14 m 12. width 9 m, length 25 m 13. width 10 km, length 68 km 14. width 5 cm, length 20 cm

Page 314

1. (5, 3) 2. (2, 6) 3. (4, 4) 4. (2, 8) 5. inconsistent 6. consistent 7. consistent 8. inconsistent 9. (3, 1) 10. (−4, −2) 11. (5, −1) 12. (3, 1) 13. (3, 6) 14. (10, 2) 15. (6, 0) 16. $\left(\frac{5}{2}, -\frac{3}{2}\right)$ 17. 3 kg at \$1.50, 2 kg at \$1.90 18. 2 kg at \$2.20, 3 kg at \$2.40 19. 2 sheets at \$.40, 4 sheets at \$.30 20. 10 at \$.30, 8 at \$.35 21. 16, 24 22. 8, 16 23. 5, 13 24. width 4, length 14

Page 315

1. (5, −1) 2. (1, 3) 3. inconsistent 4. consistent 5. inconsistent 6. (2, 6)

7. (6, −2) 8. $\left(\frac{1}{2}, 2\right)$ 9. (4, −4) 10. (2, 1) 11. (4, 1) 12. 4 kg at \$1.30, 3 kg at \$1.70 13. 6 kg at \$2.80, 4 kg at \$2.40 14. 20, 40 15. 7, 9 16. 2, 13 17. width 6, length 8

Page 316

1. They land at the same time. 2. The pencil lands first; they land at the same time. 3. 5 seconds

Page 319

1. {(−4, 5), (−2, −2), (3, 2), (3, 4), (5, 1)}; $D = \{-4, -2, 3, 5\}$; $R = \{5, -2, 2, 4, 1\}$; no 2. {(−4, −3), (−3, 2), (0, 0), (2, 2), (4, −3)}; $D = \{-4, -3, 0, 2, 4\}$; $R = \{-3, 2, 0\}$; yes 3. {(−1, −3), (0, −2), (2, 0), (3, 1), (4, 2)}; $D = \{-1, 0, 2, 3, 4\}$; $R = \{-3, -2, 0, 1, 2\}$; yes 4. $D = \{0, -1, 3, -4\}$; $R = \{1, -2, 4\}$; yes 5. $D = \{3, 4, -1, 0\}$; $R = \{2\}$; yes 6. $D = \{2\}$; $R = \{-2, -3, -1, 0\}$; no 7. $D = \{3, -3, 0\}$; $R = \{0, 3, -3\}$; no 8. $D = \{-1, -2, 0, 1, 2\}$; $R = \{1, 2, 0, -1, -2\}$; yes 9. $D = \{-1, -2, 0, 1, 2\}$; $R = \{-1, -2, 0, 1, 2\}$; yes 10. $D = \{3, -1, 2, 0\}$; $R = \{0, 2, 4, -4, -2\}$; no 11. {(4, −2), (1, −1), (4, 0)}; yes; no 12. {(3, 2), (−2, 1), (−4, 2), (0, 3)}; no; yes 13. {(1, −1), (1, −2), (1, 0), (1, 1), (1, 2)}; yes; no 14. 3, 4 15. −6, 6

Page 321

ORALS 1. function; linear function 2. not a function 3. not a function 4. function; constant function 5. function

EXERCISES (Two points belonging to each relation are given.) 1. (0, 0), (1, 3); function; linear function 2. (0, 0), (1, −2); function; linear function 3. (0, 0), (1, 1); function; linear function 4. (0, 5), (2, 5); function; constant function 5. (−4, 0), (−4, −2) 6. (0, −2), (2, −2); function; constant function 7. (3, 0), (3, 2) 8. (0, 1), (−1, 0); function; linear function 9. (0, −3), (2, 1); function; linear function 10. (0, 0), (4, 1); function; linear function 11. (−1, 0), (2, 1); function; linear function 12. (0, 0), (0, 4) 13. (0, 0), (2, 0); function;

constant function **14.** $(0, -4)$, $(-1, -2)$;
function; linear function **15.** $(0, -2)$, $(1, 1)$;
function; linear function **16.** $(0, 3)$, $(1, 1)$;
function; linear function **17.** $(-1, 0)$, $(1, -1)$;
function; linear function **18.** $(0, 0)$, $(1, -1)$;
function; linear function **19.** $(4, 0)$, $(0, 4)$;
function; linear function **20.** $(-6, 0)$, $(0, 6)$;
function; linear function **21.** $(4, 0)$, $(4, 2)$
22. $(0, -3)$, $(2, -3)$; function; constant function
23. $\left(1, -\frac{3}{4}\right)$, $\left(-2, \frac{3}{4}\right)$; function; linear function
24. $(0, 1)$, $(2, 7)$; function; linear function
25. $(-4, 0)$, $(2, 2)$; function; linear function
26. $(-1, 0)$, $(-1, 2)$ **27.** $(0, -3)$, $(2, -3)$;
function; constant function **28.** $(0, 1)$, $(2, 5)$;
function; linear function **29.** $(0, 5)$, $(-1, 2)$;
function; linear function **30.** $(0, 4)$, $(4, 0)$;
function; linear function **31.** $(-2, 4)$, $(0, 0)$,
$(2, 4)$; function **32.** $(-1, 2)$, $(0, 0)$, $(1, 2)$;
function **33.** $(-1, -2)$, $(0, -3)$, $(1, -2)$;
function **34.** $(-1, 2)$, $(0, 0)$, $(1, 2)$; function
35. $(-2, -12)$, $(0, 0)$, $(2, -12)$; function
36. $(-2, -8)$, $(0, 0)$, $(2, -8)$; function
37. $(4, 2)$, $(0, 0)$, $(4, -2)$ **38.** $(-4, 2)$, $(0, 0)$,
$(-4, -2)$ **39.** $(12, 2)$, $(0, 0)$, $(12, -2)$
40. $(-2, -1)$, $(0, 0)$, $(-2, 1)$ **41.** $(6, -2)$,
$(2, 0)$, $(6, 2)$ **42.** $(8, 3)$, $(-1, 0)$, $(8, -3)$
43. $(-2, -8)$, $(-1, -1)$, $(0, 0)$, $(1, 1)$, $(2, 8)$;
function **44.** $(-2, -6)$, $(-1, 1)$, $(0, 2)$, $(1, 3)$,
$(2, 10)$; function **45.** $(-2, -24)$, $(-1, -3)$,
$(0, 0)$, $(1, 3)$, $(2, 24)$; function **46.** $(-2, 8)$,
$(-1, 1)$, $(0, 0)$, $(1, -1)$, $(2, -8)$; function
47. $(1, -1)$, $(0, 0)$, $(1, 1)$ **48.** $(1, -1)$, $(0, 0)$,
$(-1, -1)$; function

Page 324
1. -2 **2.** 10 **3.** -8 **4.** 43 **5.** -68 **6.** 11 **7.** -13
8. -45 **9.** 35 **10.** -113 **11.** -5 **12.** 11
13. 11 **14.** 220 **15.** 395 **16.** $R = \{-3, 1, 5\}$
17. $R = \{-16, 8, 26\}$ **18.** $R = \{-13, -17, -21\}$
19. $R = \{18, 32, 46\}$ **20.** $R = \{10, 1, 82\}$
21. $R = \{131, 101, 75\}$ **22.** $R = \{5, 1, -1\}$
23. $R = \{-3, 7, 52\}$ **24.** $R = \left\{-7, -7\frac{1}{2}, -7\frac{1}{3}\right\}$
25. $R = \{5.5, 5.2, 4.9\}$ **26.** $R = \{1, 9, 25\}$
27. $R = \{25, 49, 81\}$ **28.** $R = \{4\}$
29. $R = \left\{-4\frac{3}{4}, -4\frac{15}{16}\right\}$ **30.** 10 **31.** 20 **32.** 11
33. 54 **34.** 4 **35.** 172 **36.** 71 **37.** 151

Page 325
The graph consists of disconnected unit line
segments parallel to x-axis, and resembles stair
steps. For example, $y = -1$ for all $-1 \le x < 0$,
$y = 2$ for all $2 \le x < 3$, etc.

Page 329
1. 96 **2.** 24 **3.** 84 **4.** 24 **5.** 93 **6.** 26 **7.** 38
8. 15 **9.** 49 **10.** 17 **11.** 72 **12.** 67

Page 332
1. 6 or $\frac{1}{6}$ **3.** -4 or $-\frac{1}{4}$ **5.** -2 or $-\frac{1}{2}$ **6.** 32
7. 14 **8.** 5 **9.** -54 **10.** 80 km **11.** 437.5 km
12. \$24 **13.** \$208.33 **14.** 102 m **15.** 10 cups
16. 24 kg **17.** $13\frac{1}{3}$ m by $16\frac{2}{3}$ m **18.** 900
19. $\frac{135}{4}$ **20.** 273.6 m **21.** 550 m

Page 336
ORALS **1.** 60 **3.** -8 **4.** 36 **5.** 1 **6.** 20
8. -22

EXERCISES **1.** 18 **4.** 100 **5.** -1 **6.** 48
7. 4 **8.** -14 **9.** 180 cm **10.** 80.3 kg **11.** 9 m
12. 40 m³ **13.** $4\frac{1}{6}$ hr **14.** 4 hr **15.** \$750 **16.** 4%
17. 24 cm **18.** 4.4 m **19.** $5\frac{1}{3}$ m **20.** 20 amps
21. 2.2 m **22.** 234 km **23.** 18 **24.** 196.9 kg

Page 338
1. $\{(-1, -3), (0, -1), (1, 1), (2, 3), (3, 5)\}$;
$D = \{-1, 0, 1, 2, 3\}$; $R = \{-3, -1, 1, 3, 5\}$; yes
2. $\{(-4, -2), (-1, -1), (0, 0), (-1, 1), (-4, 2)\}$;
$D = \{-4, -1, 0\}$; $R = \{-2, -1, 0, 1, 2\}$; no
3. $\{(-4, 1), (-2, -2), (3, 1), (4, -2)\}$;
$D = \{-4, -2, 3, 4\}$; $R = \{-2, 1\}$; yes
4. $D = \{-2, -1, 0\}$; $R = \{-2, -1, 0, 1, 2\}$; no
5. $D = \{-2, -1, 0, 1, 2\}$; $R = \{1\}$; yes (Two
points of the boundary line are given.) **6.** $(0, 0)$,
$(1, 2)$; function; linear function **7.** $(4, 0)$, $(4, 2)$
8. $(-2, 0)$, $(0, 2)$; function; linear function
9. $(0, -1)$, $(1, 2)$; function; linear function
10. $(0, -1)$, $(2, -1)$; function; constant function
11. $(0, 1)$, $(2, 9)$, $(-1, 3)$; function **12.** 3 **13.** 12
14. 7 **15.** 39 **16.** 147 **17.** $R = \{-2, 1, -5\}$
18. $R = \{-6, -1, 2\}$ **19.** direct variation; 3
20. inverse variation; 6 **22.** direct variation; -2
24. 6 **25.** -10 **26.** \$80 **27.** 150 cm

Page 339

1. $\{(-2, 4), (-1, 1), (0, 0), (1, 1), (2, 4)\}$;
$D = \{-2, -1, 0, 1, 2\}$; $R = \{0, 1, 4\}$; yes
2. $\{(-5, 4), (-4, 2), (-3, 0), (-2, -2), (-1, -4)\}$;
$D = \{-5, -4, -3, -2, -1\}$;
$R = \{4, 2, 0, -2, -4\}$; yes
3. $\{(-3, -2), (0, -3), (0, 3), (3, -2)\}$;
$D = \{-3, 0, 3\}$; $R = \{-3, -2, 3\}$; no (Two
points of the boundary line are given.)
4. $(-2, 0), (-2, 2)$ **5.** $(0, 3), (2, 3)$; function;
constant function **6.** $(0, 1), (-1, 2), (2, 5)$;
function **7.** 3 **8.** -3 **9.** -23 **10.** $R = \{1, -1\}$
11. $R = \{10, 4, -2\}$ **13.** inverse variation; -64
14. direct variation; -3 **15.** -32 **16.** 16
17. \$100 **18.** 1.8 m

Page 340

I decreases.

Page 344

1. -3 **2.** 15 **3.** $\frac{5}{4}$ **4.** $\frac{3}{4}$ **5.** $\frac{41}{10}$ **6.** 3 **7.** $-\frac{10}{9}$
8. $-\frac{9}{4}$ **9.** -84 **10.** $\{-2\}$ **11.** $\{13\}$ **12.** $\{-26\}$
13. $\{1\}$ **14.** $\left\{\frac{31}{10}\right\}$ **15.** $\{1\}$ **16.** $\{2\}$

Page 345

1. 24.96 **2.** \$2,837.14 **3.** 11.78 **4.** \$65.78
5. \$2.99

Page 348

1. $\frac{27}{2}$ **2.** $\frac{34}{7}$ **3.** -19 **4.** 35 **5.** $\frac{11}{5}$ **6.** 32 **7.** $\left\{\frac{45}{2}\right\}$
8. $\left\{\frac{9}{2}\right\}$ **9.** $\left\{\frac{15}{13}\right\}$ **10.** $\{-19\}$ **11.** $\{11\}$ **12.** $\left\{\frac{1}{5}\right\}$
13. $\{1, 3\}$ **14.** $\{1, 3\}$ **15.** -1 **16.** $3, -3$ **17.** 5
18. -5

Page 352

ORALS **1.** $\frac{1}{5}$ **2.** $\frac{3}{4}$ **3.** $\frac{5}{7}$ **4.** $\frac{2}{7}$ **5.** $\frac{4}{5a}$ **6.** $\frac{3}{3x + 1}$

EXERCISES **1.** Jake $\frac{3}{5}$; Bill $\frac{3}{x}$ **2.** Paula $\frac{5}{8}$;
Janet $\frac{5}{m}$ **3.** Maria $\frac{12}{x}$; Todd $\frac{6}{x}$ **4.** Rudy $\frac{6}{3x + 1}$;
Jane $\frac{6}{2x + 4}$ **5.** Lester $\frac{7}{m}$; Jim $\frac{14}{m + 1}$
6. Shirley $\frac{2}{2x + 3}$; Ruth $\frac{2}{x}$ **7.** Mark $\frac{3}{3m + 1}$;

Stuart $\frac{3}{m - 4}$ **8.** Joyce $\frac{3}{a - 2}$; Lee $\frac{3}{3a + 4}$
9. Joan $\frac{5}{7}$; Helene $\frac{2}{7}$ **10.** Mark $\frac{1}{3}$; Tina $\frac{2}{3}$
11. Eleanor $\frac{x}{5}$; Ted $\frac{x}{10}$ **12.** Martha $\frac{x}{4}$; Chris $\frac{x}{7}$
13. Donald $\frac{5}{x}$; Merv $\frac{5}{3x}$ **14.** Hank $\frac{6}{x}$;
Sylvia $\frac{6}{x + 1}$

Page 355

1. $1\frac{5}{7}$ hr **2.** $3\frac{3}{7}$ days **3.** $7\frac{1}{2}$ hr **4.** 24 hr **5.** $1\frac{1}{3}$ hr
6. Jake $4\frac{1}{2}$; Noah 9 **7.** Josephine 8 hr; Lois
24 hr **8.** $7\frac{1}{2}$ mo; 15 mo **9.** $1\frac{13}{47}$ hr **10.** $1\frac{3}{7}$ hr
11. $2\frac{2}{5}$ hr **12.** $2\frac{1}{7}$ wk **13.** 10 hr **14.** $10\frac{2}{3}$ hr

Page 356

1. 20% **2.** $33\frac{1}{3}$% **3.** 58% **4.** 43% **5.** 50 **6.** 40
7. \$200 **8.** \$392.85

Page 360

1. $\frac{20}{3}$ **2.** .05 **3.** 1,805 **4.** 35.7 **5.** .31 **6.** 2.4
7. 307.5 **8.** 7 **9.** -140 **10.** -50 **11.** 10.02
12. $\frac{25}{7}$ **13.** $\frac{15}{2}$ **14.** -3.5 **15.** 5 **16.** 6 **17.** $-296\frac{1}{3}$
18. 3 **19.** .033 **20.** 29.43

Page 363

1. $\frac{-1}{1}$ **2.** $\frac{32}{1}$ **3.** $\frac{-16}{1}$ **4.** $\frac{0}{1}$ **5.** $\frac{-24}{36}$ **6.** $\frac{706}{100,000}$
7. $\frac{-364}{100}$ **8.** $\frac{7}{9}$ **9.** $\frac{4}{9}$ **10.** $\frac{28}{45}$ **11.** $\frac{34}{45}$ **12.** $\frac{11}{9}$ **13.** $\frac{32}{9}$
14. $\frac{22}{45}$ **15.** $\frac{16}{99}$ **16.** $\frac{8}{33}$ **17.** $\frac{83}{99}$ **18.** $\frac{25}{33}$ **19.** $\frac{98}{99}$
20. $\frac{5,775,453}{999,000}$ **21.** $\frac{306,483}{99,900}$ **22.** $\frac{214,546,686}{999,900}$

Page 367

1. \$375 **2.** 6% **3.** \$1,200 at 5%, \$600 at 6%
4. \$2,000 at $5\frac{3}{4}$%, \$500 at 5% **5.** \$600 at 4%,
\$1,200 at 6% **6.** \$2,000 at 8%, \$3,200 at 5%
7. \$500 at 5%, \$800 at 6% **8.** \$500 at 5%,
\$300 at 4% **9.** \$6,000 at 5%, \$4,000 at $4\frac{1}{2}$%
10. \$2,250 at $6\frac{1}{2}$%, \$2,750 at 6% **11.** \$7,000
12. \$3,000

Page 370

1. $\frac{14}{5}$ 2. $\frac{5}{6}$ 3. $\frac{5}{11}$ 4. $\frac{7}{4}$ 5. $\frac{5(6a+1)}{2a+3}$ 6. $\frac{6a+4}{a+2}$

7. $\frac{12a+1}{6a+1}$ 8. $\frac{9b+10}{b+9}$ 9. $\frac{40a-6a^2}{15a^2+70}$

10. $\frac{6b^2-40b}{20+15b^2}$ 11. $\frac{3-5a}{2a+1}$ 12. $\frac{9b+12}{6b+5}$

13. $x+1$ 14. $x-2$ 15. $\frac{1}{m-8}$

Page 373

1. $\frac{2a-1}{6a-18}$ 2. $\frac{2x+11}{5x+3}$ 3. $\frac{3x-2}{9x-34}$ 4. 3 5. $\frac{2}{7}$

6. 2 7. $\frac{a^2+4a-8}{a-4}$ 8. $\frac{m^2-3m-7}{m-1}$

9. $\frac{x^2-6x+10}{x-3}$ 10. 4 11. $\frac{5x-8}{4x-9}$ 12. $\frac{15b-1}{15b+3}$

13. $\frac{-3x-2}{7x-6}$ 14. 2 15. $\frac{1}{4}$ 16. $\frac{x^2-2x+2}{4x+1}$

17. $\frac{2}{2x+5}$ 18. $\frac{2x^2+5x+9}{5}$ 19. $\frac{a+b}{a-b}$

20. $\frac{6x^2-36xy+7xy^2}{6x^2-294y^2}$ 21. $\frac{2x^2+9xy-19y^2}{3x}$

Page 376

1. $x=\frac{2}{a}$ 2. $x=\frac{5}{r}$ 3. $x=a$ 4. $x=\frac{bc}{2}$

5. $x=-3a$ 6. $x=a-2c$ 7. $x=4a$

8. $x=3c+5$ 9. $x=\frac{d+c}{2}$ 10. $x=\frac{3c+7}{b}$

11. $x=\frac{3b-4a}{2}$ 12. $x=\frac{6h-2a}{7}$ 13. $x=\frac{8}{k+2}$

14. $x=\frac{4}{a+c}$ 15. $\frac{b}{2a}$ 16. $x=\frac{-t}{m-p}$

17. $x=\frac{3b+c}{2}$ 18. $x=3m+5p$ 19. $x=\frac{2ab}{c}$

20. $x=cb+ab$ 21. $\frac{p}{4}$; 7 22. $i=\frac{A}{pt}$; 3

23. $s=\frac{p-b}{2}$; 19 24. $d=\frac{l-a}{15}$; 6

25. $r=\frac{C}{2\pi}$; 2 m 26. $r=\frac{i}{pt}$; $\frac{3}{80}$ 27. $h=\frac{V}{lw}$;

4 cm 28. $f=\frac{3C}{d^2}$; 15 29. $x=\frac{3c-5a}{2b}$

30. $x=4a$ 31. $x=\frac{2d+4c}{a}$ 32. $x=\frac{3}{2}$

33. $x=\frac{4b+2}{5b}$ 34. $x=a$ 35. $x=a+2$

36. $x=a+4$ 37. $x=a+b$ 38. $16+\frac{3}{2}p$; 28

39. $h=\frac{3V}{\pi r^2}$; 6 km 40. $l=\frac{T-\pi r^2}{\pi r}$; 20

41. $p=\frac{A}{rt+1}$; 120 42. $h=\frac{T-2\pi r^2}{2\pi r}$; 8

43. $a=3A-b-c$; 31

Page 377

1. $\frac{10}{3}\Omega$ 2. $\frac{75}{4}\Omega$ 3. $\frac{600}{7}\Omega$ 4. $\frac{24}{13}\Omega$

Page 378

1. -1 2. 15 3. $\frac{-1}{3}$ 4. $\frac{39}{11}$ 5. $-1,-2$ 6. $-3,3$

7. $\frac{45}{4}$ hr 8. $\frac{10}{3}$ hr 9. $\frac{28}{3}$ mo; 28 mo 10. $\frac{10}{3}$ wk

11. $\frac{700}{3}$ 12. $\frac{1,500}{39}$ 13. -230 14. $\frac{-18}{1}$ 15. $\frac{0}{1}$

16. $\frac{15}{2}$ 17. $\frac{42}{9}$ 18. $\frac{29}{90}$ 19. $\frac{2}{11}$ 20. $\frac{11}{7}$ 21. $\frac{9+15b}{6b+7}$

22. $x+3$ 23. $\frac{10a-12}{7}$ 24. $\frac{11a-11}{4a}$

25. $\frac{x^2-7x+13}{2x-1}$ 26. $\frac{3m+8}{b}$ 27. $\frac{tr-5a}{m}$

28. $\frac{8}{k+5}$ 29. $-a$ 30. $\frac{a}{mq}$; $\frac{16}{7}$ 31. $\frac{4k}{d^2}$; 7

Page 379

1. -3 2. $\frac{9}{2}$ 3. -28 4. 3 5. $\frac{28}{3}$ 6. $\frac{36}{5}$ 7. $\frac{75}{4}$; 75

8. 20 9. 80 10. $\frac{1,000}{18}$ 11. -100 12. $\frac{-14}{1}$

13. $\frac{25}{3}$ 14. $\frac{4}{9}$ 15. $\frac{12}{99}$ 16. 1 17. $\frac{12a-10}{3}$

18. $m+2$ 19. $\frac{x^2+x-1}{5x+22}$ 20. $\frac{2a+4}{m}$ 21. $\frac{7}{t-2}$

22. $6b$ 23. $\frac{m}{ad}$; 2 24. $\frac{5l}{p^2}$; 25

Page 383

1. R 2. I 3. R 4. R 5. I 6. R 7. R 8. R 9. I
10. R 11. R 12. R 13. I 14. I 15. R 16. R
17. R 18. R 19. R 20. I 21. Answers may
vary. 22. Answers may vary. 23. Answers may
vary. 24. yes; {integers} $\subseteq$ {reals} 25. irrational
26. irrational 27. irrational 28. irrational 29. F
30. T 31. T 32. F 33. T 34. T

Page 386

ORALS **1.** yes; 5 **2.** no; 2.4 **3.** yes; 10
4. no; 5.1 **5.** yes; 6 **6.** no; 6.2 **7.** no; 6.5
8. yes; 7 **9.** no; 3.3 **10.** no; 7.7 **11.** yes; 1
12. no; 8.2 **13.** no; 3.5 **14.** yes; 8 **15.** no; 2.8
16. no; 8.6 **17.** no; 6.2 **18.** no; 8.8 **19.** yes; 3
20. no; 9.6

EXERCISES **1.** 6.1 m **2.** 7.9 cm **3.** 7.4 m,
14.8 m **4.** 9.7 cm **5.** 5.5 m, 16.5 m
6. 7.1 cm, 35.5 cm **7.** 5.3 cm **8.** 8.2 m, 12.3 m
9. 33.0 m, 6.6 m **10.** 18.2 cm, 9.1 cm
11. 2.8 cm **12.** 25.8 m, 17.2 m

Page 390

1. 5.1 **2.** 1 **3.** 6.9 **4.** 5 **5.** 9.4 **6.** 7.9 **7.** 4.2
8. 7 **9.** 7.2 **10.** 2.6 **11.** 3.5 **12.** 6 **13.** 6.1
14. 8.8 **15.** 5.7 **16.** 9.5 **17.** 8.2 **18.** 7.6
19. 8.4 **20.** 10 **21.** 9.1 **22.** 15.6 **23.** 10.8
24. 16.0 **25.** 14.1 **26.** 19.4

Page 393

1. $\sqrt{10}$ **2.** $\sqrt{21}$ **3.** $\sqrt{30}$ **4.** $\sqrt{33}$ **5.** $\sqrt{14}$
6. 15 **7.** 32 **8.** 18 **9.** 35 **10.** 110 **11.** $2\sqrt{3}$
12. $4\sqrt{5}$ **13.** $3\sqrt{3}$ **14.** $5\sqrt{2}$ **15.** $7\sqrt{2}$ **16.** $2\sqrt{7}$
17. $-4\sqrt{15}$ **18.** $8\sqrt{10}$ **19.** $8\sqrt{2}$ **20.** $9\sqrt{5}$
21. $5\sqrt{3}$; 8.7 **22.** 24 **23.** $-6\sqrt{5}$; -13.4
24. $6\sqrt{6}$; 14.7 **25.** $18\sqrt{5}$; 40.2 **26.** $16\sqrt{10}$;
50.6 **27.** $-14\sqrt{7}$ **28.** $65\sqrt{6}$ **29.** $-38\sqrt{5}$
30. $-306\sqrt{3}$ **31.** $102\sqrt{11}$

Page 395

ORALS **1.** 1 **3.** -1 **5.** 5 **6.** -6 **8.** 7
11. -3 **12.** 11

EXERCISES **1.** x^4y^2 **2.** $-a^3b^5$ **3.** cd^4 **4.** $5x$
5. $-3y^2$ **6.** $7a^5$ **7.** $-9ab^3$ **8.** $8x^2y^4$ **9.** $-2c^5d$
10. $-4x^4y^6$ **11.** $3a^3b^4$ **12.** $10x^2y^7$ **13.** $a^2b^3c^4$
14. xy^3z^5 **15.** $-c^2de^6$ **16.** $-2xy^4z$ **17.** $3a^3b^4c$
18. $-7x^2y^4z$ **19.** $8a^2b^6c$ **20.** $-9x^4y^6z^2$
21. $6c^4d^5e^6$ **22.** $-10xy^6z^5$ **23.** $5a^6b^5c^2$
24. $-4cd^3e^7$ **25.** $11c^4d^3e$ **26.** $-13x^4yz^5$
27. $12a^4bc^8$ **28.** $2xy^4\sqrt{5}$ **29.** $-3a^2b^5\sqrt{3}$
30. $-2c^4d\sqrt{7}$ **31.** $-4a^3b^6\sqrt{2}$ **32.** $5xy^3\sqrt{2}$
33. $-4a^5b^6\sqrt{3}$ **34.** $10x^2yz^3\sqrt{2}$ **35.** $3a^6b^7c\sqrt{5}$
36. $5c^4de^6\sqrt{3}$ **37.** $-7a^2b^4c^8\sqrt{2}$
38. $8x^2y^5z^4\sqrt{2}$ **39.** $-9x^4yz^9\sqrt{3}$ **40.** $.2xy^4$

41. $-1.3ab^4c^{10}$ **42.** $.004x^2yz^9$ **43.** $\frac{1}{5}x^5yz^6$
44. $\frac{2}{7}x^4y^6z^{12}$ **45.** $-\frac{9}{4}ab^{18}c^{50}$

Page 397

1. $x\sqrt{x}$ **2.** $-a^3\sqrt{a}$ **3.** $3x^2\sqrt{x}$ **4.** $5\sqrt{c}$
5. $2x^2\sqrt{2x}$ **6.** $3a^4\sqrt{2a}$ **7.** $x\sqrt{7x}$ **8.** $-x^5\sqrt{5x}$
9. $x^2y^3\sqrt{y}$ **10.** $ab^2\sqrt{b}$ **11.** $-c^3d\sqrt{d}$
12. $m^4\sqrt{n}$ **13.** $x^2y^3\sqrt{xy}$ **14.** $a^4b\sqrt{ab}$
15. $c\sqrt{cd}$ **16.** $n^3\sqrt{mn}$ **17.** $a^2b^4\sqrt{a}$
18. $-2d\sqrt{c}$ **19.** $xy^2\sqrt{5x}$ **20.** $3mb^4\sqrt{11m}$
21. $6x\sqrt{y}$ **22.** $-4m^4n^3\sqrt{n}$ **23.** $x^3y^4\sqrt{6y}$
24. $2a^2b\sqrt{5b}$ **25.** $x^2y^4\sqrt{19xy}$ **26.** $2y\sqrt{10xy}$
27. $-5mn^2\sqrt{2m}$ **28.** $6b^3\sqrt{2a}$ **29.** $8yz^3\sqrt{11x}$
30. $-21ab^3c^3\sqrt{10ac}$ **31.** $12a^2c^6\sqrt{7b}$
32. $x^2z^4\sqrt{xy}$ **33.** $-c^3d^3e^3\sqrt{d}$
34. $-a^3b^5c^5\sqrt{ac}$ **35.** $-3xy^3\sqrt{xyz}$
36. $4x^3y^3z^2\sqrt{y}$ **37.** $-5b^3c^3d^4\sqrt{bc}$
38. $20a^5b^4\sqrt{3b}$ **39.** $-48x^2y^5\sqrt{2y}$
40. $64e^3f^3g\sqrt{2eg}$ **41.** xy^3 **42.** a^2b^4 **43.** $-cd^4$
44. $-x^2y^3$ **45.** $2ab^3$ **46.** $-3x^2y$ **47.** $-4ab^2\sqrt[3]{a}$
48. $-5x^2y^3\sqrt[3]{x}$ **49.** $-2b^2\sqrt[3]{5a^2b^2}$
50. $-2b^2c^3\sqrt[3]{7ac}$ **51.** $4x^2z^4\sqrt[3]{3xy}$
52. $-2x^3y^3z^3\sqrt[3]{4yz^2}$ **53.** xy^3 **54.** ab^2
55. $-2x^2y$ **56.** $2xy^2$ **57.** $3xy^2\sqrt[5]{x}$
58. $-3b\sqrt[4]{a^3b}$ **59.** $-2b\sqrt[5]{3a^2b^2c^3}$
60. $2yz^3\sqrt[4]{5x^3y^3}$ **61.** $-4acde\sqrt[5]{5de^2}$
62. $-9a^4bc^2\sqrt[4]{2a^2bc}$ **63.** $18xy^2z^2\sqrt[3]{2x^2yz^2}$
64. $-7c^4d^8\sqrt[4]{12cde}$

Page 398

1. 2.24 **2.** 2.65

Page 401

1. no **2.** yes **3.** no **4.** yes **5.** no **6.** yes **7.** no
8. yes **9.** $c = 10$ **10.** $c = 20$ **11.** $b = 12$
12. $c = 2\sqrt{10}$ **13.** $a = 4\sqrt{3}$ **14.** $a = 2\sqrt{2}$
15. $b = 48$ **16.** $a = 8$ **17.** $c = 2\sqrt{5}$ **18.** 8.5 km
19. 2.6 m **20.** 19.2 cm **21.** 5.7 m **22.** 2.8 cm
23. 4.2 m

Page 403

1. $9\sqrt{5}$ **2.** $3\sqrt{3}$ **3.** $15\sqrt{6}$ **4.** $\sqrt{2}$ **5.** $\sqrt{10}$
6. $-8\sqrt{7}$ **7.** $2\sqrt{6} + 6\sqrt{3}$ **8.** $4\sqrt{3} - 15\sqrt{2}$
9. $12\sqrt{5} - 6\sqrt{7}$ **10.** $-4\sqrt{5} + 4\sqrt{11}$
11. $8\sqrt{5} - 3\sqrt{2}$ **12.** $14\sqrt{7} + 2\sqrt{3}$ **13.** $7\sqrt{2}$
14. $6\sqrt{3}$ **15.** $-5\sqrt{6}$ **16.** $6\sqrt{3}$ **17.** $2\sqrt{11}$

18. $-38\sqrt{2}$ 19. $9\sqrt{a}$ 20. $12\sqrt{x}$ 21. $7\sqrt{mn}$
22. $11\sqrt{xy}$ 23. $-3\sqrt{xy}$ 24. $14\sqrt{c} - 8c\sqrt{c}$
25. $4x\sqrt{3z} - x\sqrt{5z}$ 26. $-13\sqrt{xy}$
27. $-21ab\sqrt{ab}$ 28. $3cd\sqrt{cd}$ 29. $4\sqrt{3x}$
30. $17\sqrt{6y}$ 31. cannot simplify 32. $-3\sqrt{2z}$
33. $-11\sqrt{10x}$ 34. $2\sqrt{3xy}$ 35. $8xy\sqrt{5x}$
36. $-6ab\sqrt{2b}$ 37. $.6y\sqrt{x}$ 38. $1.54a\sqrt{ab}$
39. $.22xy\sqrt{x}$ 40. $-.05xy\sqrt{x}$ 41. $3.56ab\sqrt{ab}$
42. $4.88xy\sqrt{xy}$

Page 405

ORALS 1. 7 2. 8 3. 5 4. 12 5. 96 6. 50
7. 60 8. -48 9. -12 10. $8\sqrt{7}$ 11. $-30\sqrt{2}$
12. $24\sqrt{30}$

EXERCISES 1. $40\sqrt{3}$ 2. $6\sqrt{35}$ 3. $24\sqrt{30}$
4. $42\sqrt{2}$ 5. $15\sqrt{30}$ 6. $-64\sqrt{3}$ 7. $2x$ 8. $15c$
9. y 10. $6x$ 11. $-72y$ 12. $80x\sqrt{3}$ 13. 0
14. $4\sqrt{10} - 16$ 15. $-20\sqrt{3} - 60\sqrt{2}$
16. $4\sqrt{10} + 80\sqrt{2}$ 17. $16 - \sqrt{6}$
18. $-2 + 2\sqrt{15}$ 19. $34 + 24\sqrt{6}$
20. $72 + 2\sqrt{21}$ 21. 2 22. 5 23. -30 24. -34
25. $19 + 4\sqrt{21}$ 26. $23 - 6\sqrt{10}$ 27. $26 - 4\sqrt{30}$
28. $38 + 12\sqrt{10}$ 29. $62 + 24\sqrt{3}$
30. $203 - 80\sqrt{6}$ 31. $522 - 72\sqrt{7}$ 32. 2
33. $120 - 80\sqrt{2}$ 34. $177 + 90\sqrt{2}$
35. $10 + 2\sqrt{6} - 2\sqrt{15} - 2\sqrt{10}$
36. $5 + 3\sqrt{2} + 2\sqrt{6} + 2\sqrt{3}$ 37. 6

Page 407
Right $\triangle$; legs 2, 1 or $\sqrt{2}$, $\sqrt{3}$; legs 2, $\sqrt{2}$ or 1, $\sqrt{5}$ or $\sqrt{3}$, $\sqrt{3}$

Page 410
1. $\frac{\sqrt{2}}{2}$ 2. $\frac{5\sqrt{3}}{3}$ 3. $\sqrt{5}$ 4. $4\sqrt{7}$ 5. $2\sqrt{3}$ 6. $\frac{\sqrt{2}}{2}$
7. $\sqrt{3}$ 8. $\frac{2\sqrt{5}}{5}$ 9. $\frac{\sqrt{10}}{2}$ 10. $\frac{4\sqrt{2}}{5}$ 11. $\frac{4\sqrt{x}}{x^3}$
12. $\frac{3\sqrt{x}}{x^4}$ 13. $\frac{2\sqrt{m}}{m^2}$ 14. $\frac{5\sqrt{m}}{m^5}$ 15. $\frac{6\sqrt{x}}{x}$
16. $\frac{2\sqrt{3a}}{3a^2}$ 17. $\frac{3\sqrt{2a}}{2a^3}$ 18. $\frac{2\sqrt{2b}}{3b^2}$ 19. $\frac{\sqrt{6x}}{2x}$
20. $\frac{9\sqrt{3a}}{a^2}$ 21. $5y\sqrt{x}$ 22. $12\sqrt{b}$ 23. $\frac{3\sqrt{y}}{y}$
24. $5c^2\sqrt{cd}$ 25. $12x^2y^2\sqrt{xy}$ 26. $6x\sqrt{x}$

27. $y\sqrt{2y}$ 28. $\frac{\sqrt{2m}}{m}$ 29. $\frac{\sqrt{5a}}{5}$ 30. $\frac{x^3\sqrt{6x}}{2}$
31. $\frac{15 + 5\sqrt{3}}{6}$ 32. $\frac{-6 + 2\sqrt{2}}{7}$ 33. $\frac{\sqrt{30} + 2\sqrt{3}}{6}$
34. $\frac{10\sqrt{5} - 5}{19}$ 35. $-\sqrt{7} - 2$

Page 412
1. $\frac{3}{4}$ 2. $\frac{5}{7}$ 3. $\frac{10}{9}$ 4. $\frac{4}{3}$ 5. $\frac{11}{5}$ 6. $\frac{\sqrt{7}}{2}$ 7. $\frac{3\sqrt{6}}{5}$
8. $\frac{\sqrt{31}}{7}$ 9. $\frac{\sqrt{67}}{9}$ 10. $\frac{3\sqrt{3}}{4}$ 11. $\frac{\sqrt{6}}{4}$ 12. $\frac{2\sqrt{3}}{9}$
13. $\frac{\sqrt{15}}{6}$ 14. $\frac{\sqrt{35}}{10}$ 15. $\frac{\sqrt{110}}{20}$ 16. $\frac{\sqrt{5y}}{y}$
17. $\frac{4\sqrt{x}}{x^2}$ 18. $\frac{\sqrt{21}}{3z}$ 19. $\frac{\sqrt{30y}}{5y^2}$ 20. $\frac{3\sqrt{3xy}}{xy^2}$
21. $\frac{3\sqrt{6xy}}{y^3}$ 22. $\frac{2\sqrt{15y}}{xy^2}$ 23. $\frac{\sqrt{2x}}{2x^2}$ 24. $\frac{2\sqrt{yz}}{y}$
25. $\frac{\sqrt{3z}}{3xz}$ 26. $\frac{\sqrt{6y}}{6y^2}$ 27. $\frac{\sqrt{77}}{7y}$ 28. $2b\sqrt{a}$
29. $\frac{y\sqrt{14yz}}{z}$ 30. $\frac{4\sqrt{5ab}}{5b}$ 31. $\frac{\sqrt{4x + 6}}{2}$
32. $\frac{\sqrt{15z - 9}}{3}$ 33. $\frac{\sqrt{28x + 49}}{7}$ 34. $\frac{\sqrt{10x + 10}}{2}$
35. $\frac{\sqrt{15 - 25z}}{5}$ 36. $\frac{\sqrt{8x^2 - 14}}{2}$ 37. $\frac{\sqrt{6z^2 + 9}}{3}$
38. $\frac{\sqrt{12y^2 - 2y}}{2}$ 39. $\frac{y + 3}{y}$ 40. $\frac{x + 5}{5}$

Page 413
1. $340.75 2. yes

Page 414
1. I 2. R 3. R 4. R 5. I 6. R 7. I 8. R
9. 6.8 cm 10. 7.3 m; 21.9 m 11. 5.9 cm;
11.8 cm 12. no 13. yes; 8.6 14. yes; 6.4
15. no 16. yes; 3.9 17. yes; 7.9 18. 21 19. 36
20. $-4\sqrt{3}$ 21. $8a^2b^5$ 22. $-7x^4yz^5$
23. $12cd^2e^5$ 24. $y\sqrt{xy}$ 25. $-6x^5y^5\sqrt{3xy}$
26. $3x^2y^3\sqrt[3]{y^2}$ 27. $4xyz^2\sqrt[3]{xy^2}$ 28. yes 29. no
30. yes 31. yes 32. $c = 17$ 33. $a = 3$
34. $b = 4\sqrt{2}$ 35. $-\sqrt{5}$ 36. $5x\sqrt{y}$
37. $15x - 10\sqrt{x}$ 38. $35 - 12\sqrt{6}$ 39. -2
40. $\frac{\sqrt{3}}{3}$ 41. $2\sqrt{2}$ 42. $\frac{\sqrt{3x}}{2x}$ 43. $6y^2\sqrt{2xy}$ 44. 7
45. $5x$ 46. $\frac{\sqrt{14ab}}{b}$ 47. $\frac{\sqrt{12x + 6}}{3}$

Page 415

1. R **2.** R **3.** R **4.** I **5.** R **6.** I **7.** I **8.** R
9. 7.7 m **10.** 20.1 cm; 26.8 cm **11.** 8.5 cm;
25.5 cm **12.** 3.2 **14.** 7.2 **16.** $\sqrt{65}$ **17.** 40
18. $-4\sqrt{5}$ **19.** $7a^2b$ **20.** $-9x^3yz^6$ **21.** $d\sqrt{15c}$
22. $-15x^2y^2\sqrt{6xy}$ **23.** $3x^3y^4\sqrt[3]{y}$ **24.** yes
25. no **26.** yes **27.** $c = 2\sqrt{5}$ **28.** $b = 5$
29. $a = 6$ **30.** $-\sqrt{3}$ **31.** $-22x\sqrt{y}$ **32.** $3 - 2\sqrt{2}$
33. -2 **34.** $6x - 15\sqrt{x}$ **35.** $\dfrac{7\sqrt{3}}{3}$ **36.** $\sqrt{2}$
37. $3x\sqrt{5x}$ **38.** $5d^2\sqrt{3cd}$ **39.** 4 **40.** $3y\sqrt{3y}$
41. $\dfrac{y\sqrt{34x}}{2x}$ **42.** $\dfrac{\sqrt{21x - 35}}{7}$

Page 416

1. $3^2 + 4^2 = 5^2$, $5^2 + 12^2 = 13^2$, $7^2 + 24^2 = 25^2$,
$9^2 + 40^2 = 41^2$, $11^2 + 60^2 = 61^2$ **2.** The first
integer of each triple is the next consecutive
odd number. Let m be the first integer in a
triple, then the second integer is $\dfrac{m^2 - 1}{2}$ and
the third integer is $\dfrac{m^2 + 1}{2}$, or one more than
the second integer. **3.** 13, 84, 85; 15, 112, 113;
17, 144, 145

Page 419

1. {9} **2.** {64} **3.** {20} **4.** {288} **5.** $\left\{\frac{1}{16}\right\}$ **6.** $\left\{\frac{1}{108}\right\}$
7. {2} **8.** {3} **9.** 1 **10.** 16 **11.** no solution **12.** 18
13. $\frac{79}{3}$ **14.** 14 **15.** 4 **16.** no solution **17.** no
solution **18.** 69 **19.** 12 **20.** 12 **21.** $-3, -2$
22. no solution **23.** 2 **24.** no solution **25.** 25
26. 100 **27.** 2 **28.** 10 **29.** 1 **30.** no solution
31. 4

Page 421

1. {1, −1} **2.** {6, −6} **3.** {2, −2} **4.** ϕ
5. {7, −7} **6.** {0} **7.** {3, −3} **8.** ϕ **9.** {8, −8}
10. {10, −10} **11.** ϕ **12.** {12, −12}
13. $\{\sqrt{15}, -\sqrt{15}\}$ **14.** $\{\sqrt{11}, -\sqrt{11}\}$
15. $\{\sqrt{13}, -\sqrt{13}\}$ **16.** $\{2\sqrt{7}, -2\sqrt{7}\}$
17. $\{2\sqrt{6}, -2\sqrt{6}\}$ **18.** $\{4\sqrt{2}, -4\sqrt{2}\}$
19. $\{3\sqrt{2}, -3\sqrt{2}\}$ **20.** $\{2\sqrt{11}, -2\sqrt{11}\}$ **21.** ϕ
22. 10, 4 **23.** −1, −9 **24.** 9, 7 **25.** $\dfrac{\sqrt{15}}{3}$,
$-\dfrac{\sqrt{15}}{3}$ **26.** $\dfrac{\sqrt{14}}{2}$, $-\dfrac{\sqrt{14}}{2}$ **27.** $\dfrac{\sqrt{65}}{5}$, $-\dfrac{\sqrt{65}}{5}$

Page 425

ORALS   **1.** 1 **2.** 9 **3.** 25 **4.** 4 **5.** 64 **6.** 16
7. 36 **8.** 81

EXERCISES   **1.** {−8, −2} **2.** {1, −3}
3. {−1, −15} **4.** {2, −4}
5. $\{4 + \sqrt{11}, 4 - \sqrt{11}\}$ **6.** {9, −3}
7. $\{-5 + \sqrt{10}, -5 - \sqrt{10}\}$ **8.** {1, −13}
9. {7, −3} **10.** $\{-4 + \sqrt{13}, -4 - \sqrt{13}\}$ **11.** {2}
12. {1, −7} **13.** {7, −11}
14. $\{-3 + 2\sqrt{3}, -3 - 2\sqrt{3}\}$ **15.** {2, 14}
16. {8, −6} **17.** {6, 12} **18.** {−6, −10}
19. {13, −3} **20.** $\{-2 + \sqrt{7}, -2 - \sqrt{7}\}$
21. {−3, −17} **22.** $\{-1 + \sqrt{6}, -1 - \sqrt{6}\}$
23. {6, 10} **24.** {−7, −11} **25.** {21, −1}
26. {4, 20} **27.** $\{-15 + \sqrt{70}, -15 - \sqrt{70}\}$
28. {5, −2} **29.** {−8, −1} **30.** {6, 1} **31.** {5, −10}
32. {4, −1} **33.** {3, −2} **34.** {4, 7} **35.** {5, −6}
36. {−2, −3} **37.** {3, −4} **38.** {10, −1}
39. {7, −2} **40.** {−3, −12} **41.** {15, 2}
42. {1, 2} **43.** {7, −8} **44.** {8, −1} **45.** {−4, −7}
46. {4, 9} **47.** {12, 7} **48.** {9, 6} **49.** {2, 19}
50. {−9, −8} **51.** {2, −17} **52.** {−3, −20}
53. {20, 5} **54.** {23, −2} **55.** $\left\{\dfrac{-7 \pm \sqrt{37}}{2}\right\}$
56. $\left\{\dfrac{-11 \pm \sqrt{41}}{2}\right\}$ **57.** $\left\{\dfrac{-5 \pm \sqrt{21}}{2}\right\}$
58. $\left\{\dfrac{3 \pm \sqrt{29}}{2}\right\}$ **59.** $\left\{\dfrac{-5 \pm \sqrt{29}}{2}\right\}$
60. $\left\{\dfrac{7 \pm \sqrt{57}}{2}\right\}$ **61.** $\left\{\dfrac{1 \pm \sqrt{13}}{2}\right\}$ **62.** ϕ
63. $\left\{\dfrac{-7 \pm \sqrt{33}}{2}\right\}$ **64.** $\left\{\dfrac{-3 \pm \sqrt{13}}{2}\right\}$ **65.** ϕ
66. $\left\{\dfrac{9 \pm \sqrt{69}}{2}\right\}$

28. 4, −4 **29.** 5, −5 **30.** $2\sqrt{3}, -2\sqrt{3}$
31. $-3 + 2\sqrt{2}, -3 - 2\sqrt{2}$ **32.** $4 + 4\sqrt{2}$,
$4 - 4\sqrt{2}$ **33.** $-6 + 2\sqrt{7}, -6 - 2\sqrt{7}$
34. $-1 + 2\sqrt{3}, -1 - 2\sqrt{3}$ **35.** $7 + 2\sqrt{6}$,
$7 - 2\sqrt{6}$ **36.** $3 + 2\sqrt{10}, 3 - 2\sqrt{10}$
37. $\left\{\dfrac{5 + 2\sqrt{3}}{2}, \dfrac{5 - 2\sqrt{3}}{2}\right\}$
38. $\left\{\dfrac{-3 + 2\sqrt{3}}{2}, \dfrac{-3 - 2\sqrt{3}}{2}\right\}$
39. $\left\{\dfrac{1 + \sqrt{5}}{2}, \dfrac{1 - \sqrt{5}}{2}\right\}$

Page 429

1. $2x^2 + 6x + 5 = 0$; $a = 2$, $b = 6$, $c = 5$
2. $4x^2 + 3x + 2 = 0$; $a = 4$, $b = 3$, $c = 2$
3. $2x^2 - 4x - 8 = 0$; $a = 2$, $b = -4$, $c = -8$
4. $2x^2 - 4x + 0 = 0$; $a = 2$, $b = -4$, $c = 0$
5. $x^2 + 2x + 0 = 0$; $a = 1$, $b = 2$, $c = 0$
6. $3x^2 + 0x + 7 = 0$; $a = 3$, $b = 0$, $c = 7$
7. $x^2 + 0x - 5 = 0$; $a = 1$, $b = 0$, $c = -5$
8. $x^2 - 6x + 3 = 0$; $a = 1$, $b = -6$, $c = 3$
9. $3x^2 - 6x - 2 = 0$; $a = 3$, $b = -6$, $c = -2$
10. $x^2 + 0x - 4 = 0$; $a = 1$, $b = 0$, $c = -4$
11. $5x^2 - 3x + 0 = 0$; $a = 5$, $b = -3$, $c = 0$
12. $4x^2 - 6x - 2 = 0$; $a = 4$, $b = -6$, $c = -2$
13. $-3, -1$ **14.** $3, 2$ **15.** 1 **16.** $2, -5$
17. $7, -3$ **18.** $6, -4$ **19.** $5, -8$ **20.** $13, -1$
21. 4 **22.** $\{2, -3\}$ **23.** $\{1, -11\}$ **24.** $\{15, -3\}$
25. $\{6, -5\}$ **26.** $\{1, -3\}$ **27.** $\{-1, -4\}$ **28.** $\{8, 1\}$
29. $\{2, -2\}$ **30.** $\{-1, -2\}$ **31.** $\{2, -1\}$
32. $\{0, -3\}$ **33.** $\{18, -2\}$

Page 433

1. 3 L **2.** 1 L **3.** 6 L **4.** 12.5 dL **5.** 87.5 L
6. 20 cm³ **7.** 48 L **8.** 1.5 dL **9.** 6.5 L **10.** 60 mL
11. 2 dL **12.** 30 cm³ **13.** 7.5 dL **14.** 25 dL

Page 436

1. $\left\{-3, \frac{1}{2}\right\}$ **2.** $\left\{2, \frac{1}{3}\right\}$ **3.** $\left\{-\frac{1}{2}, \frac{2}{3}\right\}$ **4.** $\left\{\frac{1}{2}, 3\right\}$
5. $\left\{\frac{3}{2}, 4\right\}$ **6.** $\left\{\frac{5}{4}, \frac{3}{2}\right\}$ **7.** $\left\{-2, \frac{1}{3}\right\}$ **8.** $\left\{-\frac{3}{2}, 3\right\}$
9. $\left\{\frac{10}{3}\right\}$ **10.** $\left\{\frac{5 \pm \sqrt{33}}{2}\right\}$ **11.** $\left\{\frac{7 \pm \sqrt{37}}{2}\right\}$
12. $\left\{\frac{7 \pm \sqrt{61}}{2}\right\}$ **13.** ϕ **14.** $\left\{\frac{-1 \pm \sqrt{5}}{2}\right\}$
15. $\left\{\frac{-5 \pm \sqrt{37}}{2}\right\}$ **16.** $\left\{\frac{-1 \pm \sqrt{21}}{2}\right\}$ **17.** ϕ
18. $\left\{\frac{3 \pm \sqrt{5}}{2}\right\}$ **19.** ϕ **20.** $\{3 \pm \sqrt{11}\}$
21. $\{2 \pm \sqrt{14}\}$ **22.** $\{5 \pm 2\sqrt{5}\}$ **23.** $\{4 \pm \sqrt{13}\}$
24. ϕ **25.** $\left\{-4, \frac{3}{2}\right\}$ **26.** $\left\{\frac{1}{3}, \frac{4}{3}\right\}$ **27.** $\{-2 \pm \sqrt{3}\}$
28. ϕ **29.** $\left\{\frac{7 \pm \sqrt{5}}{2}\right\}$ **30.** $\left\{\frac{3}{2}, 3\right\}$ **31.** $\left\{1, -\frac{5}{2}\right\}$
32. $\left\{1, \frac{3}{4}\right\}$ **33.** $\left\{\frac{3}{4}\right\}$ **34.** $\left\{-2, -\frac{1}{2}\right\}$
35. $\left\{\frac{2 \pm \sqrt{29}}{5}\right\}$ **36.** $\left\{\frac{-1 \pm \sqrt{17}}{2}\right\}$
37. $\{\sqrt{2} \pm 2\}$ **38.** $\left\{\frac{\sqrt{3} \pm \sqrt{21}}{3}\right\}$
39. $\{-3 \pm \sqrt{13}\}$

Page 439

ORALS **1.** $14x^2$ **2.** $x^2 + x$ **3.** $3x^2 + 15x$
4. $x^2 - 9$ **5.** $4x^2 - 25$ **6.** $6x^2 - 5x - 6$

EXERCISES **1.** $l = 8$ m, $w = 5$ m
2. $l = 10$ cm, $w = 5$ cm **3.** $l = 8$ m, $w = 4$ m
4. $l = 9$ m, $w = 3$ m **5.** $l = 11$ cm, $w = 4$ cm
6. $l = 12$ m, $w = 5$ m **7.** $l = 5$ cm, $w = 4$ cm
8. $l = 7$ m, $w = 4$ m **9.** $l = 8.4$ cm, $w = 2.4$ cm
10. $l = 17.8$ m, $w = 2.8$ m **11.** $l = 7.7$ m,
$w = 5.7$ m **12.** $l = 5.2$ km, $w = 1.2$ km
13. $l = 12$ cm, $w = 8$ cm **14.** $l = 19$ cm,
$w = 8$ cm **15.** $l = 15$ km, $w = 6$ km
16. $l = 13$ cm, $w = 7$ cm **17.** $l = 18$ km,
$w = 4$ km **18.** $l = 16$ cm, $w = 8$ cm
19. $l = 8.1$ m, $w = 3.1$ m **20.** $l = 2.4$ km,
$w = 1.8$ km **21.** $l = 7$, $w = 5$ **22.** $l = 12$, $w = 10$

Page 440

1. yes **2.** Answers will vary. **3.** Wednesday

Page 442

1. $\{75\}$ **2.** $\{36\}$ **3.** ϕ **4.** $\{2\}$ **5.** ϕ **6.** $\{2\}$
7. $\{10, -10\}$ **8.** ϕ **9.** $\{6, -6\}$ **10.** $\{12, -4\}$
11. $\{4, -20\}$ **12.** $\{3 \pm 2\sqrt{2}\}$ **13.** 16 **14.** 49
15. 1 **16.** 100 **17.** $\frac{25}{4}$ **18.** $\frac{225}{4}$ **19.** $\{13, -1\}$
20. $\{1, -3\}$ **21.** $\{9, 5\}$ **22.** $\{4, -12\}$ **23.** $\{7, -3\}$
24. $\{6, 4\}$ **25.** $\{-4, -2\}$ **26.** $\{17, 3\}$
27. $\{-6, -10\}$ **28.** $3x^2 - 5x + 4 = 0$; $a = 3$,
$b = -5$, $c = 4$ **29.** $x^2 - x + 6 = 0$; $a = 1$,
$b = -1$, $c = 6$ **30.** $3x^2 + 6x + 0 = 0$; $a = 3$,
$b = 6$, $c = 0$ **31.** $x^2 + 0x - 7 = 0$; $a = 1$, $b = 0$,
$c = -7$ **32.** $4x^2 - 3x + 0 = 0$; $a = 4$, $b = -3$,
$c = 0$ **33.** $5x^2 + 0x - 11 = 0$; $a = 5$, $b = 0$,
$c = -11$ **34.** $3x^2 - 4x - 8 = 0$; $a = 3$, $b = -4$,
$c = -8$ **35.** $7x^2 - 2x + 1 = 0$; $a = 7$, $b = -2$,
$c = 1$ **36.** $3x^2 + 24x - 1 = 0$; $a = 3$, $b = 24$,
$c = -1$ **37.** $\{4, 2\}$ **38.** $\{3, -5\}$ **39.** $\{3, 4\}$
40. $\{6, -1\}$ **41.** $\{-2, -5\}$ **42.** $\{11, -1\}$
43. $\{3, -7\}$ **44.** $\{5, 10\}$ **45.** $\{-3, 1\}$ **46.** $\{6, 4\}$
47. $\{7, 0\}$ **48.** $\{9, -6\}$ **49.** $\left\{-2, \frac{1}{3}\right\}$ **50.** $\left\{4, -\frac{3}{2}\right\}$
51. $\left\{\frac{1}{2}, -\frac{5}{2}\right\}$ **52.** ϕ **53.** $\left\{\frac{-1 \pm \sqrt{13}}{3}\right\}$
54. $\{-3 \pm \sqrt{10}\}$ **55.** $\left\{\frac{7 \pm \sqrt{5}}{2}\right\}$ **56.** ϕ
57. $\left\{\frac{2 \pm 3\sqrt{2}}{2}\right\}$ **58.** $\left\{\frac{-1 \pm \sqrt{5}}{2}\right\}$

59. $\left\{\dfrac{5 \pm \sqrt{17}}{4}\right\}$ **60.** $\left\{-1, -\dfrac{3}{2}\right\}$ **61.** $\left\{\dfrac{5 \pm \sqrt{97}}{6}\right\}$

62. $\left\{\dfrac{1 \pm 2\sqrt{2}}{7}\right\}$ **63.** $l = 5$ m, $w = 4$m

64. $l = 20$ m, $w = 4$ m

Page 443

1. $\{4\}$ **2.** ϕ **3.** $\{6\}$ **4.** $\{6, -6\}$ **5.** $\{10, -10\}$
6. $\{-5 \pm 2\sqrt{3}\}$ **7.** 25 **8.** 4 **9.** 81 **10.** $\dfrac{49}{4}$
11. $\{-3, -1\}$ **12.** $\{13, -3\}$ **13.** $\{2, -8\}$
14. $\{19, -1\}$ **15.** $2x^2 - 5x + 4 = 0$; $a = 2$,
$b = -5$, $c = 4$ **16.** $x^2 - x - 8 = 0$; $a = 1$,
$b = -1$, $c = -8$ **17.** $2x^2 - 3x - 7 = 0$; $a = 2$,
$b = -3$, $c = -7$ **18.** $3x^2 - 54x - 1 = 0$; $a = 3$,
$b = -54$, $c = -1$ **19.** $\{-3, -6\}$ **20.** $\{5, -6\}$
21. $\left\{\dfrac{-7 \pm \sqrt{57}}{2}\right\}$ **22.** $\left\{\dfrac{2}{3}, \dfrac{1}{2}\right\}$ **23.** $\left\{-1, \dfrac{3}{2}\right\}$
24. $\left\{\dfrac{1 \pm \sqrt{13}}{3}\right\}$ **25.** ϕ **26.** ϕ **27.** $\left\{\dfrac{1 \pm \sqrt{10}}{3}\right\}$
28. $\left\{-1, -\dfrac{3}{4}\right\}$ **29.** $l = 3$ m, $w = 4$ m
30. $l = 6$ km, $w = 2$ km

Page 444

1. 4.5 **2.** 2.8 **3.** 5.6 **4.** 6.7

Page 447

ORALS **1.** 70° **2.** 55° **3.** 75° **4.** 30° **5.** 5°
6. $(90 - x)°$ **7.** 60° **8.** 45° **9.** 15° **10.** 88°
11. 8° **12.** $(90 - y)°$

EXERCISES **1.** 33°, 57° **2.** 60° **3.** 65°, 25°
4. 30°, 60°, 90° **5.** 45° **6.** 14°, 76° **7.** 16°
8. 58°, 60°, 62° **9.** 15°, 75° **10.** 36°, 54°
11. 75°, 70°, 35° **12.** 20°, 26°, 134°

Page 450

1. $x = 3$, $y = 14$ **2.** $x = 4\frac{1}{2}$, $y = 2\frac{2}{3}$ **3.** $EF = 3\frac{1}{3}$,
$DF = 8\frac{2}{3}$ **4.** $BC = 4$, $DF = 13\frac{1}{2}$ **5.** $DE = 11\frac{2}{3}$,
$EF = 20$ **6.** $AB = 6$, $FE = 24$ **7.** $CB = 13\frac{1}{3}$,
$DF = 15$ **8.** $CB = 21$, $AC = 16\frac{1}{2}$ **9.** 6 m
10 45 m **11.** 9.6 m **12.** 64 m **13.** $7\frac{1}{2}$ m
14. 600 m

Page 452

ORALS **1.** q **2.** q **3.** r **4.** p **5.** p **6.** $\dfrac{p}{r}$ **7.** $\dfrac{p}{r}$
8. $\dfrac{q}{p}$ **9.** $\dfrac{q}{r}$ **10.** $\dfrac{q}{r}$

EXERCISES **1.** $\tan A = 1.333$, $\sin A = .800$,
$\cos A = .600$, $\tan B = .750$, $\sin B = .600$,
$\cos B = .800$ **2.** $\tan A = .533$, $\sin A = .471$,
$\cos A = .882$, $\tan B = 1.875$, $\sin B = .882$,
$\cos B = .471$ **3.** $\tan A = .750$, $\sin A = .600$,
$\cos A = .800$, $\tan B = 1.333$, $\sin B = .800$,
$\cos B = .600$ **4.** $\tan A = .292$, $\sin A = .280$,
$\cos A = .960$, $\tan B = 3.429$, $\sin B = .960$,
$\cos B = .280$ **5.** $\tan A = .894$, $\sin A = .667$,
$\cos A = .745$, $\tan B = 1.118$, $\sin B = .745$,
$\cos B = .667$ **6.** $\tan A = 2.000$, $\sin A = .894$,
$\cos A = .447$, $\tan B = .500$, $\sin B = .447$,
$\cos B = .894$ **7.** 1.000 **8.** $.707$ **9.** $.707$

10. $\sin A = \dfrac{a}{c}$; $\cos B = \dfrac{a}{c}$, thus $\sin A = \cos B$

11. $\sin B = \dfrac{b}{c}$; $\cos A = \dfrac{b}{c}$; thus $\sin B = \cos A$

12. $\tan A = \dfrac{a}{b}$; $\tan B = \dfrac{b}{a}$; $\dfrac{1}{\tan B} = \dfrac{1}{\dfrac{b}{a}} = \dfrac{a}{b}$;

thus $\tan A = \dfrac{1}{\tan B}$ **13.** $a^2 + b^2 = c^2$,

$\dfrac{a^2}{c^2} + \dfrac{b^2}{c^2} = \dfrac{c^2}{c^2} = 1$. Also, $\dfrac{a^2}{c^2} + \dfrac{b^2}{c^2} = \sin^2 A +$

$\cos^2 A$. By substitution, $\sin^2 A + \cos^2 A = 1$.
14. $\tan A = .250$, $\sin A = .243$, $\cos A = .970$,
$\tan B = 4.000$, $\sin B = .970$, $\cos B = .243$
15. $\tan A = .775$, $\sin A = .612$, $\cos A = .791$,
$\tan B = 1.291$, $\sin B = .791$, $\cos B = .612$
16. $\tan A = 2.646$, $\sin A = .936$, $\cos A = .354$,
$\tan B = .378$, $\sin B = .354$, $\cos B = .936$
17. Any two complementary angles may be
represented as the acute angles of a right

triangle ABC. $\sin A = \dfrac{a}{c}$; $\cos B = \dfrac{a}{c}$; thus,

$\sin A = \cos B$, or the sine of an angle is equal
to the cosine of its complement. **18.** The
hypotenuse of a right triangle is always longer
than either leg. Thus, the ratio of a leg to the
hypotenuse is between 0 and 1.

Page 454

The graph of $\{(x, y, z) \mid x = -3\}$ is a plane $\perp$ to xy − plane, parallel to yz − plane and 3 units to the left of it.

Page 457

ORALS **1.** .0872 **2.** .3839 **3.** .2079 **4.** .7265 **5.** .8572 **6.** .6691 **7.** .9903 **8.** .2126 **9.** .9976 **10.** 1.327 **11.** 13° **12.** 55° **13.** 40° **14.** 1° **15.** 88° **16.** 44°

EXERCISES **1.** .9613 **2.** .1564 **3.** .4384 **4.** .8660 **5.** 57.29 **6.** .9511 **7.** 2.145 **8.** .6691 **9.** .2588 **10.** .4848 **11.** 8° **12.** 42° **13.** 23° **14.** 22° **15.** 34° **16.** 59° **17.** 49° **18.** 54° **19.** 77° **20.** 48° **21.** 83° **22.** 4° **23.** F **24.** T **25.** T **26.** F **27.** T **28.** F **29.** F **30.** T **31.** F **32.** T **33.** T **34.** T **35.** F **36.** F **37.** T **38.** T **39.** T **40.** Sin A increases from 0 to 1. The ratio of a to c approaches 1. **41.** Cos A decreases from 1 to 0. The ratio of b to c approaches 0. **42.** Tan A increases from 0 to an infinitely large number. As $m \angle A$ increases, a becomes infinitely large, and so the ratio of a to b becomes infinitely large.

Page 460

1. $a = 8.9$ **2.** $a = 9.4$ **3.** $b = 8.5$ **4.** $m \angle B = 77$ **5.** $c = 9.7$ **6.** $m \angle B = 38$ **7.** $a = 4.7$ **8.** $m \angle B = 38$ **9.** $c = 18.3$ **10.** $a = 3.9$ **11.** $m \angle A = 30$ **12.** $m \angle A = 37$ **13.** $a = 25.7$ **14.** $a = 13.6$ **15.** $m \angle B = 74$, $BC = 5.7$,

$AB = 20.8$ **16.** $m \angle A = 40$, $BC = 10.1$, $AB = 15.7$ **17.** $m \angle B = 54$, $BC = 10.2$, $AB = 17.3$ **18.** $m \angle A = 16$, $m \angle B = 74$, $AB = 7.3$ **19.** $m \angle B = 32$, $BC = 15.3$, $AC = 9.5$ **20.** $BC = 4$, $m \angle A = 53$, $m \angle B = 37$

Page 463

1. $x = 58.5$ m **2.** $x = 22.3$ m **3.** $x = 64.7$ km **4.** $x = 37.4$ m **5.** $x = 342.9$ m **6.** $x = 16{,}181.2$ m **7.** $x = 46.6$ m **8.** 7.3 m **9.** 216.6 m **10.** 185.4 m **11.** 96.0 m **12.** 5° **13.** 32° **14.** 24.6 m **15.** 21,299.3 m **16.** 1,067.3 m **17.** 49.5 km² **18.** 6.7 m by 9.9 m

Page 464

1. $x = 8$, $y = 10$ **2.** $x = 5\frac{1}{3}$, $y = 6$ **3.** 3.000 **4.** .949 **5.** .949 **6.** .316 **7.** 72° **8.** 18° **9.** $c = 20.4$ **10.** $b = 5.7$ **11.** $a = 6.9$ **12.** $m \angle A = 53$ **13.** 93.3 m **14.** 6.7 km **15.** 44°, 44°, 92° **16.** 16°, 74° **17.** 35°, 55° **18.** 2.6 m **19.** 31.3 m **20.** 28.9 m

Page 465

1. $x = 7\frac{1}{2}$, $y = 8\frac{3}{4}$ **2.** $x = 10\frac{2}{3}$, $y = 6\frac{3}{4}$ **3.** cos $A = .943$ **4.** cos $B = .333$ **5.** sin $A = .333$ **6.** tan $B = 2.828$ **7.** $m \angle A = 19$ **8.** $m \angle B = 71$ **9.** $a = 9.9$ **10.** $c = 67.6$ **11.** $b = 16.1$ **12.** $m \angle B = 39$ **13.** $x = 9.8$ m **14.** $x = 81.7$ m **15.** 26°, 64° **16.** 55°, 50°, 75° **17.** 11.2 m **18.** 285.6 m

Page 466

1. $BC = 2\sqrt{5}$, $AC = 2\sqrt{5}$ **2.** $AB = 5$, $BC = 5$

HOLT
ALGEBRA
1

Eugene D. Nichols

Mervine L. Edwards

E. Henry Garland

Sylvia A. Hoffman

Albert Mamary

William F. Palmer

HOLT ALGEBRA 1

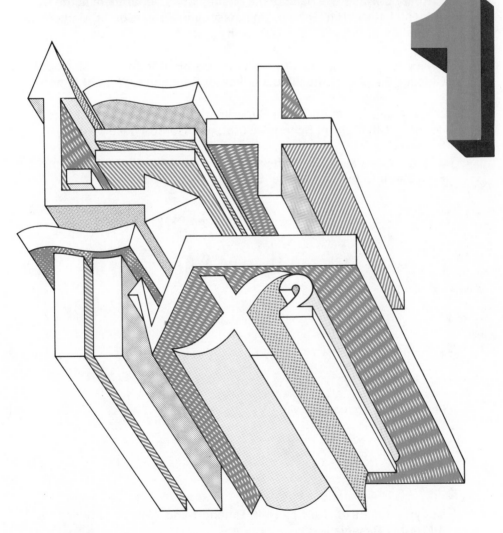

HOLT, RINEHART AND WINSTON, PUBLISHERS
New York · Toronto · London · Sydney

About the Authors

Eugene D. Nichols is Professor of Mathematics Education and Lecturer in the Department of Mathematics at Florida State University, Tallahassee, Florida.

Mervine L. Edwards is Chairman of the Mathematics Department, Shore Regional High School, West Long Branch, New Jersey.

E. Henry Garland is Head of the Mathematics Department at the Developmental Research School, and Associate Professor of Mathematics Education at Florida State University, Tallahassee, Florida.

Sylvia A. Hoffman is Curriculum Coordinator for the Metropolitan Chicago Region of the Illinois Office of Education, State of Illinois.

Albert Mamary is Assistant Superintendent of Schools for Instruction, Johnson City Central School District, Johnson City, New York.

William F. Palmer is Professor and Chairman of the Department of Education, Catawba College, Salisbury, North Carolina.

Photo credits are on page viii.

ISBN: 0-03-018901-2

890123456   071   98765432

CONTENTS

SPECIAL TOPICS

ACKNOWLEDGEMENTS FOR PHOTOGRAPHS

Page 3 Top: SAS Photo
        Bottom: © Betty Medsger
Page 87 Top and Bottom: Irene Fertik
Page 202 Top Left: HRW Photo by Russell Dian
          Top Right: Courtesy of Flooring Magazine
          Bottom: Courtesy of the DuPont Co.

Page 260 Irene Fertik
Page 303 Courtesy of Pfizer, Inc.
Page 340 HRW Photo by Russell Dian
Page 413 HRW Photo by Russell Dian

SYMBOL LIST

$=$	is equal to	1
$\ldots$	goes on forever	21
$-a$	the opposite of a	24
$\{\ \ \}$	set	57
ϕ	empty set	92
$\neq$	is not equal to	94
$<$	is less than	94
$>$	is greater than	94
$\leq$	is less than or equal to	95
$\geq$	is greater than or equal to	95
$\{x \mid x < 4\}$	the set of all numbers x such that $x < 4$	95
$\subseteq$	is a subset of	105
$\nsubseteq$	is not a subset of	105
$\cap$	intersection of sets	106
$\cup$	union of sets	106
3^4	the fourth power of 3	119
x^3	the third power of x, or x cubed	119
GCF	greatest common factor	135
LCD	least common denominator	211
$|x|$	the absolute value of x	232
$\vec{d}(PQ)$	the directed distance from P to Q	236
$\perp$	is perpendicular to	240
$P(x, y)$	point P with coordinates x, y	242
$\overleftrightarrow{MN}$	line MN	247
$\overline{AB}$	line segment AB	251
$5:7$	the ratio 5 to 7	261
$f(x)$	the value of f at x	323
$.3\overline{3}$	the 3 repeats forever	362
$\sqrt{x}$	the principal square root of x	384
$\doteq$	is approximately equal to	385
$\triangle ABC$	triangle ABC	399
$\pm$	plus or minus	428
$m\angle A$	degree measure of angle A	445
$\cong$	is congruent to	448
$\sim$	is similar to	448
$\tan A$	tangent of $m\angle A$	451
$\sin A$	sine of $m\angle A$	451
$\cos A$	cosine of $m\angle A$	451

BASIC OPERATIONS

Puzzles

PUZZLE 1.

Start with a pile of 15 tooth-picks. Each player in turn may take 1, 2, or 3 toothpicks from the pile. The player who must take the last toothpick is the loser.

PUZZLE 2.

Arrange the numbers 1, 2, 3, 4, 5, 6, 7, 8, 9 so that they meet these conditions:
(1) There are exactly three numbers in each circle.
(2) The sum of the numbers in each circle is 15.

PUZZLE 3.

All you have is a 3-minute hourglass and an 8-minute hourglass. How can you cook an egg for exactly 13 minutes?

Order of Operations

 REVIEW CAPSULE

Ways to show multiplication:

times sign	raised dot	parentheses
↓	↓	↙ ↘
2×5	$2 \cdot 5$	(2)(5), or 2(5)

Read each as 2 times 5.

EXAMPLE 1   What does this mean? (2)(5) + 3

There are two possibilities.

$$(2)(5) + 3 \qquad \qquad (2)(5) + 3$$

Multiply first. ⟶ 10 + 3   (2)(8) ← Add first.

Then add. ⟶ 13   16 ← Then multiply.

Two different answers ⟶   13 or 16?

We make this agreement to avoid confusion. ⟶

Order of Operations
When both multiplications and additions occur, we multiply first and then add.

Thus, in Example 1,   (2)(5) + 3

Multiply first. ⟶   10 + 3

Then add. ⟶   13

EXAMPLE 2   Compute 6 + (3)(4).

$$6 + (3)(4)$$
$$6 + \quad 12$$
$$18$$

Multiply first. ⟶

Then add. ⟶

Thus, 6 + 3(4) = 18.

EXAMPLE 3 Compute (4) (2) + (3) (1).

$$(4) (2) + (3) (1)$$
$$8 \quad + \quad 3$$
$$11$$

EXAMPLE 4 Compute $7 + 4 \cdot 2 + 1 + 6 \cdot 5$.

Remember the order of operations. $\longrightarrow$

$$7 + \underbrace{4 \cdot 2} + 1 + \underbrace{6 \cdot 5}$$
$$7 + \quad 8 \quad + 1 + \quad 30$$
$$46$$

EXERCISES

Answers for all exercises are given in the front of the Teacher's Edition.

PART A

Compute.

1. (4) (6) + 1 *25*   **2.** (7) (5) + 8 *43*   **3.** $6 \cdot 3 + 12$ *30*

4. $7 + 5 \cdot 8$ *47*   **5.** 8 (3) + 5 *29*   **6.** 6 + (4) (11) *50*

7. 8 + (3) (9) *35*   **8.** (9) (1) + 12 *21*   **9.** 10 + (8) (1) *18*

10. (3) (9) + 13 *40*   **11.** $6 \cdot 11 + 2$ *68*   **12.** 8 + (3) (9) *35*

13. $14 + 12 \cdot 1$ *26*   **14.** 5 (0) + 0 *0*   **15.** 3 (2) + 4 (1) *10*

16. (6) (5) + (8) (3) *54*   **17.** (7) (9) + (10) (1) *73*   **18.** (6) (2) + (5) (0) *12*

19. (4) (8) + (0) (7) *32*   **20.** (6) (3) + (17) (2) *52*   **21.** $5 \cdot 8 + 4 \cdot 9$ *76*

22. (6) (9) + 1 + (8) (2) *71*   **23.** (7) (5) + (4) (8) + 2 *69*   **24.** $0 \cdot 8 + 5 + 0 \cdot 9$ *5*

PART B

Compute.

25. 1 + (0) (18) + (2) (9) *19*   **26.** 6 + (4) (13) + 12 *70*

27. 7 (9) + 8 + 4 (2) *79*   **28.** (3) (9) + (2) (12) + 8 *59*

29. (7) (4) + 8 + 10 + (9) (3) *73*   **30.** 2 + (6) (7) + (3) (5) + 4 *63*

31. $6 + 2 \cdot 9 + 4 \cdot 6 + 5$ *53*   **32.** (1) (8) + 7 + (0) (3) + (2) (4) *23*

33. (0) (8) + 2 + (9) (4) + (3) (5) + 4 *57*   **34.** 7 + (2) (13) + (5) (7) + 1 + (4) (5) *89*

35. (2) (36) + 15 + (9) (14) + 7 *220*   **36.** $28 \cdot 5 + 4 \cdot 16 + 17 + 8 \cdot 3$ *245*

PART C

Compute.

37. (.5) (.007) + 1.18   **38.** .15 + (2.18) (.004)   **39.** (.15) (.6) + .004 + (1.1) (.007)

Mathematics in Aviation

Airplane pilots make careful checks of the instrument panel before and during flights.

Air traffic is monitored by traffic controllers in control towers of airports. They carefully calculate the flight patterns of arriving and departing planes.

Variables

▶ *REVIEW CAPSULE*

Order of Operations
Multiply first. Then add.

$$7 + 5(8)$$
$$7 + \quad 40 \quad \leftarrow \text{Multiply } 5(8) \text{ first.}$$
$$47 \qquad \leftarrow \text{Then add.}$$

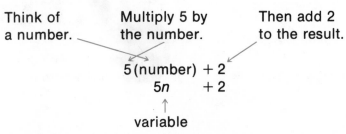

Think of a number.   Multiply 5 by the number.   Then add 2 to the result.

$$5(\text{number}) + 2$$
$$5n \qquad + 2$$
$$\uparrow$$
$$\text{variable}$$

$5n$ means $5(n)$. ⟶

A *variable* takes the place of a number. ⟶

EXAMPLE 1   Evaluate $5n + 2$ for the values of n shown.

To evaluate means to find the value.
Substitute the values for the variable. ⟶

Let n be 3.	Let n be 8.	Let n be 20.
$5n + 2$	$5n + 2$	$5n + 2$
$5(3) + 2$	$5(8) + 2$	$5(20) + 2$
$15 + 2$	$40 + 2$	$100 + 2$
17	42	102

EXAMPLE 2   Evaluate $5 + 8a + 2b$ if $a = 7$ and $b = 4$.

$$5 + 8(7) + 2(4)$$
$$5 + \quad 56 \quad + \quad 8$$
$$69$$

Order of operations:
Multiply first.
Then add.

Terms are added.

Terms

$$5 + 8a + 2b$$

8 is the coefficient of a.   2 is the coefficient of b.

A coefficient is the multiplier of a variable.

EXAMPLE 3 Name the terms and the variables in $3w + 8z + 2$.
Then name the coefficient of each variable.

Terms are added.
Variables are letters which take the
place of numbers.

The terms are 3w, 8z, and 2.
The variables are w and z.

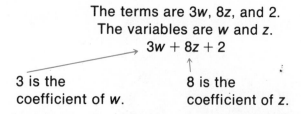

$3w + 8z + 2$

3 is the
coefficient of w.

8 is the
coefficient of z.

ORAL EXERCISES

Name the terms and the variables. Then name the coefficient of each variable.

1. $6x + 1$ **2.** $4 + 3c$ **3.** $2y + 5$
4. $5a + 6 + 4b$ **5.** $7 + 3x + 8y$ **6.** $9m + 1 + 2n$
7. $3c + 2d + 6$ **8.** $7g + 3h + 12k$ **9.** $4y + 12z + 5w$

EXERCISES

PART A

Evaluate.

1. $2x + 3$ if $x = 5$ *13*   **2.** $5 + 3y$ if $y = 4$ *17*   **3.** $7 + 6a$ if $a = 7$ *49*
4. $7y + 3$ if $y = 2$ *17*   **5.** $9a + 1$ if $a = 6$ *55*   **6.** $5 + 6z$ if $z = 1$ *11*
7. $3x + 9$ if $x = 3$ *18*   **8.** $7 + 4c$ if $c = 8$ *39*   **9.** $2m + 6$ if $m = 4$ *14*
10. $5x + 4 + 2y$ if $x = 2, y = 4$ *22*   **11.** $3a + 6b + 1$ if $a = 3, b = 6$ *46*
12. $4m + 8 + 7n$ if $m = 6, n = 1$ *39*   **13.** $2k + 8 + 5t$ if $k = 9, t = 1$ *31*
14. $2 + 4y + 5z$ if $y = 7, z = 8$ *70*   **15.** $8g + 5 + 3e$ if $g = 8, e = 3$ *78*
16. $4p + 9 + 3q$ if $p = 9, q = 2$ *51*   **17.** $6r + 7s + 2$ if $r = 6, s = 5$ *73*

PART B

EXAMPLE Evaluate $xz + 7y$ if $x = 3, y = 5,$ and $z = 2$.

$3(2) + 7(5)$
$6 \quad + \quad 35,$ or 41

Evaluate if $x = 3, y = 8,$ and $z = 5$.

18. $3x + 2y + 4z$ **19.** $5z + 4x + 7y$ *93*   **20.** $8y + 3z + 7x$
21. $2yz + xz$ **22.** $yz + 5xy$ *160*   **23.** $4xy + 8zy$
24. $6xy + 3yz + 1$ **25.** $9y + 5xy + 2zx$ *222*   **26.** $2xy + 6xz + 4yz$

Commutative and Associative Properties

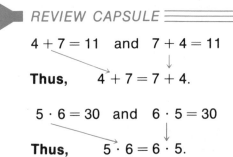

REVIEW CAPSULE

$4 + 7 = 11$ and $7 + 4 = 11$

Thus, $4 + 7 = 7 + 4.$

$5 \cdot 6 = 30$ and $6 \cdot 5 = 30$

Thus, $5 \cdot 6 = 6 \cdot 5.$

When adding or multiplying two numbers, we can change the order.

The Review suggests this. ⟶

Commutative Property

Addition: $a + b = b + a$, for all numbers a and b.

Multiplication: $a \cdot b = b \cdot a$, for all numbers a and b.

EXAMPLE 1 Is this statement true? $(3 + 1) + 9 = 3 + (1 + 9)$

$(3 + 1) + 9$	$3 + (1 + 9)$
Add inside the parentheses first. ⟶ | $4 \quad + 9$ | $3 + \quad 10$ |
Answers are the same. ⟶ | 13 | 13 |

Yes, $(3 + 1) + 9 = 3 + (1 + 9)$ is a true statement.

EXAMPLE 2 Is this statement true? $(5 \cdot 2) \cdot 4 = 5 \cdot (2 \cdot 4)$

$(5 \cdot 2) \cdot 4$	$5 \cdot (2 \cdot 4)$
Multiply inside the parentheses first. ⟶ | $10 \quad \cdot 4$ | $5 \cdot \quad 8$ |
Answers are the same. ⟶ | 40 | 40 |

Yes, $(5 \cdot 2) \cdot 4 = 5 \cdot (2 \cdot 4)$ is a true statement.

Associative Property

Addition: $(a + b) + c = a + (b + c)$, for all numbers a, b, and c.

Multiplication: $(a \cdot b) \cdot c = a \cdot (b \cdot c)$, for all numbers a, b, and c.

EXAMPLE 3   Rewrite $295 + 42 + 5$ by using the commutative and associative properties. Then compute.

Associative property of addition

Commutative property of addition
Associative property of addition

$$
\begin{aligned}
295 + 42 + 5 &= (295 + 42) + 5 \\
&= 295 + (42 + 5) \\
&= 295 + (5 + 42) \\
&= (295 + 5) + 42 \\
&= \underbrace{300} + 42 \\
&= 342
\end{aligned}
$$

Thus, $295 + 42 + 5 = 342$.

EXAMPLE 4   Rewrite $25 \cdot 7 \cdot 4$ by using the commutative and associative properties. Then compute.

Associative property of multiplication

Commutative property of multiplication

Associative property

$$
\begin{aligned}
25 \cdot 7 \cdot 4 &= (25 \cdot 7) \cdot 4 \\
&= 25 \cdot (7 \cdot 4) \\
&= 25 \cdot (4 \cdot 7) \\
&= (25 \cdot 4) \cdot 7 \\
&= \underbrace{100} \cdot 7 \\
&= 700
\end{aligned}
$$

Thus, $25 \cdot 7 \cdot 4 = 700$.

SUMMARY   **Addition can be done in any order. Multiplication can be done in any order. The commutative and associative properties make this possible.**

EXAMPLE 5 Which property is illustrated by each equation?

Comm. is short for commutative.
Assoc. is short for associative.

$6x + 8y = 8y + 6x$

$(4 \cdot r)s = 4(rs)$

$3x(8) = 8(3x)$

Answers
Comm. Prop. Add.
Assoc. Prop. Mult.
Comm. Prop. Mult.

EXERCISES

PART A

Rewrite by using the commutative and associative properties. Then compute.

1. $17 + 4 + 56$ *77*

2. $49 + 16 + 1$ *66*

3. $2 + 56 + 38$ *96*

4. $27 + 2 + 98$ *127*

5. $67 + 35 + 3$ *105*

6. $25 + 47 + 5$ *77*

7. $4 \cdot 17 \cdot 25$ *1,700*

8. $50 \cdot 23 \cdot 2$ *2,300*

9. $5 \cdot 164 \cdot 2$ *1,640*

10. $20 \cdot 39 \cdot 5$ *3,900*

11. $250 \cdot 49 \cdot 4$ *49,000*

12. $2 \cdot 78 \cdot 50$ *7,800*

Which property is illustrated?

Assoc. Prop. Mult.   *Assoc. Prop. Add.*

13. $8 + 2 = 2 + 8$

14. $(4 \cdot 5) \cdot 7 = 4 \cdot (5 \cdot 7)$

15. $(2 + 8) + 1 = 2 + (8 + 1)$

16. $9 \cdot 4 = 4 \cdot 9$

17. $(xy)z = x(yz)$

18. $5 + (8 + x) = (5 + 8) + x$

19. $4c + 8d = 8d + 4c$

20. $7(5b) = (7 \cdot 5)b$

21. $4y(9) = 9(4y)$

Comm. Prop. Add.   *Assoc. Prop. Mult.*   *Comm. Prop. Mult.*

PART B

Rewrite by using the commutative and associative properties. Then compute.

22. $29 + 44 + 6 + 1$ *80*

23. $2 + 167 + 38 + 3$ *210*

24. $121 + 136 + 4 + 9$

25. $522 + 7 + 28 + 43$

26. $632 + 271 + 29 + 68$ *1,000*

27. $285 + 24 + 15 + 66$

28. $8 \cdot 56 \cdot 125$ *56,000*

29. $2 \cdot 187 \cdot 25 \cdot 2$ *18,700*

30. $20 \cdot 36 \cdot 2 \cdot 5$ *7,200*

PART C

EXAMPLE Is division commutative?
(Is $a \div b = b \div a$ always true?)

Let's try $6 \div 2$ and $2 \div 6$.

$6 \div 2 = 3$ and $2 \div 6 = \dfrac{2}{6}$, or $\dfrac{1}{3}$. So, $6 \div 2 \neq 2 \div 6$.

Thus, division is not commutative.

31. Is subtraction commutative?
Is subtraction associative?
Illustrate your answer.

32. Is division associative?
Illustrate your answer.

Distributive Property

OBJECTIVE

■ To rewrite expressions by using the distributive property

 REVIEW CAPSULE

Rewrite $5(6)$ and $4(3+8)$ by using the commutative property of multiplication.

$$5(6)$$
$$6(5)$$

$$4(3+8)$$
$$(3+8)4$$

EXAMPLE 1   Show that $5(6+3) = 5 \cdot 6 + 5 \cdot 3$.

Compute $5(6+3)$ and $5 \cdot 6 + 5 \cdot 3$.

Answers are the same. ⟶

$5(6+3)$	$5 \cdot 6 + 5 \cdot 3$
$5(9)$	$30 + 15$
45	45

Thus, $5(6+3) = 5 \cdot 6 + 5 \cdot 3$.

EXAMPLE 2   Show that $(5+3)4 = 5 \cdot 4 + 3 \cdot 4$.

$(5+3)4$	$5 \cdot 4 + 3 \cdot 4$
$8(4)$	$20 + 12$
32	32

Answers are the same. ⟶

Thus, $(5+3)4 = 5 \cdot 4 + 3 \cdot 4$.

Examples 1 and 2 suggest this. ⟶

Distributive Property of Multiplication over Addition

$a(b+c) = a \cdot b + a \cdot c$ and $(b+c)a = b \cdot a + c \cdot a$, for all numbers a, b, and c.

EXAMPLE 3   Rewrite $5(4+7)$ by using the distributive property. Then compute both expressions.

Distribute 5. ⟶

$$5(4+7) = 5 \cdot 4 + 5 \cdot 7$$

Compute $5(4+7)$ and $5 \cdot 4 + 5 \cdot 7$.

$5(4+7)$	$5 \cdot 4 + 5 \cdot 7$
$5(11)$	$20 + 35$
55	55

Answers are the same. ⟶

EXAMPLE 4 Rewrite $(8 + 3)5$ by using the distributive property.

$$(8 + 3)5 = 8 \cdot 5 + 3 \cdot 5$$

EXAMPLE 5 Show that $3(7 + 4 + 2) = 3 \cdot 7 + 3 \cdot 4 + 3 \cdot 2$.

$3(7 + 4 + 2)$	$3 \cdot 7 + 3 \cdot 4 + 3 \cdot 2$
$3(13)$	$21 + 12 + 6$
39	39

Answers are the same. ⎯⎯⎯⎯⎯⎯⟶

The distributive property may be used with three or more terms.

Thus, $3(7 + 4 + 2) = 3 \cdot 7 + 3 \cdot 4 + 3 \cdot 2$.

EXAMPLE 6 Rewrite $3(8) + 3(1)$ by using the distributive property.

3 is distributed.
Use the property "in reverse."

$$3(8) + 3(1) = 3(8 + 1)$$

EXAMPLE 7 Rewrite $5 \cdot 10 + 5 \cdot 2 + 5 \cdot 3 + 5 \cdot 5$ by using the distributive property.

$$5 \cdot 10 + 5 \cdot 2 + 5 \cdot 3 + 5 \cdot 5 = 5(10 + 2 + 3 + 5)$$

EXAMPLE 8 Rewrite $6(2) + 9(2)$ by using the distributive property.

2 is distributed. ⎯⎯⎯⎯⎯⎯⟶

$$6(2) + 9(2) = (6 + 9)2$$

EXAMPLE 9 Rewrite $6(3) + 1(3) + 8(3)$ by using the distributive property.

$$6(3) + 1(3) + 8(3) = (6 + 1 + 8)3$$

EXAMPLE 10 Rewrite $(6)(5) + (4)(6) + (6)(8)$ by using the distributive property.

$$(6)(5) + (4)(6) + (6)(8)$$

$$(6)(5) + (6)(4) + (6)(8)$$
$$6(5 + 4 + 8)$$

Thus, $(6)(5) + (4)(6) + (6)(8) = 6(5 + 4 + 8)$.

EXERCISES

PART A

Rewrite by using the distributive property. Then compute both expressions.

1. $4(6+2)$ *$4 \cdot 6 + 4 \cdot 2$; 32* **2.** $5(3+8)$ *$5 \cdot 3 + 5 \cdot 8$; 55* **3.** $2(9+4)$ *$\overset{18}{} \overset{8}{} = 26$*

4. $(9+7)1$ *$1 \cdot 9 + 1 \cdot 7$; 16* **5.** $(2+9)6$ *$2 \cdot 6 + 9 \cdot 6$; 66* **6.** $(3+7)5$

7. Show that $7(4+8+2)=7 \cdot 4+7 \cdot 8+7 \cdot 2$. **8.** Show that $(9+4+1)6=9 \cdot 6+4 \cdot 6+1 \cdot 6$.

Rewrite by using the distributive property. *$4 \cdot 2 + 4 \cdot 7 + 4 \cdot 6$ $3 \cdot 8 + 3 \cdot 1$*

9. $6(3+5)$ *$6 \cdot 3 + 6 \cdot 5$* **10.** $8(4+9)$ *$8 \cdot 4 + 8 \cdot 9$* **11.** $3(8+1)$

12. $(8+1+9)5$ **13.** $4(2+7+6)$ **14.** $(5+4+9)3$

15. $4(6)+4(2)$ *$4(6+2)$* **16.** $7(3)+7(9)$ *$7(3+9)$*

17. $(5)(6)+(9)(6)$ *$(5+9)6$* **18.** $(1)(5)+(9)(5)$ *$(1+9)5$*

19. $3 \cdot 8+8 \cdot 7$ *$(3+7)8$* **20.** $9 \cdot 2+4 \cdot 9$ *$9(2+4)$*

21. $5 \cdot 4+5 \cdot 2+5 \cdot 7$ *$5(4+2+7)$* **22.** $1 \cdot 3+2 \cdot 3+8 \cdot 3$ *$(1+2+8)3$*

23. $(6)(8)+(4)(8)+(7)(8)$ *$(6+4+7)8$* **24.** $2(9)+2(4)+2(6)$ *$2(9+4+6)$*

25. $(4)(3)+(7)(4)+(4)(1)$ *$4(3+7+1)$* **26.** $(6)(5)+(4)(6)+(9)(6)$

27. $8 \cdot 7+7 \cdot 4+7 \cdot 2$ *$7(8+4+2)$* **28.** $1(9)+5(9)+9(3)$ *$(1+5+3)9$*

PART B

Rewrite by using the distributive property. *$1 \cdot 4 + 9 \cdot 4 + 7 \cdot 4 + 2 \cdot 4$*

29. $7(5+1+9+2)$ **30.** $(6+8+4+3)5$ **31.** $(1+9+7+2)4$

32. $3(2+6+4+8)$ **33.** $7(8+4+3+5)$ **34.** $(5+2+6+5)5$

35. $4(8+1+3+5+9)$ **36.** $(2+7+1+6+3)7$ **37.** $(8+9+1+4+6)3$

38. $6(3)+4(6)+6(1)+2(6)$ **39.** $(7)(4)+(4)(7)+(2)(4)+(7)(4)$

$6(3+4+1+2)$ *$(7+7+2+7)4$*

PART C

EXAMPLE Is subtraction distributive over multiplication? [Is it always true that $a-(b \cdot c)=(a-b) \cdot (a-c)$?]

Let's try $12-(2 \cdot 4)$ and $(12-2)(12-4)$.

$12-(2 \cdot 4)$	$(12-2)(12-4)$
$12-8$	$10(8)$
4	80

Two different answers ⟶

Subtraction is not distributive over multiplication.

40. Is multiplication distributive over subtraction? Illustrate your answer.

41. Is addition distributive over multiplication? Illustrate your answer.

42. Is division distributive over addition from the left? Illustrate your answer.

43. Is division distributive over addition from the right? Illustrate your answer.

The Metric System

The metric system of measurement is based on ten, just as our numeration system is based on ten. The commonly-used units are screened.

Place name	thousands	hundreds	tens	units	tenths	hundredths	thousandths
	1,000	100	10	1	.1	.01	.001

Unit of length Symbol	kilometer km	hectometer hm	dekameter dam	meter m	decimeter dm	centimeter cm	millimeter mm
Value	1,000 m	100 m	10 m	1 m	.1 m	.01 m	.001 m
Prefix	kilo	hecto	deka		deci	centi	milli
Meaning	1,000	100	10		.1	.01	.001

PROBLEM

Change 5 km to cm.

One Way

Think: To get from km to cm, move 5 places to the right. So, move the decimal point 5 places to the right.

5.0 0 0 0 0.

Thus, 5 km = 500,000 cm.

Another Way

$$\frac{5 \text{ km}}{1} \cdot \frac{100 \text{ cm}}{1 \text{ m}}$$

$$\frac{5 (1,000)(1 \text{ m}) \cdot 100 \text{ cm}}{1 \text{ m}}$$

$5,000 \cdot 100 \text{ cm} = 500,000 \text{ cm}$

PROJECT

Change as indicated. Use either method.

1. 3 m to mm **2.** 6 hm to cm **3.** 7 km to dm

4. 5 m to km **5.** 8 cm to m **6.** 4 mm to km

CAPACITY

The units of capacity are related in the same way as the units of length. The commonly-used units are screened.

Unit of capacity Symbol	kiloliter kL	hectoliter hL	dekaliter daL	liter L	deciliter dL	centiliter cL	milliliter mL
Value	1,000 L	100 L	10 L	1 L	.1 L	.01 L	.001 L

PROJECT

Change as indicated.

7. 3L to cL   **8.** 5 daL to cL   **9.** 6 kL to mL

10. 7 dL to hL   **11.** 8L to kL   **12.** 9 mL to kL

WEIGHT (MASS)

The commonly used units are screened.

Unit of weight Symbol	kilogram kg	hectogram hg	dekagram dag	gram g	decigram dg	centigram cg	milligram mg
Value	1,000 g	100 g	10 g	1 g	.1 g	.01 g	.001 g

PROJECT

Change as indicated.

13. 5 g to mg   **14.** 3 dag to cg   **15.** 8 kg to mg

16. 2 dg to dag   **17.** 7 g to kg   **18.** 6 mg to kg

Distributive Property and Variables

OBJECTIVE

■ To simplify and to evaluate expressions like $7x + 3 + 9y + 4x$ if $x = 4$ and $y = 7$

 ► *REVIEW CAPSULE*

Rewrite $7(4) + 2(4)$ by using the distributive property.

$$7(4) + 2(4) = (7 + 2)4$$

EXAMPLE 1   Rewrite $6y + 7y$ by using the distributive property. Simplify the result.

y is distributed. ⟶

$$6y + 7y = (6 + 7)y$$
$$= (13)y$$
$$= 13y$$

Thus, $6y + 7y = 13y$.

$6y + 7y$ $x + 9y + 4$

like terms   unlike terms

To *simplify* an expression, we combine like terms.

EXAMPLE 2   Simplify $5x + 7x$.

Combine like terms. ⟶

$$5x + 7x = 12x$$

EXAMPLE 3   Simplify $4a + 5b + 2$, if possible.

$4a$, $5b$, and 2 are unlike terms. ⟶ $4a + 5b + 2$ cannot be simplified.

EXAMPLE 4   Simplify $9x + 8y + 5x + 1 + 9$, if possible.

$9x$ and $5x$ are like terms. Rearrange terms to group $9x$ and $5x$ together.

$$9x + 8y + 5x + 1 + 9$$
$$9x + 5x + 8y + 1 + 9$$

$$14x \quad + 8y + \quad 10$$

ORAL EXERCISES

Simplify, if possible. *(3, 6, 8, 11, 13, 16, 18, 20 cannot be simplified.)*

1. $2x + 3x$ *5x*
2. $4p + 7p$ *11p*
3. $2a + 3$ *13c*
4. $6b + 7b$ *13b*

5. $5y + 6y$ *11y*
6. $5a + 8b$
7. $6r + 9r$ *15r*
8. $8 + 3y$

9. $2m + 8m$ *10m*
10. $7x + 9x$ *16x*
11. $4y + 8z$
12. $5c + 8c$

13. $4 + 9y$
14. $2x + 5x$ *7x*
15. $9w + 4w$ *13w*
16. $7e + 8f$

17. $2z + 6z$ *8z*
18. $8x + 9y$
19. $3g + 7g$ *10g*
20. $5 + 5e$

EXERCISES

PART A

Simplify, if possible.

1. $6x + 3 + 4x$ *10x + 3*
2. $6 + 8x + 7$ *13 + 8x*
3. $5y + 9 + 2y$ *7y + 9*

4. $3m + 2 + 5m$ *8m + 2*
5. $3a + 8a + 9$ *11a + 9*
6. $2r + 8 + 6r$ *8r + 8*

7. $7 + 6z + 5$ *6z + 12*
8. $9 + 5z + 8z$ *13z + 9*
9. $4b + 7 + 5b$ *9b + 7*

10. $8 + 6x + 3$ *6x + 11*
11. $5k + 7 + 4k$ *9k + 7*
12. $9 + 6x + 8$ *6x + 17*

13. $2y + 1 + 3y$ *5y + 1*
14. $2a + 7 + 5$ *2a + 12*
15. $3z + 8z + 4$ *11z + 4*

16. $2m + 3m + 8 + 1$ *5m + 9*
17. $6t + 7 + 4t + 9$ *10t + 16*
18. $7y + 3 + 7 + 3y$

19. $9 + 5z + 4 + 3z$ *8z + 13*
20. $5 + 4x + 3 + 8x$ *12x + 8*
21. $5x + 2y + 4x + 7y$

22. $6a + 7b + 8b + 2a$
23. $4m + 2q + 3m + 7q$
24. $3c + 5d + 9c + 4d$

25. $7x + 8y + 4x + 1$
26. $2 + 3z + 5 + 4y$
27. $7a + 8b + 9a + 6$

28. $5a + 4b + 9c + 5a$ ↘
    10a + 4b + 9c
29. $7x + 2y + 5z + 1$ ↘
    cannot be simplified
30. $6g + 4 + 5h + 9g$ ↘
    15g + 5h + 4

PART B

EXAMPLE   Simplify $5x + 9y + 3x + 2y$. Then evaluate if $x = 6$ and $y = 1$.

Group *x* terms together
and *y* terms together. ——————→

$$5x + 9y + 3x + 2y$$
$$5x + 3x + 9y + 2y$$
$$8x \quad + \quad 11y$$
$$\downarrow \qquad \quad \downarrow$$

Substitute 6 for *x*, 1 for *y*. ——————→

$$8(6) + 11(1)$$
$$48 + 11, \text{ or } 59$$

Simplify. Then evaluate for the given values of the variables.

31. $4a + 6a + 5$ if $a = 2$ *10a + 5; 25*
32. $9 + 5r + 7r$ if $r = 3$ *12r + 9; 45*

33. $2y + 8 + 5y$ if $y = 8$ *7y + 8; 64*
34. $8 + 4k + 7$ if $k = 9$ *4k + 15; 51*

35. $9 + 4y + 3 + 2y$ if $y = 7$ *6y + 12; 54*
36. $6x + 4 + 9 + 3x$ if $x = 3$. *12a + 9b + 4; 97*

37. $4z + 2 + 3w + 8z$ if $z = 6$, $w = 4$ ↘
    12z + 3w + 2; 86
38. $5a + 6b + 4 + 3b + 7a$ if $a = 4$, $b = 5$

Applying the Distributive Property

 REVIEW CAPSULE

Simplify $4x + 3 + 2x + 9$.

Group like terms. → $(4x + 2x) + (3 + 9)$
Combine like terms. → $\quad 6x \quad + \quad 12$

EXAMPLE 1 Simplify $7(5x)$.

Associative property →
$$7(5x) = (7 \cdot 5)x$$
$$= \quad 35x$$

EXAMPLE 2 Simplify $(9y)3$.

Rearrange and regroup. →
$$(9y)3 = (9 \cdot 3)y$$
$$= \quad 27y$$

EXAMPLE 3 Simplify $7(4x + 5)$.

Distribute 7. →
$7(4x) = (7 \cdot 4)x = 28x$ →
$$7(4x + 5) = 7(4x) + 7(5)$$
$$= \quad 28x \quad + \quad 35$$

EXAMPLE 4 Simplify $6 + 7(3c + 2) + 4c$.

$$6 + 7(3c + 2) + 4c = 6 + 7(3c) + 7(2) + 4c$$
$$= 6 + \quad 21c \quad + \quad 14 \quad + 4c$$
$$= (21c + 4c) + (6 + 14)$$
$$= 25c + 20$$

EXAMPLE 5 Simplify $8 + (2y + 5)3 + 7y$.

$(2y + 5)3 = (2y)3 + (5)3$ →
$$8 + (2y + 5)3 + 7y$$
$$8 + (2y)3 + (5)3 + 7y$$
$$8 + 6y + 15 + 7y$$
$$(6y + 7y) + (8 + 15)$$
$$13y + 23$$

Thus, $8 + (2y + 5)3 + 7y = 13y + 23$.

ORAL EXERCISES

Simplify.

1. $8(3x)$ *24x*   **2.** $7(9r)$ *63r*   **3.** $5(4y)$ *20y*   **4.** $3(9z)$ *27z*   **5.** $7(4a)$ *28a*   **6.** $8(7x)$ *56x*

7. $3(2a + 5)$ **8.** $4(3x + 2)$ **9.** $7(5c + 4)$ **10.** $(1 + 9a)5$

    6a + 15   *12x + 8*   *35c + 28*   *5 + 45a*

EXERCISES

PART A

Simplify.

1. $7(1 + 5y) + 8y$ *43y + 7*   **2.** $4z + (2z + 5)3$ *10z + 15*

3. $(6m + 9)4 + 5m$ *29m + 36*   **4.** $9 + 3(2m + 8)$ *6m + 33*

5. $8c + 7(2 + 4c)$ *36c + 14*   **6.** $7b + (1 + 8b)6$ *55b + 6*

7. $3(9x + 4) + 2x$ *29x + 12*   **8.** $(5 + 2d)4 + 9$ *8d + 29*

9. $2r + 8(7 + 5r)$ *42r + 56*   **10.** $4 + (7n + 8)2$ *14n + 20*

11. $5(6 + 4y) + 7y$ *27y + 30*   **12.** $(2d + 8)7 + 9d$ *23d + 56*

13. $(1 + 7c)5 + 4c$ *39c + 5*   **14.** $3z + 6(4 + 8z)$ *51z + 24*

15. $9 + 2(4x + 1)$ *8x + 11*   **16.** $6(7a + 2) + 5a$ *47a + 12*

17. $2x + 4(6 + 2x) + 3x$ *13x + 24*   **18.** $5 + 7(4y + 3) + 5y$ *33y + 26*

19. $5 + (4c + 2)3 + 6c$ *18c + 11*   **20.** $3g + 5(7 + 4g) + 8$ *23g + 43*

21. $2x + 6 + (5 + 3x)4$ *14x + 26*   **22.** $4z + 8(7 + 3z) + 5$ *28z + 61*

PART B

Simplify.

23. $(5 + 6r)3 + (7 + 2r)2$ *22r + 29*   **24.** $5(7y + 3) + 9(1 + 2y)$ *53y + 24*

25. $4(6e + 5) + 2(7e + 9)$ *38e + 38*   **26.** $(8a + 9)3 + (4a + 2)7$ *52a + 41*

PART C

EXAMPLE   Simplify $2[5x + 4(2x + 3)]$.

Remove inner parentheses first by distributing 4. $\longrightarrow$

$$2[5x + 4(2x + 3)] = 2[5x + 4(2x) + 4(3)]$$
$$= 2(5x + \quad 8x \quad + \quad 12)$$
$$= 2(13x + 12)$$
$$= 2(13x) + 2(12)$$
$$= 26x + 24$$

Now distribute 2. $\longrightarrow$

Simplify.

27. $5[6c + 7(4c + 2)]$ **28.** $2a + 5[(6a + 8)2 + 3a]$

29. $7x + 4[2x + (5 + 3x)6]$ **30.** $6[2y + 3(2y + 4) + 1] + 3(5 + 8y)$

Chapter One Review

Compute. $[p.\ 1]$

1. $(7)(2) + 8$
2. $9 + (3)(4)$
3. $4 + (9)(0)$
4. $0 \cdot 4 + 6 + 8 \cdot 1$
5. $6 + 2(1) + 5 + 4(3)$
6. $5 + 2 \cdot 8 + 3 \cdot 2 + 6 + 5 \cdot 2$

Evaluate for the given values of the variables. $[p.\ 4]$

7. $9 + 7r$ if $r = 8$
8. $2d + 9$ if $d = 9$
9. $6 + 5x + 3y$ if $x = 4$, $y = 6$
10. $7a + 8 + 5b$ if $a = 1$, $b = 9$
11. $4g + 9h + 2$ if $g = 5$, $h = 7$
12. $8 + 4x + 7y$ if $x = 2$, $y = 8$

Name the terms and the variables. Then name the coefficient of each variable. $[p.\ 4]$

13. $5 + 9x$
14. $5y + 1 + 4z$
15. $8a + 7b + 2c$

Rewrite by using the commutative and associative properties. Then compute. $[p.\ 6]$

16. $2 + 57 + 28$
17. $23 + 9 + 7 + 41$
18. $422 + 36 + 24 + 38$
19. $(50)(47)(2)$
20. $97 \cdot 125 \cdot 8$
21. $(25)(41)(4)(2)$

Which property is illustrated? $[p.\ 6]$

22. $6 + 5 = 5 + 6$
23. $(7 \cdot 2) \cdot 6 = 7 \cdot (2 \cdot 6)$
24. $9 + (4 + x) = (9 + 4) + x$
25. $3(x + y) = (x + y)3$

Rewrite by using the distributive property. $[p.\ 9]$

26. $7(4 + 9)$
27. $(6 + 8)3$
28. $(5 + 2 + 6)9$
29. $8(3 + 7 + 5)$
30. $5(6) + 5(3)$
31. $(8)(9) + (9)(2)$
32. $(6)(7) + (7)(1) + (7)(6)$
33. $(4)(5) + (8)(4) + (3)(4) + (1)(4)$

34. Show $5(4 + 3 + 2) = 5 \cdot 4 + 5 \cdot 3 + 5 \cdot 2$.
35. Show $(1 + 5 + 9)3 = 1 \cdot 3 + 5 \cdot 3 + 9 \cdot 3$.

Simplify. $[p.\ 14,\ 16]$

36. $3x + 8 + 7x$
37. $9 + 4y + 8y$
38. $3t + 7 + 5t + 9$
39. $4p + 6q + 7p + 8q + 3$
40. $5r + 6(1 + 3r)$
41. $(6y + 8)3 + 2y$
42. $9(5p + 2) + 4p$
43. $8 + 2(7z + 3)$
44. $(3x + 5)4 + (8x + 7)6$
45. $5(9 + 3y) + 7(8 + 6y)$

Simplify. Then evaluate for the given values of the variables. $[p.\ 14]$

46. $7x + 9 + 3x$ if $x = 8$
47. $5 + 3y + 8 + 6y$ if $y = 2$
48. $4a + 3b + 6a + 7b$ if $a = 2$, $b = 1$
49. $4 + 3x + 7y + 9x + 4y$ if $x = 8$, $y = 6$

Chapter One Test

Compute.

1. $8 + (5)(6)$

2. $0 \cdot 4 + 7 + 5 \cdot 6$

3. $7(1) + 8 + 4(6)$

4. $7 + 3 \cdot 9 + 5 + 4 \cdot 6$

Evaluate for the given values of the variables.

5. $4 + 9y$ if $y = 7$

6. $2d + 12$ if $d = 7$

7. $6a + 2b + 4$ if $a = 3$, $b = 8$

Name the terms and the variables. Then name the coefficient of each variable.

8. $4 + 7x + 9y$

Rewrite by using the commutative and associative properties. Then compute.

9. $5 + 67 + 15$

10. $25 \cdot 58 \cdot 4$

11. $47 + 21 + 3 + 39$

12. $(50)(31)(2)(6)$

Which property is illustrated?

13. $(x + y) + z = x + (y + z)$

14. $12 + y = y + 12$

15. $b(5a) = (5a)b$

16. $(4 \cdot c) \cdot d = 4 \cdot (c \cdot d)$

Rewrite by using the distributive property.

17. $6(4 + 9)$

18. $(8 + 1 + 7)3$

19. $9(7) + 9(2)$

20. $(4)(5) + (5)(6) + (7)(5)$

21. Show $3(8 + 2 + 5) = 3 \cdot 8 + 3 \cdot 2 + 3 \cdot 5$.

22. Show $(4 + 1 + 6)7 = 4 \cdot 7 + 1 \cdot 7 + 6 \cdot 7$.

Simplify.

23. $6x + 7 + 3x$

24. $5y + 8 + 4z + 7y + 3z$

25. $2a + 4(7 + 5a)$

26. $7r + (6 + 2r)3 + 9$

27. $4(3x + 2) + 5(7x + 5)$

28. $(8y + 4)5 + (2y + 9)3$

Simplify. Then evaluate for the given values of the variables.

29. $3x + 7 + 9x$ if $x = 4$

30. $5a + 9 + 6b + 4a + 8b$ if $a = 5$, $b = 2$

Temperature

Temperature is measured in degrees Celsius (°C) in the metric system.

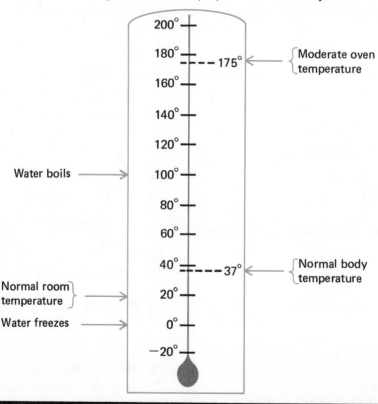

PROJECT

What is a good estimate of the temperature for the activity?

1. Wearing a sweater in the house   2. Swimming outdoors

3. Wearing woolen gloves   4. Burning toast

Adding Integers

REVIEW CAPSULE

Whole numbers on a number line

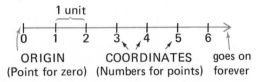

Each whole number *corresponds* to a point.

Addition on a number line

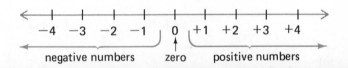

We can extend a number line to the left of 0.

Integers on a number line ⟶

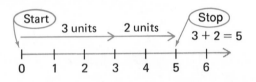

. . . means the numbers go
on forever.

The numbers, . . . , $-3, -2, -1, 0, +1, +2, +\cdot\cdot\cdot$
are *integers*.

Positive integers ⟶ $+1,$ $+2,$ $+3, . . .$
Read. ⟶ positive 1,   positive 2,   positive 3, and so on

Zero ⟶ 0 Zero is neither positive nor negative.

Negative integers ⟶ $-1,$ $-2,$ $-3, . . .$
Read. ⟶ negative 1,   negative 2,   negative 3, and so on

The regular sign + will be used
for positive integers.

To avoid confusion, we will use a heavy plus
sign + to show addition.

Adding positive integers is like adding whole numbers. For example,

Positive plus positive
Read. ——————————————————→ $+8 + +3 = +11$
Positive 8 plus positive 3 equals positive 11.

EXAMPLE 1

Add $-4 + -2$.

Negative plus negative
Read. ——————————————————→ Negative 4 plus negative 2

Start at 0. Move 4 units to the *left* to -4.
Then move 2 more units to the *left*.
The sum is -6.

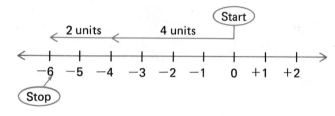

$$-4 + -2 = -6$$

EXAMPLE 2

Add $+4 + -5$.

Positive plus negative
Start at 0. Move 4 units to the *right* to $+4$.
Then move 5 units to the *left*.
The sum is -1.

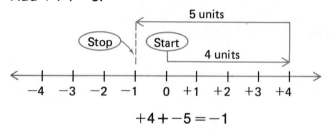

$$+4 + -5 = -1$$

EXAMPLE 3

Add $+5 + -3$.

Positive plus negative
Start at 0.
Move 5 right to $+5$.
Move 3 left.
The sum is $+2$.

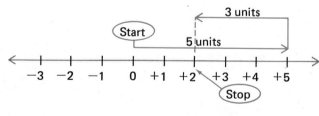

$$+5 + -3 = +2$$

EXAMPLE 4

Add $-3 + +7$.

Negative plus positive
Start at 0.
Move 3 left to -3.
Move 7 right.
The sum is $+4$.

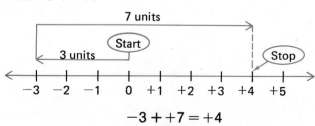

$$-3 + +7 = +4$$

EXERCISES

Add.

1. +3 + +7 *+10*
2. +8 + +5 *+13*
3. −6 + −8 *−14*
4. +4 + −2 *2*
5. −6 + −4 *−10*
6. −1 + +7 *+6*
7. +9 + −2 *+7*
8. −5 + −3 *−8*
9. +7 + −2 *+5*
10. +4 + +4 *+8*
11. +6 + −9 *−3*
12. −3 + −7 *−10*
13. +8 + −9 *−1*
14. +6 + −2 *+4*
15. −4 + −5 *−9*
16. +6 + +1 *7*
17. −4 + −6 *−10*
18. −6 + +2 *−4*
19. +5 + −9 *−4*
20. +3 + +6 *9*
21. −10 + −3 *−13*
22. +11 + +5 *+16*
23. +12 + −9 *+3*
24. −3 + +15 *12*
25. +13 + −8 *+5*
26. −17 + −2 *−19*
27. −16 + +5 *−11*
28. +8 + −19 *−11*
29. −14 + −9 *−23*
30. −6 + +17 *+11*
31. +13 + +7 *+20*
32. −18 + −8 *−26*

Add.

33. +4 + +5 *+9*
34. +5 + +4 *+9*
35. −6 + −1 *−7*
36. −1 + −6 *−7*
37. −3 + +8 *+5*
38. +8 + −3 *+5*
39. +2 + −6 *−4*
40. −6 + +2 *−4*
41. +9 + −3 *+6*
42. −3 + +9 *+6*
43. −8 + −2 *−10*
44. −2 + −8 *−10*
45. −2 + 0 *−2*
46. 0 + −2 *−2*
47. +8 + 0 *+8*
48. 0 + +8 *+18*

Add.

49. +6 + −6 *0*
50. −3 + +3 *0*
51. +8 + −8 *0*
52. −6 + +6 *0*
53. −5 + +5 *0*
54. +8 + −8 *0*
55. +3 + −3 *0*
56. −9 + +9 *0*

Add.

57. +10 + −32 *−22*
58. −27 + −31 *−58*
59. +46 + −22 *+24*
60. −38 + +28 *−10*
61. +46 + +21 *+67*
62. −37 + +56 *+19*
63. −62 + −19 *−81*
64. +45 + −45 *0*
65. −28 + +36 *+8*
66. +59 + −63 *−4*
67. +12 + −87 *−75*
68. −56 + −23 *−79*
69. −96 + −35 *−131*
70. +48 + −37 *+11*
71. −56 + +56 *0*
72. +43 + −39 *4*
73. +158 + −136 *+22*
74. +279 + +346 *+625*
75. −458 + −329 *−787*
76. +728 + −958 *−230*
77. −379 + +247 *−132*
78. −586 + −431 *−1,017*
79. +372 + +622 *+994*
80. −489 + +262 *−227*

For each case below, state a rule for addition of integers.

81. positive plus positive
82. negative plus negative
83. positive plus negative
84. negative plus positive

Add.

85. +.03 + −.86 *−.83*
86. −1.07 + +.83 *−.24*
87. −1.12 + +.046 *−1.074*
88. −2.03 + +1.42 *−1.61*
89. −.16 + +2.03 *1.87*
90. +2.06 + −6.04 *−3.98*
91. −28.4 + +114.03 *85.63*
92. −.0004 + +1.703 *1.7026*

Properties of Addition of Integers

 REVIEW CAPSULE

Adding Integers

Signs the same	Signs different
$+5 + +9 = +14$	$+8 + -3 = +5$
$-8 + -9 = -17$	$-6 + +4 = -2$

Commutative Property of Addition
$8 + 3 = 3 + 8$ ← Whole numbers
$-8 + +3 = +3 + -8$ ← Integers

EXAMPLE 1   Show that $(+4 + -6) + -3 = +4 + (-6 + -3)$.

$(+4 + -6) + -3$	$+4 + (-6 + -3)$
$-2 + -3$	$+4 + -9$
-5	-5

Add inside parentheses first. ⟶
Answers are the same. ⟶

Thus, $(-4 + -6) + -3 = +4 + (-6 + -3)$.

EXAMPLE 2   Draw a conclusion from these additions.

$$+6 + 0 = +6 \quad | \quad -4 + 0 = -4 \quad | \quad 0 + -6 = -6$$

Adding zero gives the same number.

The sum of any integer and zero is that integer.

Example 2 suggests this. ⟶
Zero is the additive identity.

Property of Additive Identity
$a + 0 = a$ and $0 + a = a$, for each number a.

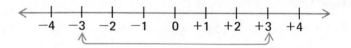

Opposites are the same distance from 0 on a number line.

-3 and $+3$ are opposites. 0 is its own opposite.

Read $-a$ as the opposite of a, or as the additive inverse of a.

The symbol $-a$ means the opposite of a, or the additive inverse of a.

EXAMPLE 3   For each value of *a*, give the value of −*a*.

−*a* (the opposite of *a*) can be positive, negative, or zero, depending upon the value of *a*.

a	*Answers* −*a*
+6	−6
−2	+2
0	0

EXAMPLE 4   Draw a conclusion from these additions.

$$+4 + -4 = 0 \qquad -2 + +2 = 0$$

The sum of any integer and its opposite is zero.

> **Property of Additive Inverses**
> $a + -a = 0$, for each number *a*.

SUMMARY

Commutative Property: $a + b = b + a$
Associative Property: $(a + b) + c = a + (b + c)$
Property of Additive Identity: $a + 0 = a$ and $0 + a = a$
Property of Additive Inverses: $a + -a = 0$

EXAMPLE 5   Which property of addition of integers is illustrated?

	Answers
$-6 + +6 = 0$	Additive Inverses
$0 + +8 = +8$	Additive Identity
$-7 + +2 = +2 + -7$	Commutative
$(-8 + -3) + +3$	
$\quad = -8 + (-3 + +3)$	Associative

ORAL EXERCISES

Give the opposite of each.

1. +2 *−2*   **2.** −6 *+6*   **3.** +10 *−10*   **4.** 0 *0*   **5.** −1 *+1*   **6.** −9 *+9*

7. +7 *−7*   **8.** −5 *+5*   **9.** +18 *−18*   **10.** −93 *+93*   **11.** +87 *−87*   **12.** −125 *+125*

13. −50 *+50*   **14.** +233 *−233*   **15.** −424 *+424*   **16.** *a* *−a*   **17.** −*x* *x*   **18.** −*n* *n*

19. Tell how to read the symbol −*x*. *the opposite of x*

20. Explain why the symbol −*a* should not be read as negative *a*.
−a is positive if a is negative.

EXERCISES

PART A

Compute to show that each statement is true.

1. $(+6 + -2) + -3 = +6 + (-2 + -3)$ *+1 = +1*
2. $(-7 + +4) + +8 = -7 + (+4 + +8)$ *+5 = +5*
3. $-10 + (-8 + +5) = (-10 + -8) + +5$ *-13 = -13*
4. $(-8 + +16) + -16 = -8 + (+16 + -16)$ *-8 = -8*

Which property of addition of integers is illustrated?

5. $+5 + -2 = -2 + +5$ *Comm.*
6. $-6 + +6 = 0$ *Add. Inv.*
7. $0 + +8 = +8$ *Add. Iden.*
8. $(+2 + -5) + +7 = +2 + (-5 + +7)$
9. $-9 + 0 = -9$ *Add. Iden.*
10. $+4 + -4 = 0$ *Add. Inv.*
11. $-7 + -4 = -4 + -7$ *Comm.*
12. $-8 + +3 = +3 + -8$ *Comm.*
13. $(-8 + +6) + +3 = -8 + (+6 + +3)$ *Assoc.*
14. $+15 + -15 = 0$ *Add. Inv.*
15. $x + -x = 0$ *Add. Inv.*
16. $y + 0 = y$ *Add. Iden.*
17. $c + d = d + c$ *Comm.*
18. $(x + y) + z = x + (y + z)$ *Assoc.*

PART B

Find the value of each.

19. $-x$ if $x = 3$ *-3*
20. $-b$ if $b = -5$ *+5*
21. a if $-a = -2$ *+2*
22. y if $-y = 8$ *-8*
23. z if $z = -7$ *-7*
24. n if $-n = 0$ *0*

Explain why each statement is true.

25. If x is negative, then $-x$ is positive. } *The opposite of a negative*
26. If $-x$ is negative, then $-(-x)$ is positive. } *number is positive.*

PART C

EXAMPLE   Prove $(-3 + +5) + -7 = (-7 + +5) + -3$.

Expression	Reason
$(-3 + +5) + -7$	Given
$-7 + (-3 + +5)$	Commutative Property
$-7 + (+5 + -3)$	Commutative Property
$(-7 + +5) + -3$	Associative Property

Prove.

27. $(-9 + +4) + -8 = (-8 + +4) + -9$
28. $(-6 + +7) + -5 = (-5 + +7) + -6$
29. $(-3 + +5) + +3 = +5$
30. $(-8 + -3) + +8 = -3$
31. $(x + y) + z = (z + y) + x$
32. $(-x + -y) + x = -y$

Probability

In tossing 3 coins $S = \{HHH, HHT, HTH, HTT, THH, THT, TTH, TTT\}$ and $P(2H) = \frac{3}{8}$.

PROBLEM

In tossing 2 dice, what is the probability that the sum is 7?

Sample Space for 2 dice

FIRST DIE

	1	2	3	4	5	6
1	2	3	4	5	6	⑦
2	3	4	5	6	⑦	8
3	4	5	6	⑦	8	9
4	5	6	⑦	8	9	10
5	6	⑦	8	9	10	11
6	⑦	8	9	10	11	12

SECOND DIE

Sum of dice

$P(\text{sum } 7) = \frac{6}{36}$, or $\frac{1}{6}$

PROJECT

1. A coin and a die are tossed. Find the sample space.

2. A die is rolled once. Find the sample space and $P(\text{even})$.

3. In tossing 2 dice, what is $P(\text{sum } 8)$? $P(\text{sum even})$?

4. In tossing 2 dice, what is $P(\text{both dice are same})$? $P(\text{sum } 0)$?

Multiplying Integers

OBJECTIVES
- To multiply two integers
- To compute expressions like (+8) (−3) (+5) (−2)

 REVIEW CAPSULE

Multiplying positive integers is like multiplying whole numbers.

Whole numbers	Positive integers
(3) (4) = 12	(+3) (+4) = +12
(1) (7) = 7	(+1) (+7) = +7
(8) (2) = 16	(+8) (+2) = +16

The Review Capsule suggests this rule. →
(+) (+) = +

The product of two positive numbers is a positive number.

$$\text{positive} \times \text{positive} = \text{positive}$$

EXAMPLE 1   Draw a conclusion from these multiplications.

$$(+3)\,(0) = 0 \qquad (0)\,(-4) = 0 \qquad (0)\,(0) = 0$$
The product of any number and 0 is 0.

Example 1 suggests this. ————→

Property of Zero for Multiplication
$a \cdot 0 = 0$ and $0 \cdot a = 0$, for each number a.

EXAMPLE 2   Determine a logical answer for the product (+5) (−3).

Start with this expression: (+5) (−3 + +3). Simplify it.

$$+5\,(-3 + +3)$$
$$+5\,(0)$$
$$0$$

−3 + +3 = 0 ————————→

So, $+5\,(-3 + +3) = 0.$
$$(+5)\,(-3) + (+5)\,(+3) = 0$$

Distribute +5. ————————→
The result is still 0.
What number plus +15 equals 0?
Answer: −15 ————————→

$$\boxed{} + +15 = 0$$
$$\boxed{-15} + +15 = 0$$

Thus, $(+5)\,(-3) = -15.$

EXAMPLE 3 Determine a logical answer for the product $(-3)(+5)$.

Use the commutative property.

$$(-3)(+5) = (+5)(-3)$$
$$= -15 \qquad \textbf{Thus, } (-3)(+5) = -15$$

Examples 2 and 3 suggest this rule. ⟶
$(+)(-) = -$ ─────────────⟶
$(-)(+) = -$ ─────────────⟶

> The product of a positive number and a negative number is a negative number.
> positive × negative = negative
> negative × positive = negative

EXAMPLE 4 Multiply $(+8)(-4)$.   Multiply $(-5)(+7)$.

$(+)(-) = -$ $(-)(+) = -$

$$(+8)(-4) = -32 \qquad\qquad (-5)(+7) = -35$$

EXAMPLE 5 Determine a logical answer for the product $(-4)(-9)$.

Start with this expression: $-4(-9 + +9)$.
Simplify it.

$$-4(-9 + +9)$$
$$-4(0)$$
$$0$$

So, $\qquad -4(-9 + +9) = 0.$

Distribute -4. ─────────────⟶

$$(-4)(-9) + (-4)(+9) = 0$$

What number plus -36 equals 0? ⟶
Answer: $+36$

$$\boxed{} + -36 = 0$$
$$\boxed{+36} + -36 = 0$$

Thus, $(-4)(-9) = +36.$

Example 5 suggests this rule. ─────⟶

$(-)(-) = +$ ─────────────⟶

> The product of two negative numbers is a positive number.
> negative × negative = positive

EXAMPLE 6 Multiply $(-8)(-7)$.

$(-)(-) = +$ ─────────────⟶

$$(-8)(-7) = +56$$

SUMMARY   **Like signs give a positive product.**
$$(+)(+) = + \qquad (-)(-) = +$$

Unlike signs give a negative product.
$$(+)(-) = - \qquad (-)(+) = -$$

ORAL EXERCISES

Is the product positive or negative?

1. $(+100)(-25)$ **2.** $(-80)(-90)$ **3.** $(+15)(+15)$ **4.** $(-37)(+83)$
      neg.   *pos.*   *pos.*   *neg.*

EXERCISES

PART A

Multiply.

1. $(+3)(+7)$ $+21$ **2.** $(-2)(+4)$ -8 **3.** $(+6)(-8)$ -48 **4.** $(-3)(-1)$ $+3$

5. $(-5)(+9)$ -45 **6.** $(-1)(0)$ 0 **7.** $(+7)(-4)$ -28 **8.** $(0)(+6)$ 0

9. $(+7)(-1)$ -7 **10.** $(-5)(-6)$ $+30$ **11.** $(-8)(+2)$ -16 **12.** $(-9)(0)$ 0

13. $(+3)(+9)$ $+27$ **14.** $(-7)(+6)$ -42 **15.** $(0)(-4)$ 0 **16.** $(-6)(-1)$

17. $(+1)(-8)$ -8 **18.** $(-3)(-9)$ $+27$ **19.** $(+6)(+10)$ $+60$ **20.** $(+5)(-12)$

21. $(-9)(-8)$ $+72$ **22.** $(0)(-12)$ 0 **23.** $(+3)(-6)$ -18 **24.** $(+10)(+13)$

25. $(-20)(0)$ 0 **26.** $(-5)(+14)$ -70 **27.** $(-25)(-4)$ $+100$ **28.** $(-7)(-11)$

29. $(0)(+36)$ 0 **30.** $(-6)(+6)$ -36 **31.** $(+10)(-10)$ -100 **32.** $(-8)(+12)$

33. $(+13)(-3)$ -39 **34.** $(-12)(+4)$ -48 **35.** $(+15)(-8)$ -120 **36.** $(-26)(0)$

37. $(+16)(-2)$ -32 **38.** $(-15)(+5)$ -75 **39.** $(-36)(-2)$ $+72$ **40.** $(0)(-40)$

41. $(+5)(+50)$ $+250$ **42.** $(-30)(-4)$ $+120$ **43.** $(+60)(-8)$ -480 **44.** $(-65)(-2)$

45. $(+80)(-9)$ -720 **46.** $(+41)(+1)$ $+41$ **47.** $(-40)(+40)$ $-1,600$ **48.** $(-1)(-89)$

49. $(-18)(-50)$ $+900$ **50.** $(+42)(-13)$ -546 **51.** $(0)(+72)$ 0 **52.** $(+63)(-63)$
                                                                     $-3,969$

PART B

EXAMPLE   Multiply $(-2)(+8)(-5)(+6)$.

Multiplication can be done in any order. $\longrightarrow$

$$(-2)(+8)(-5)(+6) = \underbrace{(-2)(-5)}\,\underbrace{(+8)(+6)}$$
$$= \quad (+10) \qquad (+48)$$
$$= \quad +480$$

Multiply.

53. $(-6)(+3)(-5)$ $+90$ **54.** $(+8)(-2)(-3)$ $+48$

55. $(-6)(+8)(+3)(-1)$ $+144$ **56.** $(+9)(-7)(-3)(+5)$ $+945$

57. $(+3)(-7)(+8)(-9)$ $+1,512$ **58.** $(+6)(0)(-7)(-9)$ 0

59. $(-3)(+8)(-5)(+6)(-7)$ $-5,040$ **60.** $(+8)(+3)(-9)(-1)(+5)$ $+1,080$

PART C

Give two examples to illustrate each property for integers.

61. Commutative property of multiplication   **62.** Associative property of multiplication   **63.** Distributive property of multiplication over addition

Dividing Integers

 REVIEW CAPSULE

Multiplication and division are related operations.

Multiplication	Division
(3) (2) = 6	$6 \div 2 = 3$, or $\dfrac{6}{2} = 3$
(5) (9) = 45	$45 \div 9 = 5$, or $\dfrac{45}{9} = 5$
(6) (8) = 48	$48 \div 8 = 6$, or $\dfrac{48}{8} = 6$

The product 3 times 2 is 6.
The quotient 6 divided by 2 is 3.

EXAMPLE 1 Divide $+8 \div +2$.   Divide $-10 \div -5$.

Start with this division sentence.
Write a related multiplication. ⟶
Replace the □ to make the sentence true. ⟶

$$+8 \div +2 = \square$$
$$(\square)(+2) = +8$$
$$\downarrow$$
$$(+4)(+2) = +8$$
Thus, $+8 \div +2 = +4$,
or $\dfrac{+8}{+2} = +4$.

$$-10 \div -5 = \square$$
$$(\square)(-5) = -10$$
$$\downarrow$$
$$(+2)(-5) = -10$$
Thus, $-10 \div -5 = +2$,
or $\dfrac{-10}{-5} = +2$.

Example 1 suggests this rule. ⟶

$\dfrac{(+)}{(+)} = +; \dfrac{(-)}{(-)} = +$ ⟶

The quotient of two numbers with like signs is a positive number.

$$\dfrac{positive}{positive} = positive \qquad \dfrac{negative}{negative} = positive$$

EXAMPLE 2 Divide $\dfrac{+15}{+3}$.   Divide $-16 \div -2$.

$$\dfrac{+15}{+3} = +5$$

$$-16 \div -2 = +8$$

EXAMPLE 3 Divide $-18 \div +3$.   Divide $+24 \div -6$.

Start with this division sentence.

Write a related multiplication. ⟶

$$-18 \div +3 = \square \qquad\qquad +24 \div -6 = \square$$
$$(\square)\,(+3) = -18 \qquad\qquad (\square)\,(-6) = +24$$

Replace the $\square$. ⟶

$$(-6)\,(+3) = -18 \qquad\qquad (-4)\,(-6) = +24$$

Thus, $-18 \div +3 = -6$,   **Thus,** $+24 \div -6 = -4$,

or $\dfrac{-18}{+3} = -6$.   or $\dfrac{+24}{-6} = -4$.

Example 3 suggests this rule. ⟶

> The quotient of two numbers with unlike signs is a negative number.

$\dfrac{(-)}{(+)} = -;\ \dfrac{(+)}{(-)} = -$ ⟶

> $\dfrac{\text{negative}}{\text{positive}} = \text{negative}$ $\dfrac{\text{positive}}{\text{negative}} = \text{negative}$

EXAMPLE 4   Divide $\dfrac{-20}{+4}$.   Divide $+21 \div -7$.

$$\dfrac{-20}{+4} = -5 \qquad\qquad\qquad +21 \div -7 = -3$$

SUMMARY   **Like signs give a positive quotient.**

$$\dfrac{(+)}{(+)} = + \qquad \dfrac{(-)}{(-)} = +$$

Unlike signs give a negative quotient.

$$\dfrac{(+)}{(-)} = - \qquad \dfrac{(-)}{(+)} = -$$

The rules for division of integers are the same as for multiplication.

ORAL EXERCISES

Is the quotient positive or negative?

1. $+76 \div +19$ 2. $-84 \div -21$ 3. $-75 \div +25$ 4. $+100 \div -20$ 5. $-800 \div -400$

6. $\dfrac{+125}{-25}$ 7. $\dfrac{-216}{-24}$ 8. $\dfrac{-527}{+527}$ 9. $\dfrac{+800}{+200}$ 10. $\dfrac{-1,926}{-18}$

EXERCISES

PART A

Divide.

1. $\dfrac{+8}{+4}$ *+2*
2. $\dfrac{-12}{+3}$ *-4*
3. $\dfrac{+35}{-7}$ *-5*
4. $\dfrac{-72}{-9}$ *+8*
5. $\dfrac{+28}{+4}$ *+7*
6. $\dfrac{-46}{+2}$

7. $\dfrac{-45}{-5}$ *+9*
8. $\dfrac{+8}{-8}$ *-1*
9. $\dfrac{-81}{+9}$ *-9*
10. $\dfrac{+100}{-25}$ *-4*
11. $\dfrac{0}{+9}$ *0*
12. $\dfrac{+85}{+5}$

13. $\dfrac{-60}{-10}$ *+6*
14. $\dfrac{-56}{+8}$ *-7*
15. $\dfrac{+21}{+7}$ *+3*
16. $\dfrac{-25}{-5}$ *+5*
17. $\dfrac{+44}{+11}$ *+4*
18. $\dfrac{-80}{+16}$

19. $\dfrac{-72}{+24}$ *-3*
20. $\dfrac{+45}{-9}$ *-5*
21. $\dfrac{-30}{-30}$ *+1*
22. $\dfrac{-42}{+7}$ *-6*
23. $\dfrac{+60}{+12}$ *+5*
24. $\dfrac{-32}{-8}$

25. $\dfrac{+42}{-1}$ *-42*
26. $\dfrac{-36}{+6}$ *-6*
27. $\dfrac{-52}{+13}$ *-4*
28. $\dfrac{-48}{-6}$ *+8*
29. $\dfrac{+49}{+7}$ *+7*
30. $\dfrac{+38}{-19}$

Divide.

31. $-63 \div +7$ *-9*
32. $+48 \div -12$ *-4*
33. $-72 \div +9$ *-8*
34. $-64 \div -8$

35. $+45 \div +3$ *+15*
36. $-50 \div +5$ *-10*
37. $-65 \div -13$ *+5*
38. $-49 \div +7$

Divide.

39. $+6 \div +1$ *+6*
40. $-8 \div +1$ *-8*
41. $-32 \div +1$ *-32*
42. $+46 \div +1$

43. $+9 \div +9$ *+1*
44. $-7 \div -7$ *+1*
45. $+12 \div +12$ *+1*
46. $-38 \div -38$

PART B

EXAMPLE Compute $-72 \div (+24 \div -3)$.

Divide within the parentheses first. $\longrightarrow$

$$-72 \div (+24 \div -3)$$
$$-72 \div -8$$
$$+9$$

Compute.

47. $-27 \div (-18 \div +6)$ *+9*
48. $-32 \div (-28 \div +7)$ *+8*
49. $(+10 \div -2) \div -5$ *+1*
50. $-60 \div (+48 \div -4)$ *+5*
51. $(-36 \div -4) \div -3$ *-3*
52. $+72 \div (-12 \div +3)$ *-18*
53. $(+100 \div -5) \div +4$ *-5*
54. $(+90 \div +3) \div -10$ *-3*
55. $-16 \div (-32 \div -4)$ *-2*
56. $+56 \div (+35 \div -5)$ *-8*

PART C

Compute.

57. $-.42 \div (+21 \div -.01)$
58. $(+8.1 \div -.003) \div +.09$

Using Integers

Integers can be used to describe many everyday situations.

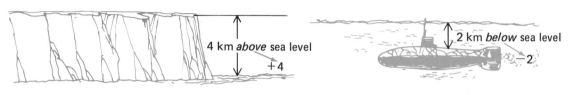

4 km *above* sea level
+4

2 km *below* sea level
-2

Deposit of $300	50 soldiers discharged from the Army	$5,000 loss in sales
+300	-50	-5,000

PROBLEM 1.

A submarine, located 60 meters below sea level, rose 15 meters. It then fired a rocket that climbed 240 meters. Find the level reached by the rocket.

To find the level reached by the rocket, add integers.

Begin with the location of the submarine.

Below   rose   rocket climbed

$$-60 + {+15} + {+240}$$
$$-60 + {+255}$$
$$+195$$

+195 means above sea level. ⟶

Thus, the rocket reached a level of 195 meters above sea level.

PROJECT

1. A submarine, located 80 m below sea level, rose 40 m. It then fired a rocket that climbed 100 m. Find the level reached by the rocket.

2. One month Lee's weight changes were a gain of 3 kg, a loss of 2 kg, a gain of 4 kg, and a loss of 5 kg. What was the net change?

PROBLEM 2.

The Shinskis had $175 in a checking account. They made deposits of $15, $45, and $60. They need to write checks for $100, $85, and $205. Can they do this?

Balance   deposit   withdrawal

$$+175 + \overbrace{+15 + +45 + +60} + \overbrace{-100 + -85 + -205}$$

$$+175 + \qquad +120 \qquad + \qquad -390$$

$$+295 + -390$$
$$-95$$

-95 means the account would be overdrawn.

Thus, they cannot write the checks.

PROJECT

3. The Carlsons had $300 in a checking account. They made deposits of $30, $70, and $100. They need to write checks for $200, $125, $20, and $130. Can they do this?

4. The population of a city was 32,000. Over the next 4 years, a planning committee recorded these population changes: gain of 3,000, loss of 4,000, gain of 6,000, loss of 5,000. Find the net change in population.

5. Several months ago, a certain bread sold for $.65 a loaf. In the meantime, the bread underwent several price changes: dropped $.04, rose $.03, rose $.02, dropped $.04. What is the current price of the bread?

6. A plane was flying at an altitude of 8,000 m. During the next 4 hours, these altitude changes were recorded: dropped 1,000 m, rose 2,000 m, dropped 500 m, rose 1,500 m. At what altitude was the plane flying then?

A New Look at Addition

REVIEW CAPSULE

Commutative Property of Addition
$$+6 + -2 = -2 + +6$$

Associative Property of Addition
$$(-4 + -8) + +3 = -4 + (-8 + +3)$$

EXAMPLE 1   Add $6 + -13$.

6 is like $+6$. ← (positive 6)
Read $6 + -13$ as

positive 6 plus negative 13.

Thus, $6 + -13 = -7$.

EXAMPLE 2   Add $-9 + 12$.

12 is like $+12$. ← (positive 12)

Thus, $-9 + 12 = 3$. ← (positive 3)

EXAMPLE 3   Add $(-18 + +25) + -2$.

Associative property ⟶
Commutative property ⟶
Associative property ⟶

$$(-18 + +25) + -2 = -18 + (+25 + -2)$$
$$= -18 + (-2 + +25)$$
$$= (-18 + -2) + +25$$
$$= \quad -20 \quad + +25$$
$$= +5, \text{ or } 5$$

We can shorten our work in Example 3.

$$(-18 + +25) + -2$$

Use the associative and commutative properties to group negatives together. ⟶

$$(-18 + -2) \quad + +25$$
$$-20 \quad + +25$$
$$+5, \text{ or } 5$$

EXAMPLE 4   Add $-3 + +8 + -7$.

$$-3 + +8 \;\; + -7$$
$$(-3 + -7) + +8$$
$$-10 \qquad + +8$$
$$-2$$

Group negatives together. ——————→

Thus, $-3 + +8 + -7 = -2$.

In Example 4 we added these three numbers.

$$-3 \qquad +8 \qquad -7$$

To simplify our writing, we will agree that we can omit the + signs when adding. That is,

The heavy plus signs are not written but are understood. ——————→

$$-3 +8 -7 \qquad \text{will mean}$$

Read. ——————→

negative 3 *plus* positive 8 *plus* negative 7

EXAMPLE 5   Read $-5 +6 -4$.

$$-5 +6 -4$$

Read. ——————→

negative 5 *plus* positive 6 *plus* negative 4

EXAMPLE 6   Read $8 -3x$.

8 means +8. + is understood. ——————→

$$8 -3x \text{ means } +8 + (-3)x$$

**Thus, $8 -3x$ is read as
positive 8 *plus* negative 3 times x.**

EXAMPLE 7   Compute $8 -7 +9$.

$$8 -7 +9 \text{ means } +8 + -7 + +9.$$

Group positives together. ——————→

$$+8 + -7 + +9 = (+8 + +9) + -7$$
$$= \qquad +17 \qquad + -7$$
$$= \qquad +10, \text{ or } 10$$

We can shorten our work in Example 7.

$$8 - 7 + 9 = (8 + 9) - 7$$
$$= \qquad 17 \qquad - 7$$
$$= \qquad 10$$

EXAMPLE 8 Compute $-5 + 8 - 6 + 4$.

Addition can be done in any order.

$$-5 + 8 - 6 + 4 = \underbrace{-5 - 6}_{} + \underbrace{8 + 4}_{}$$
$$= -11 + 12$$
$$= +1, \text{ or } 1$$

We have seen that problems like $7 - 5$ may be interpreted as addition problems.

$7 - 5$ means $+7 + -5$

These problems look like subtraction problems, but we can think of them as addition of positive and negative numbers. We will study the operation of subtraction on pages 50 and 51.

ORAL EXERCISES

Read. → *positive 3 plus negative 8*

1. $3 - 8$ **2.** $-7 + 6$ **3.** $-5 - 9$ **4.** $2 + 8$
5. $4 - 3 + 10$ **6.** $-8 + 12 - 7$ **7.** $-3 - 1 - 6$ **8.** $3 - 7 + 9$
9. $-8 + 3z - 1$ **10.** $-4x - 3$ **11.** $6x - 5y + 1$ **12.** $7x - 5y - 3$

negative 8 plus positive 3 times z plus negative 1

EXERCISES

PART A

Compute.

1. $4 - 10$ *−6*   **2.** $-9 + 3$ *−6*   **3.** $5 + 8$ *13*   **4.** $-3 - 9$ *−12*
5. $-6 - 9 + 15$ *0*   **6.** $5 + 6 - 17$ *−6*   **7.** $-16 - 31 + 3$ *−44*   **8.** $-28 + 3 + 42$
9. $-15 - 9 + 36$ *12*   **10.** $-12 + 5 - 2$ *−9*   **11.** $18 - 13 + 2$ *7*   **12.** $-42 + 7 + 16$
13. $-5 + 3 + 21$ *19*   **14.** $-36 - 8 + 14$ *−30*   **15.** $16 + 8 - 14$ *10*   **16.** $21 - 7 - 23$
17. $58 - 39 - 2$ *17*   **18.** $18 - 47 - 12$ *−41*   **19.** $-36 + 17 - 2$ *−21*   **20.** $42 - 17 - 36$
21. $-22 + 12 + 15$ *5*   **22.** $63 - 47 + 17$ *+33*   **23.** $65 - 2 - 29$ *34*   **24.** $-38 - 9 + 46$

PART B

Compute.

25. $-28 + 36 - 43 - 91$ *−126*   **26.** $-81 + 49 - 38 + 16$ *−54*   **27.** $76 - 85 - 79 + 5$ *−83*
28. $47 - 13 - 68 + 17$ *−17*   **29.** $31 - 57 + 14 + 28$ *16*   **30.** $68 - 79 - 85 - 31$ *−127*
31. $-56 + 14 - 72 + 12$ *−102*   **32.** $72 - 36 + 41 + 13$ *90*   **33.** $-62 - 58 + 43 - 17$ *−94*
34. $29 - 45 - 62 + 73$ *−5*   **35.** $58 - 46 + 71 - 83$ *0*   **36.** $-105 + 56 + 63 - 21$ *−7*

Magic Squares

In ancient China and India the people often wore jewelry which was assumed to contain mystical powers. One such ornament was the magic square.

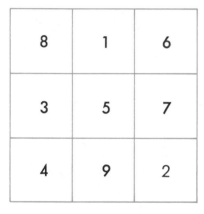

8	1	6
3	5	7
4	9	2

The sum of the numbers along any row, column, or diagonal is 15.

PROJECT Arrange the numbers 1 to 16 in each of these 4 × 4 squares to make magic squares.

1.

1		7	
	13		11
10		16	
	6		4

2.

16			
			8
		7	
4			1

Evaluating Expressions

OBJECTIVES
- To evaluate expressions like $-6x + 5y - 3z$ if $x = -2$, $y = -4$, $z = -3$
- To simplify expressions like $(7x + 3y)\, 2 + 3x + 4$ then evaluate if $x = -3$, $y = -4$

▶ REVIEW CAPSULE

$4 - 7$ means $+4 + -7$
$7 - 6 + 2$ means $+7 + -6 + +2$
$-3 + 8 - 6$ means $-3 + +8 + -6$
$4x - 5$ means $(+4)\,(x) + -5$
$6 - 5a$ means $+6 + (-5)\,(a)$
$2x - 6y$ means $(+2)\,(x) + (-6)\,(y)$

EXAMPLE 1   Evaluate $4x - 3$ if $x = 7$.

Read: positive 4 times x
 plus negative 3. ⟶
Substitute $+7$ for x. ⟶
Multiply first. Then add. ⟶
We can omit the +. ⟶

$$
\begin{aligned}
4x - 3 &= (+4)\,(x) & + -3 \\
&= (+4)\,(+7) & + -3 \\
&= \quad +28 & + -3 \\
&= \quad\quad +28 - 3 \\
&= \quad\quad\quad +25
\end{aligned}
$$

EXAMPLE 2   Evaluate $-6 + 5a$ if $a = 3$.

$5a$ means $(+5)\,(a)$. ⟶

$(+)\,(+) = (+)$ ⟶
$-6 + 15 = +9$, or 9 ⟶

$$
\begin{aligned}
-6 + 5a &= -6 + (5)\,(a) \\
&= -6 + (5)\,(3) \\
&= -6 \quad + 15 \\
&= \quad\quad 9
\end{aligned}
$$

EXAMPLE 3   Evaluate $2x - 6y$ if $x = -3$ and $y = -1$.

$2x$ means $(+2)\,(x)$. ⟶

$(+)\,(-) = (-)$ $(-)\,(-) = (+)$ ⟶

$$
\begin{aligned}
2x - 6y &= (2)\,(x) & + (-6)\,(y) \\
&= (2)\,(-3) & + (-6)\,(-1) \\
&= \quad -6 & +6 \\
&= \quad 0
\end{aligned}
$$

EXAMPLE 4   Evaluate $-5a - 8b + 7c$ if $a = -1$, $b = -3$, $c = -4$.

$$
\begin{aligned}
-5a - 8b + 7c &= (-5)\,(a) & + (-8)\,(b) & + (7)\,(c) \\
&= (-5)\,(-1) & + (-8)\,(-3) & + (7)\,(-4) \\
&= \quad 5 & +24 & -28 \\
&= \quad 1
\end{aligned}
$$

Add 5 and 24 first, then add -28.

EXERCISES

PART A

Evaluate for the given values of the variables.

1. $6x + 2$ if $x = 2$ *14*
2. $7g + 9$ if $g = 5$ *44*
3. $5a + 3$ if $a = -1$ *−2*
4. $-3x - 5$ if $x = -2$ *1*
5. $7c - 2d$ if $c = 3, d = 5$ *11*
6. $8r - 7s$ if $r = 7, s = 7$ *7*
7. $-5y + 4z$ if $y = -4, z = -2$ *12*
8. $-2k - 5t$ if $k = -4, t = -6$ *38*
9. $7e - 3f$ if $e = 6, f = -7$ *63*
10. $-5m + 3n$ if $m = -5, n = 1$ *28*
11. $4x + 5y + 3z$ if $x = 1, y = -2, z = 3$ *3*
12. $6r - 9s - 5t$ if $r = 6, s = -2, t = -8$ *94*
13. $-8e + 7f - 4g$ if $e = 3, f = -4, g = -5$ *−32*
14. $-2p - 8q + 6r$ if $p = -2, q = -9, r = -6$ *40*
15. $4f + 7g - 2h$ if $f = -5, g = -8, h = -4$ *−68*
16. $-7d + 8e - 3f$ if $d = -3, e = 7, f = -6$ *95*
17. $7a - 2b + 9c$ if $a = -1, b = -7, c = -9$ *−74*

PART B

EXAMPLE   Simplify $(6x + 3y)2 + 7x + 4$. Then evaluate if $x = -3$ and $y = -7$.

$$(6x + 3y)2 + 7x + 4$$

Distribute 2. $\longrightarrow$ $$(6x)(2) + (3y)(2) + 7x + 4$$
$$12x + 6y + 7x + 4$$

Combine like terms. $\longrightarrow$ $$19x + 6y + 4$$

Substitute −3 for x, −7 for y. $\longrightarrow$ $$(19)(-3) + 6(-7) + 4$$
$$-57 - 42 + 4$$
$$-99 + 4$$
$$-95$$

Simplify. Then evaluate if $x = -5$, $y = 3$, and $z = -1$.

18. $4(7x + 3y) + 6x + 2$ *−132*
19. $9 + 3(5x + 2y) + 7$ *−41*
20. $8 + 4z + 2(3x + 5z)$ *−36*
21. $(4y + 3z)8 + 7y + 1$ *94*
22. $(7x + 3y)4 + 8x + 9y$ *−117*
23. $6z + 2(9y + 3z) + 8y + 5$ *71*
24. $2(6x + 3y + 2z) + 8y + 4z$ *−26*
25. $(6x + 9z)4 + 5(7x + 8y)$ *−211*

PART C

Simplify. Then evaluate if $x = -2$ and $y = 3$. [Hint: Work within brackets first.]

26. $3[2x + 4(3y + 8)]$
27. $7x + 2[4 + 3(x + 6y)]$

Combining Like Terms

▶ REVIEW CAPSULE

Combine like terms.

$$3x + 5x = 8x$$
$$6a + 3a = 9a$$
$$5c + 2 + 8c = 13c + 2$$

EXAMPLE 1   Simplify $-2x + 5x$.

$-2x$ and $+5x$ are like terms.
Use the distributive property. ⟶

$$-2x + 5x = (-2 + 5)x$$
$$= 3x$$

Thus, $-2x + 5x = 3x$.

EXAMPLE 2   Simplify $8a - 3a$.

To combine like terms,
add the coefficients. ⟶

$$8a - 3a = (8 - 3)a$$
$$= 5a$$

EXAMPLE 3   Simplify $-5b - 9b$.

$$-5b - 9b = -14b$$

EXAMPLE 4   Simplify $4y - 9 - 7y + 14$.

Group like terms. ⟶

$$4y - 9 - 7y + 14 = \underbrace{4y - 7y}\ \underbrace{-9 + 14}$$
$$= -3y + 5$$

EXAMPLE 5   Simplify $6x - 4 - 2y - 9x + 7y - 8$.

$$6x - 4 - 2y - 9x + 7y - 8$$
$$\underbrace{6x - 9x}\ \underbrace{-2y + 7y}\ \underbrace{-4 - 8}$$
$$-3x + 5y - 12$$

EXERCISES

PART A

Simplify.

1. $-3y + 8y$ $5y$

2. $4a - 7a$ $-3a$

3. $-6b + 8b$ $2b$

4. $-9x - 2x$ $-11x$

5. $-7z + 5z$ $-2z$

6. $-4c - 7c$ $-11c$

7. $-8r + 3r$ $-5r$

8. $-5y - 5y$ $-10y$

9. $2r - 9r$ $-7r$

10. $4x - 5 - 2x$ $2x - 5$

11. $5z - 8 - 9z$ $-4z - 8$

12. $-7c - 8 - 5c$

13. $-5q - 9 + 3q$ $-2q - 9$

14. $8x - 4 - 3x$ $5x - 4$

15. $-6y - 4 - 3y$

16. $7 - 5t + 9 + 7t$ $2t + 16$

17. $-4x + 3 - 8x - 2$

18. $-6y + 3 + 8 - 7y$

$-12x + 1$

Simplify.

19. $6x - 2y - 4x + 3 + 8y$ $2x + 6y + 3$

20. $5a + 3b - 4 - 7a - 6b$ $-2a - 3b - 4$

21. $-5r - 9s + 9r + 3s - 6$ $4r - 6s - 6$

22. $3p - 7q - 5 + 9q - 7p$ $-4p + 2q - 5$

23. $-9x + 8 - 3y - 5x + 7y$ $-14x + 4y + 8$

24. $4d - 5 - 8d + 3e - 6$ $-4d + 3e - 11$

25. $-6x + 9y - 4 - 4x - 6y$ $-10x + 3y - 4$

26. $4j - 7k + 2 - 9j - 8$ $-5j - 7k - 6$

27. $-9 + 8a - 4c - 7 + 5a$ $13a - 4c - 16$

28. $-8q + 9s - 2 + 6q - 4s$ $-2q + 5s - 2$

29. $6b - 7 - 4a + 8 - 3b - 2a$ $-6a + 3b + 1$

30. $-7a + 4 - 5a + 6b + 4a - 2b$

$-8a + 4b + 4$

PART B

EXAMPLE   Simplify $-3x - 5 + 8y - 4x - 4y$. Then evaluate if $x = -4$ and $y = -9$.

Regroup. $\longrightarrow$

Combine like terms. $\longrightarrow$

Substitute -4 for x, -9 for y. $\longrightarrow$

$$-3x - 5 + 8y - 4x - 4y$$
$$\underbrace{-3x - 4x} + \underbrace{8y - 4y} - 5$$
$$-7x \qquad +4y \quad -5$$
$$-7(-4) + 4(-9) - 5$$
$$28 \qquad -36 \quad -5$$
$$28 - 41$$
$$-13$$

Simplify. Then evaluate for $x = -2$, $y = -3$, and $z = 8$.

31. $5x - 3 + 8y - 2y - 3x$ -25

32. $-4z + 8 - 2x - 9z + 8x$ -108

33. $-3x + 7y - 4z + 9x - 3y$ -56

34. $-7z - 8y - 3x - 4y + 5z$ 26

35. $-6x + 3 + 2y - 9 - 5x + 4y$ -2

36. $-8y + 4z + 2y - 7 - 9z - 2y$ -23

PART C

Simplify. Then evaluate for $x = -.3$, $y = 2.5$, and $z = .004$.

37. $1.5x - 4 + .007y - 1.2y - .3x$

38. $2.4 - .08x + .3y - .1 + 3.02z - .7x$

$(1)(a) = a$ and $(-1)(a) = -a$

 REVIEW CAPSULE

Simplify $4x - 7 + 5x$.

$$4x - 7 + 5x = 4x + 5x - 7$$
$$= 9x - 7$$

EXAMPLE 1 Draw a conclusion from these multiplications.

$(1)(6) = 6 \quad\vdots\quad (1)(-2) = -2 \quad\vdots\quad (8)(1) = 8$

The product of one and any number is that number.

Example 1 suggests this. ⟶
One is the multiplicative identity.

Property of Multiplicative Identity
$(1)(a) = a$ and $(a)(1) = a$, for each number a.

EXAMPLE 2 Draw a conclusion from these multiplications.

−5 is the opposite of 5. ⟶ $(-1)(5) = -5 \quad\vdots\quad (-1)(-4) = 4 \quad\vdots\quad (7)(-1) = -7$

The product of negative one and any number is the opposite (additive inverse) of the number.

Example 2 suggests this. ⟶

Multiplication Property of −1
$(-1)(a) = -a$ and $(a)(-1) = -a$,
for each number a.

EXAMPLE 3 Simplify $6a + 2a + a$.

Replace a with $1a$. ⟶ $6a + 2a + 1a = 9a$

EXAMPLE 4 Simplify $-9 + 3b + 4 - b$.

Replace $-b$ with $-1b$. ⟶ $-9 + 3b + 4 - 1b$
Rearrange terms. ⟶ $3b - 1b - 9 + 4$
Combine like terms. ⟶ $2b - 5$

EXAMPLE 5   Simplify $3m - 9 + 4m + 7 - 8m$.

Rearrange terms. $\longrightarrow$

$$\underbrace{3m + 4m - 8m}_{-1m} \underbrace{- 9 + 7}_{-2}$$

Replace $-1m$ with $-m$. $\longrightarrow$ $- m - 2$

ORAL EXERCISES

Which property is illustrated?

1. $(-1)(-8) = 8$
Mult. Prop. -1

2. $(x)(1) = x$
Mult. Iden.

3. $(-y)(1) = -y$
Mult. Iden.

4. $-c = (-1)(c)$
Mult. Prop. -1

EXERCISES

PART A

Simplify.

1. $4x - 5x + x$ *0*
3. $6b - 4b + b$ *3b*
5. $5r - r + 8r$ *12r*
7. $a - 4 - 2a + 6$ *$-a + 2$*
9. $7c + 8 - 6c - 9$ *$c - 1$*
11. $4e - 9 - 5e + 6$ *$-e - 3$*
13. $9 - q + 6 - 8q$ *$-9q + 15$*
15. $3p - 2 - 5 - p$ *$2p - 7$*
17. $-7 + d - 8 - 6d + 5$ *$-5d - 10$*
19. $-5a + 9 - a - 7 + 3a$ *$-3a + 2$*
21. $5 - 4z + 7 - 2z + 4 - z$ *$-7z + 16$*
23. $8b - 9 - b + 7b + 4 - 9$ *$14b - 14$*

2. $a + 4a - 7a$ *$-2a$*
4. $-c + 8c - 2c$ *5c*
6. $6y - y - 6y$ *$-y$*
8. $7 - z - 3z + 4$ *$-4z + 11$*
10. $9d - 4 - d + 8$ *$8d + 4$*
12. $2 + 3x - 7 - 2x$ *$x - 5$*
14. $2s - 9 - s + 5$ *$s - 4$*
16. $7a - 5 - a + 6$ *$6a + 1$*
18. $4z - 8 + z - 6 - 5z$ *-14*
20. $3r - 5 - 7r - 8 + r$ *$-3r - 13$*
22. $4y - 5 - 6y + 8 - y + 7$ *$-3y + 10$*
24. $-f + 4 - 7f - 8 + 2f + 6$ *$-6f + 2$*

PART B

Simplify. Then evaluate if $x = -2$, $y = 6$, and $z = -3$.

25. $3x - 4y - x - 8$ *-36*
27. $7x - y + 8z - 8x$ *-28*
29. $6z - 8y + x - 7z$ *-47*
31. $-8y - 4z + x - y - 2z + 1$ *-37*

26. $6y + z - 7y - 5$ *-14*
28. $5x + z - 6x + 3y$ *17*
30. $-y + 8x - z - 2x$ *-15*
32. $4z - y - 7x - 2z - 8x + 3 + y$ *27*

PART C

Simplify. Then evaluate if $x = .03$, $y = 1.04$, and $z = 2.01$.

33. $-.7x + 5z + .002y - 6z + 1.4x$

34. $-x + 2.04y + 3.1x - .05y - z$

Removing Parentheses

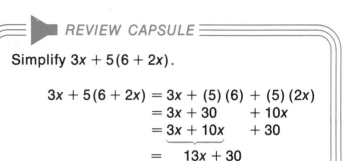

► *REVIEW CAPSULE*

Simplify $3x + 5(6 + 2x)$.

$$
\begin{aligned}
3x + 5(6 + 2x) &= 3x + (5)(6) + (5)(2x) \\
&= 3x + 30 \quad\quad + 10x \\
&= \underbrace{3x + 10x} \quad + 30 \\
&= \quad\quad 13x + 30
\end{aligned}
$$

EXAMPLE 1 Simplify $4a - 5(7 + 3a)$.

Read: 4a plus −5 times the
quantity 7 plus 3a. ⟶

Distribute −5. ⟶

Omit the + signs. ⟶

Rearrange terms. ⟶

$$
\begin{aligned}
4a - 5(7 + 3a) &= 4a + -5(7 + 3a) \\
&= 4a + (-5)(7) + (-5)(3a) \\
&= 4a - 35 - 15a \\
&= \underbrace{4a - 15a} - 35 \\
&= \quad -11a - 35
\end{aligned}
$$

EXAMPLE 2 Simplify $3n - 6(4 - 5n)$.

$$3n - 6(4 - 5n)$$

Distribute −6. Omit the + signs. ⟶

Combine like terms. ⟶

$$3n - 24 + 30n$$
$$33n - 24$$

EXAMPLE 3 Simplify $-2(7x + 3) - 8x$. Then evaluate the result
if $x = -3$.

$$-2(7x + 3) - 8x$$

$$-14x - 6 - 8x$$
$$-22x - 6$$
$$\downarrow$$

Substitute −3 for x. ⟶

Multiply first. ⟶

Then add. ⟶

$$-22(-3) - 6$$
$$66 - 6$$
$$60$$

EXERCISES

Simplify.

1. $5x - 8(2 - 3x)$ *$29x - 16$*

2. $4 - 3(7 - 9z)$ *$27z - 17$*

3. $4y - 2(7 - 5y)$ *$14y - 14$*

4. $6b - 8(3b + 7)$ *$-18b - 56$*

5. $6 - 4(2a - 8)$ *$-8a + 38$*

6. $5c - 6(8 - 4c)$ *$29c - 48$*

7. $3(2x - 9) - 4x$ *$2x - 27$*

8. $-7(3 - 2x) + 8x$ *$22x - 21$*

9. $-9(4a + 7) - 3a$ *$-39a - 63$*

10. $-6(-5d - 8) + 2d$ *$32d + 48$*

11. $-7(5a + 3) + 6a$ *$-29a - 21$*

12. $7c - 2(3c - 5)$ *$c + 10$*

13. $2x - 2(4x + 3) - 5$ *$-6x - 11$*

14. $6y - 8(4 + 7y) - 3y$ *$-53y - 32$*

15. $8 - 7(5 - 3c) + 4c$ *$25c - 27$*

16. $-7r + 6 - 3(4r - 2)$ *$-19r + 12$*

17. $5x - 2(4 - 6x) + 8$ *$17x$*

18. $-3(8 - 5z) + 2 - 6z$ *$9z - 22$*

19. $-5 - 9(4y + 8) - 2y + 3$ *$-38y - 74$*

20. $7x - 8 - 5(4x - 9) + 2x$ *$-11x + 37$*

Simplify. Then evaluate the result for the given value of the variable.

21. $4(5y - 8) - 3y$ if $y = 8$ *104*

22. $8 - 5(4 - 3c)$ if $c = -5$ *-87*

23. $-6(7x + 1) + 5x$ if $x = -4$ *142*

24. $7x - 2(4x - 6)$ if $x = 6$ *6*

25. $9 - 2(-5x + 8)$ if $x = -9$ *-97*

26. $-5y - 4(8 - 9y)$ if $y = -6$ *-218*

27. $7d - 8(4 - 3d) + 6$ if $d = 3$ *67*

28. $-6r + 5 - 3(2r - 1)$ if $r = -7$ *92*

29. $4(-3x + 2) - 5x - 9$ if $x = -1$ *16*

30. $9 - 2(8g + 7) + 2g$ if $g = -3$ *37*

EXAMPLE Simplify $-3(5x - 7) - 6(4 + 2x)$.

$$-3(5x - 7) - 6(4 + 2x)$$

Distribute -3. Then distribute -6.

$$-15x + 21 - 24 - 12x$$
$$-15x - 12x + 21 - 24$$
$$-27x - 3$$

Simplify.

31. $-4(3x - 5) - 3(2 + 7x)$ *$-33x + 14$*

32. $-5(3y - 7) - 2(6 + 4y)$ *$-23y + 23$*

33. $-5(6 + 3y) - 7(2y - 9)$ *$-29y + 33$*

34. $-3(5x - 4) + 8(-3x + 2)$ *$-39x + 28$*

35. $5(3z - 7) - 9(-8z - 6)$ *$87z + 19$*

36. $-4(7 - 8d) - 2(-6d + 5)$ *$44d - 38$*

37. $7x - 3(5x + 2) - 6(7 + 2x)$ *$-20x - 48$*

38. $-3(8 - 7z) + 6z - 9(4 - 3z)$ *$54z - 60$*

Simplify. [Hint: Work within brackets first.]

39. $4 - 2[7 - 2(3 - 5x)]$

40. $6x - 3[8 + 3x - 4(5 - 2x)]$

Applying the Property $-a = -1(a)$

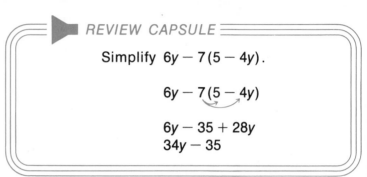

▶ REVIEW CAPSULE

Simplify $6y - 7(5 - 4y)$.

$$6y - 7(5 - 4y)$$

$$6y - 35 + 28y$$
$$34y - 35$$

EXAMPLE 1 Simplify $5x - (4 + 3x)$.

$-(a) = -1a$, so
$-(4 + 3x) = -1(4 + 3x)$

$$5x - (4 + 3x) = 5x - 1(4 + 3x)$$

Distribute -1. ───────────→
Combine like terms. ─────────→

$$= 5x - 4 - 3x$$
$$= 2x - 4$$

EXAMPLE 2 Simplify $-6b - (8 - 7b)$.

Replace $-(8 - 7b)$ with $-1(8 - 7b)$. ──→ $-6b - (8 - 7b) = -6b - 1(8 - 7b)$

$$= -6b - 8 + 7b$$
$$= 1b - 8$$

Replace $1b$ with b. ──────────→

$$= b - 8$$

EXAMPLE 3 Simplify $2 - (9 - c) + 5c$. Then evaluate the result if $c = -4$.

$-a = -1a$ ─────────────────→

$$2 - (9 - c) + 5c = 2 - 1(9 - 1c) + 5c$$

$$= 2 - 9 + 1c + 5c$$
$$= -7 + 6c$$

$$\downarrow$$

Replace c with -4. ──────────→

$$-7 + 6(-4)$$

Multiply first. ───────────────→

$$= -7 - 24$$

Then add. ───────────────────→

$$= -31$$

EXERCISES

PART A
Simplify.

1. $-5y - (6y + 2)$ $\quad -11y - 2$
2. $3 - (6x - 9)$ $\quad -6x + 12$
3. $-8 - (5z + 4)$ $\quad -5z - 12$
4. $-6x - (3 + 5x)$ $\quad -11x - 3$
5. $7c + (8 - 9c)$ $\quad -2c + 8$
6. $-(4x - 3) + 2x$ $\quad -2x + 3$
7. $-(8 - 6f) - 3f$ $\quad 3f - 8$
8. $-(7z + 8) - 9z$ $\quad -16z - 8$
9. $6y - (7 - 3y) - 2$ $\quad 9y - 9$
10. $-8 + (-4p + 7) - 9p$ $\quad -13p - 1$
11. $y - (9 - 7y) - 8$ $\quad 8y - 17$
12. $6r - 3(r - 7) + 8r$ $\quad 11r + 21$
13. $-(e + 7) - 5e - 6$ $\quad -6e - 13$
14. $4c - (3c + 2) - 10c$ $\quad -9c - 2$
15. $-5d + (8 - d) - 9$ $\quad -6d - 1$
16. $7x - 8 - (5x + 6)$ $\quad 2x - 14$
17. $-(3y - 8) + 7y - 12$ $\quad 4y - 4$
18. $9q + (8 - 3q) + 16$ $\quad 6q + 24$
19. $3z + 8 - (5z + 2) - 9z$ $\quad -11z + 6$
20. $5x - (2 - 4x) + 8x - 7$ $\quad 17x - 9$
21. $-9b - 4 - (7b + 6) - 3b$ $\quad -19b - 10$
22. $-(-5c - 8) + 6 - 9c - c$ $\quad -5c + 14$

Simplify. Then evaluate the result for the given value of the variable.

23. $-4x - (6 - 3x)$ if $x = 6$ $\quad -12$
24. $-9z - (8 + z)$ if $z = -7$ $\quad 62$
25. $-(c + 8) + 6c$ if $c = -3$ $\quad -23$
26. $-(4y - 6) + 3y$ if $y = 9$ $\quad -3$
27. $5r - (-7 + 2r) + 8$ if $r = 8$ $\quad 39$
28. $-6 - (3b - 2) + 5b$ if $b = -4$ $\quad -12$
29. $-(-7x + 2) - 8x + 1$ if $x = 6$ $\quad -7$
30. $-8z - (5z + 6) + 3z$ if $z = -9$ $\quad 84$
31. $5y - 9 - (7y - 6)$ if $y = 2$ $\quad -7$
32. $7r - (8 - r) + 12$ if $r = -8$ $\quad -60$

PART B

EXAMPLE   Simplify $-4(7 - x) - (5x + 3)$.

$-a = -1a$ $\longrightarrow$ $\qquad -4(7 - x) - (5x + 3) = -4(7 - 1x) - 1(5x + 3)$

Distribute -4. Then distribute -1. $\longrightarrow$ $\qquad = -28 + 4x - 5x - 3$

$\qquad = -1x - 31$

Replace $-1x$ with $-x$. $\longrightarrow$ $\qquad = -x - 31$

Simplify.

33. $-(7 + 3y) - 5(4y - 8)$ $\quad -23y + 33$
34. $-6(7x - 5) - (4 - x)$ $\quad -41x + 26$
35. $-(5z - 7) - (9 - z)$ $\quad -4z - 2$
36. $-(a + 4) - 3(7 - a)$ $\quad 2a - 25$
37. $-(-6r + 9) - (-7 - 3r)$ $\quad 9r - 2$
38. $-(-5 + c) - (-8 - c)$ $\quad 13$

PART C

Simplify. [Hint: Work within the brackets first.]

39. $-[3(x - 2) - (4 - 5x)]$
40. $-2a - [-2(1 - 7a) - (5 - 3a)]$

Subtracting Integers

OBJECTIVES
■ To subtract one number from another by adding its opposite
■ To subtract expressions like $-5a + 2$ from $3a - 4$

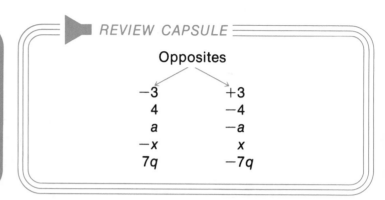

▶ REVIEW CAPSULE

Opposites

-3	$+3$
4	-4
a	$-a$
$-x$	x
$7q$	$-7q$

EXAMPLE 1   Subtract 3 from 8.

$$8 \text{ subtract } 3$$

8 subtract 3 is
8 plus the opposite of 3. ⟶

$$8 \quad - \quad 3$$
$$8 \quad + \quad -3$$
$$5$$

Subtract b *from* a means

a subtract b
a plus the opposite of b.
$a - b = a + -1(b)$, or $a + -b$, for all numbers a and b.

EXAMPLE 2   Subtract 6 from 4.

$$4 \text{ subtract } 6$$

4 subtract 6 is
4 plus the opposite of 6. ⟶

$$4 \quad - \quad 6$$
$$4 \quad + \quad -6$$
$$-2$$

EXAMPLE 3   Subtract -9 from 7.

$$7 \text{ subtract } -9$$

7 subtract -9 is
7 plus the opposite of -9. ⟶

$$7 \quad - \quad (-9)$$
$$7 \quad + \quad +9$$
$$16$$

Recall the Property of −1. ⟶ The opposite of a is equal to −1 times a.

$$-a = (-1)(a)$$

EXAMPLE 4   Subtract $-7a + 5$ from $3a - 2$.

$$3a - 2 \text{ subtract} \quad -7a + 5$$
$$3a - 2 \quad - \quad (-7a + 5)$$

Add the opposite of $(-7a + 5)$. ⟶ $\quad 3a - 2 \quad + \quad -(-7a + 5)$

$-(-7a + 5) = (-1)(-7a + 5)$ ⟶ $\quad 3a - 2 \quad + \quad -1(-7a + 5)$

Distribute −1. ⟶ $\quad 3a - 2 + 7a - 5$
$$10a - 7$$

EXERCISES

PART A

1. Subtract 2 from 5. *3*
2. Subtract −1 from 6. *7*
3. Subtract −5 from −7. *−2*
4. Subtract 5 from −8. *−13*
5. Subtract 4 from −10. *−14*
6. Subtract −7 from 0. *7*
7. Subtract −12 from −3. *9*
8. Subtract −10 from 10. *20*
9. Subtract 17 from −1. *−18*
10. Subtract $4x - 3$ from $6x - 4$. *$2x - 1$*
11. Subtract $b - 7$ from $4b + 1$. *$3b + 8$*
12. Subtract −5 from $5y + 3$. *$5y + 8$*
13. Subtract $3x + 7$ from $2x - 5$. *$-x - 12$*
14. Subtract $-2x - 5$ from $x + 4$. *$3x + 9$*
15. Subtract $-4y - 9$ from $-2y + 8$.
16. Subtract $-x - 8$ from $7x + 9$. *$8x + 17$*
17. Subtract $3x - 4$ from $-2x - 1$. *$-5x + 3$*

PART B

EXAMPLE   From $3a - 4$, subtract $-5a + 2$.

$$3a - 4 \text{ subtract} \quad -5a + 2$$
$$3a - 4 \quad - \quad (-5a + 2)$$

Add the opposite of $(-5a + 2)$
which is $(-1)(-5a + 2)$. ⟶ $\quad 3a - 4 \quad + \quad (-1)(-5a + 2)$

Distribute −1. ⟶ $\quad 3a - 4 + 5a - 2$
$$8a - 6$$

18. From $-12y - 1$, subtract $8y + 2$. *$-20y - 3$*
19. From $16z + 3$, subtract $-7 - 4z$. *$20z + 10$*
20. From $-4a - 5$, subtract $-7a - 8$. *$3a + 3$*
21. From $y - 18$, subtract $-2y + 9$.
22. From $-1 - x$, subtract $-5x + 3$. *$4x - 4$*
23. From $9z - 3$, subtract $-9z + 3$.
24. From $-y + 18$, subtract $2y - 9$. *$-3y + 27$*
25. From −9, subtract $3x + 2$. *$-3x - 11$*

PART C

26. Show that $a - b = a + (-1)b$. Justify each step.

Chapter Two Review

Add. [p. 21]

1. $+3 + +7$
2. $+6 + -2$
3. $-5 + +8$
4. $+4 + -9$
5. $-3 + -15$
6. $-7 + 0$

Compute. [p. 36]

7. $-9 + 7 - 3$
8. $6 + 7 - 4$
9. $-8 - 3 + 2$
10. $-16 + 8 - 15$
11. $-5 - 9 + 22$
12. $36 - 21 - 4$
13. $-12 + 14 - 18 + 22$
14. $31 - 55 + 14 - 18$
15. $-104 + 54 + 62 - 21$

Multiply. [p. 28]

16. $(-9)(+7)$
17. $(+8)(-2)$
18. $(+6)(+4)$
19. $(-21)(-5)$
20. $(0)(-7)$
21. $(-5)(-3)(-5)$
22. $(-7)(+3)(-4)$
23. $(-5)(-4)(+3)(-2)$
24. $(-8)(+2)(-5)(+4)$

Divide. [p. 31]

25. $\dfrac{+14}{+2}$
26. $\dfrac{-49}{+7}$
27. $\dfrac{+36}{-6}$
28. $-52 \div -4$
29. $+45 \div -9$
30. $(-63 \div +7) \div -3$

Evaluate for the given values of the variables. [p. 40]

31. $5r + 7s$ if $r = 3$, $s = -6$
32. $-2x + 7y$ if $x = 4$, $y = 9$
33. $6x + 7y - 9z$ if $x = 3$, $y = -2$, $z = -5$

Simplify. [p. 42, 44, 48]

34. $3y - 8y + 6y$
35. $x + 5x - 9x$
36. $5d - 8 - d + 6$
37. $-4p + 7 + 13 - p$
38. $4c - 2(3 - 2c)$
39. $-a + 4 - 3(-4 - 2a)$
40. $6 - (5 - x) - 4x$
41. $-(z - 2) - 8z - 7$

Simplify. Then evaluate the result for the given value of the variable. [p. 46, 48]

42. $5(6x - 7) - 3x$ if $x = 4$
43. $-6k - 8(3k - 2)$ if $k = -5$

[p. 50]

44. Subtract 5 from -8.
45. Subtract -9 from 6.
46. Subtract -4 from -1.
47. Subtract $3x - 10$ from $7x + 2$.
48. Subtract $-7a + 8$ from $4a - 2$.
49. From $4a - 3$, subtract $2a + 5$.
50. From $-3a - 4$, subtract $-2a + 5$.

Which property of addition of integers is illustrated? [p. 24]

51. $-2 + -7 = -7 + -2$
52. $0 + x = x$

Chapter Two Test

Add.

1. $+9 + -4$

2. $-6 + -7$

3. $-12 + +7$

Compute.

4. $8 - 3 - 19$

5. $-5 + 12 - 81$

6. $16 - 14 + 5$

Multiply.

7. $(-8)(-2)$

8. $(+7)(-3)$

9. $(-9)(+6)$

10. $(-7)(0)$

11. $(-5)(-9)$

12. $(+8)(+7)(-2)$

Divide.

13. $\dfrac{-24}{+6}$

14. $\dfrac{-18}{-3}$

15. $\dfrac{+42}{-3}$

16. $-9 \div -1$

17. $+56 \div +14$

18. $-72 \div (-8 \div +4)$

Evaluate for the given values of the variables.

19. $6x + 8y$ if $x = 3, y = -5$
20. $-7a - 9 + 8b$ if $a = -2, b = -8$

Simplify.

21. $-4x - 2x$

22. $6 + 8c - 2c$

23. $5a + 2b - 9 - 3a - 7b$

24. $4z + 8 - z - 3$

25. $-y + 7 - 9y - 8 + 2y$

26. $-5(3x - 2) - 5x$

27. $-4a - 8(2 - 3a) - 9$

28. $4y - (7 - 2y)$

29. $-(7b + 8) - 6b - 2$

30. $4p - (8 - p) + 5 - p$

Simplify. Then evaluate for the given value of the variable.

31. $-5r - 2(6 + 3r)$ if $r = -3$

32. $-(5y - 3) - 7y + 8$ if $y = -9$

33. Subtract -12 from -7.
34. Subtract 4 from -9.
35. Subtract $-8y + 6$ from $5y - 2$.
36. From $-2a + 3$, subtract $-4a + 6$.

Which property of addition of integers is illustrated?

37. $(-7 + +3) + -5 = -7 + (+3 + -5)$

38. $+8 + -3 = -3 + +8$

Computer Programs: Flow Charts

Instructions are given to a computer by means of a program.

PROBLEM 1.

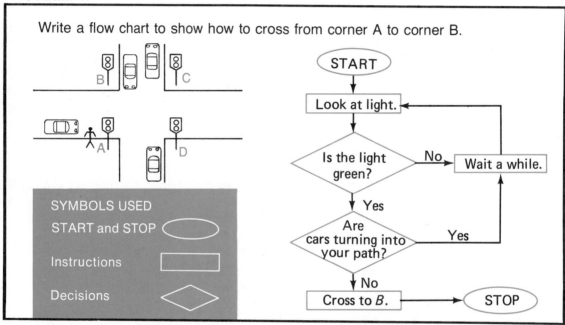

Write a flow chart to show how to cross from corner A to corner B.

SYMBOLS USED

START and STOP ⬭

Instructions ▭

Decisions ◇

START

Look at light.

Is the light green? — No → Wait a while.

↓ Yes

Are cars turning into your path? — Yes →

↓ No

Cross to *B*. → STOP

The two loops in the flow chart call for instructions to be repeated.

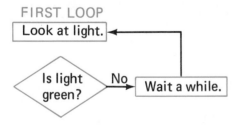

FIRST LOOP

Look at light.

Is light green? — No → Wait a while.

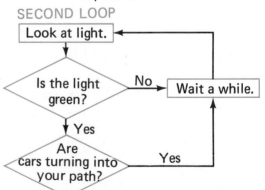

SECOND LOOP

Look at light.

Is the light green? — No → Wait a while.

↓ Yes

Are cars turning into your path? — Yes →

PROBLEM 2.

Write a flow chart to show how to cross from corner A to corner C.
The traffic is eliminated to simplify matters.

```
                    ( START )
                        |
                        v
                ┌───────────────┐
                │ Look at light.│
                └───────────────┘
                        |
                        v
                      ╱   ╲
          Yes      ╱   Is    ╲      No
       ┌─────────╱ light green ╲─────────┐
       │         ╲  from A to B? ╱        │
       │          ╲            ╱          │
       │            ╲        ╱            │
       v                                  v
┌──────────────┐                  ┌──────────────┐
│  Cross to B. │                  │  Cross to D. │
└──────────────┘                  └──────────────┘
       |                                  |
       v                                  v
     ╱   ╲                              ╱   ╲
   ╱   Is   ╲     Yes          Yes    ╱   Is   ╲
  ╱ light green ╲──────┐    ┌────────╱ light green ╲
  ╲  from B to C? ╱    │    │        ╲  from D to C? ╱
   ╲            ╱      │    │          ╲            ╱
     ╲ No     ╱        │    │            ╲ No     ╱
┌──────────────┐       v    v         ┌──────────────┐
│ Wait a while.│    ┌──────────────┐  │ Wait a while.│
└──────────────┘    │  Cross to C. │  └──────────────┘
                    └──────────────┘
                          |
                          v
                      ( STOP )
```

How many loops can you identify in the flow chart?

PROJECT

Draw a flow chart to show all of the steps for each process.

1. Unlocking a certain door with a choice of three keys.

2. Changing a burnt-out light bulb. (Start with an unused bulb.)

Open Sentences

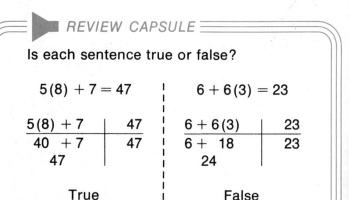

A sentence like $8x + 3 = 35$ is an open sentence. It contains a variable, x.

EXAMPLE 1   In the sentence $8x + 3 = 35$, replace x with 3. Is the resulting sentence true or false? Then replace x with 4. True or false?

Replace x with 3.

$8x + 3$	35
$8(3) + 3$	35
$24 + 3$	
27	

False

Replace x with 4.

$8x + 3$	35
$8(4) + 3$	35
$32 + 3$	
35	

True

EXAMPLE 2   The sentence below is an open English sentence.

Neither true nor false ⟶   It is the shortest month of the year.

Replace "It" with the name of a month to make a true sentence. Then replace "It" to make a false sentence.

Replace "It" with any month except February. ⟶ February is the shortest month of the year. — True
May is the shortest month of the year. — False

A solution of an open sentence is a replacement which makes it true.

EXAMPLE 3 Which members of the replacement set $\{1, 2, 3\}$ are solutions of $4x + 3 = x + 9$?

Replace x with each member of the set $\{1, 2, 3\}$.

Replace x with 1.

$4x + 3$	$x + 9$
$4(1) + 3$	$1 + 9$
$4\ + 3$	10
7	

False

Replace x with 2.

$4x + 3$	$x + 9$
$4(2) + 3$	$2 + 9$
$8\ + 3$	11
11	

True

Replace x with 3.

$4x + 3$	$x + 9$
$4(3) + 3$	$3 + 9$
$12\ + 3$	12
15	

False

2 is the only member of the replacement set which makes the sentence true. ⟶ **Thus,** 2 is the solution of $4x + 3 = x + 9$.

EXAMPLE 4 Which members of the replacement set $\{2, 0, -1, -2\}$ are solutions of $23 - 6c = 15 - 10c$?

Replace c with each member of $\{2, 0, -1, -2\}$

Replace c with 2.

$23 - 6c$	$15 - 10c$
$23 - 6(2)$	$15 - 10(2)$
$23 -\ 12$	$15 -\ 20$
11	-5

False

Replace c with 0.

$23 - 6c$	$15 - 10c$
$23 - 6(0)$	$15 - 10(0)$
$23 -\ 0$	$15 -\ 0$
23	15

False

Replace c with -1.

$23 - 6c$	$15 - 10c$
$23 - 6(-1)$	$15 - 10(-1)$
$23 +\ 6$	$15 +\ 10$
29	25

$(-)(-) = (+)$

False

Replace c with -2.

$23 - 6c$	$15 - 10c$
$23 - 6(-2)$	$15 - 10(-2)$
$23 +\ 12$	$15 +\ 20$
35	35

True

-2 is the only member which makes the sentence true. ⟶ **Thus,** -2 is the solution of $23 - 6c = 15 - 10c$.

ORAL EXERCISES

Which are open sentences?

1. $5x + 6 = 22$ O **2.** $13 = (6)(2) + 1$ T **3.** $14 - 2y = 8$ O
4. $7(5) + 8 = c$ O **5.** $6x = 9 + 2y$ O **6.** $4 + 9 = 2 + 11$ T
7. $5(9) - 12 = 17$ F **8.** $8 + 9x = 36$ O **9.** $2(4 + 5) = 20$ F
10. $3(7 + 2a) = 4$ O **11.** $23 = 3(5) + 8$ T **12.** $8 + 3(7) = 9d$ O
13. He is president of his class. O **14.** Texas is the smallest state in the U.S.A. F **15.** It is the largest planet in the solar system. O

For each sentence above which is *not* an open sentence, tell whether it is true or false. *(See above.)*

EXERCISES

Part A

Which members of the given replacement set are solutions of the sentence?

1. $6x + 5 = 35$ $\{1, 5\}$ 5 **2.** $47 = 5y + 7$ $\{4, 8, 12\}$ 8
3. $9 + 4z = 45$ $\{4, 2, 9\}$ 9 **4.** $22 = 8 + 2d$ $\{7, 8\}$ 7
5. $5r - 1 = 24$ $\{1, 3, 5\}$ 5 **6.** $29 - 4g = 21$ $\{2, 5, 8\}$ 2
7. $58 - 5x = 13$ $\{3, 4, 9\}$ 9 **8.** $56 = 29 + 9b$ $\{1, 3, 5, 7\}$ 3
9. $39 = 7y - 10$ $\{4, 7, 10\}$ 7 **10.** $8r - 38 = 26$ $\{4, 6, 8\}$ 8
11. $12x + 8 = 56$ $\{2, 4, 6, 8\}$ 4 **12.** $7m - 32 = 31$ $\{1, 5, 9, 10, 12\}$ 9
13. $5 + 6z = 35$ $\{5, 6, 7\}$ 5 **14.** $68 = 9x - 85$ $\{17, 19, 21\}$ 17
15. $10r = 7r + 21$ $\{3, 7\}$ 7 **16.** $6a - 48 = 6$ $\{9, 10, 11\}$ 9
17. $8d - 32 = 0$ $\{1, 4, 9\}$ 4 **18.** $70 = 2y + 56$ $\{5, 7, 9\}$ 7
19. $15 + y = 5y + 3$ $\{3, 4, 5, 6, 7\}$ 3 **20.** $4x - 3 = 3x - 1$ $\{1, 2, 3, 4, 5\}$ 2
21. $9c - 5 = 7c + 3$ $\{2, 4, 6\}$ 4 **22.** $2r - 6 = r + 3$ $\{2, 5, 9\}$ 9
23. $18 - 5r = 2r + 4$ $\{1, 2, 3, 4\}$ 2 **24.** $40 - 9a = 13a - 26$ $\{3, 4, 5\}$ 3
25. $10y - 22 = 8y - 10$ $\{12, 14, 6\}$ 6 **26.** $4z + 2 = -z + 27$ $\{5, 8, 9\}$ 5
27. $8x - 13 = 21x - 52$ $\{3, 8, 11\}$ 3 **28.** $5y + 2 = 8y - 10$ $\{1, 2, 4, 8\}$ 4

PART B

Which members of the given replacement set are solutions of the sentence?

29. $7y + 6 = 6 - y$ $\{0, 1, 2\}$ 0 **30.** $24 - 5t = 19 - 10t$ $\{-3, -2, -1\}$ -1
31. $6d + 7 = 2d + 8$ $\{\frac{1}{2}, \frac{1}{3}, \frac{1}{4}\}$ $\frac{1}{4}$ **32.** $1 + 5x = 9 - x$ $\{\frac{3}{2}, \frac{4}{3}, \frac{3}{4}\}$ $\frac{4}{3}$
33. $9a - 2 = 3a - 20$ $\{-1, -3, -5\}$ -3 **34.** $2x + 2 = 4x + 2$ $\{-1, 0, 1, 2\}$ 0
35. $5y + 12 = 3 + y$ $\{1, 2, 3, 4\}$ *none*   **36.** $-8z - 46 = 7z - 1$ $\{-3, -2, -1\}$ -3
37. $8r + 4 = 7 + 2r$ $\{\frac{1}{2}, \frac{1}{3}, \frac{1}{4}\}$ $\frac{1}{2}$ **38.** $5x + 8 = x - 6$ $\{2, 3, 4, 5, 6\}$ *none*

Solving Equations

OBJECTIVE
■ To solve equations like
$5x - 8 = 40$
by applying the equation
properties

REVIEW CAPSULE
Additive Inverses, or Opposites

6	−6	$6 + -6 = 0$
−3	3	$-3 + 3 = 0$
x	$-x$	$x + -x = 0$

A sentence with $=$ is an equation. To solve
an equation means to find all of its solutions.
We will assume that the replacement set is the
set of all numbers.

EXAMPLE 1   Add 8 to each side of the equation $n = 3$.
Then find the solution.

The solution of $n = 3$ is 3.

$$n = 3$$
$$n + 8 = 3 + 8$$
$$\text{or} \quad n + 8 = 11$$

3 is the solution of both equations.

The solution of $n + 8 = 11$ is 3, since $3 + 8 = 11$.

Example 1 suggests this. ⟶
We can add the same number to each
side of an equation.

Addition Property for Equations
If $a = b$ is true, then $a + c = b + c$ is also true,
for all numbers a, b, and c.

EXAMPLE 2   Multiply each side of the equation $x = 5$
by 2. Then find the solution.

The solution of $x = 5$ is 5.

$$x = 5$$
$$2(x) = 2(5)$$
$$2x = 10$$

5 is the solution of both equations.

The solution of $2x = 10$ is 5, since $2(5) = 10$.

Example 2 suggests this. →
We can multiply each side of an equation by the same number.

Multiplication Property for Equations

If $a = b$ is true, then $a(c) = b(c)$ is also true, for all numbers a, b, and c.

EXAMPLE 3 Divide each side of the equation $7x = 42$ by 7. Is the solution of the resulting equation the same as the solution of $7x = 42$?

$$7x = 42$$
$$\frac{7x}{7} = \frac{42}{7}$$

$\frac{7}{7} = 1$ →
$$1x = 6$$
$$x = 6$$

The solution of $x = 6$ is 6.

$$7x = 42$$

The solution of $7x = 42$ is 6, since $7(6) = 42$.

Yes, 6 is the solution of both equations.

Example 3 suggests this. →
We can divide each side of an equation by the same nonzero number.

Division Property for Equations

If $a = b$ is true, then $\frac{a}{c} = \frac{b}{c}$ is also true, for all numbers, a, b, and c $[c \neq 0]$.

EXAMPLE 4 Solve $3c + 5 = 17$. Then check your solution.

Get $3c$ alone; (alone if no $+5$).
-5 is the additive inverse of 5.
Add -5 to each side. →

$$3c + 5 = 17$$
$$\underline{- 5 \quad -5}$$
$$3c + 0 = 12$$ $\begin{cases} \text{Addition Property} \\ \text{for Equations} \end{cases}$

Now $3c$ is alone. →
$$3c = 12$$

Divide each side by 3. →
$$\frac{3c}{3} = \frac{12}{3}$$ $\begin{cases} \text{Division Property} \\ \text{for Equations} \end{cases}$

$\frac{3}{3} = 1$ →
$$1c = 4$$

Now c is alone. →
$$c = 4$$

Check. →
Replace c with 4. →

$3c + 5$	17
$3(4) + 5$	17
$12 + 5$	
17	

True

Thus, 4 is the solution of $3c + 5 = 17$.

EXAMPLE 5   Solve $6x - 7 = 11$. Then check your solution.

Get $6x$ alone; (alone if no -7).

7 is the additive inverse of -7.

Add 7 to each side. $\longrightarrow$

$$
\begin{array}{l}
6x - 7 = 11 \\
\underline{+7 \quad +7} \\
6x + 0 = 18
\end{array}
\quad \left\{ \begin{array}{l} \text{Addition Property} \\ \text{for Equations} \end{array} \right.
$$

Now $6x$ is alone. $\longrightarrow$

$$6x = 18$$

Divide each side by 6. $\longrightarrow$

$$\frac{6x}{6} = \frac{18}{6} \quad \left\{ \begin{array}{l} \text{Division Property} \\ \text{for Equations} \end{array} \right.$$

$$1x = 3$$

Now x is alone. $\longrightarrow$

$$x = 3$$

Check. $\longrightarrow$

Replace x with 3. $\longrightarrow$

$$
\begin{array}{c c}
6x \ -7 & \ 11 \\
\hline
6(3) - 7 & \ 11 \\
18 - 7 & \\
11 &
\end{array}
$$

True

Thus, 3 is the solution of $6x - 7 = 11$.

EXAMPLE 6   Solve $8 = -12 - 4a$.

Get $-4a$ alone; (alone if no -12).

Add 12 to each side. $\longrightarrow$

$$
\begin{array}{l}
8 = -12 - 4a \\
\underline{+12 \quad +12} \\
20 = 0 - 4a
\end{array}
\quad \left\{ \begin{array}{l} \text{Addition Property} \\ \text{for Equations} \end{array} \right.
$$

Now $-4a$ is alone. $\longrightarrow$

$$20 = -4a$$

Divide each side by -4. $\longrightarrow$

$$\frac{20}{-4} = \frac{-4a}{-4} \quad \left\{ \begin{array}{l} \text{Division Property} \\ \text{for Equations} \end{array} \right.$$

$\dfrac{20}{-4} = -5 \qquad \dfrac{-4}{-4} = 1$

$$-5 = 1a$$

Now a is alone. $\longrightarrow$

$$-5 = a$$

Check -5 in $8 = -12 - 4a$. $\longrightarrow$ **Thus, -5 is the solution of $8 = -12 - 4a$.**

SUMMARY   **To solve $ax + b = c$ for x:**

Add the additive inverse of b to each side. $\longrightarrow$

$$
\begin{array}{l}
ax + b = c \\
\underline{-b \quad -b} \\
ax + 0 = c - b
\end{array}
$$

Divide each side by a. $\longrightarrow$

$$\frac{ax}{a} = \frac{c-b}{a}$$

$$x = \frac{c-b}{a}$$

ORAL EXERCISES

To solve each equation, what number would you add to each side? By what number would you divide each side?

1. $2x + 9 = 17$ *−9; 2*
2. $-8 = 2 + 5z$ *−2; 5*
3. $-6c + 30 = -6$
4. $14 - 3y = -13$ *−14; −3*
5. $4d - 7 = -11$ *7; 4*
6. $40 - 8x = -16$
7. $7 = 19 + 4c$ *−19; 4*
8. $3z - 7 = 8$ *7; 3*
9. $7y + 20 = 6$
10. $8 = 10d - 32$ *32; 10*
11. $-58 - 9r = 14$ *58; −9*
12. $62 = 20 + 7x$
13. $4z - 5 = -9$ *5; 4*
14. $8p - 42 = 38$ *42; 8*
15. $-36 = 10y + 14$
16. $24 = 2 + 11q$ *−2; 11*
17. $-41 = 12z - 5$ *5; 12*
18. $9c + 8 = 8$
19. $10x - 17 = -7$ *17; 10*
20. $-16 = 62 + 13y$ *−62; 13*
21. $15g - 7 = -37$
22. $73 - 20r = -27$ *−73; −20*
23. $10c - 9 = -9$ *9; 10*
24. $87 = 51 - 9b$

EXERCISES

PART A

Solve each equation in Exercises 1–24 above. *Checks are optional.*

PART B

EXAMPLE   Solve $2x - 8 = -7$.

Add 8 to each side. $\longrightarrow$

$$\begin{array}{rcl} 2x - 8 &=& -7 \\ +8 & & +8 \\ \hline 2x &=& 1 \end{array}$$

Divide each side by 2. $\longrightarrow$

$$\frac{2x}{2} = \frac{1}{2}$$

The solution is a fraction. $\longrightarrow$

$$x = \frac{1}{2}$$

Check on your own. $\longrightarrow$ **Thus,** $\dfrac{1}{2}$ is the solution of $2x - 8 = -7$.

Solve.

25. $5r + 8 = 9$ $\frac{1}{5}$
26. $12 = 4y + 9$ $\frac{3}{4}$
27. $8 = 6r + 7$ $\frac{1}{6}$
28. $9 + 3x = 10$ $\frac{1}{3}$
29. $18 = 19 - 8d$ $\frac{1}{8}$
30. $17 = 20 - 4x$ $\frac{3}{4}$
31. $13 - 5z = 11$ $\frac{2}{5}$
32. $17 - 3a = 15$ $\frac{2}{3}$
33. $4x + 19 = 20$ $\frac{1}{4}$
34. $14 - 6y = 9$ $\frac{5}{6}$
35. $8x = 22 - 19$ $\frac{3}{8}$
36. $5 = 9 - 7x$ $\frac{4}{7}$

PART C

Solve.

37. $3x - .02 = -.548$
38. $6.2 - 2x = 3.4$
39. $-.07 - 5x = -2.1$

Algebra and Commissions

It is a common practice in business to encourage sales people to sell more by giving them extra money, a commission, for each item they sell.

SALES PERSON WANTED IN THE **CAMERA DEPARTMENT**
EARN **$125**/WEEK **plus $5** ON EACH POLAROID YOU SELL!!

If I sell 4 Polaroids I can earn

5 (4) + $125

COMMISSION ON EACH — NUMBER SOLD — REGULAR SALARY

20 + 125 = $145

PROBLEM

Jill earns $160 a week plus a commission of $15 for each portable TV she sells. How many must she sell to earn a total of $250?

Let n = the number she must sell

(Commission on each) (number sold) + (regular salary) = total

$$(15) \quad\quad (n) \quad + \quad 160 \quad = 250$$
$$15n + 160 = 250$$
$$15n = 90$$
$$n = 6$$

Thus, she must sell 6 portable TV's.

PROJECT

1. Mary earns $155 a week plus a commission of $4 for each mower she sells. How many must she sell to make $183?

2. Harry earns $150 a week plus a commission of $5 for each radio he sells. How many must he sell to make $190?

Equations: The Variable on Both Sides

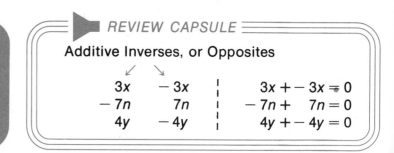

► REVIEW CAPSULE

Additive Inverses, or Opposites

$3x$	$-3x$	$3x + -3x = 0$
$-7n$	$7n$	$-7n + 7n = 0$
$4y$	$-4y$	$4y + -4y = 0$

EXAMPLE 1   Solve $5n - 4 = 3n + 18$. Check your solution.

$-3n$ is the additive inverse of $3n$.
Add $-3n$ to each side. ───────→

Now the variable term is on one
side only. ───────→

Add 4 to each side. ───────→

Divide each side by 2. ───────→

$$
\begin{array}{rl}
5n - 4 = & 3n + 18 \\
-3n & -3n \\
\hline
2n - 4 = & 0 + 18 \\
2n - 4 = & 18 \\
+4 & +4 \\
\hline
2n + 0 = & 22 \\
2n = & 22 \\
\dfrac{2n}{2} = & \dfrac{22}{2} \\
n = & 11
\end{array}
$$

Check.

$5n - 4$	$3n + 18$
$5(11) - 4$	$3(11) + 18$
$55 - 4$	$33 + 18$
51	51

Thus, 11 is the solution of $5n - 4 = 3n + 18$.

EXAMPLE 2   Solve the equation in Example 1 by adding
$-5n$, rather than $-3n$, to each side.

$-5n$ is the additive inverse of $5n$.
Add $-5n$ to each side. ───────→
Now the variable term is on one side only.

Add -18 to each side. ───────→

Divide each side by -2. ───────→

$$
\begin{array}{rl}
5n - 4 = & 3n + 18 \\
-5n & -5n \\
\hline
-4 = & -2n + 18 \\
-18 & -18 \\
\hline
-22 = & -2n + 0 \\
-22 = & -2n \\
\dfrac{-22}{-2} = & \dfrac{-2n}{-2} \\
11 = & n
\end{array}
$$

Thus, 11 is the solution of $5n - 4 = 3n + 18$.

EXAMPLE 3   Solve $4y - 21 = 9y - 16$.

Add $-9y$ to each side. $\longrightarrow$
(We could have added $-4y$ to each side.)

$$
\begin{array}{rcl}
4y - 21 = & 9y - 16 \\
-9y & -9y \\
\hline
-5y - 21 = & 0 - 16 \\
-5y - 21 = & -16
\end{array}
$$

Add 21 to each side. $\longrightarrow$

$$
\begin{array}{rcl}
+21 & +21 \\
\hline
-5y + 0 = & 5 \\
-5y = & 5
\end{array}
$$

Divide each side by -5. $\longrightarrow$

$$
\frac{-5y}{-5} = \frac{5}{-5}
$$

$$
y = -1
$$

Check on your own. $\longrightarrow$ **Thus,** -1 is the solution of $4y - 21 = 9y - 16$.

EXAMPLE 4   Solve $5x - 7 = x + 9$.

x means $1x$. $\longrightarrow$
Add $-1x$ to each side. $\longrightarrow$
(We could have added $-5x$ to each side.)

$$
\begin{array}{rcl}
5x - 7 = & 1x + 9 \\
-1x & -1x \\
\hline
4x - 7 = & 0 + 9 \\
4x - 7 = & 9
\end{array}
$$

Add 7 to each side. $\longrightarrow$

$$
\begin{array}{rcl}
+7 & +7 \\
\hline
4x + 0 = & 16 \\
4x = & 16
\end{array}
$$

Divide each side by 4. $\longrightarrow$

$$
\frac{4x}{4} = \frac{16}{4}
$$

$$
x = 4
$$

Check on your own. $\longrightarrow$ **Thus,** 4 is the solution of $5x - 7 = x + 9$.

EXAMPLE 5   Solve $8x - 12 = 15x - 4x$.

$15x - 4x = 11x$ $\longrightarrow$
Add $-11x$ to each side. $\longrightarrow$

$$
\begin{array}{rcl}
8x - 12 = & 15x - 4x \\
8x - 12 = & 11x \\
-11x & -11x \\
\hline
-3x - 12 = & 0
\end{array}
$$

Add 12 to each side. $\longrightarrow$

$$
\begin{array}{rcl}
+12 & +12 \\
\hline
-3x + 0 = & 12 \\
-3x = & 12
\end{array}
$$

Divide each side by -3. $\longrightarrow$

$$
\frac{-3x}{-3} = \frac{12}{-3}
$$

$$
x = -4
$$

Check on your own. $\longrightarrow$ **Thus,** -4 is the solution of $8x - 12 = 15x - 4x$.

EXERCISES

PART A

Solve.

1. $5x + 6 = 2x + 15$ *3*
2. $6y - 8 = 20 + 2y$ *7*
3. $5 + 9x = 7x + 11$ *3*
4. $3z + 10 = 2 + 5z$ *4*
5. $4a - 9 = 3a - 1$ *8*
6. $21r - 26 = 8r - 13$ *1*
7. $2x - 12 = x + 3$ *15*
8. $5d + 11 = 8d - 7$ *6*
9. $-x + 22 = 4x + 2$ *4*
10. $6c - 20 = 2c$ *5*
11. $9e + 14 = 11e$ *7*
12. $7c = -24 + c$ *-4*
13. $8y + 11 = 7y$ *-11*
14. $17x - 8 = 5x + 4$ *1*
15. $3y = 15y - 72$ *6*
16. $7 + 11z = 97 - 7z$ *5*
17. $18 - 9x = 2x + 7$ *1*
18. $3r - 2 = -9 + 2r$ *-7*
19. $10g - 22 = 8g - 14$ *4*
20. $7z + 8 = -16 + 3z$ *-6*
21. $x - 3 = 22 - 4x$ *5*   *21*
22. $20x - 16x = 6x - 8$ *4*
23. $5x - 2x = 24 - 9x$ *2*
24. $13x - 4x = 10x - 21$ *↗*
25. $-x + 3x = 6 + x$ *6*
26. $4y - 3y = 18 - 2y$ *6*
27. $4z - 5z = -28 + 3z$ *7*
28. $27 - 6y = 4y - 7y$ *9*
29. $3x + 8 = 2x - x$ *-4*
30. $x + x + 18 = 30$ *6*
31. $2y + 5y + 3 = 10y$ *1*
32. $8 + 2x = 5x - 13$ *7*
33. $25 - 4y = 1 + 4y$ *3*
34. $13x + 11 = 10x - 7$ *-6*
35. $7x - 8x = 4 - 2x$ *4*
36. $13y - 4y = -14 + 2y$ *↘*   *-2*

PART B

EXAMPLE   Solve $7x + 8 = 5 + 3x$.

$$7x + 8 = 5 + 3x$$

Add $-3x$ to each side. $\longrightarrow$ $4x + 8 = 5$

Add -8 to each side. $\longrightarrow$ $4x = -3$

Divide each side by 4. $\longrightarrow$ $x = \frac{-3}{4}$

Thus, $\frac{-3}{4}$ **is the solution.**

Solve.

37. $7x + 6 = 9 + 8x$ -3
38. $3y + 9 = -2y + 7$ $\frac{-2}{5}$
39. $y + 6 = 7 - 3y$ $\frac{1}{4}$
40. $-6a - 15 = -17 - 9a$ $\frac{-2}{3}$
41. $2 + 6c = -1 + 11c$ $\frac{3}{5}$
42. $10x - 5 = -9 + 3x$ $\frac{-4}{7}$
43. $2x + 13 = -4x + 18$ $\frac{5}{6}$
44. $-11 + 4x = -13 - 3x$ $\frac{-2}{7}$
45. $12 - 5y = 7 - y$ $\frac{5}{4}$
46. $13z - 3 = 8z + 6$ $\frac{9}{5}$
47. $2y - 15 = -3y - 22$ $\frac{-7}{5}$
48. $a + 11 = -2a + 7$ $\frac{-4}{3}$

PART C

Solve.

49. $3x + x - 2 = 7 - 2x$
50. $7c + 4 - c = 2c - 3$
51. $6a + 8 = 19 + 9a + 7 - 15a$
52. $-4 - d + 2d = 3 + 4d$
53. $8y + 7 = 22 - y + 3y$
54. $3x + 6x + 2 = 4x - 3 - 2x$
55. $12x - 1.2 = 3x + 1.5$
56. $.04 - 3x = -5x - .002$
57. $7x - .05 = 3.15 + 2x$

Number Mysteries

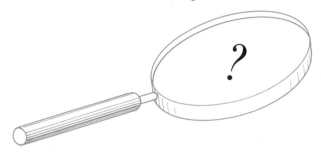

GAME

Play this game with a friend. You can always tell what your friend's starting number was. Here's how.

Ask your friend to do the following:	You think:
1. Choose a number.	1. x
2. Add 2.	2. $x + 2$
3. Multiply by 8.	3. $8x + 16$
4. Subtract 10.	4. $8x + 6$
5. Divide by 2.	5. $4x + 3$
6. Add 9.	6. $4x + 12$
7. Divide by 4.	7. $x + 3$
8. Give the result.	8. $x + 3$

The result will always be 3 more than the starting digit.

PROJECT

1. Now try this. Explain how to find the mystery number.
   Choose a mystery number.
   Double it.
   Add 6.
   Add the mystery number.
   Divide by 3.
   Give the result.

2. Make up some mystery numbers of your own.

Equations with Parentheses

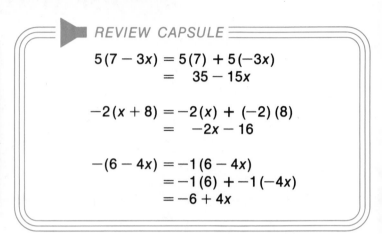

REVIEW CAPSULE

$$5(7 - 3x) = 5(7) + 5(-3x)$$
$$= 35 - 15x$$

$$-2(x + 8) = -2(x) + (-2)(8)$$
$$= -2x - 16$$

$$-(6 - 4x) = -1(6 - 4x)$$
$$= -1(6) + -1(-4x)$$
$$= -6 + 4x$$

EXAMPLE 1   Solve $10x - 3(5 - 3x) = 23$. Then check your solution.

$-3(5 - 3x) = -15 + 9x$

$10x + 9x = 19x$ ⟶

Add 15 to each side. ⟶

Divide each side by 19. ⟶

$$
\begin{array}{rl}
10x - 3(5 - 3x) = & 23 \\
10x - 15 + 9x = & 23 \\
19x - 15 = & 23 \\
+15 \quad +15 & \\
\hline
19x \quad\quad = & 38 \\
x = 2 &
\end{array}
$$

Check.

$10x - 3(5 - 3x)$	23
$10(2) - 3[5 - 3(2)]$	23
$20 - 3(5 - 6)$	
$20 - 3(-1)$	
$20 + 3$	
23	

Thus, 2 is the solution.

EXAMPLE 2   Solve $7x - (9 - 4x) = 3(x - 11)$.

$-(9 - 4x) = -1(9 - 4x)$ ⟶

$-1(9 - 4x) = -9 + 4x; \ 3(x - 11) = 3x - 33$

$7x + 4x = 11x$ ⟶

Add $-3x$ to each side. ⟶

Add 9 to each side. ⟶

Divide each side by 8. ⟶

$$
\begin{array}{rl}
7x - \ \ (9 - 4x) = & 3(x - 11) \\
7x - 1(9 - 4x) = & 3(x - 11) \\
7x \ \ - 9 + 4x = & 3x - 33 \\
11x - 9 = & 3x - 33 \\
-3x & -3x \\
\hline
8x - 9 = & -33 \\
+9 & +9 \\
\hline
8x \quad = & -24 \\
x = -3 &
\end{array}
$$

Check on your own. ⟶ **Thus,** -3 is the solution.

EXERCISES

PART A

Solve.

1. $4(x - 2) = 20$ *7*
2. $2(5 + x) = 22$ *6*
3. $-5(x + 4) = 15$ *-7*
4. $8 - 4(y - 1) = -36$ *12*
5. $5(z - 6) = 10$ *8*
6. $3(c - 1) + 8 = -10$ *-5*
7. $2(2s + 3) = -18$ *-6*
8. $-4(2x + 6) = 16$ *-5*
9. $y - (8 - y) = 32$ *20*
10. $(50 - x) - (3x + 2) = 0$ *12*
11. $20 - (8 + x) = -(1 - x) + 29$ *-8*
12. $3c + 2(c + 2) = 13 - (2c - 5)$ *2*
13. $5z + 10(-z + 14) = 95$ *9*
14. $x + (x + 1) + (x + 2) = 15$ *4*
15. $2(c + 3) + 5c = 15 - (2c + 18)$ *-1*
16. $5d - (d + 3) = (d + 2) + 7$ *4*
17. $(x + 4) - (x - 6) = 5(x - 8)$ *10*
18. $5 + 7x = -(3 - 2x) - 3x$ *-1*
19. $3y - (4 - 2y) = 3(y + 2)$ *5*
20. $6(x + 2) = 4 - (3 - 2x) - 1$ *-3*
21. $2(2 - 3z) = 8 - 2(4z + 5)$ *-3*
22. $7y - (4 - 2y) = 3(y + 3) - 1$ *2*
23. $5 - 3(4 - 2x) = 4(x - 3) - 3$ *-4*
24. $2(x + 1) + 15x = -(3x - 17) + 5x$ *1*
25. $7y - 2(3 - y) = 4(y + 1)$ *2*
26. $7(x - 1) + 5 = -2(3 - 4x) + 5$ *-1*
27. $2(3 - z) = 16 - 2(3 + 2z)$ *2*
28. $8y - 3(4 - 2y) = 6(y + 1) - 2$ *2*
29. $3 + 7(x + 1) = 6 - (5 + 2x)$ *-1*
30. $7(a - 1) + 4 = -(2a - 4) + 6a + 2$ *3*
31. $-2(3 - 4z) + 7z = 13z - 4$ *1*
32. $-4(2x - 5) + 3x = x - 28$ *8*
33. $5 - (x + 8) + 6x = 4(x + 2)$ *11*
34. $7 - 3(y + 1) + 8 = 4 - 5(y - 2)$ *1*
35. $-(2x + 6) + 3x = 1 + 2(4 - 2x)$ *3*
36. $5 - 3(x + 1) = -(x - 9) + 5x$ *-1*
37. $6y + 3(4 - y) = 8 - 2(y + 3)$ *-2*
38. $-(6 - 4c) + 3c = 10 - 2(c - 1)$ *2*
39. $16 - 4(2a + 1) = 6a + (1 - 3a)$ *1*
40. $7 - 2(4 - 3x) + 8x = -(x + 31)$ *-2*

PART B

Solve.

41. $7(2x - 2) - 5x = 4x + 2$ $\frac{16}{5}$
42. $4z - 3 - 7(z + 1) = 6z$ $\frac{-10}{9}$
43. $-5y - 2(y + 4) = 6y - 9$ $\frac{1}{13}$
44. $8y + 5(1 - y) = 4y - 6$ *11*
45. $3(-2x + 1) = 4(1 + 3x) + 2$ $-\frac{1}{6}$
46. $5r + 3(r - 7) = -(r + 8)$ $\frac{13}{9}$
47. $7(1 - 3a) + a = 6 - (a - 4)$ $-\frac{3}{19}$
48. $2z - 8(z + 1) = 6z + (3z - 4)$ $\frac{-4}{15}$
49. $9 - 4(2 - y) = 7y - (3 + y)$ *2*
50. $6(r - 2) - 3r - 1 = 8(5r + 1) - 10r$ $\frac{-7}{9}$
51. $5z + 3(z - 2) - 6z = 12$ *9*
52. $-3(6 - 2x) + 4x = -(2x - 8)$ $\frac{13}{6}$

PART C

Solve.

53. $6[5 - 3(x - 4)] = 4x + 18$
54. $3 - 2x = -[4 + 5(2x - 1)]$
55. $-7x - [2(3x + 1) + 4] = 3x$
56. $-2[4 - (2 + 3x)] = 4x + 5$
57. $-[7 + 2(1 - 2x)] = 1 - 5x$
58. $4x - 2[5(x + 1) + 3] = 8x$

English Phrases to Algebra

▶ REVIEW CAPSULE

English phrase: 6 decreased by 2

Mathematical terms: 6   —   2
6 decreased by 2 means 6 made smaller by 2, or $6 - 2$

English phrase: 8 increased by 3

Mathematical terms: 8   +   3
8 increased by 3 means 8 made greater by 3, or $8 + 3$

EXAMPLE 1   Write in mathematical terms.

Decreased by means made smaller by. Use —.

7 decreased by 5   9 increased by 4
7   —   5   9   +   4

EXAMPLE 2   Write in mathematical terms.

The value of x is not known.

3 decreased by x
3   — x

EXAMPLE 3   Write in mathematical terms.

Let a variable represent the number.

12 increased by 4 times a number
12   + $(4)(y)$, or $12 + 4y$

EXAMPLE 4   Write in mathematical terms.

7 less than 10 does not mean $7 - 10$.
It means $10 - 7$.

7 less than 10
10   —   7

EXAMPLE 5   Write in mathematical terms.

9 more than 5 means 5 made greater by 9.

$$\text{9 more than 5}$$
$$5 \quad + \quad 9$$

EXAMPLE 6

Write in mathematical terms.

5 less than 3 times a number

Let n represent the number.

$$(3)\,(n) \quad - \quad 5, \text{ or } 3n - 5$$

EXAMPLE 7   Write in mathematical terms.

8 more than twice x

Twice x means 2 times x.

$$(2)\,(x) \quad + \quad 8, \text{ or } 2x + 8$$

EXERCISES

PART A

Write in mathematical terms.

1. 8 decreased by 5 $\ 8 - 5$
2. 9 increased by 7 $\ 9 + 7$
3. 12 increased by 6 $\ 12 + 6$
4. 8 less than 15 $\ 15 - 8$
5. 2 more than 23 $\ 23 + 2$
6. 15 decreased by x $\ 15 - x$
7. y increased by 4 $\ y + 4$
8. 7 more than x $\ x + 7$
9. 8 less than n $\ n - 8$
10. 8 decreased by twice x $\ 8 - 2x$
11. 3 more than 5 times y $\ 5y + 3$
12. 7 times a number, decreased by 2
13. 6 less than 3 times a number $\ 3n - 6$
14. 5 decreased by twice n $\ 5 - 2n$
15. 25 decreased by 4 times a number $\ 25 - 4n$
16. 8 more than 7 times a number
17. 4 times x, increased by 8 $\ 4x + 8$
18. 12 less than 3 times a number
19. 14 increased by twice a number $\ 14 + 2n$
20. 2 times n, decreased by 4 $\ 2n - 4$
21. 9 times a number, decreased by 7 $\ 9n - 7$
22. twice a number, increased by 1

$$7n + 8 \qquad 3n - 12$$

$$2n + 1$$

PART B

Write in mathematical terms.

23. x increased by y $\ x + y$
24. x more than y $\ y + x$
25. 7 times x, decreased by twice y $\ 7x - 2y$
26. m less than 3 times n $\ 3n - m$
27. 9 more than x times y $\ xy + 9$
28. m times n less than 20 $\ 20 - mn$
29. y decreased by 5 times x $\ y - 5x$
30. 6 times x, increased by 5 times y
31. 5 increased by 8 more than 7 times y $\ 5 + 7y + 8$
32. 7 more than twice a number, increased by 6 $\ 2x + 7 + 6$

$$6x + 5y$$

33. 2 less than 5 times a number, increased by 9 $\ 5n - 2 + 9$
34. x more than 8 times y, decreased by twice x $\ 8y + x - 2x$

Number Problems

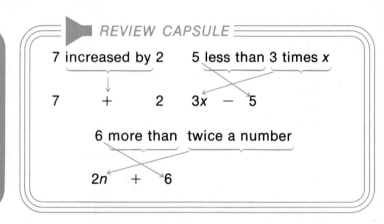

REVIEW CAPSULE

7 increased by 2   5 less than 3 times x

7   +   2 $3x$ —   5

6 more than twice a number

$2n$ +   6

EXAMPLE 1   Write an equation for each sentence.

Three more than a number is 9.

$$n + 3 = 9$$

A number decreased by 7 is 8 times the number.

$$n - 7 = 8n$$

EXAMPLE 2   Seven more than 4 times a number is 31. Find the number.

Let $n =$ the number

7 more than 4 times n is 31.

Write an equation. ⟶
Add −7 to each side. ⟶

$$4n + 7 = 31$$
$$\underline{ - 7 \quad -7}$$
$$4n = 24$$

Divide each side by 4. ⟶

$$n = 6$$

Check 6 in the problem. ⟶

7 more than 4 times 6 is 31.

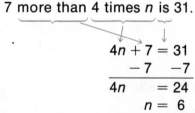

4 (6) + 7	31
24 + 7	
31	

Thus, the number is 6.

EXAMPLE 3 A number decreased by 14 is the same as 8 times the number. Find the number.

Let n = the number

n decreased by 14 is the same as 8 times n.

Write an equation. $\longrightarrow$
$n = 1n$ $\longrightarrow$
Add $-1n$ to each side. $\longrightarrow$

$$\begin{array}{rcl} n - 14 &=& 8n \\ 1n - 14 &=& 8n \\ -1n && -1n \\ \hline -14 &=& 7n \end{array}$$

Divide each side by 7. $\longrightarrow$
$$-2 = n$$

Check -2 in the problem. $\longrightarrow$

n decreased by 14 is 8 times n.

$-2 - 14$	$8(-2)$
-16	-16

Thus, the number is -2.

EXAMPLE 4 Three less than twice a number is the same as the number increased by 8. Find the number.

Let x = the number

Twice x is $2x$.

3 less than $2x$ is the same as x increased by 8.

$$\begin{array}{rcl} 2x - 3 &=& x + 8 \\ 2x - 3 &=& 1x + 8 \\ -1x && -1x \\ \hline 1x - 3 &=& 8 \\ +3 && +3 \\ \hline x &=& 11 \end{array}$$

$1x = x$ $\longrightarrow$

Check 11 in the problem. $\longrightarrow$ **Thus,** the number is 11.

EXAMPLE 5 A number increased by 6 times the number is -63. Find the number.

Let n = the number

$$\begin{array}{rcl} n + 6n &=& -63 \\ 7n &=& -63 \\ n &=& -9 \end{array}$$

$n + 6n = 1n + 6n = 7n$ $\longrightarrow$

Check -9 in the problem. $\longrightarrow$ **Thus,** the number is -9.

ORAL EXERCISES

Give an equation for each sentence.

1. Five more than twice x is 14. $2x + 5 = 14$
2. Six decreased by 4 times n is 18. $6 - 4n = 18$
3. Seven times n is 3 more than n.
4. Two less than a number is 20.
5. Eight more than twice a number is 2.
6. The sum of x and 6 is 8 times x.
7. Two decreased by 4 times x is 15.
8. Twelve is 5 more than 6 times x.
9. Sixteen less than twice x is 32. $2x - 16 = 32$
10. Nine increased by 5 times n is 18. $9 + 5n = 18$

EXERCISES

PART A

1. Nine more than a number is 13. Find the number. 4
2. A number decreased by 10 is 16. Find the number. 26
3. Eleven increased by twice a number is 17. Find the number. 3
4. Eight less than 5 times a number is 22. Find the number. 6
5. Twelve decreased by 3 times a number is 9. Find the number. 1
6. Three more than 8 times a number is -29. Find the number. -4
7. Sixteen is 5 less than 7 times a number. Find the number. 3
8. Thirteen increased by 9 times a number is 4. Find the number. -1
9. Ten less than twice a number is the same as 7 times the number. Find the number. -2
10. A number increased by 30 is 14 decreased by 3 times the number. Find the number. -4
11. Nine more than 5 times a number is the same as 2 times the number. Find the number. -3
12. Twice a number is the same as 6 more than 8 times the number. Find the number. -1
13. Seven less than 6 times a number is the same as the number decreased by 2. Find the number. 1
14. Five times a number is the same as 30 more than 8 times the number. Find the number. -10
15. Two less than 2 times a number is the same as the number decreased by 38. Find the number. -36
16. A number increased by 5 is the same as 37 decreased by 7 times the number. Find the number. 4
17. Eight times a number decreased by the number is 35. Find the number. 5
18. Twice a number plus 4 times the number is -54. Find the number. -9
19. A number plus 3 more than the number is 17. Find the number. 7
20. Six more than a number increased by the number is 40. Find the number. 17
21. Seven times a number decreased by the number is -48. Find the number. -8
22. Five less than 3 times a number is -20. Find the number. -5
23. Eight times a number is the same as 30 less than 5 times the number. Find the number. -10
24. Three less than 3 times a number is the same as 5 less than twice the number. Find the number. -2

PART B

EXAMPLE   Three times the sum of a number and 2 is the same as 8 increased by the number. Find the number.

Let $x =$ the number

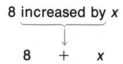

3 times the sum of x and 2

$3(x + 2)$

8 increased by x

$8 + x$

$3(x + 2)$ is the same as $8 + x$

$$3(x + 2) = 8 + x$$

Remove parentheses. $\longrightarrow$ $3x + 6 = 8 + x$
Add $-1x$ to each side. $\longrightarrow$ $2x + 6 = 8$
Add -6 to each side. $\longrightarrow$ $2x = 2$
Divide each side by 2. $x = 1$

Check 1 in the problem. $\longrightarrow$ **Thus,** the number is 1.

---

25. Five times the sum of a number and 2 is 45. Find the number. *7*

26. Six times the sum of a number and -4 is 30. Find the number. *9*

27. Five more than a number is 4 times the sum of the number and 8. Find the number. *-9*

28. Three times the sum of 4 and a number is the same as 18 increased by the number. Find the number. *3*

29. Twice the sum of 6 and a number is the same as 15 decreased by the number. Find the number. *1*

30. Eight more than three times a number is the same as twice the number decreased by 6. Find the number. *-14*

PART C

31. If 6 times the sum of twice a number and 8 is decreased by 4, the result is 1 less than 3 times the sum of the number and 6. Find the number.

32. If 15 is decreased by 7 times the sum of 5 and 3 times a number, the result is 12 more than twice the sum of the number and 7. Find the number.

More Number Problems

<table>
<tr><td>

OBJECTIVES

■ To solve word problems involving two or more numbers

</td></tr>
</table>

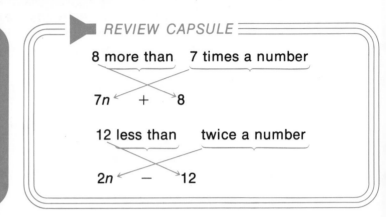

▶ REVIEW CAPSULE

8 more than   7 times a number

7n   +   8

12 less than   twice a number

2n   −   12

EXAMPLE 1   Clyde is thinking of two numbers. The second number is 5 more than twice the first. Repesent the two numbers.

Let f = first number

5 more than twice the first ——————→ $2f + 5$ = second number

Thus, f and $2f + 5$ represent the two numbers.

EXAMPLE 2   The greater of two numbers is 8 less than 4 times the smaller. Represent the two numbers.

Let s = smaller number
$4s - 8$ = greater number

Thus, s and $4s - 8$ represent the two numbers.

EXAMPLE 3   The second of three numbers is 6 times the first. The third is 1 more than the second. Represent the three numbers.

Let f = first number

6 times the first ——————————→ $6f$ = second number

1 more than the second —————→ $6f + 1$ = third number

Thus, f, $6f$, and $6f + 1$ represent the three numbers.

EXAMPLE 4   The greater of two numbers is 12 more than 8 times the smaller. Their sum is 21. Find the numbers.

Represent the two numbers.

Let s = smaller number
$8s + 12$ = greater number

Smaller + greater = 21. ────────────→
Write an equation and solve it.

$$s + (8s + 12) = 21$$
$$9s + \;\; 12 = 21$$
$$9s = 9$$
$$s = 1$$

Find both numbers.

Smaller number, s is 1.
Greater number, $8s + 12$ is $8(1) + 12$, or 20.

Check 1 and 20 in the first part of the problem.

Greater is 12 more than 8 times smaller.

20	$8(1) + 12$
20	20

Check 1 and 20 in the second part of the problem.

Their sum is 21.

$1 + 20$	21
21	

Thus, 1 and 20 are the two numbers.

EXAMPLE 5   The second of two numbers is 16 less than 3 times the first. Their sum is 24. Find the two numbers.

Let f = first number
$3f - 16$ = second number

First + second = 24. ────────────→

$$f + (3f - 16) = 24$$
$$4f - 16 = 24$$
$$4f = 40$$
$$f = 10$$

Find both numbers. $3(10) - 16 = 30 - 16$, or 14

First number, f is 10.
Second number, $3f - 16$ is $3(10) - 16$, or 14.

Check. ────────────────→

The sum is 24.

$10 + 14$	24
24	

Second is 16 less than 3 times first.

14	$3(10) - 16$
	14

Thus, 10 and 14 are the two numbers.

EXAMPLE 6   Separate $90 into two parts so that the first part is $30 less than twice the second part.

Let s = second part
$2s - 30$ = first part
$$s + (2s - 30) = 90$$
$$3s - 30 = 90$$
$$3s = 120$$
$$s = 40$$

First is 30 less than twice second.
Their sum is 90. ————————→
Separate 90 into two parts means the sum of the parts is 90.

Find both parts.
$2(40) - 30 = 80 - 30$, or 50 }

Second part, s is 40.
First part, $2s - 30$ is $2(40) - 30$, or 50.

Thus, $50 and $40 are the two parts.

EXAMPLE 7   The second of three numbers is 6 times the first. The third is 1 more than the second. Their sum is 27. Find the three numbers.

Let f = first number
$6f$ = second number

1 more than second ————————→ $6f + 1$ = third number
Their sum is 27. ————————→
$$f + 6f + 6f + 1 = 27$$
$$13f + 1 = 27$$
$$13f = 26$$
$$f = 2$$

First, f is 2.
Second, $6f$ is $6(2)$, or 12.

$6(2) + 1 = 12 + 1 = 13$ ————————→ Third, $6f + 1$ is $6(2) + 1$, or 13.

Thus, 2, 12, and 13 are the three numbers.

EXERCISES

PART A

1. The second of two numbers is 5 times the first. Their sum is 42. Find the numbers. *7; 35*

2. The greater of two numbers is 3 more than twice the smaller. Their sum is 24. Find the numbers. *7; 17*

3. The sum of two numbers is 50. The first is 5 less than 4 times the second. Find the numbers. *39; 11*

4. Find two numbers whose sum is 55 if the second is 7 more than 5 times the first. *8; 47*

5. The greater of two numbers is 9 more than the smaller. Their sum is 83. Find the numbers. *37; 46*

6. The sum of two numbers is 19. The second is 8 less than twice the first. Find the numbers. *9; 10*

7. Sixty-eight students are separated into two groups. The first group is 3 times as large as the second. How many students are in each group? *51; 17*

8. Separate $115 into two parts so that the greater part is $12 more than the smaller part.
$51.50; $63.50

9. Separate $89 into two parts so that the second part is $4 less than twice the first part. *$31; $58*

10. Separate 43 people into two groups so that the first group is 5 less than 3 times the second. *31, 12*

11. The sum of three numbers is 34. The first is 3 less than the second, while the third is 4 more than the second. Find the numbers. *8, 11, 15*

12. The sum of three numbers is 26. The second number is twice the first, and the third is 6 more than the second. Find the numbers.
4, 8, 14

PART B

EXAMPLE The smaller of two numbers is 3 less than the greater. If the greater is decreased by twice the smaller, the result is -5. Find the numbers.

Let g = greater number
$g - 3$ = smaller number

greater decreased by twice smaller is -5

$$g \quad - \quad 2(g - 3) \quad = -5$$

$-2(g - 3) = -2g + 6 \longrightarrow$

$$g - 2g + 6 = -5$$
$$1g - 2g + 6 = -5$$
$$-1g + 6 = -5$$
$$-1g = -11$$
$$g = 11$$

Greater number, g is 11.
Smaller number, $g - 3$ is $11 - 3$, or 8.
Thus, the numbers are 11 and 8.

13. The greater of two numbers is 3 more than the smaller. If twice the smaller is added to the greater, the result is 30. Find the numbers. *9; 12*

14. The second of two numbers is 4 more than the first. If the second is increased by 1, the result is twice the first. Find the numbers. *5; 9*

15. The first of two numbers is twice the second. Seven more than the second number is equal to the first number decreased by 6. Find the numbers. *26; 13*

16. The second of two numbers is 3 more than the first. If 4 times the first is increased by the second, the result is 73. Find the numbers.
14; 17

Coin Problems

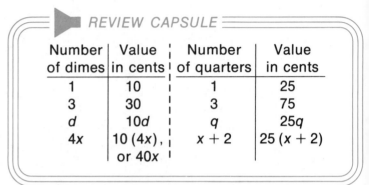

Number of dimes	Value in cents	Number of quarters	Value in cents
1	10	1	25
3	30	3	75
d	$10d$	q	$25q$
$4x$	$10(4x)$, or $40x$	$x + 2$	$25(x + 2)$

EXAMPLE 1 Find the total value in cents.
3 nickels and 7 dimes

$$\text{Total value} = 3(5) + 7(10)$$
$$= 15 \quad + 70, \quad \text{or } 85 \text{ cents}$$

EXAMPLE 2 Represent the total value in cents.
d dimes and q quarters

Number of coins ⟶

Value in cents ⟶

	Dimes	Quarters
Number	d	q
Value	$10d$	$25q$

Thus, the total value in cents is $10d + 25q$.

EXAMPLE 3 Represent the total value in cents.
x quarters and $15 - x$ nickels

	Quarters	Nickels
Number	x	$15 - x$
Value	$25x$	$5(15 - x)$

$$\text{Total value} = 25x + 5(15 - x)$$
$$= 25x + 75 - 5x$$
$$= 20x + 75$$

Thus, the total value in cents is $20x + 75$.

EXAMPLE 4 Eleanor had three times as many quarters as nickels. She had $1.60 in all. How many nickels and how many quarters did she have?

	Nickels	Quarters
Number	n	$3n$
Value	$5n$	$25\,(3n)$

Let n = number of nickels ⎫
$3n$ = number of quarters ⎰

$1.60 = 160 cents
total value = 160 cents

$$5n + 25\,(3n) = 160$$
$$5n + 75n = 160$$
$$80n = 160$$
$$n = 2$$

Find both numbers.

Number of nickels, n is 2.
Number of quarters, $3n$ is 3 (2), or 6.

Check 2 and 6 in the first part of the problem.

Number of quarters is 3 times number of nickels.

6	3 (2)
	6

Check 2 and 6 in the second part of the problem.

Total value is 160 cents.

5 (2) + 25 (6)	160
10 + 150	
160	

Thus, she had 2 nickels and 6 quarters.

EXAMPLE 5 Paul had 23 coins in nickels and dimes. Their total value was $1.55. How many were nickels and how many were dimes?

	Nickels	Dimes
Number	n	$23 - n$
Value	$5n$	$10\,(23 - n)$

23 coins in all.
Let n = number of nickels ⎫
$23 - n$ = number of dimes ⎰

$1.55 = 155 cents
total value = 155 cents

$$5n + 10\,(23 - n) = 155$$
$$5n + 230 - 10n = 155$$
$$230 - 5n = 155$$
$$-5n = -75$$
$$n = 15$$

Find both numbers.

Number of nickels, n is 15.
Number of dimes, $23 - n$ is $23 - 15$, or 8.

Check 15 and 8 in the problem.

Thus, he had 15 nickels and 8 dimes.

EXAMPLE 6   Bob has 4 more dimes than nickels. He has $1.45 in all. Write an equation to find the number of nickels he has.

Let n = number of nickels.

4 more than n

$n + 4$ = number of dimes.

	Nickels	Dimes
Number	n	$n + 4$
Value	$5n$	$10(n + 4)$

Equation $\longrightarrow$

$$5n + 10(n + 4) = 145$$

EXERCISES

PART A

1. John has 4 times as many nickels as dimes. He has $.90 in all. How many coins of each type does he have? *12n; 3d*

2. Chris has 5 times as many nickels as quarters. Their value is $1.50. How many nickels does she have? *15*

3. Gladys has $.85. She has 3 times as many quarters as dimes. How many coins of each type does she have? *1d; 3q*

4. Jose has 7 times as many dimes as nickels. Their value is $3.00. How many dimes does he have? *28*

5. Jim has 11 coins in dimes and quarters. Their value is $1.70. How many of each does he have? *7d; 4q*

6. A collection of 24 dimes and half dollars amounts to $3.60. How many dimes are there? *21*

7. Beth has 7 more nickels than pennies. She has $1.19 in all. How many of each does she have? *14p; 21n*

8. The number of dimes is 5 less than the number of quarters. The total value is $2.30. How many dimes are there? *3*

PART B

9. For a school play, 738 tickets valued at $856 were sold. Some cost $1 and some cost $1.50. How many $1 tickets were sold? *502*

10. Angelo has $6.25 in dimes and quarters. The number of dimes is 2 more than 3 times the number of quarters. How many of each does he have? *35d; 11q*

11. Bill has 6 times as many dimes as nickels and 2 more pennies than dimes. He has $2.15 in all. How many of each does he have? *3n; 18d; 20p*

12. Mary has $3.41. She has 2 more dimes than half dollars and 3 times as many pennies as dimes. How many pennies does she have? *21*

PART C

13. Kay has 5 more nickels than pennies, twice as many dimes as nickels, and 2 more quarters than dimes. She has $17.17 in all. How many dimes does she have?

14. In changing a $5 bill, Sarah received 9 more dimes than nickels and 7 fewer quarters than dimes. How many coins of each type did she receive?

Vacationing by Rental Car

Many people fly to a resort and then rent a car for touring.

CHAN'S
CAR RENTALS
$75/wk plus 9¢/km

THE TRIP IS 450 KM.
THAT WOULD COST
$75 + $.09(450) =
$75 + $40.50
FLAT + COST/KM = $115.50
RATE

PROBLEM

A car renting agency charges $85/week plus 8¢/km. How far can you travel, to the nearest km, on a maximum budget of $200?

Use the formula. ⟶

$(.08)(n) = .08n$
Add -85 to each side. ⟶
Divide each side by .08. ⟶

$$.08 \overline{)115.00\,0} = 1,437.5$$

Let n = the number of km you can travel
flat rate plus $(.08)$ (number of km)

$$85 \quad + \quad .08n = 200$$
$$.08n = 115$$
$$n = 1,437.5$$

Thus, you can travel 1,438 km.

PROJECT

Round answers to the nearest unit.

1. Earl budgeted $150 for renting a car. How far can he travel if the charges are $75 plus 23¢/km?

2. Jill budgeted $250 for renting a car. How far can she travel if the charges are $90 plus 18¢/km?

3. Which is more economical? A 200-km bus tour for $85, or renting a car for $75 plus 8¢/km?

4. The Byrnes budgeted $240 for renting a car. The charges are $16.45/day plus 13¢/km. How far can they travel in a week?

Perimeter Problems

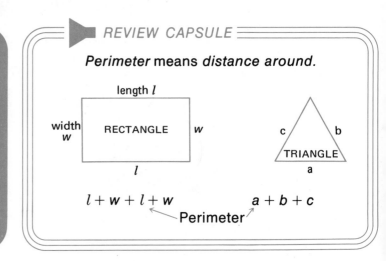

▶ *REVIEW CAPSULE*

Perimeter means *distance around.*

$$l + w + l + w \qquad a + b + c$$
Perimeter

EXAMPLE 1   The length of a rectangle is 5 meters (m) greater than the width. The perimeter is 38 meters. Find the length and the width.

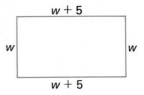

Length is 5 greater than width. ⟶

Let w = width
$w + 5$ = length

Formula for perimeter ⟶
Substitute $w + 5$ for l. ⟶

$$2l + 2w = \text{perimeter}$$
$$2(w + 5) + 2w = 38$$
$$2w + 10 + 2w = 38$$
$$4w + 10 = 38$$
$$4w = 28$$
$$w = 7$$

Width, w is 7.
Length, $w + 5$ is $7 + 5$, or 12.

Check 7 and 12 in the problem.

Length is 5 greater than width.

12	7 + 5
12	12

Perimeter	is 38.
$2(12) + 2(7)$	38
38	

Thus, the length is 12 m and the width is 7 m.

EXAMPLE 2 The length of a rectangle is 8 kilometers (km) more than 6 times the width. The perimeter is 156 km. Find the length and the width.

Let w = width
$6w + 8$ = length

$6w + 8$
w ⸻ w
$6w + 8$

Substitute $6w + 8$ for l. ⟶

$$2l + 2w = \text{perimeter}$$
$$2(6w + 8) + 2w = 156$$
$$12w + 16 + 2w = 156$$
$$14w + 16 = 156$$
$$14w = 140$$
$$w = 10$$

Check.
Perimeter $= 2l + 2w$
$\quad = 2(68) + 2(10)$
$\quad = 136 + 20$
$\quad = 156$ km

Width, w is 10.
Length, $6w + 8$ is $6(10) + 8$, or 68.

Thus, the length is 68 km and the width is 10 km.

EXAMPLE 3 Side b of a triangle is twice as long as side c. Side a is 3 meters longer than side b. The perimeter is 48 meters. Find the length of each side.

Let c = side c
$2c$ = side b
$2c + 3$ = side a

It is easy to represent a and b in terms of c.

c b $(2c)$
a
$(2c + 3)$

$$a \quad + \ b \ + c = \text{perimeter}$$
$$(2c + 3) + 2c + c = 48$$
$$5c + 3 = 48$$
$$5c = 45$$
$$c = 9$$

Side c is 9.
Side b, $2c$ is $2(9)$, or 18.
Side a, $2c + 3$ is $2(9) + 3$, or 21.

Check.
Perimeter $= a + b + c$
$\quad = 21 + 18 + 9$
$\quad = 48$ meters

Thus, the lengths of the sides are 21 meters, 18 meters, and 9 meters.

EXERCISES

PART A

1. The length of a rectangle is 6 m greater than the width. The perimeter is 40 m. Find the length and the width. *13 m; 7 m*

2. The length of a rectangle is twice the width. The perimeter is 42 cm. Find the length and the width. *14 cm; 7 cm*

3. The length of a rectangle is 3 km more than twice the width. The perimeter is 54 km. Find the length and the width. *19 km; 8 km*

4. The length of a rectangle is 2 m less than 3 times the width. The perimeter is 68 m. Find the length and the width. *25 m; 9 m*

5. Side *x* of a triangle is 2 cm longer than side *y*. Side *z* is 5 cm shorter than twice side *y*. The perimeter is 49 cm. Find the length of each side.

6. The perimeter of a triangle is 40 m. The first side is twice the second. The third side is 5 m more than the first. Find the length of each side.

7. The perimeter of a triangle is 38 cm. The first side is 3 cm less than the second, and the third is 5 cm more than the second. Find the lengths of the three sides. *9 cm; 12 cm; 17 cm*

8. The perimeter of a triangle is 47 km. The first side is 5 km less than twice the second, and the third is 2 km more than the first. Find the lengths of the sides.

9. The base of an isosceles triangle is 8 m. The perimeter is 30 m. Find the lengths of the two congruent sides. *11 m; 11 m*

10. One of the two congruent sides of an isosceles triangle is 7 cm. The perimeter is 24 cm. Find the base. *10 cm*   *17 km; 11 km; 19 km*

PART B

11. A square and an equilateral triangle have the same perimeter. Each side of the square is 12 m. Find the length of each side of the triangle. *16 m*

12. A square and an equilateral triangle have the same perimeter. Each side of the triangle is 20 cm. Find the length of each side of the square.

13. A rectangle and an equilateral triangle have the same perimeter. The length of the rectangle is twice the width. Each side of the triangle is 18 cm. Find the length and width of the rectangle. *18 cm; 9 cm*

14. Each side of an equilateral triangle is 2 m more than each side of a square. Their perimeters are the same. Find the length of each side of the triangle. *8 m*   *15 cm*

PART C

15. The length of a rectangle is 3 cm less than twice the width. If the length is decreased by 2 cm and the width by 1 cm, the perimeter will be 24 cm. Find the dimensions of the original rectangle.

16. A rectangular field is 4 times as long as it is wide. If the length is decreased by 10 m and the width is increased by 2 m, the perimeter will be 64 m. Find the dimensions of the original field.

Mathematics in the Hospital

Many important jobs are done in hospitals by technicians and lab specialists. Pictured above is a technician setting up one of the many machines that are used to monitor a patient's health. Below is a lab specialist analyzing blood samples.

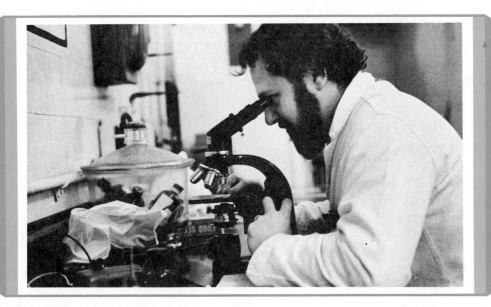

Chapter Three Review

Which members of the given replacement set are solutions of the sentence? $[p.\ 56]$

1. $20 = 2x + 6$ $\{7, 8, 9\}$
2. $13 + 2x = 3 + 6x$ $\{1, 2, 3, 4, 5\}$
3. $23 + 9y = 50$ $\{1, 3, 5, 7\}$
4. $7x - 21 = 5x - 9$ $\{5, 6\}$
5. $8y - 36 = 24$ $\{4, 6, 8\}$
6. $6y - 13 = -52 + 19y$ $\{3, 8, 11\}$
7. $-4c - 46 = -2$ $\{-9, -10, -11\}$
8. $4x - 4 = 3x - 2$ $\{1, 2, 3, 4\}$

Solve. $[p.\ 59,\ 64,\ 68]$

9. $-7 = 5x + 1$
10. $8r - 22 = 58$
11. $3y - 6 = 9$
12. $-39 = -3 + 12y$
13. $10c - 15 = -5$
14. $5x - 8 = -8$
15. $1 + 4x = 55 - 8$
16. $-42 + 39 = 11 - 2z$
17. $5 + 8x = 6x + 11$
18. $3c + 2 = -70 + 15c$
19. $9x - 20 = 8x + 2$
20. $27 - 5y = 4y - 6y$
21. $3z - 2z = -8 - z$
22. $33 - 4x = 1 + 4x$
23. $x + 12 + x = -14$
24. $16 - 9 = 5x - 8$
25. $-4(2x + 6) = -3x + 1$
26. $5 - 10x = -(3 - 2x)$
27. $6(y + 3) = 9 - (3 - 2y)$
28. $7(x - 1) = -2(-4x + 3)$
29. $5x - 4(2x - 6) = 3x - 24$
30. $-3(2x + 1) + 5 = -(4x - 9) + 5x$
31. $8y - 2(-3y + 4) = -(y + 38)$
32. $12 - 3(y + 1) = 1 - 5(y - 2)$

Write in mathematical terms. $[p.\ 70]$

33. 6 increased by x
34. 12 less than y
35. n decreased by 3
36. 6 more than 3 times x
37. 5 less than twice y
38. 7 less than 9 times a number

Solve each problem. $[p.\ 72,\ 76,\ 80,\ 84]$

39. A number increased by 8 is the same as 3 times the number. Find the number.

40. The sum of two numbers is 26. The second is 2 less than 3 times the first. Find the two numbers.

41. One number is 17 more than another. If the greater number is increased by 3, the result is 5 times the smaller. Find the two numbers.

42. Paula had 7 times as many nickels as quarters. Their value was $1.80. How many quarters did she have?

43. The perimeter of a rectangle is 68 cm. The length is 2 cm more than 3 times the width. Find the length and the width.

44. Side x of a triangle is 3 m longer than side y. Side z is 2 m shorter than twice side y. The perimeter is 17 m. Find the lengths of the three sides.

Chapter Three Test

Which members of the given replacement set are solutions of the sentence?

1. $13 + x = 5x + 1$ $\{3, 4\}$
2. $9y - 7 = 11 + 7y$ $\{7, 8, 9\}$
3. $5x + 2 = 8x - 10$ $\{1, 2, 4, 5\}$
4. $-6 + 8z = 21z - 45$ $\{3, 8, 11\}$
5. $5x - 7 = 4x - 12$ $\{-4, -5, -6\}$
6. $8y - 9 = 5y + 3$ $\{1, 2, 4, 5\}$

Solve.

7. $38 - 8x = -18$
8. $6y + 7 = 7$
9. $15r - 5 = -35$
10. $8c - 9 = -2c - 9$
11. $9 + 15 = 10z - 7$
12. $-2 + 5x = 38 - 10$
13. $3(x + 5) = x + 21$
14. $-(3x + 2) = x - 50$
15. $6y + (1 - 3y) = 16 - 4(2y + 1)$
16. $7(x + 1) - 1 = 2 - (5 + 2x)$
17. $2(3 - x) - 7 = 9 - 2(3 + 2x)$
18. $(x + 2) + (x + 4) = 42 - (x + 6)$

Write in mathematical terms.

19. 7 decreased by 2
20. 5 increased by x
21. x less than twice y
22. 8 more than 3 times a number

Solve each problem.

23. Seven less than 4 times a number is the same as the number increased by 8. Find the number.

24. The greater of two numbers is 8 less than 3 times the smaller. Their sum is 36. Find the two numbers.

25. A collection of 25 dimes and quarters amounts to $5.05. How many of each kind of coin are there?

26. The length of a rectangle is 3 m less than 3 times the width. The perimeter is 66 m. Find the length and the width.

Sequences

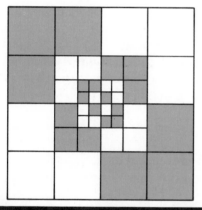

Mathematics is concerned with patterns formed by numbers. A pattern is displayed in each sequence of numbers below.

PROJECT

See if you can find the pattern. Then give the next three numbers in the sequence.

1. −6, −7, −8, −9, −10, . . .

2. 3, 9, 27, 81, . . .

3. −3, −3, −3, −3, . . .

4. 2, −2, 2, −2, 2, . . .

5. .1, .01, .001, .0001, . . .

6. 3, −6, 12, −24, . . .

7. 1, 2, 4, 5, 7, 8, 10, 11, . . .

8. 1, 4, 9, 16, 25, . . .

9. 1, 8, 27, 64, . . .

10. −6, −2, 2, 6, 10, . . .

11. $\dfrac{1}{2}, \dfrac{2}{3}, \dfrac{3}{4}, \dfrac{4}{5}, \ldots$

12. $\dfrac{1}{2}$, 2, 8, 32, . . .

13. 0, 3, 8, 15, . . .

14. $\dfrac{1}{2}, \dfrac{4}{3}, \dfrac{9}{4}, \dfrac{16}{5}, \ldots$

15. 0, 7, 26, 63, . . .

16. 0, 1, 1, 2, 3, 5, 8, 13, . . .

Sets

OBJECTIVES

- To identify equal sets
- To identify and describe finite and infinite sets
- To find and graph solution sets of equations like
  $$3x - 14 = 5x - 16$$

 REVIEW CAPSULE

A *set* is a collection of objects. The objects are *members,* or *elements* of the set. Braces are used to enclose the names of the elements of a set.

Set A   Set B
↓   ↓
$A = \{2, 4, 6\}$ $B = \{-2, -1, 0, 1, 2\}$

elements of A   elements of B

Definition of equal sets ⟶

Two sets are *equal* if they have the same elements.

Examples of equal sets

The order of listing the elements does not matter. ⟶

$\{-1, 3, 8\} = \{3, 8, -1\}$ $\{1, 2, 3\} = \{1, 1+1, 1+2\}$

Finite sets	Infinite sets
↙ ↘	↙ ↘
$\{1, 2, 3\}$ $\{-1, 0, 1, 2\}$	$\{1, 2, 3, 4, \ldots\}$ $\{\text{integers}\}$
A definite number of elements	No definite number of elements

The three dots mean the pattern continues forever.

It is not possible to list all the members of an infinite set.

EXAMPLE 1   Tell whether each set is finite or infinite. Then describe each set in words.

$\{5, 6, 7\}$ finite
$\{2, 4, 6, 8, \ldots\}$ infinite

Between 4 and 8 means *not* including 4 and 8.
Other descriptions are possible.

$\{5, 6, 7\}$ is the set of whole numbers between 4 and 8.
$\{2, 4, 6, 8, \ldots\}$ is the set of positive even integers.

EXAMPLE 2 $C = \{$integers between -3 and $2\}$. Describe set C by listing its elements.

Examine the integers on a number line.

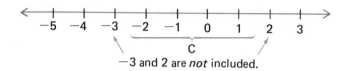

-3 and 2 are *not* included.

Thus, $C = \{-2, -1, 0, 1\}$.

EXAMPLE 3 $A = \{$integers between 5 and $6\}$. Describe set A by listing its elements.

There are no integers between 5 and 6. A set can have no elements. ⟶ Thus, $A = \phi$ (the set with no elements).

Definition of empty set ⟶

> The set with no elements is the empty set.
>
> Symbol for the empty set: ϕ

EXAMPLE 4 Find the set of all solutions of $6x - 9 = 2x + 19$. Then graph the set.

The replacement set is {all numbers}.

$$6x - 9 = 2x + 19$$
$$4x - 9 = 19$$
$$4x = 28$$
$$x = 7$$

7 is the solution. ⟶

A set can have only 1 element. ⟶ Thus, $\{7\}$ is the set of all solutions.

To graph $\{7\}$, place a dot at 7 on a number line. $\Big\}$

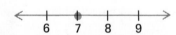

Definition of solution set ⟶
For Example 4, the solution set is $\{7\}$.

> The *solution set* of an open sentence is the set of all members of the replacement set which are solutions of the sentence.

EXAMPLE 5 Find the solution set of $x + 5 = x + 2$.

$$\begin{array}{r} x + 5 = x + 2 \\ \underline{-x \qquad -x} \\ 5 = 2 \end{array}$$ ← False sentence

Add $-x$ to each side. ⟶

There is no number which makes $x + 5 = x + 2$ true. ⟶ Thus, the solution set of $x + 5 = x + 2$ is ϕ.

EXERCISES

PART A

Which sets are equal to $\{1, 3, 5, 6\}$?

1. $\{1, 6, 3, 5\}$ E

2. $\{1, 3, 7, 6\}$ NE

3. $\{5, 2, 1, 6\}$ NE

4. $\{6, 3, 1, 5\}$ E

5. $\{1, 1+2, 1+4, 1+5\}$ E

6. $\{3, 8-1, 7-1, 1\}$ NE

For each set, tell whether it is finite or infinite. Then describe the set in words.

7. $\{0, 1, 2, 3, 4\}$ *fin.*

8. $\{0, 1, 2, 3, 4, \ldots\}$ *inf.*

9. $\{1, 3, 5, 7, \ldots\}$ *inf.*

10. $\{-1, -2, -3, -4\}$ *fin.*

11. ϕ *fin.*

12. $\{\ldots -2, -1, 0, 1, 2, \ldots\}$

Describe each set by listing its elements.

$\{9, 10, 11, \ldots\}$

13. $A = \{$positive integers less than 6$\}$

14. $B = \{$positive integers greater than 8$\}$

15. $C = \{$negative integers between -4 and $-1\}$ $\{-3, -2\}$

16. $D = \{$integers between 8 and 9$\}$ ϕ

Find the solution set of each sentence. Then graph it.

17. $5y - 8 = 20 + y$ $\{7\}$

18. $3x - 5 = 7 + 3x$ ϕ

19. $9z + 17 = 11z + 3$ $\{7\}$

20. $9 + 4y = 4y - 12$ ϕ

21. $8y - 22 = -14 + 6y$ $\{4\}$

22. $3x + 4 = -68 + 15x$ $\{6\}$

23. $-8y + 7y = 4 - 2y$ $\{4\}$

24. $13 + 20 = 10x - 7$ $\{4\}$

25. $27 - 6y = -8y + 5y$ $\{9\}$

26. $-3x + 2 = x - 8 - 4x$ ϕ

27. $x + x + 5x = -7$ $\{-1\}$

28. $6x + 8 + x = -4 + 7x$ ϕ

PART B

EXAMPLE Find the solution set of $7x + 2 = 2 + 3x + 4x$. Then graph it.

$$7x + 2 = 2 + \underbrace{3x + 4x}$$
$$7x + 2 = 2 + \quad 7x$$

Add -2 to each side. ⟶

Divide each side by 7. ⟶

$$7x = 7x$$
$$x = x$$

Every number also makes $7x + 2 = 2 + 3x + 4x$ true.

Every number makes $x = x$ true.
Thus, the solution set is $\{$all numbers$\}$.

Graph of $\{$all numbers$\}$ ⟶

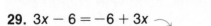

$$\begin{array}{ccccccccc} & | & | & | & | & | & | & | & | & \\ -4 & -3 & -2 & -1 & 0 & 1 & 2 & 3 & 4 \end{array}$$

Find the solution set of each sentence. Then graph it.

$\{$all numbers$\}$

29. $3x - 6 = -6 + 3x$

$\{$all numbers$\}$

30. $x + x - 2x = -12$ ϕ

31. $4x + 7 + 5x = 7 + 9x$ $\{$all numbers$\}$

PART C

Graph the solution set of each.

32. $8 - [5 - (4 + x)] = 8 - (6 - x)$

33. $8x - 3[4 - (2 - x)] = 5x - 6$

Inequalities

▶ *REVIEW CAPSULE*

SENTENCES

Types & Symbols		Examples	
EQUATIONS	True	False	Open
$=$ is equal to	$2+3=5$	$4+6=9$	$x+3=8$
INEQUALITIES	True	False	Open
$\neq$ is not equal to	$5 \neq 7$	$1+2 \neq 3$	$y \neq 6$
$<$ is less than	$4 < 8$	$10 < 7$	$x < 2$
$>$ is greater than	$7 > 2$	$3 > 9$	$c+2 > 4$

$a < b$ means $b > a$.

EXAMPLE 1 Graph the solution set of $x < 4$.

Read: x is less than 4. ———————→
Many numbers make $x < 4$ true.

$$
\begin{aligned}
x &< 4 \\
3\tfrac{1}{2} &< 4 \\
3 &< 4 \\
1 &< 4 \\
0 &< 4 \\
-2 &< 4 \\
-4\tfrac{1}{3} &< 4 \\
-5 &< 4
\end{aligned}
$$

We could go on forever. ———————→

Mark the points with the ———————→
coordinates listed above.

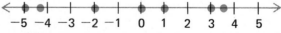

Any point to the left of the point with coordinate
4 has a coordinate less than 4. We draw an
arrow to show all such points.

Graph of solution set of $x < 4$:

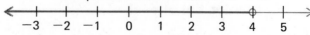

Note the circle around 4.
4 is not in the solution set.

Read: the set of all numbers x, such that x is less than 4. ⟶

The solution set of $x < 4$ is an infinite set.
$$\{x \mid x < 4\}$$

EXAMPLE 2 Graph the solution set of $x > -2$.

Read: x is greater than −2. ⟶
Substitute numbers for x. ⟶

$$
\begin{array}{rcl}
x & > & -2 \\
\hline
-1 & > & -2 \\
-\dfrac{1}{2} & > & -2 \\
0 & > & -2 \\
3 & > & -2 \\
20 & > & -2
\end{array}
$$

We could go on forever. ⟶

Graph of $\{x \mid x > -2\}$ ⟶
−2 is not in the solution set.

−1 > −2. For example, a temperature of 1° below 0° is warmer than a temperature of 2° below 0°.

Any point to the right of the point with coordinate −2 has a coordinate greater than −2.

EXAMPLE 3 Graph the solution set of $x \le 1$.
$x \le 1$ means x is less than or equal to 1.

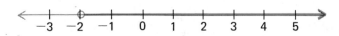

Graph of $\{x \mid x \le 1\}$ ⟶
The dot shows that 1 is in the solution set.

Any number which is less than or equal to 1 makes $x \le 1$ true. **Thus,** the graph includes 1 and all points to the left.

EXAMPLE 4 Graph the solution set of $-3 \le x$.

$$-3 \le x \text{ means } x \ge -3$$

Read the variable first. ⟶
x is greater than or equal to −3

Graph of $\{x \mid x \ge -3\}$ ⟶
−3 is in the solution set.

Any number which is greater than or equal to −3 makes $x \ge -3$ true. **Thus,** the graph includes −3 and all points to the right.

ORAL EXERCISES

Tell which inequality symbol, > or <, will make the sentence true.

1. 5 ? 8 <   **2.** 9 ? 6 >   **3.** −5 ? −2 <   **4.** −3 ? −5 >   **5.** −4 ? −1 <
6. −13 ? −18 >   **7.** −5 ? 1 <   **8.** −6 ? 14 <   **9.** 5 ? −3 >   **10.** −8 ? −12 >

Read each inequality. [Hint: Read the variable first.]
Then replace x with a number that will make the inequality true.

11. $x > -5$ **12.** $-8 \leq x$ **13.** $x < +3$ **14.** $-6 \geq x$ **15.** $-4 < x$ **16.** $x \leq -8$

EXERCISES

PART A

Graph the solution set of each sentence.

1. $b < 3$	**2.** $y > 1$	**3.** $x \leq 5$	**4.** $d \geq -5$
5. $x \leq -2$	**6.** $y > -4$	**7.** $2 < c$	**8.** $r < 4$
9. $-6 \leq y$	**10.** $x > -5$	**11.** $2 > g$	**12.** $x \leq 0$
13. $4 < y$	**14.** $z \geq 4$	**15.** $r \geq 4$	**16.** $y < -1$
17. $a < -3$	**18.** $r > 0$	**19.** $x \geq 1$	**20.** $a \leq 3$
21. $b \leq -3$	**22.** $1 > z$	**23.** $y < -2$	**24.** $3 \leq c$
25. $c \geq -1$	**26.** $-2 \geq x$	**27.** $r \leq -4$	**28.** $x < -5$
29. $x > -2$	**30.** $x > -1$	**31.** $a \geq 2$	**32.** $y \leq 2$
33. $1 \leq b$	**34.** $y < -3$	**35.** $5 \geq g$	**36.** $r < -4$

PART B

EXAMPLE   Graph the solution set of $y \neq -\frac{1}{3}$.

Every number except $-\frac{1}{3}$
is in the solution set. ──────────→

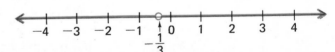

Graph the solution set of each sentence.

37. $x \neq 2\frac{1}{2}$ **38.** $-\frac{1}{4} > y$ **39.** $x < \frac{5}{4}$ **40.** $-\frac{3}{2} \leq x$

41. $\frac{1}{2} \geq y$ **42.** $0 \neq x$ **43.** $x \geq -\frac{2}{3}$ **44.** $0 \geq y$

PART C

Graph the solution set of each sentence.

45. $x \not\leq 5$ **46.** $-8 \not> x$ **47.** $-2.5 \not\geq x$ **48.** $x \not< -8.1$

Computer Programs: Input and Output

Some computer programs call for information to be entered into the machine before calculations can be done and the answer printed out.

PROBLEM

Write a flow chart to evaluate $4x + 3y - 5$ for given values of x and y.

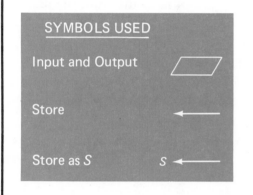

SYMBOLS USED

Input and Output

Store

Store as S $S \leftarrow$

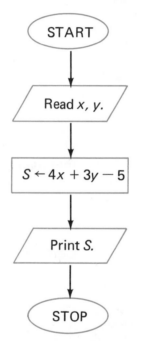

START

Read x, y.

$S \leftarrow 4x + 3y - 5$

Print S.

STOP

Input: Feed the values of x and y into the machine.

Replace x and y with input values. Compute. Store as S.

Output: Print the result.

PROJECT

Evaluate $4x + 3y - 5$ for the given values of x and y. Use the flow chart above.

1. $x = 2$, $y = -3$ **2.** $x = 5$, $y = 4$ **3.** $x = -1$, $y = 5$

4. Write a flow chart to show how to find the average of three numbers.

Properties for Inequalities

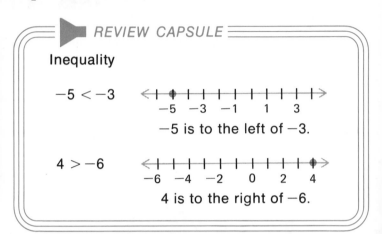

▶ REVIEW CAPSULE

Inequality

$-5 < -3$ -5 is to the left of -3.

$4 > -6$ 4 is to the right of -6.

EXAMPLE 1 Consider the inequality $4 < 7$. Add 2 to each side. Use the symbol, $<$ or $>$, to write a true inequality.

Different numbers ──────────→
Same number ──────────→
Different numbers ──────────→

$$
\begin{array}{rr}
4 < & 7 \\
+2 & +2 \\
\hline
6 < & 9
\end{array}
$$ same order

EXAMPLE 2 Consider $-6 < -1$. Add -3 to each side. Write a true inequality.

$$
\begin{array}{rr}
-6 < & -1 \\
-3 & -3 \\
\hline
-9 < & -4
\end{array}
$$ same order

EXAMPLE 3 Consider $4 \geq -2$. Add 7 to each side. Write a true inequality.

$$
\begin{array}{rr}
4 \geq & -2 \\
+7 & +7 \\
\hline
11 > & 5
\end{array}
$$ same order

EXAMPLE 4 Consider $8 > -1$. Add -10 to each side. Write a true inequality.

$$
\begin{array}{rr}
8 > & -1 \\
-10 & -10 \\
\hline
-2 > & -11
\end{array}
$$ same order

Examples 1–4 suggest this property.

Addition Property for Inequalities

If $a < b$,   If $a > b$,

then $a + c < b + c$.   then $a + c > b + c$.

Adding the same number to each side of an inequality does not change the order.

EXAMPLE 5   Consider $2 < 7$. Multiply each side by 3 and write a true inequality. Then multiply each side by -3 and write a true inequality.

Multiplying by a negative number reverses the order.

$$2 < 7$$
$$2(3) \ ? \ 7(3)$$
$$6 < 21$$
same order

$$2 < 7$$
$$2(-3) \ ? \ 7(-3)$$
$$-6 > -21$$
reverse order

EXAMPLE 6   Consider $3 \geq -5$. Multiply each side by 2 and write a true inequality. Then multiply each side by -2 and write a true inequality.

Multiplying by a negative number reverses the order.

$$3 \geq -5$$
$$3(2) \ ? \ -5(2)$$
$$6 \geq -10$$
same order

$$3 \geq -5$$
$$3(-2) \ ? \ -5(-2)$$
$$-6 \leq 10$$
reverse order

Examples 5 and 6 suggest this property.

Multiplication Property for Inequalities

If $a < b$ and $c > 0$, c is positive. The order of the inequality is the same.

then $ac < bc$.

If $a < b$ and $c < 0$, c is negative. The order of the inequality is reversed.

then $ac > bc$.

EXAMPLE 7 Consider 9 > 6. Divide each side by 3 and write a true inequality. Then divide each side by −3 and write a true inequality.

$$9 > 6$$
$$\frac{9}{3} \;?\; \frac{6}{3} \quad \text{same order}$$
$$3 > 2$$

$$9 > 6$$
$$\frac{9}{-3} \;?\; \frac{6}{-3} \quad \text{reverse order}$$
$$-3 < -2$$

EXAMPLE 8 Consider −4 ≤ 12. Divide each side by 4 and write a true inequality. Then divide each side by −4 and write a true inequality.

$$-4 \le 12$$
$$\frac{-4}{4} \;?\; \frac{12}{4} \quad \text{same order}$$
$$-1 \le 3$$

$$-4 \le 12$$
$$\frac{-4}{-4} \;?\; \frac{12}{-4} \quad \text{reverse order}$$
$$1 \ge -3$$

Examples 7 and 8 suggest this property.

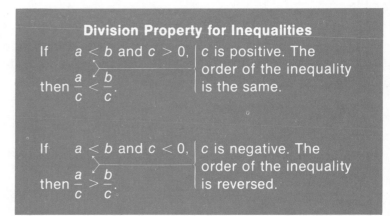

Division Property for Inequalities

If $a < b$ and $c > 0$, then $\dfrac{a}{c} < \dfrac{b}{c}$. | c is positive. The order of the inequality is the same.

If $a < b$ and $c < 0$, then $\dfrac{a}{c} > \dfrac{b}{c}$. | c is negative. The order of the inequality is reversed.

EXAMPLE 9 Tell what operation was performed on each side of the first inequality to give the second inequality.
$$-21 < 14 \qquad 3 > -2$$

$$\left.\begin{array}{cc} \dfrac{-21}{-7}; & \dfrac{14}{-7} \\ \downarrow & \downarrow \\ 3 & -2 \end{array}\right\}$$

Thus, each side of −21 < 14 was divided by −7 to give 3 > −2.

SUMMARY — Properties for Inequalities

Operation	Addition		Multiplication		Division	
Sign of operator	pos.	neg.	pos.	neg.	pos.	neg.
Order of resulting inequality	same	same	same	reverse	same	reverse

ORAL EXERCISES

If the indicated operation is performed, will the order of the inequality change?

1. $4 > 3$ Add 6. *No*
2. $-6 < -2$ Divide by -2. *Yes*
3. $6 > -1$ Multiply by -4. *Yes*
4. $8 > -4$ Divide by 4. *No*
5. $-8 < -2$ Divide by 2. *No*
6. $9 > -2$ Add -5. *No*
7. $-3 < 2$ Multiply by 7. *No*
8. $4 > 0$ Multiply by 5. *No*
9. $0 < 5$ Multiply by -3. *Yes*
10. $-9 \leq -3$ Divide by -3. *Yes*
11. $-24 < 12$ Divide by 3. *No*
12. $-8 < 1$ Add 7. *No*
13. $7 > -1$ Multiply by -6. *Yes*
14. $-6 \leq 2$ Divide by -2. *Yes*
15. $2 \leq 3$ Divide by 1. *No*
16. $-5 \leq 0$ Add -4. *No*
17. $0 > -4$ Add 2. *No*
18. $6 \geq 3$ Divide by -3. *Yes*
19. $9 \geq -4$ Add -6. *No*
20. $0 < 8$ Multiply by 6. *No*
21. $0 \leq 5$ Multiply by 3. *No*
22. $-4 < 0$ Multiply by -5. *Yes*
23. $3 \leq 7$ Add 4. *No*
24. $-8 < 6$ Multiply by -1. *Yes*
25. $-2 > -3$ Add 8. *No*
26. $-6 > -7$ Multiply by 4. *No*

EXERCISES

PART A

For each inequality in Exercises 1–26 above, write a true inequality by performing the indicated operation on each side.

PART B

Tell what operation was performed on each side of the first inequality to give the second inequality.

27. $5 > 3$ $2 > 0$ *Add -3.*
28. $4 \leq 7$ $8 \leq 14$ *Mult. by 2.*
29. $-6 < 2$ $18 > -6$ *Mult. by -3.*
30. $8 > 4$ $2 > 1$ *Divide by 4.*
31. $-2 \geq -3$ $3 \geq 2$ *Add 5.*
32. $3 \geq -1$ $12 \geq -4$ *Mult. by 4.*
33. $-9 < -6$ $3 > 2$ *Divide by -3.*
34. $-8 < 2$ $-5 < 5$ *Add 3.*
35. $2 > 0$ $-6 < 0$ *Mult. by -3.*
36. $-7 < 14$ $1 > -2$ *Divide by -7.*

PROPERTIES FOR INEQUALITIES **101**

Solving Inequalities

 REVIEW CAPSULE

Find the solution set of $6x + 7 = -2x + 31$.

$$6x + 7 = -2x + 31$$

$$\underline{+2x \qquad\qquad +2x}$$

$$8x + 7 = \qquad\qquad 31$$

$$\underline{\quad -7 \qquad\qquad -7}$$

$$8x \quad = \qquad\qquad 24$$

$$\frac{8x}{8} = \frac{24}{8}$$

$$x = 3$$

Thus, the solution set is {3}.

EXAMPLE 1

Find and graph the solution set of
$4x + 7 > 3x + 10$.

Add $-3x$ to each side. ⟶

The order is the same. ⟶

Add -7 to each side. ⟶

Same order ⟶

$$4x + 7 > \quad 3x + 10$$

$$\underline{-3x \qquad\quad -3x}$$

$$1x + 7 > \qquad\quad 10$$

$$\underline{\quad -7 \qquad\qquad - 7}$$

$$1x \quad > \qquad\qquad 3, \text{ or } x > 3$$

Any number greater than 3 should make
$4x + 7 > 3x + 10$ true.

Check two numbers greater than 3.

Try 4.

$4x + 7 >$	$3x + 10$
$4(4) + 7$	$3(4) + 10$
$16 + 7$	$12 + 10$
23	22

$23 > 22$ True

Try 7.

$4x + 7 >$	$3x + 10$
$4(7) + 7$	$3(7) + 10$
$28 + 7$	$21 + 10$
35	31

$35 > 31$ True

Check two numbers *not* greater than 3.

Try 3.

$4x + 7 >$	$3x + 10$
$4(3) + 7$	$3(3) + 10$
$12 + 7$	$9 + 10$
19	19

$19 > 19$
False

Try -2.

$4x + 7 >$	$3x + 10$
$4(-2) + 7$	$3(-2) + 10$
$-8 + 7$	$-6 + 10$
-1	4

$-1 > 4$
False

We could check numbers forever!

It appears that any number greater than 3 makes the sentence true. Any number less than or equal to 3 makes the sentence false.

Thus, the solution set of $4x + 7 > 3x + 10$ is $\{x \mid x > 3\}$.

Graph of $\{x \mid x > 3\}$ ————————→

3 is not a solution.

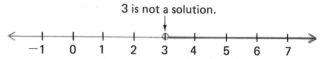

EXAMPLE 2 Find and graph the solution set of $5x - 10 \le 6x - 8$.

$$
\begin{array}{rcl}
5x - 10 & \le & 6x - 8 \\
-5x & & -5x \\
\hline
-10 & \le & 1x - 8 \\
+8 & & +8 \\
\hline
-2 & \le & x \\
& & x \ge -2
\end{array}
$$

$-2 \le x$ means $x \ge -2$. ————————→

Check -2 and several numbers greater than -2.

Thus, the solution set is $\{x \mid x \ge -2\}$.

-2 is a solution.

Graph of $\{x \mid x \ge -2\}$ ————————→

EXAMPLE 3 Find and graph the solution set of $10x + 3 < 7x - 9$.

$$
\begin{array}{rcl}
10x + 3 & < & 7x - 9 \\
-7x & & -7x \\
\hline
3x + 3 & < & -9 \\
-3 & & -3 \\
\hline
3x & < & -12 \\
\dfrac{3x}{3} & < & \dfrac{-12}{3} \\
x & < & -4
\end{array}
$$

Divide each side by 3. ————————→

The order is the same since 3 is positive.

Thus, the solution set is $\{x \mid x < -4\}$.

Graph of $\{x \mid x < -4\}$ ————————→

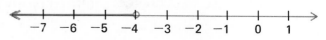

EXAMPLE 4 Solve $10x + 3 < 7x - 9$ again. This time add $-10x$ to each side rather than $-7x$. Is the result the same?

$$10x + 3 < 7x - 9$$

Add $-10x$ to each side. ⟶

$$\underline{-10x -10x}$$

$$3 < -3x - 9$$

Add 9 to each side. ⟶

$$\underline{+9 +9}$$

$$12 < -3x$$

Divide each side by -3.

Reverse the order, since -3 is ⟶
negative.

$$\frac{12}{-3} > \frac{-3x}{-3}$$

$$-4 > x$$

$-4 > x$ means $x < -4$. ⟶

$$x < -4$$

Yes, the result is the same.

EXERCISES

PART A

Find and graph the solution set.

1. $2 + 5x > -8$ $\{x \mid x > -2\}$
2. $10x + 14 \geq -36$ $\{x \mid x \geq -5\}$
3. $-17 < 9y - 8$ $\{y \mid y > -1\}$
4. $7 > 3x - 8$ $\{x \mid x < 5\}$
5. $-2x - 28 > -5x - 7$ $\{x \mid x > 7\}$
6. $5y + 8 < -4 + 17y$ $\{y \mid y > 1\}$
7. $4a + 1 \leq 3a + 9$ $\{a \mid a \leq 8\}$
8. $8x - 11 \geq 5x + 7$ $\{x \mid x \geq 6\}$
9. $7d - 6 < -24 + d$ $\{d \mid d < -3\}$
10. $7y + 3 > 10y - 12$ $\{y \mid y < 5\}$
11. $-3r + 13 \leq 2r - 7$ $\{r \mid r \geq 4\}$
12. $-22 + 10x > -14 + 8x$ $\{x \mid x > 4\}$
13. $25 - 4x \geq 4x + 1$ $\{x \mid x \leq 3\}$
14. $8 - 7y < y + 8$ $\{y \mid y > 0\}$
15. $-x + 12 > 3x - 4$ $\{x \mid x < 4\}$
16. $8 - 3x < -4x + 7$ $\{x \mid x < -1\}$
17. $9x - 5 \leq 25 + 4x$ $\{x \mid x \leq 6\}$
18. $9y + 7 \geq 13 + 11y$ $\{y \mid y \leq -3\}$
19. $10y - 24 > 3y - 3$ $\{y \mid y > 3\}$
20. $6x - 18 \leq 3x - 6$ $\{x \mid x \leq 4\}$
21. $6x + 3 \geq 91 - 5x$ $\{x \mid x \geq 8\}$
22. $4y + 3 > 9y - 17$ $\{y \mid y < 4\}$
23. $12y - 8 > 55 + 5y$ $\{y \mid y > 9\}$
24. $4x + 8 > -9 + 5x$ $\{x \mid x < 17\}$

PART B

Find and graph the solution set. [Hint: Remove parentheses first.]

25. $2(x + 5) > x + 15$ $\{x \mid x > 5\}$
26. $4(y + 1) < 7y - 2(3 - y)$ $\{y \mid y > 2\}$

PART C

Find and graph the solution set. [Hint: Work within brackets first.]

27. $7 - [4 - (3x - 2)] < 13 + 3x$
28. $2x - [8 - (3 -x)] > 2 - (5 - x)$

Intersection and Union of Sets

OBJECTIVES
- To determine if one set is a subset of another
- To list all the subsets of a given finite set
- To describe the intersection and the union of two sets

> ▶ *REVIEW CAPSULE*
>
> $A = \{1, 2, 3\}$ $B = \{1, 2, 3, 4, 5\}$
>
> *A* is a subset of *B*
> means
> every element of *A* is also in *B*.
>
> Write $A \subseteq B$ to mean *A* is a subset of *B*.

EXAMPLE 1 Consider sets *A* and *B* above. Is *B* a subset of *A*?

Think: Is every element of *B* also an element of *A*? $B \nsubseteq A$ means *B* is not a subset of *A*. ⟶

B contains the elements 4 and 5, which are not in *A*. **Thus,** $B \nsubseteq A$.

We make these agreements about subsets.

> Every set is a subset of itself.
> The empty set is a subset of every set.

EXAMPLE 2 List all the subsets of *C*. How many are there?
$$C = \{5, 7, 9\}$$

Subsets of *C*:

Every set is a subset of itself. ⟶
$$\{5, 7, 9\}$$
$$\{5, 7\}$$
$$\{5, 9\}$$
$$\{7, 9\}$$
$$\{5\}$$
$$\{7\}$$
$$\{9\}$$

The empty set is a subset of every set. ⟶
$$\phi$$

Thus, *C* has 8 subsets.

Consider sets R and S.

$$R = \{2, 4, 6, 8\} \quad S = \{2, 6, 10\}$$

$$\{2, 6\}$$

The *intersection* of two sets contains all the elements common to *both* sets.

The *intersection* of sets R and S is $\{2, 6\}$.

$\cap$ is the symbol for intersection.

We write $\{2, 4, 6, 8\} \cap \{2, 6, 10\} = \{2, 6\}$,
or $\quad R \quad \cap \quad S \quad = \{2, 6\}$.

EXAMPLE 3 $X = \{-3, -2, 0, 1, 2\}$ and $Y = \{-2, 1, 2, 3\}$.
Find $X \cap Y$.

-2, 1, and 2 are common to sets X and Y.

$$X \cap Y = \{-2, 1, 2\}.$$

Consider sets P and Q.

$$P = \{1, 2, 3, 7\} \quad Q = \{2, 3, 4\}$$

$$\{1, 2, 3, 4, 7\}$$

The *union* of two sets contains the elements which are in the 1st set, or 2nd set, or in both sets.

The *union* of sets P and Q is $\{1, 2, 3, 4, 7\}$.

$\cup$ is the symbol for union.

We write $\{1, 2, 3, 7\} \cup \{2, 3, 4\} = \{1, 2, 3, 4, 7\}$
or $\quad P \quad \cup \quad Q \quad = \{1, 2, 3, 4, 7\}$

EXAMPLE 4 $A = \{2, 4, 6\}$ and $B = \{5, 7, 9, 10\}$. Find $A \cap B$.

There are no elements common to both sets.

$$A \cap B = \{ \ \}, \text{ or } \phi$$

EXAMPLE 5 $C = \{0, 2, 4, 6\}$ and $D = \{0, 1, 2\}$. Find $C \cup D$.

Each element in $C \cup D$ is in C, or in D, or in both.

$$C \cup D = \{0, 1, 2, 4, 6\}.$$

SUMMARY

Intersection
$A \cap B$ is the set of all elements common to both set A and set B.

Union
$A \cup B$ is the set of elements belonging to set A or set B or both set A and set B.

EXERCISES

PART A

For each pair of sets, determine if $A \subseteq B$. Then determine if $B \subseteq A$.

$A \subseteq B$ and $B \subseteq A$

1. $A = \{0, 2, 4\}$ $B = \{0, 4\}$ *$B \subseteq A$*
2. $A = \{1, 2, 3\}$ $B = \{2, 3, 4\}$ *neither*
3. $A = \{-1, -2\}$ $B = \{-3, -2, -1\}$
4. $A = \{4, 5, 6\}$ $B = \{6, 4, 5\}$
5. $A = \{2, 4, 6\}$ $B = \{2, 4, 6, 8, 10\}$
6. $A = \{-6, 0, 6\}$ $B = \{-7, 0, 7\}$ *neither*
7. $A = \phi$ $B = \{2, 3, 6\}$ *$A \subseteq B$*
8. $A = \{1, 2, 3, 4\}$ $B = \{1, 3\}$ *$B \subseteq A$*
9. $A = \{1, 2, 3\}$ $B = \{1, 1+1, 1+2\}$
10. $A = \{-1, 0, 1\}$ $B = \{-2, -1, 0, 1, 2\}$
11. $A = \{5\}$ $B = \{6, 7, 8\}$ *neither*
12. $A = \{0\}$ $B = \phi$ *$B \subseteq A$*
13. $A = \{\text{integers}\}$ $B = \{\text{negative integers}\}$
14. $A = \{0\}$ $B = \{\text{integers}\}$
15. $A = \{\text{positive integers}\}$
    $B = \{\text{whole numbers}\}$ *$A \subseteq B$*
16. $A = \{\text{negative integers}\}$
    $B = \{\text{positive integers}\}$ *neither*

List all the subsets of each set. Then give the number of subsets.

17. $\{1, 2\}$
18. $\{2, 4, 6\}$
19. $\{8\}$ *$\{8\}, \phi; 2$*
20. ϕ *$\phi; 1$*
21. $\{-1, 0\}$
    $\{-1\}, \{0\}, \{-1, 0\}, \phi; 4$
22. $\{1, 3, 5, 7\}$

For each pair of sets, find the intersection. Then find the union.

23. $\{1, 3, 5\}$ $\{3, 5\}$
24. $\{2, 4, 6\}$ $\{6, 4, 2\}$
25. $\{4, 5, 6\}$ $\{7\}$
26. $\{1, 4, 5, 9\}$ $\{1, 2, 5\}$
27. ϕ $\{0, 2, 4\}$ *$I = \phi, U = \{0, 2, 4\}$*
28. $\{-4, 0, 4\}$ $\{-8, 0, 8\}$
29. $\{-1, -2, -3\}$ $\{1, 2, 3\}$
30. $\{1, 2, -1, -2\}$ $\{0, -1, -2\}$
31. $\{1, 4, 5\}$ $\{1, 2, 3, 4, 5\}$
32. $\{0\}$ ϕ *$I = \phi, U = \{0\}$*
33. $\{2, 4, 6\}$ $\{6, 8, 10\}$
34. $\{1, 3, 5, 7\}$ $\{2, 4, 6, 8\}$
35. $\{5, 8, 9, 2\}$ $\{2, 5, 8, 9\}$
    $I = \{2, 5, 8, 9\}$ $U = \{2, 5, 8, 9\}$
36. $\{0, 2, 4, 6\}$ $\{0, 3, 6, 9\}$
    $I = \{0, 6\}, \quad U = \{0, 2, 3, 4, 6, 9\}$

PART B

For each pair of sets, find the intersection. Then find the union.

37. $\{0, 2, 4, 6, 8, \ldots\}$ $\{1, 3, 5, 7, 9, \ldots\}$
38. $\{0, -1, -2, -3, \ldots\}$ $\{0, 1, 2, 3, \ldots\}$
39. $\{0, 2, 4, 6, 8, \ldots\}$ $\{0, 3, 6, 9, 12, \ldots\}$
40. $\{0, -2, -4, -6, -8, \ldots\}$
    $\{0, -4, -8, -12, -16, \ldots\}$
41. $\{0\}$ $\{\text{integers}\}$
42. $\{\text{negative integers}\}$ $\{\text{positive integers}\}$
43. $\{\text{positive integers}\}$ $\{\text{whole numbers}\}$
    $I = \{\text{positive integers}\},$
    $U = \{\text{whole numbers}\}$
44. $\{\text{integers}\}$ $\{\text{negative integers}\}$
    $I = \{\text{negative integers}\}$
    $U = \{\text{integers}\}$

PART C

$A = \{0, 1, 2, 3, 4\}$ $B = \{1, 3, 5\}$, and $C = \{0, 2, 4, 6\}$. **List each set.**

45. $(A \cup B) \cup C$
46. $A \cup (B \cup C)$
47. $(A \cap B) \cap C$
48. $A \cap (B \cap C)$
49. $(A \cup B) \cap C$
50. $(A \cap B) \cup C$

Motion Problems *(optional)*

<table>
<tr><td>

OBJECTIVE

■ To solve problems about motion

</td></tr>
</table>

EXAMPLE 1

Read 10 km/h as 10 km per hour.

Two cars traveled in opposite directions from the same point. The rate of one car was 10 km/h less than the rate of the other car. After 10 hours, the cars were 900 kilometers apart. Find the rate of each car.

Draw a diagram. ────────────→

Represent the rates algebraically. ──────→

Let x = rate of faster car in km/h
$x - 10$ = rate of slower car in km/h

Make a chart. ──────────────→

	Rate	Time	Distance ($d = rt$)
Faster car	x	10	$10x$
Slower car	$x - 10$	10	$10(x - 10)$

Write an equation. ───────────→

$\begin{pmatrix}\text{Distance of}\\\text{faster car}\end{pmatrix} + \begin{pmatrix}\text{Distance of}\\\text{slower car}\end{pmatrix} = \begin{pmatrix}\text{Total}\\\text{distance}\end{pmatrix}$

Substitute. ────────────────→
Solve the equation.

$10x \quad + \quad 10(x - 10) \quad = \quad 900$
$10x + 10x - 100 = 900$
$20x = 1,000$
$x = 50$

Rate of faster car, x is 50 km/h.
Rate of slower car, $x - 10$ is 40 km/h.

Thus, the faster car traveled at 50 km/h and the slower car traveled at 40 km/h.

EXAMPLE 2 Two trains left the same station at the same time but traveled in opposite directions. The E train averaged 120 km/h. The A train averaged 130 km/h. In how many hours were they 750 km apart?

Draw a diagram. ——————→

Station

| E train | | A train |

|←—————— 750 km ——————→|

Represent the time algebraically. ——————→ Let x = number of hours when they were 750 km apart

Make a chart. ——————→

	Rate	Time	Distance ($d = rt$)
E train	120	x	$120x$
A train	130	x	$130x$

Write an equation. ——————→ $\begin{pmatrix}\text{Distance of}\\\text{E train}\end{pmatrix} + \begin{pmatrix}\text{Distance of}\\\text{A train}\end{pmatrix} = \begin{pmatrix}\text{Total}\\\text{Distance}\end{pmatrix}$

Substitute. ——————→ $\qquad 120x \qquad + \qquad 130x \qquad = \qquad 750$

Solve the equation.

$$250x = 750$$
$$x = 3$$

Thus, in 3 hours the trains were 750 km apart.

EXAMPLE 3 The Dawns drove to the beach at 50 km/h. On their return trip they averaged 40 km/h. The total trip took 9 hours. How far was it to the beach?

Draw a diagram. ——————→

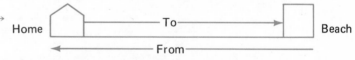

Home $\qquad$ —To— $\qquad$ Beach

←———————— From ————————

Represent the times algebraically. ——————→ Let x = time in hours of trip to the beach
$9 - x$ = times in hours of return trip

Make a chart. ——————→

	Rate	Time	Distance ($d = rt$)
To beach	50	x	$50x$
Return trip	40	$9 - x$	$40(9 - x)$

Write an equation. ——————→ (Distance to beach) = (Distance of return trip)

Substitute. ——————→ $\qquad 50x = 40(9 - x)$

Solve. $\begin{pmatrix}50x = 360 - 40x\\90x = 360\end{pmatrix}$ $\qquad 50x = 360 - 40x$

$$x = 4$$

Thus, it was 50(4), or 200 km to the beach.

EXAMPLE 4   Abe started out in his car at a rate of 40 km/h. Two hours later, Carla left from the same point. She drove along the same road at 50 km/h. How many hours had Carla driven when she caught up up with Abe?

Draw a diagram. ───────────→

Represent the times algebraically. ───────────→ Let x = time Carla traveled
$x + 2$ = time Abe traveled

Make a chart. ───────────→

	Rate	Time	Distance ($d = rt$)
Abe	40	$x + 2$	$40(x + 2)$
Carla	50	x	$50x$

Write an equation. ───────────→ (Abe's distance) = (Carla's distance)
Substitute. ───────────→ $40(x + 2) = 50x$
Solve. $\left(\begin{array}{l} 40x + 80 = 50x \\ 80 = 10x \end{array} \right)$
$40x + 80 = 50x$
$8 = x$

Thus, it took Carla 8 hours to catch up with Abe.

EXAMPLE 5   A train left a station at 3:00 pm and traveled at 100 km/h. Another train left the station at 4:00 pm and traveled in the same direction at 125 km/h. At what time did it overtake the first train?

Draw a diagram. ───────────→

Represent the times algebraically. ───────────→ Let x = time second train traveled
$x + 1$ = time first train traveled

Make a chart. ───────────→

	Rate	Time	Distance ($d = rt$)
First train	100	$x + 1$	$100(x + 1)$
Second train	125	x	$125x$

Write an equation. ───────────→ (First train's distance) = (Second train's distance)
Substitute. ───────────→ $100(x + 1) = 125x$
Solve. $\left(\begin{array}{l} 100x + 100 = 125x \\ 100 = 25x \end{array} \right)$
$100x + 100 = 125x$
$4 = x$

4:00 + 4 hr = 8:00 ───────────→ **Thus,** the second train overtook the first at 8:00 pm.

EXERCISES

1. Two trucks started toward each other at the same time from towns 500 km apart. One truck traveled at a rate of 65 km/h, the other at 60 km/h. After how many hours did they meet?

2. The Foy's rode at 40 km/h to a bus stop where they boarded a chartered bus. The bus traveled at 80 km/h. Their total trip was 280 km and took 4 hours. How long were the Foy's on the bus?

3. Jan and Joel started from the same point at the same time. They traveled in opposite directions on their bicycles. Jan traveled at 8 km/h and Joel at 7 km/h. In how many hours were they 45 km apart?

4. A car and a truck were traveling in opposite directions. They passed each other at a crossroad in the country. The car was traveling at 75 km/h and the truck at 50 km/h. In how many hours were they 375 km apart?

5. A train left a station and traveled north at 110 km/h. Two hours later, another train left the station and traveled south at 90 km/h. How many hours had the first train traveled when they were 420 km apart?

6. A train left a station and traveled south at 100 km/h. Two hours later, another train left the station and traveled in the same direction at 110 km/h. How many hours had the first train traveled when the second train overtook it?

7. Sheila and Kevin drove to the service station at 60 km/h. They returned home by bicycle at 15 km/h. The entire trip took 4 hours. How far was it from their home to the service station?

8. Dick and Roby left home for a fishing trip at 8:30 am. They were traveling at 30 km/h. Part of the way there, their car broke down. They walked back at a rate of 10 km/h and returned home at 10:30 am. How far from home were they when the car broke down?

9. An airplane left an airport and traveled due north at 1,200 km/h. Two hours later, another plane left the airport and traveled due south at 1,000 km/h. How many hours had the first plane flown when they were 9,000 km apart?

10. Amos and Russ were walking toward town at 3 km/h. Half an hour later, Theresa and Claire left from the same point and walked in the same direction at 4 km/h. For how many hours had the boys walked when the girls caught up with them?

Graphing Intersections and Unions

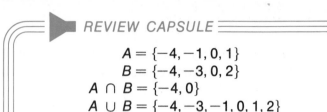

▶ REVIEW CAPSULE

$A = \{-4, -1, 0, 1\}$
$B = \{-4, -3, 0, 2\}$
$A \cap B = \{-4, 0\}$
$A \cup B = \{-4, -3, -1, 0, 1, 2\}$

EXAMPLE 1 $P = \{x \mid x \geq -2\}$ and $Q = \{x \mid x < 3\}$. Graph P, Q, and $P \cap Q$. Then describe the intersection.

Graph of $P = \{x \mid x \geq -2\}$ ⟶

Graph of $Q = \{x \mid x < 3\}$ ⟶

Graph of $P \cap Q$ ⟶

$P \cap Q$ contains all numbers common to sets P and Q.

Description of $P \cap Q$ ⟶ **Thus, $P \cap Q = \{x \mid \geq -2 \text{ and } x < 3 \}$.**

x is between -2 and 3. ⟶ We may also write $P \cap Q = \{x \mid -2 \leq x < 3\}$.

EXAMPLE 2 $P = \{x \mid x \geq -2\}$ and $Q = \{x \mid x < 3\}$. Graph P, Q, and $P \cup Q$. Then describe the union.

Graph of $P = \{x \mid x \geq -2\}$ ⟶

Graph of $Q = \{x \mid x < 3\}$ ⟶

Graph of $P \cup Q$ ⟶

$P \cup Q$ contains all numbers belonging to P, or Q, or both P and Q.

We may also write
$P \cup Q = \{x \mid x \geq -2 \text{ or } x < 3\}$. ⟶ **Thus, $P \cup Q = \{$all numbers$\}$.**

EXAMPLE 3 $R = \{x \mid x < -1\}$ and $S = \{x \mid x \geq 2\}$. Graph
R, S, and $R \cap S$. Then describe the intersection.

Graph of $R = \{x \mid x < -1\}$ ⟶

Graph of $S = \{x \mid x \geq 2\}$ ⟶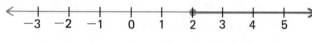

Graph of $R \cap S$ ⟶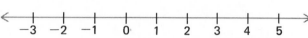

There are no numbers common to sets R and S.

Description of $R \cap S$ ⟶ **Thus,** $R \cap S = \phi$, or
$$R \cap S = \{x \mid x < -1 \text{ and } x \geq 2\}.$$

EXAMPLE 4 Consider sets R and S graphed in Example 3.
Graph $R \cup S$. Then describe the union.

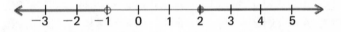

Graph of $R \cup S$ ⟶

$R \cup S$ contains all numbers belonging to R, or S,
or both R and S.

Description of $R \cup S$ ⟶ **Thus,** $R \cup S = \{x \mid x < -1 \text{ or } x \geq 2\}.$

EXAMPLE 5 $C = \{x \mid x < 4\}$ and $D = \{x \mid x \leq -1\}$. Graph
C, D, $C \cap D$, and $C \cup D$. Then describe the
intersection and the union.

Graph of $C = \{x \mid x < 4\}$ ⟶

Graph of $D = \{x \mid x \leq -1\}$ ⟶

Graph of $C \cap D = \{x \mid x \leq -1\}$ ⟶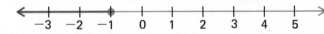

Graph of $C \cup D = \{x \mid x < 4\}$ ⟶

Description of $C \cap D$;
actually, $C \cap D = D$. ⟶ **Thus,** $C \cap D = \{x \mid x \leq -1\}$

Description of $C \cup D$;
actually, $C \cup D = C$. ⟶ and $C \cup D = \{x \mid x < 4\}.$

EXERCISES

Graph _A_, _B_, _A_ ∩ _B_, and _A_ ∪ _B_ on four separate number lines. Then describe the intersection and the union.

1. $A = \{x \mid x > -2\}$ $B = \{x \mid x < 5\}$
2. $A = \{x \mid x > 3\}$ $B = \{x \mid x < -1\}$
3. $A = \{x \mid x \geq -4\}$ $B = \{x \mid x < 2\}$
4. $A = \{x \mid x > 4\}$ $B = \{x \mid x \leq 0\}$
5. $A = \{x \mid x > -3\}$ $B = \{x \mid x \geq -1\}$
6. $A = \{x \mid x \leq 5\}$ $B = \{x \mid x < 3\}$
7. $A = \{x \mid x \geq -1\}$ $B = \{x \mid x \leq 3\}$
8. $A = \{x \mid x \leq 1\}$ $B = \{x \mid x \geq 4\}$
9. $A = \{x \mid x < 4\}$ $B = \{x \mid x < 0\}$
10. $A = \{x \mid x > -1\}$ $B = \{x \mid x > -7\}$
11. $A = \{x \mid x \geq 1\}$ $B = \{x \mid x \leq 1\}$
12. $A = \{x \mid x > 3\}$ $B = \{x \mid x \leq 3\}$
13. $A = \{x \mid x > -5\}$ $B = \{x \mid x > -4\}$
14. $A = \{x \mid x > -1\}$ $B = \{x \mid x \leq 0\}$
15. $A = \{x \mid x \leq 2\}$ $B = \{x \mid x > -1\}$
16. $A = \{x \mid x < -3\}$ $B = \{x \mid x > -3\}$
17. $A = \{x \mid x > 3\}$ $B = \{x \mid x \geq 3\}$
18. $A = \{x \mid x > 2\}$ $B = \{x \mid x < -2\}$
19. $A = \{x \mid x \geq 0\}$ $B = \{x \mid x < 0\}$
20. $A = \{x \mid x < -2\}$ $B = \{x \mid x \leq -2\}$
21. $A = \{x \mid x = 5\}$ $B = \{x \mid x > 5\}$
22. $A = \{x \mid x \geq 3\}$ $B = \{x \mid x \leq -3\}$
23. $A = \{x \mid x \geq -3\}$ $B = \{x \mid x \leq 3\}$
24. $A = \{x \mid x = 0\}$ $B = \{x \mid x \geq 0\}$
25. $A = \{x \mid x = -3\}$ $B = \{x \mid x \leq -3\}$
26. $A = \{x \mid x > 0\}$ $B = \{x \mid x = 0\}$
27. $A = \{x \mid x > 3\}$ $B = \{x \mid x \leq 4\}$
28. $A = \{x \mid x \leq 1\}$ $B = \{x \mid x > 2\}$
29. $A = \{\text{all numbers}\}$ $B = \{x \mid x > 2\}$
30. $A = \{\text{all numbers}\}$ $B = \{x \mid x = -1\}$

EXAMPLE   Describe the set graphed.

$-2 \quad 0 \quad 2$

Also written $\{x \mid -2 < x \leq 1\}$ ⟶ The set graphed is $\{x \mid x > -2 \text{ and } x \leq 1\}$.

Describe the set graphed.

31.
$-4\ -3\ -2\ -1\ 0\ 1\ 2\ 3\ 4$
$\{x \mid x \geq \mid \text{ and } x < 4\}$

32.
$-4\ -3\ -2\ -1\ 0\ 1\ 2\ 3\ 4$
$\{x \mid x \leq -1 \text{ or } x > 3\}$

33.
$-4\ -3\ -2\ -1\ 0\ 1\ 2\ 3\ 4$
$\{x \mid x > -4 \text{ and } x < 3\}$

34.
$-5\ -4\ -3\ -2\ -1\ 0\ 1\ 2\ 3$
$\{x \mid x < 0\}$

35.
$-4\ -3\ -2\ -1\ 0\ 1\ 2\ 3\ 4$
$\{x \mid x < -2 \text{ or } x \geq 0\}$

36.
$-5\ -4\ -3\ -2\ -1\ 0\ 1\ 2\ 3$
$\{x \mid x < -4 \text{ or } x > -3\}$

37.
$-4\ -3\ -2\ -1\ 0\ 1\ 2\ 3\ 4$
$\{x \mid x > 2 \text{ and } x \leq 3\}$

38.
$-5\ -4\ -3\ -2\ -1\ 0\ 1\ 2\ 3$
$\{x \mid x < -2 \text{ or } x > -2\}$

If $A = \{x \mid x > -4\}$, $B = \{x \mid x \leq 5\}$, and $C = \{x \mid x \geq 0\}$, graph the following.

39. $(A \cap B) \cap C$
40. $(A \cup B) \cup C$
41. $(A \cap B) \cup C$
42. $(A \cup B) \cap C$

René Descartes

René Descartes
(1596–1650)

René Descartes was known not only as a great mathematician but as a great scientist and philosopher as well. He was very sickly as a child and throughout his life. Because of his condition, he would spend the morning hours in bed and would often use this time to think. Sometimes he would watch a fly walking on the ceiling and try to derive a mathematical equation for its path. Descartes, also called Cartesius, is regarded as the founder of analytic geometry which defines geometric functions using algebraic expressions. Whenever ordered pairs of real numbers are assigned to points in the plane, we have a Cartesian coordinate system.

Descartes was a founder of modern philosophy and one of the Western world's most influential thinkers. His famous statement, "Cogito, ergo sum" (I think, therefore I am), provided a basis for his philosophical system, Cartesianism.

PROJECT You might be interested in learning more about Descartes. One reference that we suggest is E. T. Bell's *Men of Mathematics*.

Chapter Four Review

Which sets are equal to {2, 5, 8, 9}? $[p.\,91]$
1. {8, 9, 5, 2} **2.** {2, 9, 6, 5} **3.** {5, 8, 3, 9} **4.** {2, 2 + 3, 2 + 6, 2 + 7}

For each set, tell whether it is finite or infinite. The describe the set in words. $[p.\,91]$
5. {1, 3, 5, 7, . . .} **6.** {2, 4, 6, 8} **7.** {−1, −2, −3, −4, . . .}

Describe each set by listing its elements. $[p.\,91]$
8. {negative integers greater than −5} **9.** {positive integers less than 1}

Find the solution set of each sentence. Then graph it. $[p.\,91]$
10. $6x - 3 = 8 + 6x$ **11.** $10z + 17 = -9 + 8z$ **12.** $3x - 8 + 4x = -8 + 7x$

Graph the solution set of each sentence. $[p.\,94]$
13. $x > -2$ **14.** $y \le 5$ **15.** $y \ne -\frac{1}{2}$ **16.** $y \le -4$ **17.** $2 < y$ **18.** $-3 \ge x$

For each inequality, write a true inequality by performing the indicated operation on each side. $[p.\,98]$
19. $-3 \le 9$ Divide by −3. **20.** $-7 \ge -8$ Multiply by −8. **21.** $8 > -1$ Add −5.

What operation was performed on each side of the first inequality to give the second inequality? $[p.\,98]$
22. $-18 < -6$ $6 > 2$ **23.** $6 > 2$ $4 > 0$ **24.** $-3 < -1$ $6 > 2$

Find and graph the solution set. $[p.\,102]$
25. $11x + 8 \le -14$ **26.** $24 - 4x \ge -16 + 4x$ **27.** $6 - (4 - x) > 2x + 1$

For each pair of sets, determine if $A \subseteq B$. Then determine if $B \subseteq A$. $[p.\,105]$
28. $A = \{2, 4\}$ $B = \{6, 4, 2\}$ **29.** $A = \phi$ $B = \{0, 1\}$ **30.** $A = \{6, 10, 12\}$ $B = \{10, 6, 12\}$

List all the subsets of each set. Then give the number of subsets. $[p.\,105]$
31. {3} **32.** {4, 1} **33.** {9, 8, 7}

For each pair of sets, find the intersection. Then find the union. $[p.\,105]$
34. {4, 5, 9} {9, 5} **35.** {1, 3, 5} {2, 4, 6} **36.** {−2, 0, 2} {−1, 0, 1}

Graph A, B, $A \cap B$, and $A \cup B$ on four separate number lines. Then describe the intersection and the union. $[p.\,112]$
37. $A = \{x \mid x > 3\}$ $B = \{x \mid x \le 4\}$ **38.** $A = \{x \mid x \ge -4\}$ $B = \{x \mid x < 1\}$

Describe the set graphed. $[p.\,112]$

39.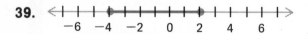

40.

Chapter Four Test

Which sets are equal to $\{3, 6, 8, 9\}$?
1. $\{6, 3, 9, 8\}$ **2.** $\{9, 8, 3, 7\}$ **3.** $\{1 + 2, 7 + 1, 7 - 1, 8 + 1\}$

For each set, tell whether it is finite or infinite. Then describe the set in words.
4. $\{5, 6, 7, 8, \ldots\}$ **5.** $\{1, 3, 5, 7\}$ **6.** $\{-2, -4, -6, -8, \ldots\}$

Describe each set by listing its elements.
7. {integers between -3 and 2}   **8.** {positive integers less than 4}

Find the solution set of each sentence. Then graph it.
9. $4y + 9 = -17 + 4y$ **10.** $3x + 8 = -3x - 16$ **11.** $8r + 12 = 15r - 9 - 7r$

Graph the solution set of each sentence.
12. $x \geq -3$ **13.** $4 < y$ **14.** $x \neq 5$

For each inequality, write a true inequality by performing the indicated operation on each side.
15. $6 > -5$ Add -8.   **16.** $-12 \leq -8$ Divide by -4.

What operation was performed on each side of the first inequality to give the second inequality?
17. $-4 < 8$ $16 > -32$ **18.** $7 < 9$ $4 < 6$

Find and graph the solution set.
19. $6 - 9x < -21$ **20.** $x - 2x \geq 18 + 2x$ **21.** $4 - (3 - y) < 3y + 9$

For each pair of sets, determine if $A \subseteq B$. Then determine if $B \subseteq A$.
22. $A = \{3, 5, 7, 9\}$ $B = \{9, 5\}$ **23.** $A = \{1, 6, 8\}$ $B = \{8, 1, 6\}$

List all the subsets of each set. Then give the number of subsets.
24. $\{7\}$ **25.** $\{1, 3, 5\}$

For each pair of sets, find the intersection. Then find the union.
26. $\{-5, 0, 5\}$ $\{-4, 0, 4\}$ **27.** $\{0, 2, 4\}$ $\{1, 3, 5\}$

Graph A, B, $A \cap B$, and $A \cup B$ on four separate number lines. Then describe the intersection and the union.
28. $A = \{x \mid x \geq -3\}$ $B = \{x \mid x < 1\}$ **29.** $A = \{x \mid x < -4\}$ $B = \{x \mid x \geq -1\}$

Describe the set graphed.

30.

31.

5 FACTORING

Sophie Germain

Sophie Germain
(1776–1831)

Sophie Germain was born in Paris on the brink of the French Revolution. Confined to her house, Sophie amused herself by spending long hours in her father's library. Here, she read of the violent death of Archimedes as he contemplated a mathematical figure in the sand. Impressed by this, Sophie decided to study mathematics, much against the wishes of her parents.

Germain would get up at night and study the language of analysis until dawn. During the reign of terror, she studied differential calculus. She was able to get the lecture notes of various professors from the École Polytechnique, even though the school did not accept women. She began a correspondence with the famous mathematician Lagrange but signed herself M. Leblanc. Lagrange was very impressed with this young mathematician. He eventually learned of her identity and openly praised her work. Germain began to think of herself as a mathematician.

Most of her work was in the fields of number theory and mathematical analysis. In 1815, she was awarded a prize by the Institut de France. She was also recommended for an honorary degree from the University of Gottingen. Unfortunately, she died before the degree could be awarded.

Exponents

OBJECTIVES
■ To evaluate expressions like $-2m^2y^3$ if $m = -4$ and $y = -2$
■ To evaluate expressions like $(-xy^2)^3$ if $x = 2$ and $y = -3$

REVIEW CAPSULE

(3) (3) (3) (3)

3^4 — Exponent

Base — 3^4

3^4
Fourth power of 3

A positive integer exponent tells the number of times the base is used as a factor.

x^1 means x, for each number x.

EXAMPLE 1 Find the value of 2^5.

Use 2 as a factor 5 times. $\longrightarrow$
2^5 does not mean $2(5)$.

$$2^5 = \underbrace{(2)\,(2)\,(2)\,(2)\,(2)}$$
$$= \qquad 32$$

EXAMPLE 2 Rewrite x^3 without an exponent.

Write x as a factor 3 times. $\longrightarrow$

$$x^3 \qquad = (x)\,(x)\,(x)$$

EXAMPLE 3 Evaluate a^5 if $a = -2$.

Write a as a factor 5 times. $\longrightarrow$

$$(a)\quad(a)\quad(a)\quad(a)\quad(a)$$

Substitute -2 for a. $\longrightarrow$

$$(-2)\,(-2)\,(-2)\,(-2)\,(-2)$$
$$\underbrace{(4)}\quad\underbrace{(4)}\quad(-2)$$
Multiply. $\longrightarrow$
$$\underbrace{(16)\,(-2)}$$
$$-32$$

EXAMPLE 4 Evaluate $-2a^3$ if $a = -3$.

Use a as a factor 3 times. $\longrightarrow$
Substitute -3 for a. $\longrightarrow$

$$-2a^3 = (-2)\,(a)\,(a)\,(a)$$
$$(-2)\,\underbrace{(-3)\,(-3)\,(-3)}$$
$$= (-2)\qquad (-27)$$
$$= \quad 54$$

EXAMPLE 5   Evaluate $-m^2b^3$ if $m=-2$, $b=3$.

Replace $-m^2b^3$ with $-1m^2b^3$. $\longrightarrow$

$m^2 = (m)(m)$; $b^3 = (b)(b)(b)$ $\longrightarrow$

Substitute -2 for m, 3 for b. $\longrightarrow$

$$
\begin{aligned}
-m^2b^3 &= -1m^2b^3 \\
&= -1(m)(m)(b)(b)(b) \\
&= -1(-2)(-2)(3)(3)(3) \\
&= -1 \quad (4) \qquad (27) \\
&= -1 \quad (108) \\
&= -108
\end{aligned}
$$

EXERCISES

PART A

Rewrite without exponents.

$$m \cdot m \cdot m \cdot m \cdot m \cdot m \qquad a \cdot a \cdot a \cdot b \cdot b$$

1. x^5 **2.** x^3 **3.** a^4 **4.** a^2 **5.** $4n^3$ **6.** m^6 **7.** $-3a^2$ **8.** a^3b^2

$x \cdot x \cdot x \cdot x \cdot x$ $a \cdot a \cdot a \cdot a$ $4 \cdot n \cdot n \cdot n$ $-3 \cdot a \cdot a$

Evaluate for the given values of the variables.

9. a^3 if $a=-3$ -27 **10.** b^5 if $b=-2$ -32 **11.** m^4 if $m=2$ 16

12. $-2m^2$ if $m=-3$ -18 **13.** $-3x^3$ if $x=2$ -24 **14.** $2a^5$ if $a=-2$ -64

15. $-x^3$ if $x=-4$ 64 **16.** $-a^2$ if $a=5$ -25 24 **17.** $-x^5$ if $x=-3$ 243

18. $2ab^4$ if $a=-1$, $b=2$ -32 **19.** $-3x^3y^2$ if $x=-2$, $y=-1$ **20.** $-xy^5$ if $x=-2$, $y=-2$

21. $-x^3y^3$ if $x=-1$, $y=-3$ **22.** $-a^3b^2c$ if $a=-4$, $b=2$, **23.** $-2x^3yz$ if $x=1$, $y=1$,

-27 $c=-1$ -256 $z=2$ -4

PART B

EXAMPLE   Evaluate $(5b)^2$ if $b=4$.

$$
\begin{aligned}
[(5)(4)]^2 &= (20)^2 \\
&= (20)(20) \\
&= 400
\end{aligned}
$$

Evaluate for the given values of the variables.

24. $(4a)^3$ if $a=-1$ -64 **25.** $(-2m)^3$ if $m=-2$ 64 **26.** $(-4a)^2$ if $a=-2$ 64

27. $(x^2y^3)^2$ if $x=-2$,   **28.** $(x^3y^2)^3$ if $x=-1$,   **29.** $(-x^3y^4)^5$ if $x=-1$,

$y=3$ $11,664$ $y=4$ $-4,096$ $y=2$ $1,048,576$

PART C

Evaluate for the given values of the variables.

30. $-x^my^n$ if $x=-2$, $m=3$, $y=5$, $n=2$ **31.** $(kb)^m$ if $k=-2$, $b=3$, $m=3$

Properties of Exponents

EXAMPLE 1   Simplify $a^3 \cdot a^4$.

Same base
$\underbrace{(3 \text{ factors, } a) + (4 \text{ factors, } a)}$
7 factors, a

$$\underbrace{a \cdot a \cdot a \cdot a \cdot a \cdot a \cdot a}$$
$$a^7$$

Example 1 suggests this. ⟶
Add exponents.

Product of Powers
$$x^m \cdot x^n = x^{m+n}$$

EXAMPLE 2   Simplify $y^2 \cdot y^7$.   Simplify $x^5 \cdot x^4$.

$x^m \cdot x^n = x^{m+n}$ ⟶

$$y^{2+7}$$ $$x^{5+4}$$
$$y^9$$ $$x^9$$

EXAMPLE 3   Simplify $(-5t^3)(-3t)$.   Simplify $(4a^3)(-6a^4)$.

t means t^1. ⟶
Group like factors. ⟶

$$(-5t^3)(-3t^1)$$ $$4 \cdot -6 \cdot a^3 \cdot a^4$$
$$-5 \cdot -3 \cdot t^3 \cdot t^1$$ $$-24 \cdot a^{3+4}$$
$$15 \quad \cdot t^{3+1}$$ $$-24a^7$$
$$15t^4$$

EXAMPLE 4   Simplify $x^2 \cdot y^3$.

Different bases ⟶

$$x^2 \cdot y^3 = x \cdot x \cdot y \cdot y \cdot y$$
$$x^2 \quad \cdot \quad y^3$$

Thus, $x^2 \cdot y^3$ cannot be simplified.

EXAMPLE 5   Show that $(x^4)^3 = x^{4 \cdot 3}$.

$(x^4)^3$	$x^{4 \cdot 3}$

Use x^4 as a factor three times. ⟶ $x^4 \cdot x^4 \cdot x^4$ | x^{12}

x^{4+4+4}

Same answers ⟶ x^{12}

Thus, $(x^4)^3 = x^{4 \cdot 3}$.

Example 5 suggests this. ⟶
$(x^4)^3 = x^{4 \cdot 3} = x^{12}$

Power of a Power

$$(x^m)^n = x^{m \cdot n}$$

EXAMPLE 6   Simplify $(x^3)^2$. $\quad$ Simplify $(a^8)^3$.

$(\overset{\frown}{x^3})^2$ Multiply exponents.

$$(x^3)^2 = x^{3 \cdot 2} \qquad (a^8)^3 = a^{8 \cdot 3}$$
$$= x^6 \qquad\qquad = a^{24}$$

EXAMPLE 7   Show that $(a^3b^2)^4 = a^{3 \cdot 4}b^{2 \cdot 4}$.

$(a^3b^2)^4$	$a^{3 \cdot 4}b^{2 \cdot 4}$

Use a^3b^2 as a factor 4 times. ⟶ $a^3b^2 \cdot a^3b^2 \cdot a^3b^2 \cdot a^3b^2$ | $a^{3 \cdot 4}b^{2 \cdot 4}$

$a^3 \cdot a^3 \cdot a^3 \cdot a^3 \cdot b^2 \cdot b^2 \cdot b^2 \cdot b^2$

$a^{\underbrace{3+3+3+3}} \qquad b^{\underbrace{2+2+2+2}}$

$3 + 3 + 3 + 3$ means $4 \cdot 3$, or $3 \cdot 4$. ⟶ $a^{3 \cdot 4} \qquad b^{2 \cdot 4}$

Thus, $(a^3b^2)^4 = a^{3 \cdot 4}b^{2 \cdot 4}$, or $a^{12}b^8$.

Example 7 suggests this. ⟶
$(a^{\overset{\frown}{3}}b^2)^4 = a^{3 \cdot 4} \cdot b^{2 \cdot 4}$

Power of a Product

$$(x^m \cdot y^n)^p = x^{m \cdot p} \cdot y^{n \cdot p}$$

EXAMPLE 8   Simplify $(2a^2b^4)^3$.

$2 = 2^1$ ⟶

$$(2a^2b^4)^3 = (2^1a^2b^4)^3$$

Multiply exponents. ⟶
$$= 2^{1 \cdot 3} \cdot a^{2 \cdot 3} \cdot b^{4 \cdot 3}$$
$$= 2^3 \cdot a^6 \cdot b^{12}$$

2^3 is $2 \cdot 2 \cdot 2$, or 8. ⟶
$$= 8a^6b^{12}$$

EXAMPLE 9   Simplify $(-3x^3y^5)^3$.

$-3 = 3^1$ ⟶

$$(-3x^3y^5)^3 = (-3^1x^3y^5)^3$$

Multiply exponents. ⟶
$$= (-3)^{1 \cdot 3} \cdot x^{3 \cdot 3} \cdot y^{5 \cdot 3}$$
$$= (-3)^3 \cdot x^9 \cdot y^{15}$$

$(-3)^3$ is $(-3)(-3)(-3)$, or -27. ⟶
$$= -27x^9y^{15}$$

ORAL EXERCISES

Simplify.

Read as 5 factors b times 1 factor b.

1. $(m^3)(m^2)$ m^5 **2.** $(b^3)(b^7)$ b^{10} **3.** $(b^2)(b^5)$ b^7 **4.** $(c^6)(c^5)$ c^{11} **5.** $(b^5)(b)$ $b^6\!\uparrow$
6. $(m^4)(m)$ m^5 **7.** $(b)(b)$ b^2 **8.** $(a)(a^6)$ a^7 **9.** $(x)(x^3)$ x^4 **10.** $(m)(m^9)$ m^{10}
11. $(c^2)^3$ c^6 **12.** $(a^4)^5$ a^{20} **13.** $(x^8)^2$ x^{16} **14.** $(y^3)^4$ y^{12} **15.** $(x^6)^3$ x^{18}

EXERCISES

PART A

Simplify.

1. $(3a^2)(4a^6)$ $12a^8$ **2.** $(5a^4)(3a^7)$ $15a^{11}$ **3.** $(2m^5)(3m^6)$ **4.** $(2b^3)(3b^4)$
5. $(4x^2)(7x^{10})$ $28x^{12}$ **6.** $(2n^5)(4n^2)$ $8n^7$ **7.** $(5a^4)(3a^5)$ **8.** $(2y^3)(5y^4)$
9. $(a^2)(4a^3)$ $4a^5$ **10.** $(3b^5)(b^2)$ $3b^7$ **11.** $(6a^5)(a^6)$ **12.** $(m^5)(3m^5)$
13. $(-4a^3)(2a^5)$ $-8a^8$ **14.** $(-6b^5)(-2b^7)$ **15.** $(4m^3)(-2m^5)$ **16.** $(a^7)(-3a^8)$
17. $(4a^3)(2a)$ $8a^4$ **18.** $(5b^2)(-4b)$ $-20b^3$ **19.** $(-3b)(5b^7)$ **20.** $(4b^4)(-3b)$
21. $(3a^3b^2)(4a^2b^4)$ $12a^5b^6$ **22.** $(4x^2y^3)(2x^3y^4)$ $8x^5y^7$ **23.** $(5m^2n^3)(-4m^2n^4)$
24. $(-2a^2b^3)(4ab^5)$ $-8a^3b^8$ **25.** $(-2ab^3)(-3a^4b)$ $6a^5b^4$ **26.** $(ab)(ab)$
27. $(a^2)^3$ a^6 **28.** $(b^3)^4$ b^{12} **29.** $(x^2)^6$ x^{12} **30.** $(y^5)^3$ y^{15} **31.** $(z^6)^5$ z^{30} **32.** $(c^9)^3$
33. $(r^3)^{10}$ r^{30} **34.** $(f^7)^7$ f^{49} **35.** $(g^{15})^3$ g^{45} **36.** $(d^{25})^4$ d^{100} **37.** $(c^4)^7$ **38.** $(h^{10})^{20}$
39. $(2x^2)^4$ $16x^8$ **40.** $(-3y^3)^2$ $9y^6$ **41.** $(-2z^4)^3$ $-8z^{12}$ **42.** $(5a^5)^3$ $125a^{15}$ **43.** $(4x^3)^4$ $256x^{12}$

PART B

Simplify.

44. $(4a^3m^2)^2$ **45.** $(3a^2x^3)^2$ $9a^4x^6$ **46.** $(2x^2y^3)^2$ $4x^4y^6$ **47.** $(2m^3n^4)^3$ **48.** $(5a^2b^3)^3$
49. $(-4a^3m^4)^3$ **50.** $(3x^2y^4)^4$ **51.** $(2xa^2)^3$ **52.** $(-3a^2b^3)^3$ **53.** $(-3xy^2m)^5$
54. $(x^3y^2z^4)^3$ $x^9y^6z^{12}$ **55.** $(a^2b^4c^3)^5$ $a^{10}b^{20}c^{15}$ **56.** $(x^2y^3z^4)^7$
57. $(3a^3b^2)^3$ $27a^9b^6$ **58.** $(2x^6y^4)^3$ $8x^{18}y^{12}$ **59.** $(-3x^3y^4z^2)^3$

PART C

EXAMPLE Simplify $(x^3)^{2a} \cdot (x^a)^3$.

$(x^m)^n = x^{m \cdot n}$ ⟶ $x^{3 \cdot 2a} \cdot x^{a \cdot 3}$
$x^{6a} \cdot x^{3a}$

$x^{6a} \cdot x^{3a} = x^{6a+3a}$, or x^{9a} ⟶ x^{9a}

Simplify.

60. $(x^{2a})(x^{2a})$ **61.** $(y^b)(y^{3b})$ **62.** $(2x^3)(3x^a)$
63. $(x^{3a})^2$ **64.** $(y^{5b})^3$ **65.** $(2x^{5a})^a$

Polynomials

OBJECTIVES
- ■ To classify polynomials
- ■ To simplify polynomials by combining like terms

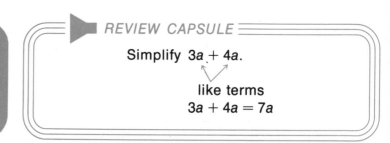

▶ REVIEW CAPSULE

Simplify $3a + 4a$.

like terms

$3a + 4a = 7a$

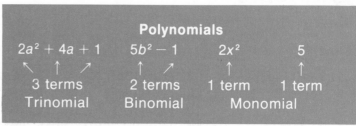

Polynomials

$2a^2 + 4a + 1$	$5b^2 - 1$	$2x^2$	5
3 terms	2 terms	1 term	1 term
Trinomial	Binomial	Monomial	

EXAMPLE 1 Classify each polynomial.

Tri means three; bi means two; mono means one.

$2a^2 + 7a + 9$	$4m^2 - 6$	$12x^2$
3 terms	2 terms	1 term
Trinomial	Binomial	Monomial

EXAMPLE 2 Simplify $9 + 7x^3 + 2x^2 - 5x^2 + 4x^3 - 8$.

Group like terms together. ⟶ $(7x^3 + 4x^3) + (2x^2 - 5x^2) + (9 - 8)$

$(7x^3 + 4x^3) = (7 + 4)x^3$

$\quad\quad\quad 11x^3 \quad\quad\quad -3x^2 \quad\quad +1$, or $11x^3 - 3x^2 + 1$

EXAMPLE 3 Simplify $8x^3 - 7x^5 + 5x - 4x^2 + 3x^3 - 2x + 6$. Then write the result in descending order of exponents.

Group like terms. ⟶

$\quad\quad 8x^3 + 3x^3 - 7x^5 + 5x - 2x - 4x^2 + 6$

Combine like terms. ⟶

$\quad\quad\quad 11x^3 \quad - 7x^5 \quad\quad +3x \quad - 4x^2 + 6$

Now write the result in descending order of exponents.

Arrange terms in order of exponents with highest exponent first. ⟶

$\quad\quad\quad -7x^5 + 11x^3 - 4x^2 + 3x + 6$

EXAMPLE 4 Simplify $7x^3 + 4x^2$.

$\quad\quad 7x^3$ and $4x^2$ are not like terms.

$7x^3 + 4x^2$ is not $11x^5$. ⟶ **Thus, $7x^3 + 4x^2$ cannot be simplified.**

EXAMPLE 5 Simplify $x^2 - 8 + 5x^4 - 7x + 3x^3 - 2x^4 + 5x^2 + 6x + 3$.

Group like terms. $\longrightarrow$ $\qquad$ $1x^2 + 5x^2 - 8 + 3 + 5x^4 - 2x^4 - 7x + 6x + 3x^3$

Combine like terms. $\longrightarrow$ $\qquad\quad$ $6x^2 \qquad -5 \qquad + 3x^4 \qquad -1x \quad + 3x^3$

Descending order $\longrightarrow$ $\qquad\qquad$ $3x^4 + 3x^3 + 6x^2 - x - 5$

ORAL EXERCISES

Classify each polynomial. *(Monomial, M; Binomial, B; Trinomial, T)*

1. $3x^3 - 5x$ *B* $\qquad$ **2.** $-4x^2$ *M* $\qquad$ **3.** $5x^3 - 4x^2 + 7x$ *T* $\qquad$ **4.** 3 *M*

Arrange each polynomial in descending order of exponents.

5. $3x^2 - 5x^3 + 7x - 4$ $\qquad$ **6.** $5x - 4x^2 - 3$ $\qquad\qquad$ $-5a^3 + 4a^2 + 2a + 1$

7. $4a^2 - 5a^3 + 2a + 1$

8. $-4x^2 - 7x^3 + x^4 + 5x + 1$ $\qquad\qquad$ **9.** $5x - 4x^3 + 7x^2 + 2$

10. $6 - 5x^3 + 2x + 3x^2 + x^4$ $\searrow$ $\qquad\qquad$ **11.** $6x^4 - 3x^2 + 2x^3 - 5 + x$

$\qquad\qquad x^4 - 5x^3 + 3x^2 + 2x + 6$ $\qquad\qquad\qquad 6x^4 + 2x^3 - 3x^2 + x - 5$

$\qquad\qquad\qquad\qquad\qquad\qquad\qquad\qquad\qquad -4x^3 + 7x^2 + 5x + 2$

EXERCISES

PART A

Simplify. Then write the result in descending order of exponents.

1. $3x^2 - 5x + 2x - 8$ $3x^2 - 3x - 8$ $\qquad$ **2.** $5x^2 - 8x + 3x + 4$ $5x^2 - 5x + 4$

3. $5x^2 - 3x + 2 + 4x^2 + 7x + 3$ $9x^2 + 4x + 5$ $\qquad$ **4.** $4 + 8x^2 - 2x + 6x^2 - 4x - 6$

5. $-7x + 2x^2 - 5 + 3x^2 + 8 - 4x$ $5x^2 - 11x + 3$ $\qquad$ **6.** $8x - 2x^2 + 5x - 4 + 5x^2 - 3$

7. $-4 + 3m^2 - 5 - 2m^2$ $m^2 - 9$ $\qquad$ **8.** $5m^2 - 4 - 7m^2 + 8$ $-2m^2 + 4$

9. $4x - 6x^2 + 5x^3 - 3x^2 + 2x^3 + 5x$ $\qquad$ **10.** $4x^3 - 5x + 2x^2 + 7x - 3x^3 + 5x^2$

11. $4m^3 - 5m^3 + 4m^2 - 4m^2 - 3m + 8m$ $\qquad$ **12.** $m^3 - 9m - 5m^2 + 9m + 4m^2 + 5m^3$

13. $6a^4 - 3a^2 + 2a^4 + 4a^2$ $8a^4 + a^2$ $\qquad$ **14.** $5a - 3a^4 + 7a + 2a^4$ $-a^4 + 12a$

15. $3 + 6a - 2a^2 - 5a + 4a^2 - 4$ $2a^2 + a - 1$ $\qquad$ **16.** $7a - 3 - a^2 + 5a - 4 - 2a^2$

17. $7b^3 - 4b - 2b^2 + 3b + 8$ $7b^3 - 2b^2 - b + 8$ $\qquad$ **18.** $4b - 3 - 9b^3 + 5b + 2b^2 - 8$

$\qquad\qquad -m^3 + 5m$ $\qquad\qquad\qquad\qquad\qquad\qquad\qquad\qquad -9b^3 + 2b^2 + 9b - 11$

PART B $\qquad 7x^3 - 9x^2 + 9x$

Simplify. $\qquad 10a^3 + 2a^2 - 12a - 4$ $\qquad\qquad\qquad\qquad\qquad 3a^3 + 3a^2 + 3a + 2$

19. $1 + 3a^3 - 4a - 2a^2 + 7a^3 - 8a + 4a^2 - 5$ $\qquad$ **20.** $6a^2 - 5a - 3 + a^2 - 4a^2 + 3a^3 + 8a + 5$

21. $a^2 + a^4 - 2a^3 - 7a - 2 + 2a^4 - 5a^3 + 8a - 4 + a^2$ $3a^4 - 7a^3 + 2a^2 + a - 6$

22. $7b^2 - 5b^4 + 2b^3 + 2b - 1 - 4b^4 - 3b^3 + 2b^2 - 8b - 2$ $-9b^4 - b^3 + 9b^2 - 6b - 3$

23. $1 - 3m^9 - 7m^6 - 19m^9 + 6m^6 - 4$ $-22m^9 - m^6 - 3$

24. $3b^5 - 6b^7 + b^5 - b^7 - b^4 - 2b^2 + 5b^4$ $-7b^7 + 4b^5 + 4b^4 - 2b^2$

25. $-3a^2 + 7a - 2a^2 + 4a^3 + 6a - 9 + 8a^3 - 10 + a^4 - 5a^2$ $a^4 + 12a^3 - 10a^2 + 13a - 19$

Flow Chart: Ordering Numbers

PROBLEM

Write a flow chart to show how to arrange a given finite set of numbers in order from smallest to largest.

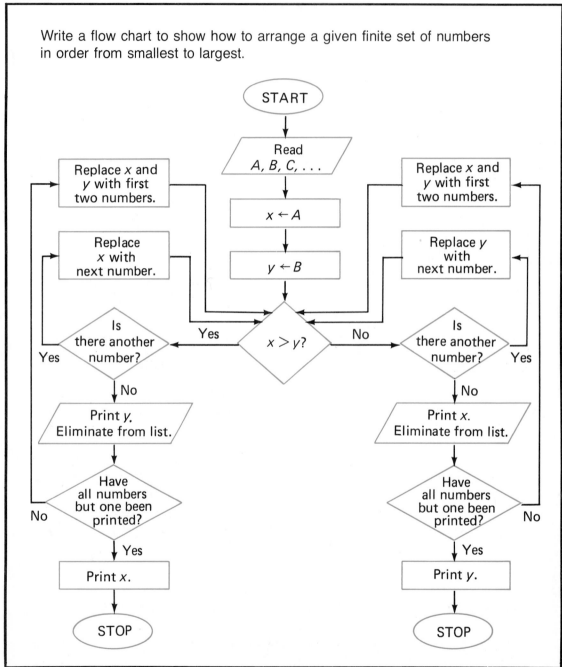

Follow the steps on the flow chart to list the numbers
17, 6, 1, 100 in order from smallest to largest.

Start.
Read 17, 6, 1, 100.
$x = 17$ $y = 6$
$x > y$? Yes.
Is there another number? Yes.
Replace x with the next number.
$x = 1$ $y = 6$
$x > y$? No.
Is there another number? Yes.
Replace y with the next number.
$x = 1$ $y = 100$
$x > y$? No.
Is there another number? No.
Print x.   *Machine prints 1. 1 is removed
$x = 17$ $y = 6$ from list. New list 17, 6, 100.
$x > y$? Yes.
Is there another number? Yes.
Replace x with the next number.
$x = 100$ $y = 6$
$x > y$? Yes.
Is there another number? No.
Print y.   *Machine prints 6. 6 is removed
$x = 17$ $y = 100$ from list. New list 17,100.
$x > y$? No.
Is there another number? No.
Print x.   *Machine prints 17. 17 is removed
Have all the numbers but one   from list.
been printed? Yes.
Print y.   *Machine prints 100.
Stop.

PROJECT

Write the steps in using the flow chart to list each sequence
of numbers from smallest to largest.

1. 8, 6, 10   **2.** 7, 2, 38, 14   **3.** −8, 20, 6, −2   **4.** 59, 26, −3, 18, 3
5. Write a flow chart for listing a sequence of numbers in order from
largest to smallest.

Simplifying Polynomials

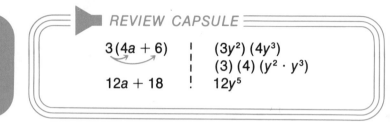

REVIEW CAPSULE

$3(4a + 6)$ $(3y^2)(4y^3)$

           $(3)(4)(y^2 \cdot y^3)$

$12a + 18$ $12y^5$

EXAMPLE 1   Multiply $a^2(3a^3 + 2a^2)$.

Distribute a^2. $a^2(3a^3) + a^2(2a^2)$

Regroup factors. $3 \cdot a^2 \cdot a^3 + 2 \cdot a^2 \cdot a^2$

$x^m \cdot x^n = x^{m+n}$ $3a^5 + 2a^4$

EXAMPLE 2   Multiply $4m^5(2m^6 - 3m^3 + 4m)$.

m means m^1. $4m^5(2m^6 - 3m^3 + 4m^1)$

Distribute $4m^5$. $4m^5(2m^6) + 4m^5(-3m^3) + 4m^5(4m^1)$

                                $4 \cdot 2 \cdot m^5 \cdot m^6 + 4 \cdot -3 \cdot m^5 \cdot m^3 + 4 \cdot 4 \cdot m^5 \cdot m^1$

                                $8m^{11} - 12m^8 + 16m^6$

EXAMPLE 3   Simplify $-(p^2 + 2p - 4)$.

$-a = -1 \cdot a$ $-1(1p^2 + 2p - 4)$

                                $(-1)(1p^2) + (-1)(2p) + (-1)(-4)$

                                $-1p^2 \qquad -2p \qquad +4$

$-1p^2 = -p^2$ $-p^2 - 2p + 4$

EXAMPLE 4   Simplify $x^3 + 2x^2 - 8x - (-2x^2 + 7x - 5)$.

$a = 1a, -a = -1a$ $1x^3 + 2x^2 - 8x - 1(-2x^2 + 7x - 5)$

Distribute -1. $1x^3 + 2x^2 - 8x + 2x^2 - 7x + 5$

Group like terms. $1x^3 + 2x^2 + 2x^2 - 8x - 7x + 5$

Combine like terms. $1x^3 + 4x^2 - 15x + 5$

$1x^3 = x^3$ $x^3 + 4x^2 - 15x + 5$

EXAMPLE 5   Add $(c^4 - 5c + 8) + (c^5 - c^4 + c^3)$.

$$(1c^4 - 5c + 8) + (1c^5 - 1c^4 + 1c^3)$$

Group like terms. $\longrightarrow$ $1c^4 - 1c^4 - 5c + 8 + 1c^5 + 1c^3$
Combine like terms. $\longrightarrow$ $0 - 5c + 8 + 1c^5 + 1c^3$
Descending order of exponents $\longrightarrow$ $1c^5 + 1c^3 - 5c + 8$
$1c^5 = c^5;\ 1c^3 = c^3$ $\longrightarrow$ $c^5 + c^3 - 5c + 8$

EXAMPLE 6   Simplify $m^2 + 3m + 7 + 2(m^2 - 5m + 7)$

m^2 means $1m^2$. $\longrightarrow$ $1m^2 + 3m + 7 + 2(1m^2 - 5m + 7)$

Distribute 2. $\longrightarrow$ $1m^2 + 3m + 7 + 2m^2 - 10m + 14$
$1m^2 + 2m^2 + 3m - 10m + 7 + 14$
Combine like terms. $\longrightarrow$ $3m^2 - 7m + 21$

EXAMPLE 7   Subtract $y^3 - 3y^2$ from $6y^4 - 5y^3 + 7y^2 - 8$.

$$(6y^4 - 5y^3 + 7y^2 - 8) - (y^3 - 3y^2)$$
$-a = -1a;\ a = 1a$ $\longrightarrow$ $(6y^4 - 5y^3 + 7y^2 - 8) - 1(1y^3 - 3y^2)$

$6y^4 - 5y^3 + 7y^2 - 8 - 1y^3 + 3y^2$
$6y^4 - 5y^3 - 1y^3 + 7y^2 + 3y^2 - 8$
$6y^4 - 6y^3 + 10y^2 - 8$

ORAL EXERCISES

Multiply.

$6a^2 - 18a - 12$ $10a^2 - 20a + 15$ $6a^2 - 10a + 12$

1. $3(2a^2 - 6a - 4)$ **2.** $5(2a^2 - 4a + 3)$ **3.** $2(3a^2 - 5a + 6)$
4. $5(4a^3 - 2a^2 + 5a - 2)$ **5.** $2(3a^3 - 2a^2 + 5a - 2)$ **6.** $4(4a^3 - 2a^2 + 7a - 3)$
7. $a^2(a^3 + a^2)$ $a^5 + a^4$ **8.** $b^3(b^4 + b^2)$ $b^7 + b^5$ **9.** $b^5(b^3 + b^2)$ $b^8 + b^7$
10. $m^2(m^2 + m)$ $m^4 + m^3$ **11.** $m^3(m^4 + m)$ $m^7 + m^4$ **12.** $a^2(a^2 + a)$ $a^4 + a^3$
13. $a^4(a^2 + a)$ $a^6 + a^5$ **14.** $a^2(a^2 + a + 5)$ **15.** $a^3(a^2 + a + 1)$
$a^4 + a^3 + 5a^2$ $a^5 + a^4 + a^3$

EXERCISES

PART A

Multiply.

$3f^4 - 5f^3 + 4f^2$ $3t^4 - 5t^3 + 6t^2$ $15a^5 - 35a^4$
                                                $2a^3 - 5a^2 + 4a$

1. $f^2(3f^2 - 5f + 4)$ **2.** $t^2(3t^2 - 5t + 6)$ **3.** $a(2a^2 - 5a + 4)$
4. $5b(3b^2 - 4b + 3)$ **5.** $2x^3(3x^2 - 7x)$ **6.** $5a^3(3a^2 - 7a)$
$15b^3 - 20b^2 + 15b$ $6x^5 - 14x^4$

Simplify.

$20c^4 - 25c^3$

7. $6b(4b^2 - 5b)$ 8. $3m(2m^2 - 5m)$ *$6m^3 - 15m^2$*   9. $5c(4c^3 - 5c^2)$

10. $-(2b^2 - 5b)$ *$-2b^2 + 5b$*   11. $-(4x^2 - 5x)$ *$-4x^2 + 5x$*   12. $-(3x^2 - 4x + 2)$

13. $-(2x^2 + 5x - 7)$ 14. $-(-b^2 - 5b)$ *$b^2 + 5b$*   15. $-(-b^2 + 2b)$ *$b^2 - 2b$*

16. $-(-x^2 - x - 2)$ 17. $-(a^2 - a - 4)$ *$-a^2 + a + 4$*   18. $-(-c^3 + c - 5)$

19. $-3a(-3a^2 - 5a + 2)$ 20. $-5b(-2b^2 - 3b - 4)$ 21. $-2a^2(2a^2 - 6a - 8)$

22. $-a(2a^2 - a - 3)$ 23. $-m(-m^2 - m - 5)$ 24. $-g(-g^2 - 2g + 5)$

25. $x^3 + 5x^2 - 7x - (-3x^2 + 5x - 9)$ 26. $x^3 + 4x^2 - 5x - (-2x^2 + 3x - 8)$

27. $2x^3 - x^2 - x - 4 - (-x^2 - 2x + 5)$ 28. $-3c^2 - 5c + 2 - (-2c^2 - 3c - 4)$

$2x^3 + x - 9$ *$-c^2 - 2c + 6$*

Add.

$x^5 + x^3 - 8x + 7$

29. $(x^4 - 8x + 7) + (x^5 - x^4 + x^3)$ 30. $(a^3 - 3a + 5) + (a^4 - a^3 + a^2)$

31. $(a^2 - a - 4) + (2a^2 - a - 3)$ 32. $(-3b^2 - 5b + 2) + (-2b^2 - 3b - 4)$

$3a^2 - 2a - 7$ *$-5b^2 - 8b - 2$*

Simplify.

$4x^2 - 9x + 17$

33. $x^2 + 3x + 2 + 3(x^2 - 4x + 5)$ 34. $y^2 - 4y + 3 + 4(y^2 + y - 5)$

35. $2a^2 - 5a - 10 + 2(2a^2 - 3a + 5)$ 36. $3c^2 - c + 6 + 3(c^2 - 3c - 5)$

$5x^4 - 2x^3 + 4x^2 - 3$

37. Subtract $x^3 - 2x^2$ from $5x^4 - x^3 + 2x^2 - 3$.   38. Subtract $a^2 - 2a$ from $5a^3 - 7a^2 + 8a - 3$.

39. Subtract $-x^3 - 2x$ from $x^4 + 3x^2 - 5x + 3$.   40. Subtract $-c^2 + 5$ from $3c^3 - 2c^2 + c - 5$.

$x^4 + x^3 + 3x^2 - 3x + 3$ *$3c^3 - c^2 + c - 10$*

PART B

EXAMPLE   Simplify $a^2b^3(2a^2 - 3ab + b^2)$.

Distribute a^2b^3. $\longrightarrow$ $a^2b^3(2a^2) + a^2b^3(-3ab) + a^2b^3(b^2)$

Regroup factors. $\longrightarrow$ $2(a^2)(a^2)(b^3) + (-3)(a^2)(a^1)(b^3)(b^1)$
$$+ (a^2)(b^3)(b^2)$$

$x^m \cdot x^n = x^{m+n}$ $\longrightarrow$ $2(a^4)(b^3) \qquad -3 \quad (a^3) \quad (b^4) + 1(a^2)(b^5)$
$$2a^4b^3 - 3a^3b^4 + a^2b^5$$

Simplify.

$2m^5n^2 - 3m^4n^3 + m^3n^4$ *$a^3b - 5a^2b^2 + 7ab^3$*

41. $m^3n^2(2m^2 - 3mn + n^2)$ 42. $ab(a^2 - 5ab + 7b^2)$

43. $2ab(a^2 - 3ab + 5b^2)$ 44. $3m^2n^2(m^3 - 3m^2n + mn^2 + n^3)$

45. $-xy^2(2x^2 - xy + y^2)$ 46. $-pq(p^2 - pq + q^2)$ *$-p^3q + p^2q^2 - pq^3$*

47. $-2ac(a^3 - a^2c + ac^2 - c^3)$ 48. $-3x^2y(-x^2 - 2xy - y^2)$

$-2a^4c + 2a^3c^2 - 2a^2c^3 + 2ac^4$ *$3x^4y + 6x^3y^2 + 3x^2y^3$*

PART C

Simplify.

49. $m^3n^2(2m^2 - 3mn + n^2) + m^3n^2(m^2 - 2mn + 3n^2)$

50. $2ab(a^2 - 3ab + 5b^2) - 3ab(3a^2 - 7ab - 9b^2)$

51. $-xy^2(3x^2 - 2xy + 5y^2) + xy^2(x^2 - xy - y^2)$

52. $-3ab^2(-a^3 - 2a^2b + ab^2 - b^3) - 2ab^2(a^3 + 3a^2b - ab^2 + 2b^3)$

Perfect Numbers

A whole number is perfect if it is the sum of all of its factors less than itself.

Perfect number ⟶ **28**

$$1 + 2 + 4 + 7 + 14 = 28$$

Factors of 28 less than 28

PROJECT

1. Is 18 a perfect number?

2. There is one perfect number less than 28. Can you find it?

3. Is 36 a perfect number?

4. The next perfect number is between 490 and 500. Can you find it?

5. The fourth perfect number is between 8,120 and 8,130. Can you find it?

6. Were any of the first four perfect numbers odd numbers?

Concept of Factoring

OBJECTIVES
■ To factor a number into primes
■ To find the missing factor given a sentence like $(6a)(?) = 12a^3$

REVIEW CAPSULE

Simplify $(3a^2b^3)(4a^4b^5)$.

$$(3a^2b^3)(4a^4b^5)$$
$$(3)(4)(a^2)(a^4)(b^3)(b^5)$$
$$12a^{2+4}b^{3+5}$$
$$12a^6b^8$$

Numbers which are multiplied are *factors*.

24 can be factored into $8 \cdot 3$,
or $12 \cdot 2$,
or $2 \cdot 3 \cdot 4$,
or $2 \cdot 2 \cdot 2 \cdot 3$.

In the last case, none of the factors can be factored further except for itself and 1.

The only factors of 3 are 3 and 1.

itself and 1

2 is a prime number.
3 is also a prime number.

Definition of prime number ⟶

A *prime number* is a whole number greater than 1 whose only factors are itself and 1.

EXAMPLE 1   Factor 40 into primes.

Three ways to begin

$$40 = 20 \cdot 2 \qquad 40 = 8 \cdot 5 \qquad 40 = 10 \cdot 4$$
$$= 5 \cdot 4 \cdot 2 \qquad = 4 \cdot 2 \cdot 5$$
Each gives the same 4 factors. ⟶ $= 5 \cdot 2 \cdot 2 \cdot 2 \qquad = 2 \cdot 2 \cdot 2 \cdot 5 \qquad = 5 \cdot 2 \cdot 2 \cdot 2$

Each factor is prime. ⟶ **Thus, $40 = 5 \cdot 2 \cdot 2 \cdot 2$.**

$5 \cdot 2 \cdot 2 \cdot 2$ is the prime factorization of 40.

EXAMPLE 2   Factor 32 into primes.

Begin with any factorization.
16 is NOT prime.
8 is NOT prime.
4 is NOT prime.

$$32 = 16 \cdot 2$$
$$= 8 \cdot 2 \cdot 2$$
$$= 4 \cdot 2 \cdot 2 \cdot 2$$
$$= 2 \cdot 2 \cdot 2 \cdot 2 \cdot 2$$

EXAMPLE 3   Find the missing factor.
$$(a^5)(?) = a^8$$

$x^m \cdot x^n = x^{m+n}$ $\longrightarrow$

$8 = 5 + \boxed{3}$ $\longrightarrow$

$(a^5)(a^{\square})$
$a^{5+\square}$
$a^{5+\boxed{3}}$
$(a^5)(a^{\boxed{3}})$

$(a^5)(a^3) = a^{5+3}$, or a^8 $\longrightarrow$ **Thus,** the missing factor is a^3.

EXAMPLE 4   Find the missing factor.
$$(5a^4)(?) = -20a^7$$

We need a number factor and a
factor $a^{\square}$. $\longrightarrow$

$-20 = (5)(-4)$

$a^7 = (a^4)(a^{\boxed{3}})$ $\longrightarrow$

Check by multiplying.

$(5a^4)(-4a^3) = -20a^7$ $\longrightarrow$

$$-20 \qquad a^7$$
$$(5)(?) \quad (a^4)(a^{\square})$$
$$\downarrow \qquad \downarrow$$
$$(5)(-4)(a^4)(a^{\boxed{3}})$$

Thus, $-4a^3$ is the missing factor.

ORAL EXERCISES

Tell whether each is prime.

1. 8 *no*	**2.** 19 *yes*	**3.** 21 *no*	*yes* **4.** 37
5. 7 *yes*	**6.** 49 *no*	**7.** 15 *no*	*yes* **8.** 41
9. 52 *no*	**10.** 2 *yes*	**11.** 27 *no*	*yes* **12.** 31
13. 40 *no*	**14.** 5 *yes*	**15.** 29 *yes*	*no* **16.** 25

Factor each as the product of two factors.

17. 12	**18.** 60	**19.** 28	**20.** 30
21. 36	**22.** 52	**23.** 42	**24.** 20
25. 18	**26.** 48	**27.** 32	**28.** 44

EXERCISES

PART A

Factor into primes.

1. 12 *(2)(2)(3)*
2. 24 *(2)(2)(2)(3)*
3. 18 *(3)(3)(2)*
4. 28 *(2)(2)(7)*

5. 45 *(5)(3)(3)*
6. 60 *(2)(2)(5)(3)*
7. 26 *(2)(13)*
8. 35 *(5)(7)*

9. 50 *(2)(5)(5)*
10. 72 *(3)(3)(2)(2)(2)*
11. 44 *(2)(2)(11)*
12. 30 *(3)(5)(2)*

13. 80 *(2)(2)(2)(2)(5)*
14. 42 *(7)(2)(3)*
15. 48 *(2)(2)(2)(2)(3)*
16. 27 *(3)(3)(3)*

Find the missing factor.

17. $(a^7)(?) = a^{10}$ a^3
18. $(a^6)(?) = a^9$ a^3

19. $(6m^5)(?) = 36m^8$ $6m^3$
20. $(4a^3)(?) = 32a^7$ $8a^4$

21. $(-3x^5)(?) = 27x^7$ $-9x^2$
22. $(-3x^3)(?) = 18x^6$ $-6x^3$

23. $(?)(5x^5) = 35x^{10}$ $7x^5$
24. $(?)(4m^5) = 8m^9$ $2m^4$

25. $(?)(3x^3) = -30x^7$ $-10x^4$
26. $(?)(-20a^8) = 40a^{13}$ $-2a^5$

27. $(3b^2)(?) = 3b^7$ b^5
28. $(?)(5b^9) = 5b^{12}$ b^3

29. $(-8b^5)(?) = 16b^6$ $-2b$
30. $(-b^7)(?) = 5b^8$ $-5b$

PART B

EXAMPLE

We need a number factor, a factor $a^\square$,
and a factor $b^\triangle$. ———————————→

Check by multiplying.
$(2a^2b^3)(4a^5b^6) = 8a^7b^9$ ————————→

Find the missing factor.
$$(2a^2b^3)(?) = 8a^7b^9$$

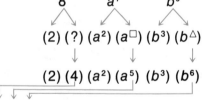

Thus, $4a^5b^6$ is the missing factor.

Find the missing factor.

31. $(3a^2b^3)(?) = 27a^5b^4$ $9a^3b$
32. $(4a^3m^5)(?) = 24a^7m^9$ $6a^4m^4$

33. $(?)(4a^3m^7) = -32a^5m^9$ $-8a^2m^2$
34. $(3a^2b^5)(?) = 39a^4b^7$ $13a^2b^2$

35. $(?)(2a^2b^5) = -2a^3b^6$ $-ab$
36. $(?)(4x^3y^2) = -8x^4y^3$ $-2xy$

37. $(?)(3x^3y^4) = -3x^5y^8$ $-x^2y^4$
38. $(2ab^2)(?) = -16a^2b^3$ $-8ab$

39. $(3x^3y)(?) = 3x^4y$ x
40. $(8a^3m)(?) = -8a^7m$ $-a^4$

PART C

Find the missing factor.

41. $(a^{2m})(?) = a^{5m}$
42. $(x^{3a})(?) = x^{8a}$
43. $(a^{2m+5})(?) = a^{4m+9}$

Factoring Out a Common Monomial

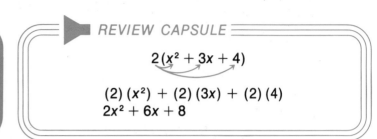

REVIEW CAPSULE

$$2(x^2 + 3x + 4)$$

$$(2)(x^2) + (2)(3x) + (2)(4)$$
$$2x^2 + 6x + 8$$

Use the distributive property in reverse. ⟶

We can rewrite $2m^3 - 6m^2 + 10m - 8$
as $2(m^3 - 3m^2 + 5m - 4)$.

2 is a common monomial factor.

EXAMPLE 1   Factor a common monomial factor from
$3b^2 + 9b + 6$.

3 divides each term evenly. Use 3 as a factor of each term.

$$3b^2 + \quad 9b \quad + 6$$

$$3(b^2) + 3(3b) + 3(2)$$

Use the distributive property in reverse. ⟶

$$3(b^2 + 3b + 2)$$

EXAMPLE 2   Factor the greatest common factor from
$4x^2 - 8x + 4$.

4 is the greatest number that divides each term evenly. Use 4 as a factor of each term.

Distributive property in reverse ⟶

$$4x^2 - \quad 8x \quad + 4$$

$$4(x^2) + 4(-2x) + 4(1)$$
$$4(x^2 - 2x + 1)$$

4 is the GCF (short for greatest common factor) of $4x^2 - 8x + 4$.

EXAMPLE 3   Find the GCF of $6x^2 + 12$.

Factor 6 and 12 into primes. ⟶

$$(3)(2)(x^2) \quad + \quad (2)(3)(2)$$

$$\underbrace{\quad}_{\text{one 3, one 2}} \quad \underbrace{\quad}_{\text{two 2's, one 3}}$$

At most, one 2 and one 3 are common to each term.

Thus, the GCF is $(2)(3)$, or 6.

Example 3 shows a technique for finding the GCF. You need not use that process if you can recognize the GCF immediately.

EXAMPLE 4 Factor the GCF from $20b^2 - 24b + 48$.

Factor into primes. $\longrightarrow$ $(2)(2)(5)(b^2) - (2)(2)(2)(3)(b) + (2)(2)(2)(2)(3)$

At most, two 2's are common to each term, so the GCF is $(2)(2)$, or 4.

$$20b^2 - 24b + 48$$

Use 4 as a factor of each term. $\longrightarrow$ $4(5b^2) + 4(-6b) + 4(12)$
Distributive property in reverse $\longrightarrow$ $4(5b^2 - 6b + 12)$

EXAMPLE 5 Factor $x^3 + x^2 + x$.

x means x^1. $\longrightarrow$
$$x^3 \quad + \quad x^2 \quad + \quad x^1$$
$$\uparrow \qquad\qquad \uparrow \qquad\qquad \uparrow$$

Think. $\longrightarrow$ three x's   two x's   one x
At most, one x is common to each term, so the GCF is x^1.

$$x^3 + x^2 + x^1$$
Use x^1 as a factor of each term. $\longrightarrow$ $x^1(x^2) + x^1(x^1) + x^1(1)$
$x^1 = x$ $\qquad\qquad\qquad$ $x^1(x^2 + x^1 + 1)$, or $x(x^2 + x + 1)$

EXAMPLE 6 Factor $2x^4 + 4x^3 + 6x^2$.

First step $\longrightarrow$ Look for the greatest common whole number factor.
Factor coefficients into primes. $\longrightarrow$ $(2)(x^4) + (2)(2)(x^3) + (2)(3)(x^2)$
2 is common to each term. $\longrightarrow$ 2 is the greatest common whole number factor.

Second step $\longrightarrow$ Now look for the greatest common variable factor.
$$2x^4 \quad + \quad 4x^3 \quad + \quad 6x^2$$
$$\uparrow \qquad\qquad \uparrow \qquad\qquad \uparrow$$

Think. $\longrightarrow$ four x's   three x's   two x's
x^2 is common to each term. $\longrightarrow$ x^2 is the greatest common variable factor.
$2x^2$ divides each term evenly. $\longrightarrow$ The GCF of $2x^4 + 4x^3 + 6x^2$ is $2x^2$.
Use $2x^2$ as a factor of each term. $\longrightarrow$ $2x^2(x^2) + 2x^2(2x^1) + 2x^2(3)$
Distributive property in reverse $\longrightarrow$ $2x^2(x^2 + 2x + 3)$

Thus, $2x^4 + 4x^3 + 6x^2 = 2x^2(x^2 + 2x + 3)$.

EXAMPLE 7   Factor $5x^6 - 20x^4 + x^3$.

First step ⟶ Look for a common whole number factor.
$$(5)\,(x^6) - (5)\,(4)\,(x^4) + 1\,(x^3)$$
1 is the common whole number factor. We do not bother to factor out the 1.

Second step ⟶ Now look for the greatest common variable factor.
$$5x^6 \quad - \quad 20x^4 \quad + \quad 1x^3$$
↑   ↑   ↑

Think. ⟶   six x's   four x's   three x's

x^3 is common to each term. ⟶ x^3 is the greatest common variable factor.

$$5x^6 - 20x^4 + 1x^3$$

Use x^3 as a factor of each term. ⟶ $x^3(5x^3) + x^3(-20x^1) + x^3(1)$

Distributive property in reverse ⟶ $x^3(5x^3 - 20x^1 + 1)$, or $x^3(5x^3 - 20x + 1)$

SUMMARY

To factor out the greatest common monomial factor:
First, factor out the greatest common whole number factor other than 1, if any. | Second, factor out the greatest common variable factor, if any.

EXERCISES

PART A

Factor.

1. $3x^2 + 27x + 9$
2. $4a^2 + 32a + 20$ $4(a^2 + 8a + 5)$
3. $6b^2 + 18b + 30$ $6(b^2 + 3b + 5)$
4. $2m^2 - 10m + 4$ $2(m^2 - 5m + 2)$
5. $7a^2 - 21a + 49$
6. $m^3 + m^2 + m$
7. $x^5 + x^4 - x^3$
8. $b^4 - 2b^3 + b^2$
9. $2a^3 - a^2 + a$
10. $y^3 - 7y^2 + y$
11. $7a^2 - 28a$
12. $3x^2 - 9x$
13. $4a^3 + 8a^2$
14. $5b^3 - 10b$
15. $6a^2 - 24a$
16. $4a^3 - 16a^2 + 32a$
17. $4a^3 - 12a^2 + 8a$
18. $7b^3 - 14b^2 + 49b$
19. $12x^3 - 6x^2 + 18x$
20. $4m^3 - 24m$
21. $4m^2 - 20$ $4(m^2 - 5)$
22. $3a^3 - 5a^2$ $a^2(3a - 5)$
23. $4m^3 - 32m^2$ $4m^2(m - 8)$
24. $5a^3 - 35a$ $5a(a^2 - 7)$

PART B

Factor.

25. $7a^5 - 35a^4 + 21a^3$ $7a^3(a^2 - 5a + 3)$
26. $6a^4 - 12a^3 + 24a^2 + 3a$
27. $3a^2 + 12ab + 36b^2$ $3(a^2 + 4ab + 12b^2)$
28. $39a^3 - 52a^2 + 26a$
29. $18m^4 - 27m^3 - 45m^2 + 36m$ $9m(2m^3 - 3m^2 - 5m + 4)$
30. $6y^3 - 18y^2 - 12y$ $6y(y^2 - 3y - 2)$

Chapter Five Review

Evaluate for the given values of the variables. $[\,p.\,119\,]$

1. a^3 if $a = -2$

2. $-3x^2$ if $x = -2$

3. $-2a^3$ if $a = -2$

4. $2m^3$ if $m = -4$

5. x^2y^2 if $x = 2, y = -3$

6. $-2a^3b$ if $a = -1, b = -3$

7. $(-2a)^3$ if $a = -2$

8. $(3m)^2$ if $m = -2$

9. $(x^3y^2)^2$ if $x = -2, y = 1$

Simplify. $[\,p.\,121\,]$

10. $(x^3)(x^7)$

11. $(a^7)(a^9)$

12. $(2a^3)(5a^4)$

13. $(3b^2)(5b)$

14. $(-3a^2)(4a^5)$

15. $(-3a^2b)(7a^3b^6)$

16. $(3a^2)^3$

17. $(4b)^2$

18. $(-2m^2n^3)^3$

Classify each polynomial. $[\,p.\,124\,]$

19. $a^2 + 7a$

20. $4x^3$

21. $6x^2 - 4x + 2$

Simplify. Then write the result in descending order of exponents. $[\,p.\,124\,]$

22. $2x^2 + 7x + 3x + 5$

23. $5a^2 - 4a + 2a + 8$

24. $-3 + 5m^2 - 8 - 2m^2$

25. $5b^3 - 3b + b^2 + 8b + 5 + 4b^2 + 2 + 4b^3$

Simplify. $[\,p.\,128\,]$

26. $a^2(a^3 + a^2)$

27. $2b^5(b^3 + b^2 + b)$

28. $a(a^2 - 2a + 3)$

29. $-m(-m^2 - 5m - 2)$

30. $-(-a^2 - a - 1)$

31. $(a^4 - 3a^2 - 5a) - (-3a^3 + 6a - 7)$

32. $x^4 - 3x^2 + 5 + 3(x^5 - x^4 + 2x^3)$

33. $c^2 + 8c + 9 + 2(c^2 - 3c - 5)$

34. $3ab(a^2 - 5ab + 4b^2)$

35. $-3ac^2(a^3 - 2a^2c + ac^2 - c^3)$

Add. $[\,p.\,128\,]$

36. $(x^3 - 2x^2 + 9) + (x^4 - 3x^3 + x^2)$

37. $(a^2 - 5a + 6) + (-4a^2 - a - 1)$

38. Subtract $x^2 - 5x$ from $2x^3 - 5x^2 + 3x - 2$.

39. Subtract $-y^3 - 3y$ from $y^3 + 2y^2 - 5y + 4$.

Factor into primes. $[\,p.\,132\,]$

40. 18

41. 32

42. 28

Find the missing factor. $[\,p.\,132\,]$

43. $(a^2)(?) = a^7$

44. $(x^4)(?) = x^9$

45. $(?)(5a^3) = 5a^4$

46. $(4a)(?) = 20a^2$

47. $(4a^2b^3)(?) = -36a^3b^7$

48. $(-x^5y^2)(?) = x^7y^6$

Factor. $[\,p.\,135\,]$

49. $4a^2 - 8a + 6$

50. $6x - 2$

51. $4x^2 - 7x$

52. $a^3 - 7a^2 + 3a$

53. $4y^3 - 8y^2 + 12y$

54. $5a^4 - 30a^3 + 20a^2 - 15a$

Chapter Five Test

Evaluate for the given values of the variables.

1. $-3a^3$ if $a = -3$
2. $-2m^3n^3$ if $m = -3, n = -2$
3. $(2ab^2)^3$ if $a = -2, b = -1$

Simplify.

4. $(3b^2)(7b)$
5. $(-3a^2b)(4ab^3)$
6. $(3x^2y^3)^2$

Classify each polynomial.

7. $5a^2 + 2a$
8. $7a$
9. $4a^2 - 6a + 5$

Simplify. Then write the result in descending order of exponents.

10. $4x^2 - 8x + 5x + 7$
11. $3a^2 - 7 + 5a^2 + 9$
12. $-3 - 2a + 3a^2 - 5a - 7a^2 + 9$

Simplify.

13. $2a^2(4a^3 - 5a^2)$
14. $m^3(m^2 + 7m - 5)$
15. $-(-e^2 - 2e - 5)$
16. $(a^2 - 5a + 1) - (-a^2 + 2a^2 - a + 1)$
17. $4a^3 - 5a^2 + a + 2(a^2 - 3a^2 - a)$
18. $c^2 + 2a + 5 + 3(c^2 - 2a - 4)$
19. $-8ac^2(a^3 - 3a^2c + 2ac^2 + c^3)$

Add.

20. $(x^4 - 2x^3 + 3x) + (5x^3 - x + 2)$
21. $(c^3 - c^2 - c) + (-2c^3 - c^2 - 3c)$
22. Subtract $x^2 - 3x$ from $4x^3 - 6x^2 + 5x - 1$.
23. Subtract $-y^3 - 2y$ from $y^3 + 3y^2 - 4y + 2$.

Factor into primes.

24. 12
25. 50

Find the missing factor.

26. $(x^4)(?) = x^{10}$
27. $(x^5)(?) = x^6$
28. $(4m^2)(?) = 32m^9$
29. $(?)(-3a^2) = 18a^5$
30. $(?)(-5a) = 35a^2$
31. $(-2a^2b^3)(?) = 8a^3b^7$

Factor.

32. $3a^2 - 18$
33. $5a^2 - 10a$
34. $8a^2 - 16a + 40$
35. $a^3 - a^2 - 7a$
36. $m^3 - m^2 - m$
37. $6x^3 - 12x^2 + 18x$
38. $3a^2 - 7a - 25$
39. $4a^4 - 24a^3 + 12a^2 - 28a$

6 FACTORING TRINOMIALS

Scientific Notation

Scientific notation is used to write very large numbers.

The distance from the sun to earth is about 1.5×10^8 kilometers.

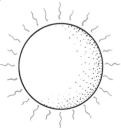

$1.5 \times 10^8 = 1.5 \times \underbrace{100,000,000}_{8 \text{ zeros}}$

$= \underbrace{150,000,000}_{\text{Standard notation}}$ kilometers

The diameter of the earth is about 13,000 kilometers.

$13,000 = 13 \times 1,000$
$\qquad = \underbrace{1.3 \times 10^4}_{\text{Scientific notation}}$ kilometers.

PROBLEM

Multiply. Use scientific notation.

$$36,000 \times 25$$
$$3.6 \times 10^4 \times 2.5 \times 10^1 = (3.6 \times 2.5) \times (10^4 \times 10^1)$$
$$= 9.0 \times 10^5, \text{ or } 900,000$$

PROJECT

Write in standard notation.
1. 4×10^2 **2.** 5.8×10^6 **3.** 2.63×10^7

Write in scientific notation.
4. 400,000,000   **5.** 63,000   **6.** 23,200,000,000

Multiply. Use scientific notation.
7. $250 \times 7,000$ **8.** $9,300 \times 30$ **9.** $54,200 \times 8,100$

Multiplying Polynomials

OBJECTIVE

■ To multiply polynomials like $(3x + 5)(2x - 4)$

REVIEW CAPSULE

Simplify $4x(x + 2)$.

$$4x(x + 2) = (4x)(x) + (4x)(2)$$
$$= 4x^2 + 8x$$

EXAMPLE 1   Multiply $(3x + 5)(2x + 4)$.

Think. ————————→

Distribute ☐ . ————————→

☐ is $3x + 5$. ————————→

Distribute $2x$. Then distribute 4.

Multiply. ————————→

Combine like terms. ————————→

$$(3x + 5)(2x + 4)$$
$$(\boxed{})(2x + 4)$$

$$(\boxed{})(2x) + (\boxed{})(4)$$

$$(3x + 5)(2x) + (3x + 5)(4)$$

$$(3x)(2x) + (5)(2x) + (3x)(4) + (5)(4)$$
$$6x^2 + 10x + 12x + 20$$
$$6x^2 + 22x + 20$$

There is a more convenient way to arrange the work.

Rewrite in vertical form.
$(3x)(2x) = 6x^2$ ⎫
$\quad(5)(4) = 20$ ⎬ ————————→
⎭

$$\begin{array}{lr} 3x & +5 \\ 2x & +4 \\ \hline 6x^2 & +20 \end{array}$$

end terms

Find the middle term by multiplying along the diagonals and adding.

$$\begin{array}{lr} 3x & +5 \\ 2x & +4 \\ \hline & +10x \end{array}$$

$(2x)(5) = 10x$ ————————————→

$(4)(3x) = 12x$ ————————————→

$+10x + 12x = +22x$ ————————————→

$$\begin{array}{lll} & +10x & \\ 6x^2 & +12x & +20 \\ \hline & +22x & \end{array}$$

Thus, $(3x + 5)(2x + 4) = 6x^2 + 22x + 20$.

EXAMPLE 2 Multiply $(2x - 5)(3x + 4)$.

Rewrite in vertical form.
Find the end terms.
$(3x)(2x) = 6x^2$; $(4)(-5) = -20$ ⟶

$$
\begin{array}{ll}
2x & -5 \\
3x & +4 \\
\hline
6x^2 & -20
\end{array}
$$

More compact form

$$
\begin{array}{ll}
2x & -5 \\
3x & +4 \\
\end{array}
$$
$$-15x$$
$$6x^2 \quad +8x \quad -20$$
$$\overline{-7x}$$

Find the middle term.
$(3x)(-5) = -15x$
$(4)(2x) = +8x$
$-15x + 8x = -7x$

$$
\begin{array}{ll}
2x & -5 \\
3x & +4 \\
\end{array}
$$
$$-15x$$
$$6x^2 \quad +8x \quad -20$$
$$\overline{-7x}$$

Thus, $(2x - 5)(3x + 4) = 6x^2 - 7x - 20.$

EXAMPLE 3 Multiply $(x + 5)(x - 5)$.

Write x as $1x$.
Find the middle term.
$(1x)(5) = +5x$
$(-5)(1x) = -5x$
$+5x - 5x = 0x$
$0x = 0$; $1x^2 = x^2$ ⟶
The product of two binomials
may be a binomial.

$$
\begin{array}{ll}
1x & +5 \\
1x & -5 \\
\end{array}
$$
$$+5x$$
$$1x^2 \quad -5x \quad -25$$
$$\overline{0x}$$

$$1x^2 + 0 - 25, \text{ or } x^2 - 25$$

Thus, $(x + 5)(x - 5) = x^2 - 25.$

EXAMPLE 4 Simplify $(2x - 3)^2$.

$(2x - 3)^2 = (2x - 3)(2x - 3)$
Find the middle term.
$(2x)(-3) = -6x$
$(-3)(2x) = -6x$
$-6x - 6x = -12x$

$$
\begin{array}{ll}
2x & -3 \\
2x & -3 \\
\end{array}
$$
$$-6x$$
$$4x^2 \quad -6x \quad +9$$
$$\overline{-12x}$$

Thus, $(2x - 3)^2 = 4x^2 - 12x + 9.$

EXAMPLE 5 Multiply $(4a - b)(a - 2b)$.

Write $-b$ as $-1b$.
Write a as $1a$.
$(1a)(-1b) = (1)(-1)(a)(b)$, or $-1ab$
$(-2b)(4a) = (-2)(4)(a)(b)$, or $-8ab$
$-1ab - 8ab = -9ab$

$$
\begin{array}{ll}
4a & -1b \\
1a & -2b \\
\end{array}
$$
$$-1ab$$
$$4a^2 \quad -8ab \quad +2b^2$$
$$\overline{-9ab}$$

Thus, $(4a - b)(a - 2b) = 4a^2 - 9ab + 2b^2.$

EXERCISES

PART A

Multiply.

$20x^2 + 37x + 15$

1. $(3x + 2)(2x + 7)$ 2. $(4x + 5)(5x + 3)$ 3. $(3m + 5)(2m + 1)$

4. $(2x - 1)(3x + 1)$ 5. $(2a - 1)(4a + 7)$ 6. $(2b - 5)(3b + 5)$

7. $(m - 5)(m + 5)$ $m^2 - 25$ 8. $(y - 4)(y + 4)$ $y^2 - 16$ 9. $(2r - 3)(2r + 3)$

10. $(3x - 1)(x + 2)$ 11. $(3a - 2)(a - 1)$ 12. $(2m - 6)(2m - 6)$

13. $(2y - 5)(y + 4)$ 14. $(3t - 1)(3t + 1)$ $9t^2 - 1$ 15. $(2b - 5)(b + 2)$

16. $(4d - 1)(d + 2)$ 17. $(3x + 5)(x - 7)$ 18. $(2n - 1)(n + 8)$

19. $(3y - 1)(3y + 1)$ $9y^2 - 1$ 20. $(7a - 1)(2a + 3)$ 21. $(6a - 5)(a + 2)$

22. $(3a - 8b)(a - 5b)$ 23. $(2y - m)(2y + 9m)$ 24. $(3p + q)(2p + 3q)$

$3a^2 - 23ab + 40b^2$ $4y^2 + 16my - 9m^2$

Simplify.

$4x^2 + 12x + 9$

25. $(3y - 5)^2$ 26. $(4x - 1)^2$ 27. $(2x + 3)^2$ 28. $(5n + 1)^2$

$9y^2 - 30y + 25$ $16x^2 - 8x + 1$

PART B

EXAMPLE   Multiply $(2x + 3)(3x^2 + 2x - 5)$.

Rewrite in vertical form.

$$
\begin{array}{r}
3x^2 + 2x - 5 \\
2x + 3 \\
\hline
6x^3 + 4x^2 - 10x \\
9x^2 + 6x - 15 \\
\hline
6x^3 + 13x^2 - 4x - 15
\end{array}
$$

$2x(3x^2 + 2x - 5)$ ⟶

$3(3x^2 + 2x - 5)$ ⟶

Combine like terms. ⟶

Multiply.

$8x^3 + 22x^2 - 17x + 14$

29. $(3x - 1)(2x^2 + 4x + 3)$ 30. $(2x + 7)(4x^2 - 3x + 2)$ 31. $(x + 7)(3x^2 - x + 5)$

32. $(x - 5)(x^2 - 7x + 1)$ 33. $(3x + 2)(x^3 - 7x^2 + 3x)$ 34. $(2x + 3)(x^3 - 2x^2 + x - 3)$

$3x^4 - 19x^3 - 5x^2 + 6x$

PART C

EXAMPLE   Simplify $(a + b)^2$. Apply the pattern to $(x + 4)^2$.

Think: $(a + b)^2 = (a + b)(a + b)$.

$$
\begin{array}{ccc}
a & & +b \\
a & \times & +b \\
\hline
 & +1ab & \\
a^2 & +1ab & +b^2 \\
\hline
 & +2ab &
\end{array}
$$

Pattern for squaring a binomial ⟶   **Thus,** $(a + b)^2 = a^2 + 2ab + b^2$

Replace a with x and b with 4. ⟶ $(x + 4)^2 = x^2 + 2(x)(4) + (4)^2$, or

$$x^2 + 8x + 16.$$

Simplify by using $(a + b)^2 = a^2 + 2ab + b^2$.

35. $(x - 7)^2$ 36. $(2x + 3)^2$ 37. $(2m - 1)^2$ 38. $(3a - 4b)^2$

Rectangle Products

Areas of rectangles and squares can be used to show the product of two binomials.

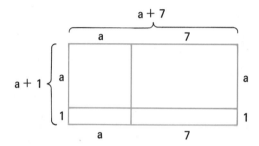

Area = length × width
= $(a + 7)(a + 1)$

But, the area of the rectangle is the sum of the areas of all of its parts.

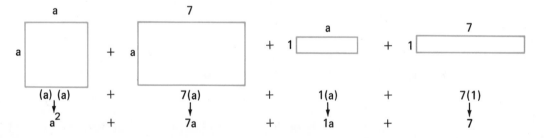

Thus, $(a + 7)(a + 1) = a^2 + 8a + 7$.

PROJECT

Use the rectangle method to multiply the binomials.

1. $(a + 2)(a + 3)$ **2.** $(x + 8)(x + 5)$ **3.** $(x + 2)(x + 5)$

Factoring Trinomials

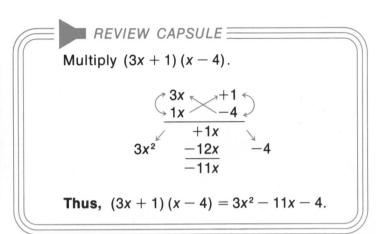

OBJECTIVE

■ To factor a trinomial into two binomials

▶ REVIEW CAPSULE

Multiply $(3x + 1)(x - 4)$.

$$
\begin{array}{c}
3x \quad\quad +1 \\
1x \quad\quad -4 \\
\hline
\quad +1x \\
3x^2 \quad -12x \quad\quad -4 \\
\hline
-11x
\end{array}
$$

Thus, $(3x + 1)(x - 4) = 3x^2 - 11x - 4.$

EXAMPLE 1 Factor $2x^2 + 5x + 3$ into two binomials.

Write a pattern to test factors.

$\left.{2 \atop 1}\right\}$Factors of 2 $\left.{3 \atop 1}\right\}$Factors of 3

$$
\begin{array}{cc}
2x & \square 3 \\
1x & \square 1
\end{array} \rightarrow \text{Omit signs for now.}
$$

Does choice of factors give correct middle term?

$(1x)(\square 3) = \square 3x$

$(\square 1)(2x) = \square 2x$

$$
\begin{array}{c}
2x \quad\quad \square 3 \\
1x \quad\quad \square 1 \\
\hline
\quad \square 3x \\
2x^2 \quad \square 2x \quad\quad +3 \\
\hline
+5x
\end{array}
$$

Check all sign combinations. ⟶

$$
\begin{array}{cccc}
+3x & +3x & -3x & -3x \\
+2x & -2x & +2x & -2x \\
\hline
+5x & +1x & -1x & -5x
\end{array}
$$

└─ One sign combination works.

Check by multiplying.

$(1x)(\boxplus 3) = +3x$ $\Big\}$
$(\boxplus 1)(2x) = +2x$ $\Big\}$
$+3x + 2x = +5x$

$$
\begin{array}{c}
2x \quad\quad \boxplus 3 \\
1x \quad\quad \boxplus 1 \\
\hline
\quad +3x \\
2x^2 \quad +2x \quad\quad +3 \\
\hline
+5x
\end{array}
$$

The factors are $(2x + 3)$ and $(1x + 1)$. ⟶ **Thus,** $2x^2 + 5x + 3 = (2x + 3)(x + 1).$

EXAMPLE 2   Factor $6x^2 - 7x + 2$.

$\left.\begin{matrix}2\\3\end{matrix}\right\}$ Factors of 6 $\left.\begin{matrix}2\\1\end{matrix}\right\}$ Factors of 2

$(3x)(\square 2) = \square 6x$

$(\square 1)(2x) = \square 2x$

No sign combination works.

Try reversing factors of 2 $\left\{\begin{matrix}1\\2\end{matrix}\right.$.

$(3x)\ (\square 1) = \square 3x$

$(\square 2)(2x)\ = \square 4x$

One sign combination works.
Check by multiplying.

$(3x)(\boxminus 1) = -3x$
$(\boxminus 2)(2x) = -4x$
$-3x - 4x = -7x$
$\left.\right\}$

Write factors horizontally. ⟶

$\begin{matrix}2x & \searrow\nearrow & \square 2\\ 3x & \nearrow\searrow & \square 1\end{matrix}$

$\begin{matrix}6x^2 & \dfrac{\begin{matrix}\square 6x\\ \square 2x\end{matrix}}{-7x} & +2\end{matrix}$

Check sign combinations.

$+6x$	$+6x$	$-6x$	$-6x$
$+2x$	$-2x$	$+2x$	$-2x$
$+8x$	$+4x$	$-4x$	$-8x$

None gives $-7x$.

$\begin{matrix}2x & \searrow\nearrow & \square 1\\ 3x & \nearrow\searrow & \square 2\end{matrix}$

$\begin{matrix}6x^2 & \dfrac{\begin{matrix}\square 3x\\ \square 4x\end{matrix}}{-7x} & +2\end{matrix}$

Check sign combinations.

$+3x$	$+3x$	$-3x$	$-3x$
$+4x$	$-4x$	$+4x$	$-4x$
$+7x$	$-1x$	$+1x$	$-7x$

One gives $-7x$.

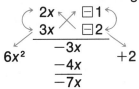

$\begin{matrix}2x & \searrow & \boxminus 1\\ 3x & \times & \boxminus 2\end{matrix}$

$\begin{matrix}6x^2 & \dfrac{\begin{matrix}-3x\\ -4x\end{matrix}}{-7x} & +2\end{matrix}$

Thus, $6x^2 - 7x + 2 = (2x - 1)(3x - 2)$.

EXAMPLE 3   Factor $x^2 + x - 20$.

$x^2 = 1x^2,\ x = 1x$ ⟶

$\left.\begin{matrix}1\\1\end{matrix}\right\}$ Factors of 1 $\left.\begin{matrix}10\\2\end{matrix}\right\}$ Factors of 20

$(1x)(\square 10) = \square 10x$

$(\square 2)(1x)\ = \square\ 2x$

No sign combination works.

Try $\left.\begin{matrix}5\\4\end{matrix}\right\}$ Factors of 20.

One sign combination works.
Check by multiplying.

$(1x)\ (\boxplus 5) = +5x$
$(\boxminus 4)(1x)\ = -4x$
$+5x - 4x = +1x$
$\left.\right\}$

The factors are
$(x + 5)$ and $(x - 4)$. ⟶

$1x^2 \quad +1x \quad -20$

$\begin{matrix}1x & \searrow\nearrow & \square 10\\ 1x & \nearrow\searrow & \square 2\end{matrix}$

$\begin{matrix}1x^2 & \square 10x & -20\\ & \square 2x & \\ & +1x & \end{matrix}$

Check sign combinations.

$+10x$	$+10x$	$-10x$	$-10x$
$+2x$	$-2x$	$+2x$	$-2x$
$+12x$	$+8x$	$-8x$	$-12x$

None gives $+1x$.

$\begin{matrix}1x & \searrow\nearrow & \square 5\\ 1x & \nearrow\searrow & \square 4\end{matrix}$

$\begin{matrix}1x^2 & \square 5x & -20\\ & \square 4x & \\ & +1x & \end{matrix}$

Check sign combinations.

$+5x$	$+5x$
$+4x$	$-4x$
$+9x$	$+1x$

One gives $+1x$.

$\begin{matrix}1x & \searrow & \boxplus 5\\ 1x & \times & \boxminus 4\end{matrix}$

$\begin{matrix}1x^2 & +5x & -20\\ & -4x & \\ & +1x & \end{matrix}$

Thus, $x^2 + x - 20 = (x + 5)(x - 4)$.

EXAMPLE 4 Factor $2x^2 - 5x - 12$.

$\left.\begin{array}{c}2\\1\end{array}\right\}$ factors of 2 $\left.\begin{array}{c}6\\2\end{array}\right\}$ factors of 12

$(1x)(\square 6) = \square 6x$

$(\square 2)(2x) = \square 4x$

No sign combination works.

$$2x \searrow\nearrow \square 6$$
$$1x \nearrow\searrow \square 2$$
$$2x^2 \begin{array}{c}\square 6x\\\square 4x\end{array} -12$$
$$\overline{-5x}$$

Check sign combinations.

$+6x$	$+6x$	$-6x$	$-6x$
$+4x$	$-4x$	$+4x$	$-4x$
$+10x$	$+2x$	$-2x$	$-10x$

None gives $-5x$.

Try $\left.\begin{array}{c}2\\6\end{array}\right\}$ factors of 12.

$$2x \searrow\nearrow \square 2$$
$$1x \nearrow\searrow \square 6$$
$$2x^2 \begin{array}{c}\square 2x\\\square 12x\end{array} -12$$
$$\overline{-5x}$$

No sign combination works.

Check sign combinations.

$+2x$	$+2x$	$-2x$	$-2x$
$+12x$	$-12x$	$+12x$	$-12x$
$+14x$	$-10x$	$+10x$	$-14x$

None gives $-5x$.

Try $\left.\begin{array}{c}3\\4\end{array}\right\}$ factors of 12.

$(1x)(\square 3) = \square 3x$

$(\square 4)(2x) = \square 8x$

One sign combination works.

$$2x \searrow\nearrow \square 3$$
$$1x \nearrow\searrow \square 4$$
$$2x^2 \begin{array}{c}\square 3x\\\square 8x\end{array} -12$$
$$\overline{-5x}$$

Check sign combinations.

$+3x$	$+3x$
$+8x$	$-8x$
$+11x$	$-5x$

One gives $-5x$.

Check by multiplying.

$(1x)(\boxplus 3) = +3x$

$(\boxminus 4)(2x) = -8x$

$+3x - 8x = -5x$

$$2x \searrow\nearrow \boxplus 3$$
$$1x \nearrow\searrow \boxminus 4$$
$$2x^2 \begin{array}{c}+3x\\-8x\end{array} -12$$
$$\overline{-5x}$$

We can also write $(x-4)(2x+3)$.   **Thus,** $2x^2 - 5x - 12 = (2x+3)(x-4)$.

EXERCISES

PART A

Factor.

1. $2x^2 + 7x + 5$
2. $3x^2 + 10x + 7$
3. $5x^2 + 7x + 2$
4. $8x^2 - 10x + 3$
5. $6x^2 - 17x + 5$
6. $10x^2 - 19x + 7$
7. $x^2 + x - 6$
8. $x^2 + x - 12$
9. $x^2 + x - 30$
10. $2a^2 - 7a - 4$
11. $3x^2 - 10x - 25$
12. $2x^2 - x - 3$
13. $x^2 + 7x + 10$
14. $b^2 + 5b + 6$
15. $a^2 + 4a + 3$
16. $y^2 - 10y + 16$
17. $m^2 - 9m + 20$
18. $d^2 - 11d + 30$

19. $a^2 - a - 20$ **20.** $y^2 - 2y - 15$ **21.** $a^2 - 7a - 18$

22. $x^2 + 2x + 1$ **23.** $b^2 - 6b + 9$ **24.** $k^2 + 12k + 36$

25. $2a^2 - 7a + 6$ **26.** $2x^2 + 5x - 3$ **27.** $2a^2 - 7a - 4$

28. $2m^2 + 9m - 5$ **29.** $2a^2 + 13a + 15$ **30.** $3b^2 - 11b + 6$

31. $3x^2 + 10x - 25$ **32.** $2m^2 + 11m + 15$ **33.** $2m^2 - 7m + 5$

34. $6a^2 + a - 1$ **35.** $3y^2 + 7y - 20$ **36.** $2p^2 - 15p + 25$

37. $2b^2 + 17b + 30$ **38.** $2x^2 + 5x + 2$ **39.** $12y^2 + 7y + 1$

PART B

Factor.

40. $2x^2 - 11x - 40$ **41.** $2x^2 + 23x + 45$ **42.** $3x^2 + 10x - 48$

43. $2a^2 - 25a + 50$ **44.** $3a^2 + 8a - 35$ **45.** $2b^2 - 29b + 60$

46. $3m^2 + 29m + 40$ **47.** $5x^2 - 42x - 27$ **48.** $3y^2 - 31y + 56$

PART C

EXAMPLE   Factor $6x^2 - 7x - 20$.

$\left.\begin{matrix}6\\1\end{matrix}\right\}$ factors of 6 $\left.\begin{matrix}5\\4\end{matrix}\right\}$ factors of 20

$6x \diagdown \square 5$
$1x \diagup \square 4$

$6x^2 \begin{matrix}\square 5x\\\square 24x\end{matrix} - 20$

Check sign combinations.

$+5x$	$+5x$	$-5x$	$-5x$
$+24x$	$-24x$	$+24x$	$-24x$
$+29x$	$-19x$	$+19x$	$-29x$

None gives $-7x$.

No combination works.

Try some other combinations of factors.

$1x \diagdown \square 5$
$6x \diagup \square 4$ or $1x \diagdown \square 10$
$6x \diagup \square 2$ or $3x \diagdown \square 4$
$2x \diagup \square 5$ etc.

Only this one works. $3x \diagdown \boxplus 4$
$2x \diagup \boxminus 5$

Check by multiplying.

$3x \diagdown \boxplus 4$
$2x \diagup \boxminus 5$

$6x^2 \quad \begin{matrix}+8x\\-15x\\\hline -7x\end{matrix} \quad -20$

Thus, $6x^2 - 7x - 20 = (3x + 4)(2x - 5)$.

Factor.

49. $15d^2 - 19d + 6$ **50.** $15y^2 + 17y - 18$ **51.** $14b^2 - 15b - 9$

52. $4a^2 - 20a + 25$ **53.** $9a^2 - 12a + 4$ **54.** $6a^2 - a - 15$

55. $15x^2 - 29x + 12$ **56.** $16y^2 + 14y - 15$ **57.** $18a^2 - 9a - 35$

Flow Chart: Solving a Simple Equation

PROBLEM

Write a flow chart to solve an equation of the form $ax + b = c$.

START

↓

Read a, b, c.

↓

$R \leftarrow c - b$

↓

Is $a = 0$? —— Yes ——→ Print "No solution." ——→ STOP

↓ No

$S \leftarrow \dfrac{R}{a}$

↓

Print S.

↓

STOP

PROJECT

1. Follow the flow chart to solve $2x + 7 = 13$.
2. Write a flow chart to solve an equation of the form $ax + b = cx + d$. Use it to solve $5x + 3 = 3x + 13$.

The Difference of Two Squares

OBJECTIVE

■ To factor the difference of two squares

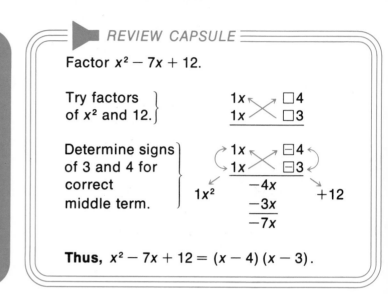

▶ REVIEW CAPSULE

Factor $x^2 - 7x + 12$.

Try factors of x^2 and 12.

$1x$ ⤫ $\square4$
$1x$ ⤫ $\square3$

Determine signs of 3 and 4 for correct middle term.

$1x$ ⤫ $\boxminus4$
$1x$ ⤫ $\boxminus3$

$$1x^2 \quad \begin{array}{c} -4x \\ -3x \\ \hline -7x \end{array} \quad +12$$

Thus, $x^2 - 7x + 12 = (x - 4)(x - 3)$.

EXAMPLE 1 Factor $x^2 - 36$.

Think of $x^2 - 36$ as a disguised trinomial with middle term $0x$. ⟶ Rewrite $x^2 - 36$ as $x^2 + 0x - 36$.

$\left.\begin{array}{c} 1 \\ 1 \end{array}\right\}$ factors of 1; $\left.\begin{array}{c} 9 \\ 4 \end{array}\right\}$ factors of 36

$(1x)(\square9) = \square9x$
$(\square4)(1x) = \square4x$

No sign combination works.

$1x$ ⤫ $\square9$
$1x$ ⤫ $\square4$

$$1x^2 \quad \begin{array}{c} \square9x \\ \square4x \\ \hline 0x \end{array} \quad -36$$

Check sign combinations.

$+9x$	$+9x$	$-9x$	$-9x$
$+4x$	$-4x$	$+4x$	$-4x$
$+13x$	$+5x$	$-5x$	$-13x$

None gives $0x$.

Try $\left.\begin{array}{c} 6 \\ 6 \end{array}\right\}$ factors of 36.

$(1x)(\square6) = \square6x$
$(\square6)(1x) = \square6x$

One sign combination works.
Check by multiplying.

$1x$ ⤫ $\square6$
$1x$ ⤫ $\square6$

$$1x^2 \quad \begin{array}{c} \square6x \\ \square6x \\ \hline 0x \end{array} \quad -36$$

Check sign combinations.

$+6x$	$+6x$
$+6x$	$-6x$
$+12x$	$0x$

One gives $0x$.

$(1x)(\boxplus6) = +6x$
$(\boxminus6)(1x) = -6x$
$+6x - 6x = \quad 0x$

$1x$ ⤫ $\boxplus6$
$1x$ ⤫ $\boxminus6$

$$1x^2 \quad \begin{array}{c} +6x \\ -6x \\ \hline 0x \end{array} \quad -36$$

The factors are $(x + 6)$ and $(x - 6)$.

Thus, $x^2 - 36 = (x + 6)(x - 6)$.

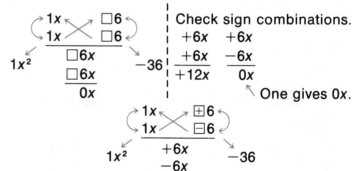

150 THE DIFFERENCE OF TWO SQUARES

$$x^2 = (x)(x), \text{ or } (x)^2$$
$$36 = (6)(6), \text{ or } (6)^2 \longrightarrow$$

$$x^2 - 36$$
$$\downarrow \qquad \downarrow$$
$$= (x)^2 - (6)^2$$
$$\uparrow$$

$x^2 - 36$ is the difference of two squares.

EXAMPLE 2 Factor $4m^2 - 25$.

Rewrite as a trinomial. $\longrightarrow$

$$4m^2 + 0m - 25$$

$\left.\begin{array}{l}2\\2\end{array}\right\}$ factors of 4; $\left.\begin{array}{l}5\\5\end{array}\right\}$ factors of 25

$(2m)(\square 5) = \square 10m$
$(\square 5)(2m) = \square 10m$
One sign combination works.

Check by multiplying.

$(2m)(\boxplus 5) = +10m$
$(\boxminus 5)(2m) = -10m$
$+10m - 10m = 0$

We can also write $(2m - 5)(2m + 5)$.

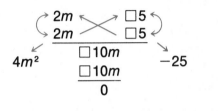

Check sign
combinations.
$\begin{array}{cc}+10m & +10m \\ +10m & -10m \\ \hline +20m & \quad 0\end{array}$
One gives 0.

Thus, $4m^2 - 25 = (2m + 5)(2m - 5)$.

$4m^2 - 25$
$(2m)^2 - (5)^2$
$\qquad$ difference

$4m^2 - 25$ is also the difference of two squares.
$$(2m)^2 - (5)^2$$

Observe a pattern for factoring the difference of two squares.

	$x^2 - 36$		$4m^2 - 25$
Rewrite. $\longrightarrow$	$(x)^2 - (6)^2$		$(2m)^2 - (5)^2$
Factor. $\longrightarrow$	$(x - 6)(x + 6)$		$(2m - 5)(2m + 5)$

EXAMPLE 3 Factor $x^2 - 4$.

Rewrite. $\longrightarrow$
Factor. $\longrightarrow$

$$(x)^2 - (2)^2$$
$$(x - 2)(x + 2)$$

EXAMPLE 4 Factor $36 - y^2$.

Rewrite. $\longrightarrow$
Factor. $\longrightarrow$

$$(6)^2 - (y)^2$$
$$(6 - y)(6 + y)$$

EXAMPLE 5   Factor $144b^2 - 49$.

Rewrite. ⟶ $(12b)^2 - (7)^2$

Factor. ⟶ $(12b - 7)(12b + 7)$

ORAL EXERCISES

Express each term in the form (a)².

1. 9 3^2 **2.** 64 8^2 **3.** 36 6^2 **4.** 100 10^2 **5.** 16 4^2

6. 144 12^2 **7.** $16b^2$ $(4b)^2$ **8.** $81x^2$ $(9x)^2$ **9.** $121x^2$ **10.** $49m^2$

11. c^2 c^2 **12.** $100x^2$ **13.** $9t^2$ $(3t)^2$ **14.** $25b^2$ $(5b)^2$ **15.** $225k^2$ $(15k)^2$

$(10x)^2$

Tell which are differences of two squares.

16. $x^2 - 16$ *yes*   **17.** $m^2 + 49$ *no*   *no* **18.** $y^2 - 35$

19. $25a^2 - 121$ *yes*   **20.** $100x^2 - 50$ *no*   *yes* **21.** $64 - 49t^2$

22. $81k^2 + 225$ *no*   **23.** $625 + 10x^2$ *no*   *no* **24.** $169 - 13y^2$

EXERCISES

PART A

Factor.

$(4m - 1)(4m + 1)$⟵

1. $x^2 - 16$ $(x - 4)(x + 4)$ **2.** $m^2 - 49$ $(m - 7)(m + 7)$ **3.** $b^2 - 25$

4. $a^2 - 81$ $(a + 9)(a - 9)$ **5.** $b^2 - 1$ $(b - 1)(b + 1)$ **6.** $m^2 - 100$

7. $m^2 - 64$ $(m + 8)(m - 8)$ **8.** $x^2 - 36$ $(x - 6)(x + 6)$ **9.** $4b^2 - 49$

10. $9a^2 - 25$ $(3a + 5)(3a - 5)$ **11.** $25a^2 - 36$ $(5a + 6)(5a - 6)$ **12.** $16x^2 - 25$

13. $49y^2 - 4$ $(7y + 2)(7y - 2)$ **14.** $16m^2 - 1$ **15.** $25m^2 - 4$

16. $36a^2 - 25$ $(6a + 5)(6a - 5)$ **17.** $4t^2 - 25$ $(2t - 5)(2t + 5)$ **18.** $4b^2 - 1$

19. $25 - x^2$ $(5 + x)(5 - x)$ **20.** $64 - y^2$ $(8 - y)(8 + y)$ **21.** $81 - t^2$

22. $36 - a^2$ $(6 - a)(6 + a)$ **23.** $49 - b^2$ $(7 + b)(7 - b)$ **24.** $100 - c^2$

25. $1 - y^2$ $(1 - y)(1 + y)$ **26.** $100 - 49x^2$ **27.** $64 - 81c^2$

28. $1 - 9x^2$ $(1 + 3x)(1 - 3x)$ **29.** $16 - 81y^2$ **30.** $64 - 49b^2$

$(4 - 9y)(4 + 9y)$

$(10 - 7x)(10 + 7x)$⟵

PART B $(15a - 13)(15a + 13)$

Factor. $(11 + 4b)(11 - 4b)$⟵

$(13p - 4)(13p + 4)$

$(10x - 7)(10x + 7)$

31. $144a^2 - 81$ **32.** $100x^2 - 49$ **33.** $25m^2 - 144$

34. $4m^2 - 169$ **35.** $36x^2 - 25$ $(6x + 5)(6x - 5)$ **36.** $25 - 144b^2$

37. $169p^2 - 16$ **38.** $x^2 - 196$ $(x - 14)(x + 14)$ **39.** $49 - 225x^2$

40. $121 - 16b^2$ **41.** $16t^2 - 225$ **42.** $100a^2 - 49$

43. $225a^2 - 169$ **44.** $36a^2 - 169$ **45.** $121m^2 - 225$

$(6a - 13)(6a + 13)$

Combined Types of Factoring

 REVIEW CAPSULE

Factor the GCF from $4x^3 - 12x^2 + 8x$.
$$4(x^3) + 4(-3x^2) + 4(2x)$$
4 is the greatest common whole
number factor.
$$4x^3 \quad - \quad 12x^2 \quad + \quad 8x$$
$$\uparrow \qquad\qquad \uparrow \qquad\qquad \uparrow$$
three x's   two x's   one x
x is the greatest common variable
factor. The GCF is $4x$.
$$4x^3 - 12x^2 + 8x$$
$$4x(x^2) + 4x(-3x) + 4x(2)$$
$$4x(x^2 - 3x + 2)$$

We have factored out the GCF from a polynomial.
We have factored a polynomial into two binomials.
Now, we combine these two types of factoring to
factor a polynomial completely.

EXAMPLE 1   Factor $4x^3 - 12x^2 + 8x$ completely.

Use the steps in the Review to factor out
the GCF. ——————————————————→

Factor $x^2 - 3x + 2$ into two binomials.

$(1x)(\Box 2) = \Box 2x$
$(\Box 1)(1x) = \Box 1x$

Check by multiplying.

$(1x)(\boxminus 2) = -2x$
$(\boxminus 1)(1x) = -1x$
$-2x - 1x = -3x$

$$4x(x^2 - 3x + 2)$$

$1x \diagdown \Box 2$
$1x \diagup \Box 1$

$1x^2$
$\quad \Box 2x$
$\quad \Box 1x$
$\quad \overline{-3x}$

$+2$

Check sign combinations.

$+2x$	$+2x$	$-2x$	$-2x$
$+1x$	$-1x$	$+1x$	$-1x$
$+3x$	$+1x$	$-1x$	$-3x$

One gives $-3x$.

$1x \diagdown \boxminus 2$
$1x \diagup \boxminus 1$

$1x^2$
$\quad -2x$
$\quad -1x$
$\quad \overline{-3x}$
$\qquad\qquad +2$

$$x^2 - 3x + 2 = (x - 2)(x - 1)$$

Put all factors together. ——————————————————→ **Thus,** $4x^3 - 12x^2 + 8x = 4x(x - 2)(x - 1)$.

EXAMPLE 2 Factor $2x^3 - 4x^2 - 48x$ completely.

Find the GCF.

Greatest common whole number factor is 2.

Greatest common variable factor: x

GCF is $2x$.

Factor out the GCF. ⟶

$$2(x^3) + 2(-2x^2) + 2(-24x)$$

↑   ↑   ↑

three x's   two x's   one x

$2x(x^2) + 2x(-2x) + 2x(-24)$

$2x(x^2 - 2x - 24)$

Factor $x^2 - 2x - 24$ into two binomials.

$1x \diagdown \diagup \square 6$

$1x \diagup \diagdown \square 4$

$1x^2$ $\dfrac{\begin{array}{c}\square 6x\\ \square 4x\end{array}}{-2x}$ -24

Check sign combinations.

+6x	+6x	−6x
+4x	−4x	+4x
+10x	+2x	−2x

One gives $-2x$.

Check by multiplying.

$(1x)(\boxminus 6) = -6x$

$(\boxplus 4)(1x) = +4x$

$-6x + 4x = -2x$

$1x \diagdown \diagup \boxminus 6$

$1x \diagup \diagdown \boxplus 4$

$1x^2$ $\dfrac{\begin{array}{c}-6x\\ +4x\end{array}}{-2x}$ -24

$x^2 - 2x - 24 = (x - 6)(x + 4)$

Put all factors together. ⟶ **Thus, $2x^3 - 4x^2 - 48x = 2x(x - 6)(x + 4)$.**

EXAMPLE 3 Factor $3x^3 - 3x$ completely.

Find the GCF.

Greatest common whole number factor is 3.

Greatest common variable factor: x

GCF is $3x$. Factor it out.

$x^2 - 1 = (x)^2 - (1)^2$; factor as the difference of 2 squares.

Put all factors together. ⟶

$$3(x^3) + 3(-1x)$$

↑   ↑

three x's   one x

$3x(x^2 - 1)$

$3x(x - 1)(x + 1)$

Thus, $3x^3 - 3x = 3x(x - 1)(x + 1)$.

EXAMPLE 4 Factor $x^2 - 6x + 8$ completely.

First look for the GCF.

No common whole number factor, other than 1

No common variable factor

$$1(x^2) + 2(-3x) + 2(4)$$

↑   ↑   ↑

two x's   one x no x's

The GCF is one. Don't bother to factor it out.

Factor $x^2 - 6x + 8$ into two binomials.

$1x \diagdown \diagup \square 4$

$1x \diagup \diagdown \square 2$

$\dfrac{\begin{array}{c}\square 4x\\ \square 2x\end{array}}{\square 6x}$

Check sign combinations.

+4x	+4x	−4x	−4x
+2x	−2x	+2x	−2x
+6x	+2x	−2x	−6x

One gives $-6x$.

Check by multiplying. ⟶ **Thus, $x^2 - 6x + 8 = (x - 4)(x - 2)$.**

EXERCISES

Factor completely.

1. $2a^2 - 10a + 8$ **2.** $2b^2 - 6b + 4$ **3.** $2a^2 + 4a - 70$
4. $2m^3 - 5m^2 + 3m$ **5.** $3x^3 + 4x^2 - 4x$ **6.** $m^3 - 9m$
7. $2x^3 - 2x$ **8.** $3a^3 - 27a$ **9.** $8m^3 - 50m$
10. $2x^3 - 14x^2 + 24x$ **11.** $2m^3 - 20m^2 + 18m$ **12.** $3x^3 - 24x^2 + 36x$
13. $4a^3 - 12a^2 - 40a$ **14.** $6x^3 - 28x^2 - 10x$ **15.** $6b^3 - 3b^2 - 30b$
16. $4a^2 - 24a + 20$ **17.** $2a^3 + 16a^2 + 30a$ **18.** $12m^2 + 33m - 9$
19. $2a^2 + 13a - 7$ **20.** $4y^2 + 7y - 2$ **21.** $2a^2 + 3a + 1$

PART B

Factor completely.

22. $18x^2 - 98$ **23.** $6x^2 + 9x - 105$ $\nearrow$ **24.** $169a - 25a^3$
                     $3(2x - 7)(x + 5)$
25. $3y^4 - 7y^3 - 20y^2$ **26.** $30e^3 - 32e^2 - 14e$ **27.** $12a^3 - 72a^2 + 33a$
28. $15a^2 - 57a + 54$ $\searrow$ **29.** $9a^3 + 66a^2 - 48a$ $\searrow$ **30.** $18m^3 - 512m$
      $3(5a - 9)(a - 2)$ $3a(3a - 2)(a + 8)$

PART C

EXAMPLE   Factor $am + bm + an + bn$.

$$a(m) + b(m) + a(n) + b(n)$$

Treat $(a + b)$ as a single common factor. Factor it out.

$$m(a + b) + n(a + b)$$
$$(a + b)(m + n)$$

Thus, $am + bm + an + bn = (a + b)(m + n)$.

EXAMPLE   Factor $x^2m + x^2 - 4m - 4$.

$$x^2(m) + x^2(1) + (-4)(m) + (-4)(1)$$
$$x^2(m + 1) - 4(m + 1)$$

Factor out $(m + 1)$. ⟶ $(m + 1)(x^2 - 4)$
Factor $x^2 - 4$. ⟶ $(m + 1)(x - 2)(x + 2)$

Thus, $x^2m + x^2 - 4m - 4 = (m + 1)(x - 2)(x + 2)$.

Factor.

31. $xm + xn - am - an$ **32.** $4x + 4y + bx + by$
33. $pr + pt - 2r - 2t$ **34.** $x^2a + x^2b - 16a - 16b$
35. $p^2y + p^2 - 25y - 25$ **36.** $16a + 16 - y^2a - y^2$

Factoring Polynomials in Two Variables

OBJECTIVE

■ To factor polynomials like
$2x^3 - 6x^2y + 4xy^2$

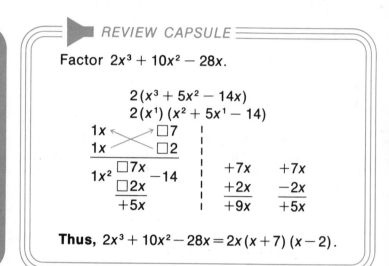

REVIEW CAPSULE

Factor $2x^3 + 10x^2 - 28x$.

$$2(x^3 + 5x^2 - 14x)$$
$$2(x^1)(x^2 + 5x^1 - 14)$$

$1x$	$\square 7$		$+7x$	$+7x$
$1x$	$\square 2$		$+2x$	$-2x$
$1x^2$ $\begin{matrix}\square 7x\\ \square 2x\end{matrix}$ -14			$+9x$	$+5x$
	$+5x$		

Thus, $2x^3 + 10x^2 - 28x = 2x(x+7)(x-2)$.

EXAMPLE 1   Factor $x^2 + 3xy + 2y^2$ completely.

Check for GCF. ────────────→ 1 is the GCF of $x^2 + 3xy + 2y^2$.

$\left.\begin{matrix}1x\\1x\end{matrix}\right\}$ factors of x^2 $\left.\begin{matrix}2y\\1y\end{matrix}\right\}$ factors of $2y^2$

$(1x)(\square 2y) = \square 2xy$
$(\square y)(1x) = \square 1xy$

$\begin{matrix}1x & \square 2y\\ 1x & \square y\end{matrix}$

$1x^2$ $\begin{matrix}\square 2xy\\ \square 1xy\end{matrix}$ $+2y^2$
$+3xy$

Check sign combinations.
$+2xy$
$+1xy$
$+3xy$
↖ This one works.

Check by multiplying.

$\left.\begin{matrix}(1x)(\boxplus 2y) = +2xy\\ (\boxplus 1y)(1x) = +1xy\\ +2xy + 1xy = +3xy\end{matrix}\right\}$

$\begin{matrix}1x & \boxplus 2y\\ 1x & \boxplus 1y\end{matrix}$

$1x^2$ $\begin{matrix}\boxplus 2xy\\ \boxplus 1xy\end{matrix}$ $+2y^2$
$+3xy$

Thus, $x^2 + 3xy + 2y^2 = (x + 2y)(x + y)$.

EXAMPLE 2   Factor $5x^2 - 20y^2$ completely.

The GCF is 5. ────────────→

$x^2 - 4y^2$
$\downarrow \quad \downarrow$
$(x)^2 - (2y)^2$
        difference of two squares

$$5(x^2 - 4y^2)$$
$$5[(x)^2 - (2y)^2]$$
$$5(x - 2y)(x + 2y)$$

Thus, $5x^2 - 20y^2 = 5(x - 2y)(x + 2y)$.

EXAMPLE 3 Factor $2a^2 - 4ab - 70b^2$ completely.

The GCF is 2. $\longrightarrow$ $2(a^2 - 2ab - 35b^2)$

$\left.\begin{array}{l}1a\\1a\end{array}\right\} a^2 \qquad \left.\begin{array}{l}7b\\5b\end{array}\right\} 35b^2$

$$
\begin{array}{l}
1a \diagdown\!\!\!\diagup \square 7b \\
1a \diagup\!\!\!\diagdown \square 5b \\
\hline
1a^2 \;\; \dfrac{\square 7ab}{\square 5ab} \;\; -35b^2 \\
\;\; -2ab
\end{array}
$$

Check sign combinations.

$+7ab$	$+7ab$	$-7ab$
$+5ab$	$-5ab$	$+5ab$
$+12ab$	$+2ab$	$-2ab$

One works.

Check by multiplying.

$(1a)(\boxminus 7b) = -7ab$
$(\boxplus 5b)(1a) = +5ab$
$-7ab + 5ab = -2ab$

$$
\begin{array}{l}
1a \diagdown\!\!\!\diagup \boxminus 7b \\
1a \diagup\!\!\!\diagdown \boxplus 5b \\
\hline
1a^2 \;\; \dfrac{\boxminus 7ab}{\boxplus 5ab} \;\; -35b^2 \\
\;\; -2ab
\end{array}
$$

Thus, $2a^2 - 4ab - 70b^2 = 2(a - 7b)(a + 5b)$.

EXERCISES

PART A

Factor completely.

1. $a^2 + 4ab + 3b^2$
2. $x^2 + 5xy + 4y^2$ $(x + 4y)(x + y)$
3. $c^2 + 7cd + 6d^2$ $(c + 6d)(c + d)$
4. $4a^2 - 36b^2$
5. $5x^2 - 45y^2$
6. $4a^2 - 100b^2$
7. $2m^2 - mb - 10b^2$
8. $2a^2 - 5ab - 3b^2$
9. $2a^2 - 9ab - 5b^2$
10. $a^2 - ab - 42b^2$
11. $a^2 - 3ab + 2b^2$
12. $x^2 - 13xy + 42y^2$
13. $2a^2 + 20ab + 42b^2$
14. $8x^2 + 24xy + 18y^2$
15. $2y^2 + 20yz + 18z^2$
16. $2m^2 - 2mn - 40n^2$ $2(m - 5n)(m + 4n)$
17. $6x^2 - 26xy - 20y^2$ $2(3x + 2y)(x - 5y)$
18. $3x^2 - 9xy - 30y^2$

PART B

Factor completely.

19. $a^2b^3 - 25b$
20. $x^3 - 3x^2y + 2xy^2$ $x(x - y)(x - 2y)$
21. $a^3b - ab^3$ $ab(a + b)(a - b)$
22. $7x^2 + 19xy - 6y^2$
23. $6x^2 - 57xy + 105y^2$
24. $2m^2 + 17mn + 30n^2$
25. $4k^2 - 42kr + 80r^2$ $2(2k - 5r)(k - 8r)$
26. $12m^2 - 75y^2$ $3(2m + 5y)(2m - 5y)$
27. $3a^2 + 13ab - 30b^2$

PART C

Factor completely.

28. $20m^2 + 60mn + 45n^2$
29. $6a^2 + 5ab - 21b^2$
30. $12x^2 + xy - 6y^2$
31. $10x^2 + 21xy + 9y^2$
32. $2a^3b + 11a^2b^2 - 21ab^3$
33. $6x^3y + 7x^2y^2 - 20xy^3$

Quadratic Equations

■ To solve equations like
$2x^2 + 9x - 5 = 0$
by factoring.

REVIEW CAPSULE

Factor $x^2 - 7x + 12$.

$$x^2 - 7x + 12 = (x - 4)(x - 3)$$

EXAMPLE 1   Find the missing factor. Then draw a conclusion.

Multiplying by 0 gives 0. ──────────→

$(4)(?) = 0$	$(?)(-7) = 0$	$(0)(?) = 0$
$(4)(0) = 0$	$(0)(-7) = 0$	$(0)(0) = 0$

If a product is 0, then at least one factor must be 0.

Either factor or both factors must be 0.

> If $a \cdot b = 0$, then $a = 0$ or $b = 0$.
> If a product is 0, then at least one factor is 0.

EXAMPLE 2   For what values of x will $(2x - 8)(x - 7) = 0$ be true?

If $a \cdot b = 0$, then $a = 0$ or $b = 0$.
Solve each equation for x.

$$2x - 8 = 0 \quad \text{or} \quad x - 7 = 0$$
$$\underline{ 8 \quad 8} \qquad \underline{ 7 \quad 7}$$
$$2x = 8 \qquad\qquad x = 7$$

Divide each side by 2. ────────────→

$$x = 4$$

Check. ──────────────────────→

$$
\begin{array}{c|c}
(2x-8)\ (x-7)\,|\,0 & (2x-8)\ (x-7)\,|\,0 \\
x=4 \quad (2\cdot4-8)\,(4-7)\,|\,0 & x=7 \quad (2\cdot7-8)\,(7-7)\,|\,0 \\
(8-8)\quad(-3) & (14-8)\quad(0) \\
(0)\quad(-3) & (6)\quad(0) \\
0 & 0
\end{array}
$$

$(2x - 8)(x - 7)$ is 0. ─────────→

Thus, $(2x - 8)(x - 7) = 0$ if $x = 4$ or $x = 7$.

Each equation contains an x^2 term.

Equations like $2x^2 + 9x - 5 = 0$, $x^2 - 36 = 0$, and $x^2 - 3x = 0$ are quadratic equations.

EXAMPLE 3   Solve $x^2 - 8x + 12 = 0$.

Factor $x^2 - 8x + 12$:
No GCF.

$$x^2 - 8x + 12 = 0$$
$$(x - 6)(x - 2) = 0$$

If $ab = 0$, then $a = 0$ or $b = 0$. ⟶

$$x - 6 = 0 \quad \text{or} \quad x - 2 = 0$$

Solve each equation for x.

$$\underline{6 \quad 6} \qquad \underline{2 \quad 2}$$
$$x = 6 \qquad\qquad x = 2$$

Check. ⟶

$$\begin{array}{c|c}
 & x^2 - 8x + 12 \mid 0 \\
x = 6 & 6^2 - 8 \cdot 6 + 12 \mid 0 \\
 & 36 - 48 + 12 \mid \\
 & - 12 + 12 \mid \\
 & 0 \mid
\end{array}
\qquad
\begin{array}{c|c}
 & x^2 - 8x + 12 \mid 0 \\
x = 2 & 2^2 - 8 \cdot 2 + 12 \mid 0 \\
 & 4 - 16 + 12 \mid \\
 & - 12 + 12 \mid \\
 & 0 \mid
\end{array}$$

Thus, the solutions are 2 and 6.

The solutions are also called roots.

A quadratic equation may have two solutions.

EXAMPLE 4   Find the solution set of $2x^2 + 5x - 3 = 0$.

Factor $2x^2 + 5x - 3$:
No GCF.
Set each factor $= 0$.
Solve each equation for x.

$$2x^2 + 5x - 3 = 0$$
$$(2x - 1)(x + 3) = 0$$
$$2x - 1 = 0 \quad \text{or} \quad x + 3 = 0$$
$$\underline{1 \quad 1} \qquad \underline{-3 \quad -3}$$
$$2x = 1 \qquad\qquad x = -3$$
$$x = \frac{1}{2}$$

Check on your own. ⟶   The solutions are $\frac{1}{2}$ and -3.

Thus, the solution set is $\left\{\frac{1}{2}, -3\right\}$.

EXAMPLE 5   Solve $x^2 - 7x = 0$.

Look for the GCF.
Factor out x, the GCF. ⟶
Set each factor $= 0$. ⟶
Solve each equation for x.

$$x^2 - 7x = 0$$
$$x(x - 7) = 0$$
$$x = 0 \quad \text{or} \quad x - 7 = 0$$
$$\underline{7 \quad 7}$$
$$x = 7$$

Check on your own. ⟶   **Thus,** the solutions are 0 and 7.

ORAL EXERCISES

For what values of x will each be true?

1. $(2x - 4)(x + 3) = 0$ $2, -3$ **2.** $x(x + 5) = 0$ $0, -5$ **3.** $5x(x - 7) = 0$ $0, 7$
4. $(3x - 1)(2x - 4) = 0$ $\frac{1}{3}, 2$ **5.** $(x - 3)(x - 3) = 0$ 3 **6.** $(x - 5)(x + 5) = 0$
$\quad\quad\quad\quad\quad\quad\quad\quad\quad\quad\quad\quad\quad\quad\quad\quad\quad\quad\quad\quad\quad\quad\quad\quad\quad\quad\quad\quad 5, -5$

EXERCISES

PART A

Solve.

1. $x^2 - 5x + 6 = 0$ $2, 3$ **2.** $x^2 - 7x + 10 = 0$ $5, 2$ **3.** $x^2 - 9x + 8 = 0$ $1, 8$
4. $x^2 - 6x = 0$ $0, 6$ **5.** $x^2 - 36 = 0$ $6, -6$ **6.** $x^2 + 8x + 12 = 0$
$\quad\quad\quad\quad\quad\quad\quad\quad\quad\quad\quad\quad\quad\quad\quad\quad\quad\quad\quad\quad\quad\quad\quad\quad\quad\quad\quad\quad -2, -6$

Find the solution set.

$\quad\quad\quad\quad\quad\quad\quad\quad\quad\quad\quad\quad\quad\quad\quad\quad\quad\quad\quad\quad\quad\quad\quad \{\frac{1}{2}, -3\}$
7. $2a^2 + 9a - 5 = 0$ $\{\frac{1}{2}, -5\}$ **8.** $3m^2 + 8m - 3 = 0$ $\{\frac{1}{3}, -3\}$ **9.** $2p^2 + 5p - 3 = 0$ ↗
10. $3x^2 + 14x - 5 = 0$ $\{\frac{1}{3}, -5\}$ **11.** $2t^2 + 7t - 15 = 0$ $\{\frac{3}{2}, -5\}$ **12.** $2b^2 + 3b - 9 = 0$ ──
13. $3a^2 - 22a + 7 = 0$ $\{\frac{1}{3}, 7\}$ **14.** $a^2 - 10a + 16 = 0$ $\{2, 8\}$ **15.** $2y^2 - 11y + 5 = 0$ ──
16. $2g^2 - 15g - 8 = 0$ $\{8, -\frac{1}{2}\}$ **17.** $4a^2 - 25 = 0$ $\{\frac{5}{2}, -\frac{5}{2}\}$ **18.** $x^2 - 64 = 0$ $\{8, -8\}$
19. $2n^2 - 13n + 15 = 0$ $\{\frac{3}{2}, 5\}$ **20.** $m^2 + 17m = 0$ $\{0, -17\}$ **21.** $3k^2 - 5k = 0$ $\{0, \frac{5}{3}\}$
$\quad\quad\quad\quad\quad\quad\quad\quad\quad\quad\quad\quad\quad\quad\quad\quad\quad \{\frac{3}{2}, -3\}\quad \{\frac{1}{2}, 5\}$ ←

PART B

Solve.

$\quad\quad\quad\quad\quad\quad\quad\quad\frac{3}{2}, -8$ $\quad\quad\quad\quad\quad\quad\quad\quad\frac{5}{3}, -7$ $\quad\quad\quad\quad\quad\quad\quad\quad\frac{1}{5}, -7$
22. $2x^2 + 13x - 24 = 0$ ↗   **23.** $3y^2 + 16y - 35 = 0$ ↗   **24.** $5a^2 + 34a - 7 = 0$ ↗
25. $2a^2 + 5a - 42 = 0$ $\frac{7}{2}, -6$ **26.** $5a^2 - 22a + 21 = 0$ $\frac{7}{5}, 3$ **27.** $2a^2 + 23a + 56 = 0$
28. $3b^2 - 31b + 36 = 0$ $\frac{4}{3}, 9$ **29.** $a^2 - 20a + 100 = 0$ 10 **30.** $x^2 + 18x + 81 = 0$ -9

PART C

$\quad\quad\quad\quad\quad\quad$ **EXAMPLE** Solve $x^3 - 25x = 0$.

Factor out the GCF. ⟶ $\quad\quad\quad\quad\quad\quad\quad\quad\quad x(x^2 - 25) = 0$
$x^2 - 25 = (x)^2 - (5)^2$; factor. ⟶ $\quad\quad\quad\quad x(x - 5)(x + 5) = 0$
If $a \cdot b \cdot c = 0$, then $a = 0$ ⟶ $x = 0$ or $\quad x - 5 = 0$ or $\quad x + 5 = 0$
or $b = 0$ or $c = 0$. $\quad\quad\quad\quad\quad\quad\quad\quad\quad\quad\quad\quad \underline{\quad 5 \quad 5}\quad\quad\quad\quad\quad \underline{-5 \quad -5}$
$\quad\quad\quad\quad\quad\quad\quad\quad\quad\quad\quad\quad\quad\quad\quad\quad\quad\quad\quad\quad\quad x = 5 \quad\quad\quad\quad\quad\quad x = -5$

$\quad\quad\quad\quad\quad\quad$ **Thus,** the solutions are 0, 5, and −5.

Solve.

31. $x^3 - 9x = 0$ **32.** $x^3 - 4x = 0$ **33.** $4b^3 - 16b = 0$
34. $x^3 - 2x^2 = 0$ **35.** $m^3 - 49m = 0$ **36.** $3x^3 - 75x = 0$

Computing Mentally

We can use our ability to multiply binomials to find the square of a two- or three-digit number mentally.

PROBLEM

Square 35. Think: $(35)^2 = (35)(35) = (30 + 5)(30 + 5)$

$$
\begin{array}{c}
30 \quad + \quad 5 \\
30 \quad + \quad 5 \\
\hline
+150 \\
\end{array}
$$

$(3)(3) = 3^2 \longrightarrow$ $\underline{900 \qquad +150 \qquad +25}$

$900 \qquad +300 \qquad +25 = 1{,}225 \leftarrow$ four-digit number

Let's find the pattern.

$(35)^2 = \underbrace{900 + 300} + 25 = 1{,}200 + 25$

$100(9 + 3) = 900 + 300 \rightarrow 100(9 + 3) + 25 = 1{,}225$

$9 = 3^2 \longrightarrow 100(\underline{3^2 + 3}) + 25 = 1{,}225$

$\boxed{3^2 + 3} \quad (25)$

first two digits ⟶   ⟵ last two digits

Short Cut for Squaring a Number Ending in 5

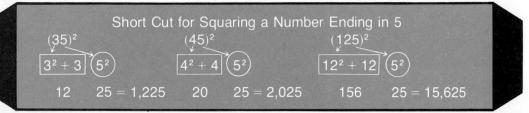

$(35)^2$ $(45)^2$ $(125)^2$

$\boxed{3^2 + 3}\;(5^2)$ $\boxed{4^2 + 4}\;(5^2)$ $\boxed{12^2 + 12}\;(5^2)$

12   25 = 1,225   20   25 = 2,025   156   25 = 15,625

PROJECT Find each mentally.

1. $(75)^2$ **2.** $(65)^2$ **3.** $(95)^2$ **4.** $(135)^2$ **5.** $(205)^2$

Quadratic Equations: Standard Form

◀ REVIEW CAPSULE

Solve $2x^2 + 5x - 3 = 0$.
$$(2x - 1)(x + 3) = 0$$
$$2x - 1 = 0 \quad \text{or} \quad x + 3 = 0$$
$$\underline{ 1 \quad 1} \qquad \qquad \underline{ -3 \quad -3}$$
$$2x = 1 \qquad \qquad \qquad x = -3$$
$$x = \frac{1}{2}$$

The solutions are $\frac{1}{2}$ and -3.

This quadratic equation is in standard form.

$2x^2 - 5x + 2 = 0$

↖ positive

$2x^2 - 5x + 2 = 0$

↑   ↑   ↑

x^2 term x^1 term   constant

$$2x^2 - 5x + 2 = 0$$
(1) Coefficient of the x^2 term ($2x^2$) is positive.
(2) Polynomial ($2x^2 - 5x + 2$) is equal to 0.
(3) Terms are arranged in descending order of exponents.

EXAMPLE 1   Solve $7x = -x^2 - 10$.

Get coefficient of x^2 term positive.
Add $1x^2$ to each side.
Coefficient of x^2 term is positive.

$$7x = -1x^2 - 10$$
$$\underline{ 1x^2 \qquad 1x^2}$$
$$1x^2 + 7x = -10$$

Get polynomial equal to 0.
Add 10 to each side.
Polynomial is equal to 0.

$$1x^2 + 7x = -10$$
$$\underline{ 10 \qquad 10}$$
$$1x^2 + 7x + 10 = 0 \quad \leftarrow \text{order of exponents}$$

Terms arranged
in descending
← order of exponents

$$x^2 + 7x + 10 = 0 \quad \leftarrow \text{Standard form}$$

Factor. ⟶
Set each factor = 0. ⟶
Solve each equation for x.

$$(x + 5)(x + 2) = 0$$
$$x + 5 = 0 \quad \text{or} \quad x + 2 = 0$$
$$\underline{ -5 \quad -5} \qquad \underline{ -2 \quad -2}$$
$$x = -5 \qquad \qquad \qquad x = -2$$

Thus, the solutions are -5 and -2.

EXAMPLE 2   Solve and check $5 - 9x = 2x^2$.

x^2 term is already positive.

Get polynomial equal to 0.

Add $9x$ to each side.

Add -5 to each side.

Polynomial is equal to 0.

$$5 - 9x = 2x^2$$
$$\underline{9x \quad 9x}$$
$$5 = 2x^2 + 9x$$
$$\underline{-5 \quad -5}$$
$$0 = 2x^2 + 9x - 5 \quad \leftarrow$$

Terms arranged in descending order of exponents

Factor. ⟶

Set each factor $= 0$. ⟶

Solve each equation for x.

$$0 = (2x - 1)(x + 5)$$
$$2x - 1 = 0 \quad \text{or} \quad x + 5 = 0$$
$$\underline{1 \quad 1} \qquad \underline{-5 \quad -5}$$
$$2x = 1 \qquad\qquad x = -5$$
$$x = \frac{1}{2}$$

Check. ⟶

$$x = \frac{1}{2} \quad \begin{array}{c|c} 5 - 9x & 2x^2 \\ \hline 5 - 9\left(\frac{1}{2}\right) & 2\left(\frac{1}{2}\right)^2 \\ 5 - 4\frac{1}{2} & 2\left(\frac{1}{4}\right) \\ \frac{1}{2} & \frac{1}{2} \end{array}$$

$$x = -5 \quad \begin{array}{c|c} 5 - 9x & 2x^2 \\ \hline 5 - 9(-5) & 2(-5)^2 \\ 5 + 45 & 2(25) \\ 50 & 50 \end{array}$$

Thus, the solutions are $\frac{1}{2}$ and -5.

EXAMPLE 3   Find the solution set of $-x^2 = 3x$.

Get x^2 term positive.

Add $1x^2$ to each side.

x^2 term is positive.

$$-1x^2 = 3x$$
$$\underline{1x^2 \quad 1x^2}$$
$$0 = 1x^2 + 3x \quad \leftarrow$$

Terms arranged in descending order of exponents

Polynomial is equal to 0. ⟶

Factor out the GCF. ⟶

Set each factor $= 0$. ⟶

Solve each equation for x.

$$0 = x^2 + 3x$$
$$0 = x(x + 3)$$
$$x = 0 \quad \text{or} \quad x + 3 = 0$$
$$\underline{-3 \quad -3}$$
$$x = -3$$

Check. ⟶

$$x = 0 \quad \begin{array}{c|c} -x^2 & 3x \\ \hline -(0)^2 & 3(0) \\ 0 & 0 \end{array}$$

$$x = -3 \quad \begin{array}{c|c} -x^2 & 3x \\ \hline -(-3)^2 & 3(-3) \\ -1(9) & -9 \\ -9 & \end{array}$$

The solutions are 0 and -3.

Thus, the solution set is $\{0, -3\}$.

EXERCISES

PART A

Solve and check.

1. $8x = -x^2 - 15$ $-3, -5$
2. $9x = -x^2 - 20$ $-4, -5$
3. $12m = -m^2 - 32$ $-4, -8$
4. $18 - 7b = b^2$ $2, -9$
5. $12 - 4m = m^2$ $2, -6$
6. $6 - 5p = p^2$ $1, -6$
7. $-x^2 = 9x$ $0, -9$
8. $-x^2 = 10x$ $0, -10$
9. $-x^2 = 7x$ $0, -7$

Find the solution sets.

10. $x^2 + 4x = 5$ $\{1, -5\}$
11. $9m^2 = 4$ $\{\frac{2}{3}, -\frac{2}{3}\}$
12. $a^2 - 10 = 3a$ $\{5, -2\}$
13. $13g = -g^2$ $\{0, -13\}$
14. $2a^2 + a = 10$ $\{-\frac{5}{2}, 2\}$
15. $b^2 = 49$ $\{7, -7\}$
16. $2a^2 + 3a = -1$ $\{-\frac{1}{2}, -1\}$
17. $5b - 2 = 3b^2$ $\{\frac{2}{3}, 1\}$
18. $n^2 - 7n = 18$ $\{9, -2\}$
19. $2x^2 + x = 1$ $\{\frac{1}{2}, -1\}$
20. $2a^2 + 7 = 15a$ $\{\frac{1}{2}, 7\}$
21. $3k^2 = -2k + 1$ $\{\frac{1}{3}, -1\}$
22. $4n^2 = 1$ $\{\frac{1}{2}, -\frac{1}{2}\}$
23. $2x^2 - 21 = 11x$ $\{-\frac{3}{2}, 7\}$
24. $3a^2 - 22a = 16$ $\{-\frac{2}{3}, 8\}$
25. $2p^2 = -11p + 6$ $\{\frac{1}{2}, -6\}$
26. $3x - 20 = -2x^2$ $\{\frac{5}{2}, -4\}$
27. $25 = 4b^2$ $\{\frac{5}{2}, -\frac{5}{2}\}$

PART B

Solve.

28. $12x^2 = 35 - x$ $-\frac{7}{4}, \frac{5}{3}$
29. $19a - 6 = 15a^2$ $\frac{3}{5}, \frac{2}{3}$
30. $4m^2 - 42 = 17m$ $-\frac{7}{4}, 6$
31. $11b - 10 = -6b^2$ $\frac{2}{3}, -\frac{5}{2}$
32. $12y^2 + 15 = 29y$ $\frac{3}{4}, \frac{5}{3}$
33. $6x^2 = 35 - 11x$ $\frac{5}{3}, -\frac{7}{2}$
34. $4m^2 = 225$ $\frac{15}{2}, -\frac{15}{2}$
35. $4a + 35 = 4a^2$ $\frac{7}{2}, -\frac{5}{2}$
36. $6b^2 + 13b = 28$ $\frac{4}{3}, -\frac{7}{2}$
37. $24b = -3b^2$ $0, -8$
38. $17x - 14 = -6x^2$ $\frac{2}{3}, -\frac{7}{2}$
39. $10a^2 - 29a = -10$ $\frac{2}{5}, \frac{5}{2}$

PART C

EXAMPLE Solve $(2x + 3)(x - 5) = x^2 + 9x - 43$.

$$2x^2 - 7x - 15 = x^2 + 9x - 43$$
$$\underline{-x^2 \qquad\qquad -x^2}$$
$$x^2 - 7x - 15 = 9x - 43$$
$$\underline{-9x \qquad\qquad -9x}$$
$$x^2 - 16x - 15 = -43$$
$$\underline{\qquad 43 \qquad\qquad 43}$$
$$x^2 - 16x + 28 = 0$$
$$(x - 14)(x - 2) = 0$$
$$x - 14 = 0 \quad \text{or} \quad x - 2 = 0$$
$$x = 14 \qquad\qquad x = 2$$

Check on your own. ⟶ **Thus,** the solutions are 14 and 2.

Solve.

40. $(3x - 2)(2x + 5) = 5x^2 + 5x - 18$

41. $(x - 3)(x + 3) = 2x^2 - 18$

Consecutive Integers

 REVIEW CAPSULE

Even integers have 2 as a factor.
For example: $-4, 0, 28, 40, 90$.

Odd integers do not have 2 as a factor.
For example: $-5, 3, 15, 35, 47$.

EXAMPLE 1 Write the next two consecutive integers.

Add 1 to get the next consecutive integer.
$(a + 2) + 1 = a + 3$

	Answers
$7, 8, 9, 10, \ldots$	$11, 12$
$-2, -1, 0, 1, 2, \ldots$	$3, 4$
$a, a + 1, a + 2, \ldots$	$a + 3, a + 4$

Example 1 suggests this. ⟶

$x, x + 1, x + 2, \ldots$ represent consecutive integers
for each integer x.

EXAMPLE 2 Write three consecutive integers, beginning with
the given integer.

-28 7 n

Begin with. ⟶ -28 7 n
$-28 + 1 = -27$ ⟶ -27 8 $n + 1 = n + 1$
$-28 + 1 + 1 = -26$ ⟶ -26 9 $n + 1 + 1 = n + 2$

EXAMPLE 3 Write the next two consecutive even integers.

Add 2 to an even integer to get the next
consecutive even integer.

	Answers
$0, 2, 4, \ldots$	$6, 8$
$-8, -6, -4, \ldots$	$-2, 0$
$b, b + 2, b + 4, \ldots$	$b + 6, b + 8$

Example 3 suggests this. ⟶

$x, x + 2, x + 4, \ldots$ represent consecutive even
integers, for each even integer x.

EXAMPLE 4 Write three consecutive even integers, beginning with the given even integer.

n $\qquad$ -8

Begin with $\longrightarrow$

Add 2 to get the next consecutive even $\big\}$
integer.

$$\begin{array}{ll} & n \\ n + 2 & = n + 2 \\ n + 2 + 2 = n + 4 \end{array} \quad \bigg| \quad \begin{array}{ll} & -8 \\ -8 + 2 & = -6 \\ -8 + 2 + 2 = -4 \end{array}$$

EXAMPLE 5 Write the next two consecutive odd integers.

	Answers
5, 7, 9, . . .	11, 13
$-9, -7, -5, . . .$	$-3, -1$
$c, c + 2, c + 4, . . .$	$c + 6, c + 8$

Add 2 to an odd integer to get the next $\big\}$
consecutive odd integer.

Example 5 suggests this. $\longrightarrow$

$x, x + 2, x + 4, . . .$ represent consecutive odd integers, for each odd integer x.

EXAMPLE 6 Write three consecutive odd integers, beginning with the given odd integer.

-9 $\qquad$ 5 $\qquad$ n

Add 2 to get the next consecutive odd $\big\}$
integer.

$$\begin{array}{c|c|c} -9 & 5 & n \\ -9 + 2 = -7 & 7 & n + 2 \qquad = n + 2 \\ -7 + 2 = -5 & 9 & n + 2 + 2 = n + 4 \end{array}$$

EXAMPLE 7 Write an equation.
The sum of three consecutive integers is 21.

Represent the integers. Add 1 to get the $\big\}$
next consecutive integer.

Sum means add. $\longrightarrow$

Write the equation. $\longrightarrow$

Let $\quad x =$ first integer
$x + 1 =$ second integer
$x + 2 =$ third integer
Their sum is 21.
$x + (x + 1) + (x + 2) = 21$

EXAMPLE 8 Write an equation.
The product of two consecutive odd integers is 15.

Represent the integers. Add 2 to get the $\big\}$
next odd integer.

Product means multiply. $\longrightarrow$

Let $\quad x =$ first odd integer
$x + 2 =$ second odd integer
$x(x + 2) = 15$

ORAL EXERCISES

Give three consecutive integers, beginning with the given integer.

1. 7   **2.** 11   **3.** 26   **4.** −2   **5.** −6   **6.** −40   **7.** a

$7, 8, 9$ $11, 12, 13$ $-2, -1, 0$ $-6, -5, -4$ $-40, -39, -38$ $a, a+1, a+2$

Give four consecutive even integers, beginning with the given integer.

8. 8   **9.** 6   **10.** 38   **11.** −4   **12.** −10   **13.** n **14.** $n + 8$

$8, 10, 12, 14$ $6, 8, 10, 12$ $-4, -2, 0, 2$ $-10, -8, -6, -4$ $n+8, n+10, n+12, n+14$

Give five consecutive odd integers beginning with the given integer.

15. 7   **16.** 19   **17.** 53   **18.** −5   **19.** −23   **20.** b **21.** $b + 6$

$7, 9, 11, 13, 15$ $-5, -3, -1, 1, 3$ $b+6, b+8, b+10, b+12, b+14$

EXERCISES

PART A

Write an equation.

1. The sum of three consecutive integers is 27. $x + (x + 1) + (x + 2) = 27$

2. The sum of three consecutive integers is 33. $x + (x + 1) + (x + 2) = 33$

3. The sum of three consecutive integers is −15. $x + (x + 1) + (x + 2) = -15$

4. The sum of three consecutive integers is −21.

5. The product of two consecutive odd integers is 35. $x(x + 2) = 35$

6. The product of two consecutive odd integers is 99. $x(x + 2) = 99$

7. The product of three consecutive even integers is 48. $x(x + 2)(x + 4) = 48$

8. The product of three consecutive even integers is 192.

9. The sum of four consecutive odd integers is 40. $x + (x + 2) + (x + 4) + (x + 6) = 40$

10. The sum of four consecutive even integers is 36. $x + (x + 2) + (x + 4) + (x + 6) = 36$

PART B

Write an equation.

11. Twice the second of two consecutive integers, increased by the first is 35. $2(x + 1) + x = 35$

12. Twice the second of two consecutive even integers, decreased by the first is 10. $2(x + 2) - x = 10$

13. Twice the second of two consecutive odd integers, increased by the first is 19. $2(x + 2) + x = 19$

14. Three times the second of two consecutive integers, decreased by three times the first is 3. $3(x + 1) - 3x = 3$

15. Three times the second of two consecutive even integers, increased by twice the first is 46. $3(x + 2) + 2x = 46$

16. Three times the first of two consecutive odd integers, decreased by twice the second is 21.

17. The product of three consecutive integers is the same as 8 times their sum.

18. The product of three consecutive even integers is the same as 4 times their sum.

Consecutive Integer Problems

REVIEW CAPSULE

Write an equation.
The sum of three consecutive odd integers is 27.

$$x + (x + 2) + (x + 4) = 27$$

EXAMPLE 1   Find two consecutive integers whose sum is 67.

Represent the integers.
Add 1 to get the next integer.
Sum means add. ⟶
Write an equation. ⟶
Combine like terms. ⟶
Solve for x.
First integer ⟶
Second integer ⟶

Let x = first integer
    $x + 1$ = second integer
Their sum is 67.

$$x + (x + 1) = 67$$
$$2x + 1 = 67$$
$$2x = 66$$
$$x = 33$$
$$x + 1 = 33 + 1, \text{ or } 34$$

Check: $33 + 34 = 67$.

Thus, the integers are 33 and 34.

EXAMPLE 2   Find two consecutive integers whose product is 20.

Represent the integers.

Product means multiply. ⟶
Write an equation. ⟶
$x(x + 1) = x(x) + x(1)$ ⟶
Get equation in standard form.
Add -20 to each side.
Factor. ⟶
Set each factor = 0. ⟶
First integer ⟶
Second integer ⟶
There are two pairs of integers.

Check the first solution in the problem. ⟶

Check 4 and 5 in the problem. There are two pairs of solutions. ⟶

Let x = first integer
    $x + 1$ = second integer
Their product is 20.

$$x(x + 1) = 20$$
$$x^2 + x = 20$$
$$\underline{ -20 \quad -20}$$
$$x^2 + x - 20 = 0$$
$$(x + 5)(x - 4) = 0$$
$$x + 5 = 0 \quad \text{or} \quad x - 4 = 0$$
$$x = -5 \quad \text{or} \quad x = 4$$
$$x + 1 = -5 + 1, \text{ or } -4 \quad \text{or} \quad x + 1 = 4 + 1, \text{ or } 5$$

-5 and -4 are consecutive integers, since $-5 + 1 = -4$.
Their product is 20, since $(-5)(-4) = 20$.

Thus, the integers are -5 and -4, or 4 and 5.

EXAMPLE 3 Find two consecutive integers such that the sum of the first and the square of the second is 19.

Represent the integers algebraically.

Let x = first integer
$x + 1$ = second integer
Sum of the first and the square of the second is 19.

$(x + 1)^2 = (x + 1)(x + 1)$
$\qquad = x^2 + 2x + 1$ $\longrightarrow$
Combine like terms. $\longrightarrow$
Add -19 to each side. $\longrightarrow$
Factor. $\longrightarrow$
Set each factor $= 0$. $\longrightarrow$
First integer $\longrightarrow$
Second integer $\longrightarrow$
Check both solutions in the problem.

$$x + (x + 1)^2 = 19$$
$$x + x^2 + 2x + 1 = 19$$
$$x^2 + 3x + 1 = 19$$
$$x^2 + 3x - 18 = 0$$
$$(x + 6)(x - 3) = 0$$
$$x + 6 = 0 \quad \text{or} \quad x - 3 = 0$$
$$x = -6 \text{ or} \qquad x = 3$$
$$x + 1 = -6 + 1, \text{ or } -5 \text{ or } x + 1 = 3 + 1 = 4$$

Sum of the first and square of the second is 19.

$-6 + (-5)^2$	19	$3 + (4)^2$	19
$-6 + 25$	19	$3 + 16$	19
19		19	

Two pairs of solutions $\longrightarrow$

Thus, the two consecutive integers are -6 and -5, or 3 and 4.

EXAMPLE 4 Find two consecutive odd integers such that the square of the second, decreased by the first is 44.

Represent the integers algebraically.

Let x = first integer
$x + 2$ = second integer
Square of second, decreased by first is 44.

Write the equation. $\longrightarrow$
$(x + 2)^2$
Add -44 to each side; standard form. $\longrightarrow$
Factor. $\longrightarrow$
Set each factor $= 0$. $\longrightarrow$
First integer $\longrightarrow$
Second integer $\longrightarrow$
There is only one pair of integers.

$$(x + 2)^2 - x = 44$$
$$x^2 + 4x + 4 - x = 44$$
$$x^2 + 3x + 4 = 44$$
$$x^2 + 3x - 40 = 0$$
$$(x - 5)(x + 8) = 0$$

$$x - 5 = 0 \qquad \text{or} \qquad x + 8 = 0$$
$$x = 5 \qquad\qquad\qquad x = -8$$
$$x + 2 = 5 + 2, \text{ or } 7 \qquad \text{First integer, } x \text{ cannot be}$$
$$-8, \text{ since } -8 \text{ is not odd.}$$

Check 5 and 7 in the problem.

Square of second, decreased by first is 44.

$(7)^2 - 5$	44
$49 \;- 5$	44
44	

There is only one solution. $\longrightarrow$ **Thus,** the two consecutive odd integers are 5 and 7.

EXERCISES

1. Find two consecutive integers whose sum is 45. *22, 23*

2. Find three consecutive odd integers whose sum is 63. *19, 21, 23*

3. Find five consecutive integers whose sum is 155. *29, 30, 31, 32, 33*

4. Find three consecutive even integers whose sum is 120. *38, 40, 42*

5. Find three consecutive integers such that twice the first added to the last is 23. *7, 8, 9*

6. Find four consecutive odd integers such that twice the second added to the last is 25. *5, 7, 9, 11*

7. Find three consecutive odd integers such that twice the first, decreased by the second is 35. *37, 39, 41*

8. Find three consecutive integers such that three times the second, increased by the last is 81. *19, 20, 21*

9. Find two consecutive integers whose product is 12. *−4, −3, or 3, 4*

10. Find two consecutive integers whose product is 30. *5, 6 or −6, −5*

11. Find two consecutive even integers whose product is 24. *4, 6 or −6, −4*

12. Find two consecutive odd integers whose product is 35. *5, 7 or −7, −5*

13. Find two consecutive odd integers such that the sum of their squares is 130. *7, 9 or −9, −7*

14. Find two consecutive even integers such that the sum of their squares is 52. *4, 6 or −6, −4*

15. Find three consecutive integers such that the square of the first, added to the last is 8.

16. Find three consecutive integers such that the square of the first, decreased by the last is 18.

17. Find three consecutive integers such that the square of the first is 18 more than the last.

18. Find three consecutive integers such that the square of the first is equal to the third. *2, 3, 4 or −1, 0, 1*

19. Find two consecutive odd integers such that the square of the second, decreased by the first is 14. *−5, −3*

20. Find two consecutive even integers such that the square of the second increased by twice the first is 44. *4, 6 or −10, −8*

21. Find four consecutive integers such that 3 times the third, decreased by the second is the last. *−2, −1, 0, 1*

22. Find four consecutive even integers such that the sum of the squares of the first and second is 12 more than the last. *2, 4, 6, 8*

23. Find four consecutive integers such that the sum of the squares of the second and third is 61. *−7, −6, −5, −4 or 4, 5, 6, 7*

24. Find five consecutive integers such that the square of the third, decreased by the square of the second is 3 times the first. *3, 4, 5, 6, 7*

Braking Distance

Braking distance is an important factor in safe driving. Braking distance is the distance traveled by a car from the time the driver applies the brakes until the car actually stops.

$$B \doteq .006s^2$$

Braking distance in meters   is about   Speed in kilometers per hour

PROBLEM

A car is traveling at a speed of 50 km/h. How far will the car travel after the brakes are applied?

Use the formula.	$\longrightarrow$	$B \doteq .006s^2$
Substitute for s.	$\longrightarrow$	$\doteq .006\,(50)^2$
$(50)^2$ means $(50)(50)$.	$\longrightarrow$	$\doteq .006\,(50)\,(50)$
$(50)(50) = 2,500$	$\longrightarrow$	$\doteq .006\,(2,500)$
		$\doteq 15.000$

$$\begin{array}{r} 2{,}500 \\ \times\ .006 \\ \hline 15{,}000 \end{array}$$

Thus, the car will travel about 15 meters before coming to a complete stop.

PROJECT

1. A car is traveling at a speed of 80 km/h. The driver suddenly applies the brakes. How far will the car travel before coming to a stop?

2. A car is traveling at a speed of 85 km/h. Suddenly the driver spots a stalled car, and hits the brakes. The stalled car is 45 meters away. Will the driver stop in time?

Chapter Six Review

Multiply. $[p.\ 141]$

1. $(x + 5)(x + 3)$

2. $(x - 7)(x + 9)$

3. $(2x + 3)(x + 5)$

4. $(3x - 1)(x + 6)$

5. $(2b - 3)(b + 4)$

6. $(m - 1)(m + 1)$

7. $(4z - 1)(3z - 2)$

8. $(3x - 5)(x + 5)$

9. $(3x - 1)(5x + 4)$

10. $(x - 5)(x^2 + 7x + 3)$

11. $(2x - 3)(x^2 + 3x - 4)$

12. $(3x - 1)(x^2 + 2x - 4)$

Simplify. $[p.\ 141]$

13. $(3a - 5)^2$

14. $(4x - 1)^2$

15. $(2x + 3)^2$

16. $(7x + 1)^2$

Factor completely. $[p.\ 145,\ 150,\ 153,\ 156]$

17. $x^2 - 7x + 12$

18. $p^2 + 7p + 10$

19. $2a^2 + 9a - 5$

20. $x^2 - 5x + 6$

21. $3y^2 + 17y + 10$

22. $3x^2 + 16x - 12$

23. $2m^2 + 3m - 20$

24. $2m^2 + 7m + 6$

25. $2x^2 - 9x + 9$

26. $4a^2 + 2a - 2$

27. $6x^2 - x - 1$

28. $12b^2 + 5b - 2$

29. $a^2 - 4$

30. $x^2 - 36$

31. $4a^2 - 25$

32. $49x^2 - 36y^2$

33. $3x^2 + 21x + 36$

34. $2a^2 - 8a + 6$

35. $2a^2 - 2a - 40$

36. $3b^2 + 6b - 45$

37. $3k^3 + 3k^2 - 90k$

38. $3b^2 - 21b - 90$

39. $6x^3 - 24x^2 + 18x$

40. $b^3 - 49b$

41. $x^2 + 3xy + 2y^2$

42. $a^2 - 9b^2$

43. $a^2 - 3ab - 28b^2$

44. $2p^2 + 13pq + 15q^2$

45. $144x^2 - 169y^2$

46. $4y^2 - 14yb - 30b^2$

47. $3x^2 - 31xy + 56y^2$

48. $yx^2 - 4y^3$

49. $12x^2 - 27$

50. $12x^2 - 60x + 75$

Solve. $[p.\ 158,\ 162]$

51. $a^2 - 3a + 2 = 0$

52. $x^2 - 4 = 0$

53. $a^2 - 9a - 36 = 0$

54. $4 = a^2$

55. $24 + p^2 = 10p$

56. $-9r + 14 = -r^2$

Find the solution set. $[p.\ 158,\ 162]$

57. $x^2 - 5x = 0$

58. $9m^2 - 49 = 0$

59. $9a - 5 = -2a^2$

60. $2x^2 = 13x - 21$

61. $6x = x^2$

62. $2a^2 = -15a - 28$

Solve these problems. $[p.\ 165,\ 168]$

63. Find two consecutive integers whose product is 72.

64. Find two consecutive integers whose sum is 35.

65. Find three consecutive integers such that the square of the first, decreased by 5 times the second is 9.

66. Find three consecutive even integers such that the square of the first, added to the sum of the second and third is 30.

Chapter Six Test

Multiply.

1. $(x + 5)(x + 8)$

2. $(2x - 1)(3x + 4)$

3. $(3x - 2)(3x + 2)$

4. $(2a + 3)(a^2 - 7a + 4)$

Simplify.

5. $(3a - 2)^2$

6. $(4x + 1)^2$

Factor completely.

7. $a^2 - 7a + 10$

8. $x^2 - 2x - 35$

9. $4m^2 + 18m - 36$

10. $p^2 - 49$

11. $2b^3 - 8b^2 - 64b$

12. $16a^3 - 25a$

13. $2x^2 + 5xy - 3y^2$

14. $8b^2 - 8bc - 6c^2$

Solve.

15. $x^2 - 5x + 4 = 0$

16. $a^2 - 4a - 12 = 0$

17. $a^2 - 7a = 0$

18. $m^2 - 10m = -24$

19. $3p + 28 = p^2$

20. $x^2 = 64$

Find the solution set.

21. $m^2 + 14m = 0$

22. $25 = x^2$

23. $-11m - 21 = -2m^2$

24. $2k^2 = -21k - 40$

25. $2b^2 - 9b = 5$

26. $2m^2 - 21 = -m$

Solve these problems.

27. Find two consecutive integers whose sum is 81.

28. Find two consecutive integers whose product is 56.

29. Find two consecutive odd integers such that the square of the second increased by 4 times the first is 37.

30. Find two consecutive even integers such that the square of the first increased by the second is 22.

SIMPLIFYING FRACTIONS

Mathematics in Music

The distance from middle *C* to the next *C* is one octave.

> The frequency of a note is the number of vibrations per second.

Note	Frequency	Note	Frequency
Middle C	264	G	396
D	297	A	440
E	330	B	495
F	352	Higher C	528

From the table, $\dfrac{\text{frequency of higher C}}{\text{frequency of middle C}} = \dfrac{528}{264}$, or $\dfrac{2}{1}$. ← { All octaves are in this ratio.

Simple frequency ratios indicate pleasing combinations of notes.

$\dfrac{E}{C} = \dfrac{330}{264}$, or $\dfrac{5}{4}$
└─ pleasing

$\dfrac{G}{B} = \dfrac{396}{495}$, or $\dfrac{132}{165}$
└─ not pleasing

PROJECT Find as many pleasing combinations of notes as you can. Try your combinations on a piano, if possible.

Fractions

OBJECTIVES

■ To find products of the form $a\left(\dfrac{1}{b}\right)$

■ To find reciprocals of fractions

■ To find the values of x for which fractions like $\dfrac{x-3}{x+2}$ are undefined

▶ REVIEW CAPSULE

$3(2)$ means $2 + 2 + 2$, or 6
$2(-5)$ means $-5 + (-5)$, or -10
$4(x)$ means $x + x + x + x$, or $4x$
$3(-a)$ means $-a + (-a) + (-a)$, or $-3a$

Fractions on a Number Line

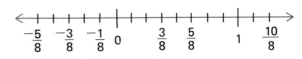

$\dfrac{3}{8}$ ⟵ Numerator
$\dfrac{3}{8}$ ⟵ Denominator

EXAMPLE 1 Give the coordinates of points A and B.

Each subdivision is $\dfrac{1}{5}$.

Count from 0.

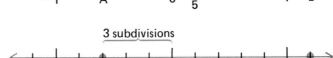

Count $-\dfrac{1}{5}, -\dfrac{2}{5}, -\dfrac{3}{5}$. ⟶

Point A	Point B
3 subdivisions *left* of 0	6 subdivisions *right* of 0
$-\dfrac{3}{5}$	$\dfrac{6}{5}$

EXAMPLE 2 Show that $\dfrac{16}{8} = 2$.

$\dfrac{16}{8}$ means $16 \div 8$, or $8\overline{)16}$.

Check by multiplying. If $\dfrac{a}{b} = c$, then $b \cdot c = a$.

$16 \div 8 = 2$ **Thus,** $\dfrac{16}{8} = 2$.

EXAMPLE 3   Show that $\dfrac{6}{0}$ is undefined, or meaningless.

Is $\dfrac{6}{0} = 6$?   Is $\dfrac{6}{0} = 0$?

If $\dfrac{a}{b} = c$, then $b \cdot c = a$. ──────→ Check: $0 \cdot 6 = 0$ *not* 6.   Check: $0 \cdot 0 = 0$ *not* 6.

Let $\dfrac{6}{0} = x$. Then $0 \cdot x = 6$. But $0 \cdot x = 0$ for *every*

number *x*.

There is no number that can be
multiplied by 0 to get 6. ──────→ **Thus,** $\dfrac{6}{0}$ is undefined, or meaningless.

Definition of rational number ──────→ A *rational number* is a number which can be

written in the form $\dfrac{a}{b}$, where *a* and *b* are

integers and $b \neq 0$.

$\dfrac{4}{5}, \dfrac{-7}{8}, \dfrac{24}{8}$ are rational numbers.

EXAMPLE 4   Write each in the form $\dfrac{a}{b}$.

Think. ──────────────────→
$$5 \qquad\qquad 16 \div 4 \qquad -2 \div 8$$
$$5 \div 1$$
$$\dfrac{5}{1} \qquad\qquad \dfrac{16}{4} \qquad\qquad \dfrac{-2}{8}$$

EXAMPLE 5   Show that $3\left(\dfrac{1}{6}\right) = \dfrac{3}{6}$.

$$3\left(\dfrac{1}{6}\right) \text{ means } \dfrac{1}{6} + \dfrac{1}{6} + \dfrac{1}{6}.$$

Mark off sixths on a number line.

Count 3 subdivisions from 0 to $\dfrac{3}{6}$.

Thus, $3\left(\dfrac{1}{6}\right) = \dfrac{3}{6}$.

Example 5 suggests this. ──────→
$$a\left(\dfrac{1}{b}\right) = \dfrac{a}{b}, \; b \neq 0.$$

EXAMPLE 6 Multiply $-2\left(\dfrac{1}{7}\right)$. Multiply $(x+3)\left(\dfrac{1}{x-5}\right)$.

$a\left(\dfrac{1}{b}\right)=\dfrac{a}{b},\ b\neq 0$ ⟶ $-2\left(\dfrac{1}{7}\right)=\dfrac{-2}{7}$ $(x+3)\left(\dfrac{1}{x-5}\right)=\dfrac{x+3}{x-5}$

EXAMPLE 7 Multiply $4\left(\dfrac{1}{4}\right)$.

$$4\left(\dfrac{1}{4}\right)=\dfrac{4}{4}$$

$\dfrac{4}{4}$ means $4\div 4$ and $4\div 4=1$.

Thus, $4\left(\dfrac{1}{4}\right)=1$.

Example 7 suggests this. ⟶

$$a\left(\dfrac{1}{a}\right)=1.$$

Reciprocals are sometimes called
multiplicative inverses.

a and $\dfrac{1}{a}$ are *reciprocals* of each other if $a\neq 0$.

EXAMPLE 8 Find the reciprocal of each of the following:
$$6,\ \dfrac{1}{7},\ 0,\ -8$$

Number	Reciprocal
6	$\dfrac{1}{6}$
$\dfrac{1}{7}$	7
0	No reciprocal
-8	$-\dfrac{1}{8}$

$6(?)=1,\ 6\left(\dfrac{1}{6}\right)=1$

$\left(\dfrac{1}{7}\right)(?)=1,\ \left(\dfrac{1}{7}\right)(7)=1$

$(-8)\,(?)=1,\ (-8)\left(-\dfrac{1}{8}\right)=1$

EXAMPLE 9 Find the missing factor or product.

$$(?)\left(\dfrac{1}{a}\right)=\dfrac{b}{a}\quad a(?)=\dfrac{a}{m}\quad (x-2)\left(\dfrac{1}{x+4}\right)=?$$

$$b\left(\dfrac{1}{a}\right)=\dfrac{b}{a}\quad a\left(\dfrac{1}{m}\right)=\dfrac{a}{m}\quad (x-2)\left(\dfrac{1}{x+4}\right)=\dfrac{x-2}{x+4}$$

EXERCISES

PART A

Find the missing factor.

1. $4(?) = \dfrac{4}{7}$ $\tfrac{1}{7}$ **2.** $p(?) = \dfrac{p}{q}$ $\tfrac{1}{q}$ **3.** $(?)(y) = \dfrac{y}{x}$ $\tfrac{1}{x}$ **4.** $(?)(-7) = \dfrac{-7}{13}$ $\tfrac{1}{13}$

5. Give the reciprocal of $-3, 0, 1, -1,$ and $-\dfrac{1}{5}$. $-\tfrac{1}{3}; \; no \; reciprocal; \; 1; -1; -5$

Give the coordinate of each point A.

6.

7.

8.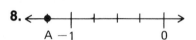

Write each in the form $\dfrac{a}{b}$.

9. 6 $\dfrac{6}{1}$ **10.** -3 $\dfrac{-3}{1}$ **11.** $12 \div 3$ $\dfrac{12}{3}$ **12.** $-8 \div 2$ $\dfrac{-8}{2}$ **13.** $-6 \div 12$

Multiply.

14. $4\left(\dfrac{1}{5}\right)$ $\dfrac{4}{5}$ **15.** $-5\left(\dfrac{1}{17}\right)$ $\dfrac{-5}{17}$ **16.** $(x+5)\left(\dfrac{1}{x-4}\right)$ $\dfrac{x+5}{x-4}$ **17.** $(a-4)\left(\dfrac{1}{a+2}\right)$

PART B

EXAMPLE   For what value of x is $\dfrac{x+2}{2x-4}$ undefined?

$\dfrac{a}{b}$ is undefined for $b = 0.$ ⟶ $\dfrac{x+2}{2x-4}$ is undefined when $2x - 4 = 0.$

Solve. $2x - 4 = 0$

                         $2x = 4$

                $x = 2$ Thus, $\dfrac{x+2}{2x-4}$ is undefined when $x = 2.$

Find the value(s) of x for which the fraction is undefined.

18. $\dfrac{2x-1}{x-7}$ 7 **19.** $\dfrac{3x+2}{2x-10}$ 5 **20.** $\dfrac{7x+1}{3x-12}$ 4 **21.** $\dfrac{x+5}{x^2-9}$ $3, -3$ **22.** $\dfrac{3x+2}{x^2-7x+12}$

PART C

Find the value(s) of x for which the fraction is undefined.

23. $\dfrac{3x-2}{x^3-25x}$ **24.** $\dfrac{x+4}{x^3-7x^2+12x}$ **25.** $\dfrac{2x+5}{x^4-16}$

Zero and Negative Exponents

Consider this pattern.

Exponents
decrease
by 1.

$$2^5 = 2 \cdot 2 \cdot 2 \cdot 2 \cdot 2 = 32$$
$$2^4 = 2 \cdot 2 \cdot 2 \cdot 2 \quad = 16$$
$$2^3 = 2 \cdot 2 \cdot 2 \quad\quad = 8$$
$$2^2 = 2 \cdot 2 \quad\quad\quad = 4$$
$$2^1 = 2 \quad\quad\quad\quad = 2$$
$$2^0 = \underrightarrow{\qquad\qquad} = 1$$

Powers
are divided
by 2.

Thus, $2^0 = 1$.

Continue the pattern for three more entries.

$$2^0 = \underrightarrow{\qquad\qquad} = 1$$
$$2^{-1} = \frac{1}{2} \qquad\quad = \frac{1}{2}$$
$$2^{-2} = \frac{1}{2 \cdot 2} \qquad = \frac{1}{4}$$
$$2^{-3} = \frac{1}{2 \cdot 2 \cdot 2} \quad = \frac{1}{8}$$

For any $a \neq 0$, $a^0 = 1$. For any $a \neq 0$, $a^{-n} = \dfrac{1}{a^n}$.

0^0 is undefined.

PROJECT Find the value.

1. 4^0

2. 3^{-2}

3. $(-2)^0$

4. 5^{-3}

5. 6^{-1}

6. $\dfrac{1}{2^{-1}}$

7. $\dfrac{2^0}{3}$

8. $3^{-2} \cdot 5^0$

9. $(2 \cdot 3)^0$

10. $5^{-1} + 2^{-1}$

Multiplying Fractions

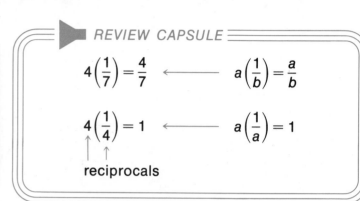

▶ REVIEW CAPSULE

$$4\left(\frac{1}{7}\right) = \frac{4}{7} \longleftarrow a\left(\frac{1}{b}\right) = \frac{a}{b}$$

$$4\left(\frac{1}{4}\right) = 1 \longleftarrow a\left(\frac{1}{a}\right) = 1$$

reciprocals

EXAMPLE 1 Show that $\dfrac{1}{3} \cdot \dfrac{1}{4} = \dfrac{1}{12}$.

A number has exactly one reciprocal.

First show the reciprocal of 12 as $\dfrac{1}{3} \cdot \dfrac{1}{4}$.

$$12 \cdot \frac{1}{3} \cdot \frac{1}{4}$$

Factor: $12 = 3 \cdot 4.$ —————→

$$3 \cdot 4 \cdot \frac{1}{3} \cdot \frac{1}{4}$$

Regroup. —————————→

$$\left(3 \cdot \frac{1}{3}\right)\left(4 \cdot \frac{1}{4}\right)$$

$a \cdot \dfrac{1}{a} = 1$ —————————→

$$1 \cdot 1$$
$$1$$

Two numbers whose product is 1 are reciprocals. ⎱

Since $12 \cdot \dfrac{1}{3} \cdot \dfrac{1}{4} = 1$, $\dfrac{1}{3} \cdot \dfrac{1}{4}$ is the reciprocal of 12.

$12 \cdot \dfrac{1}{12} = 1$ —————————→ But, $\dfrac{1}{12}$ is also the reciprocal of 12.

Thus, $\dfrac{1}{3} \cdot \dfrac{1}{4} = \dfrac{1}{12}$.

A technique for multiplying fractions like $\dfrac{1}{5} \cdot \dfrac{1}{4}$ —————————→

$$\frac{1}{a} \cdot \frac{1}{b} = \frac{1}{ab}, \, a \neq 0, \, b \neq 0$$

EXAMPLE 2 Multiply $\frac{1}{5} \cdot \frac{1}{6}$. Multiply $\frac{1}{3}\left(-\frac{1}{8}\right)$. Multiply $\frac{1}{x^2} \cdot \frac{1}{x^3}$.

$\frac{1}{a} \cdot \frac{1}{b} = \frac{1}{ab}$

$\frac{1}{5} \cdot \frac{1}{6} = \frac{1}{5 \cdot 6}$ $\frac{1}{3}\left(-\frac{1}{8}\right) = -\frac{1}{3 \cdot 8}$ $\frac{1}{x^2} \cdot \frac{1}{x^3} = \frac{1}{x^2 \cdot x^3}$

$= \frac{1}{30}$ $= -\frac{1}{24}$ $= \frac{1}{x^5}$

EXAMPLE 3 Multiply $\frac{4}{5} \cdot \frac{3}{7}$.

$\frac{a}{b} = a \cdot \frac{1}{b}$

·Multiplication can be done in any order}

$\frac{1}{a} \cdot \frac{1}{b} = \frac{1}{ab}$

$a \cdot \frac{1}{b} = \frac{a}{b}$

$\frac{4}{5} \cdot \frac{3}{7} = 4 \cdot \frac{1}{5} \cdot 3 \cdot \frac{1}{7}$

$= (4 \cdot 3)\left(\frac{1}{5} \cdot \frac{1}{7}\right)$

$= 12 \cdot \frac{1}{35}$

$= \frac{12}{35}$

Thus, $\frac{4}{5} \cdot \frac{3}{7} = \frac{12}{35}$.

Product of Two Fractions

$\frac{\text{Product of numerators}}{\text{Product of denominators}}$

$\frac{a}{b} \cdot \frac{c}{d} = \frac{ac}{bd}, \; b \neq 0, \; d \neq 0.$

EXAMPLE 4 Multiply $5 \cdot \frac{3}{7}$.   Multiply $\left(-\frac{2}{5}\right)\left(-\frac{6}{11}\right)$.

$5 = \frac{5}{1}$

$\frac{a}{b} \cdot \frac{c}{d} = \frac{ac}{bd}$

$5 \cdot \frac{3}{7} = \frac{5}{1} \cdot \frac{3}{7}$ $\left(-\frac{2}{5}\right)\left(-\frac{6}{11}\right)$

$= \frac{5 \cdot 3}{1 \cdot 7}$ $+\frac{12}{55}$ ← $(-)\,(-) = +$

$= \frac{15}{7}$ or $\frac{12}{55}$

EXAMPLE 5 Multiply $\frac{7}{9}\left(-\frac{2}{3}\right)$.   Multiply $\frac{4}{5}\left(\frac{2}{3}\right)$.

$(+)\,(-) = -$

$-\frac{7 \cdot 2}{9 \cdot 3} = -\frac{14}{27}$ $\frac{4 \cdot 2}{5 \cdot 3} = \frac{8}{15}$

EXAMPLE 6   Multiply $\dfrac{1}{2} \cdot \dfrac{3}{4} \cdot \dfrac{3}{2}$.

Extend rule for multiplication.

$$\frac{a}{b} \cdot \frac{c}{d} \cdot \frac{e}{f} = \frac{ace}{bdf}$$

$$\frac{1}{2} \cdot \frac{3}{4} \cdot \frac{3}{2} = \frac{1 \cdot 3 \cdot 3}{2 \cdot 4 \cdot 2}, \text{ or } \frac{9}{16}$$

EXAMPLE 7   Multiply $\dfrac{3a^2}{2b^3} \cdot \dfrac{4a^3}{5b^6}$.

$$\frac{3a^2}{2b^3} \cdot \frac{4a^3}{5b^6} = \frac{3a^2 \cdot 4a^3}{2b^3 \cdot 5b^6}$$

$a^2 \cdot a^3 = a^{2+3}$, or a^5
$b^3 \cdot b^6 = b^{3+6}$, or b^9

$$= \frac{3 \cdot 4 \cdot a^2 \cdot a^3}{2 \cdot 5 \cdot b^3 \cdot b^6}$$

$$= \frac{12a^5}{10b^9}$$

EXAMPLE 8   Multiply $\left(\dfrac{x+1}{x+3}\right)\left(-\dfrac{2x-1}{2x+1}\right)$.

$(-)(+) = -$

$2x^2 + x - 1$ $2x^2 + 7x + 3$

$$\left(\frac{x+1}{x+3}\right)\left(-\frac{2x-1}{2x+1}\right) = -\frac{(x+1)(2x-1)}{(x+3)(2x+1)}$$

$$= -\frac{2x^2 + x - 1}{2x^2 + 7x + 3}$$

EXAMPLE 9   Multiply $2\left(\dfrac{x-1}{x+3}\right)$.

Rewrite 2 as $\dfrac{2}{1}$.

$2(x-1) = 2x - 2$

$$2\left(\frac{x-1}{x+3}\right) = \frac{2}{1}\left(\frac{x-1}{x+3}\right)$$

$$= \frac{2(x-1)}{1(x+3)}$$

$$= \frac{2x-2}{x+3}$$

EXAMPLE 10   Multiply $(x-1)\left(\dfrac{2x+5}{x-3}\right)$.

$x - 1 = \dfrac{x-1}{1}$

$2x^2 + 3x - 5$

$$(x-1)\left(\frac{2x+5}{x-3}\right) = \left(\frac{x-1}{1}\right)\left(\frac{2x+5}{x-3}\right)$$

$$= \frac{(x-1)(2x+5)}{1(x-3)}$$

$$= \frac{2x^2 + 3x - 5}{x-3}$$

ORAL EXERCISES
Multiply.

1. $\frac{1}{8} \cdot \frac{1}{2}$ *$\frac{1}{16}$*
2. $\frac{1}{5} \cdot \frac{1}{6}$ *$\frac{1}{30}$*
3. $\frac{1}{m^2} \cdot \frac{1}{m^3}$ *$\frac{1}{m^5}$*
4. $\frac{1}{a^5} \cdot \frac{1}{a^3}$ *$\frac{1}{a^8}$*
5. $\frac{1}{3} \cdot \frac{1}{2a}$ *$\frac{1}{6a}$*
6. $5 \cdot \frac{1}{2a}$ *$\frac{5}{2a}$*
7. $\frac{1}{5} \cdot \frac{1}{46}$ *$\frac{1}{230}$*
8. $\left(-\frac{2}{3}\right)\left(-\frac{4}{7}\right)$ *$\frac{8}{21}$*
9. $-\frac{3}{5} \cdot \frac{1}{2}$ *$-\frac{3}{10}$*
10. $4 \cdot \frac{2}{3}$ *$\frac{8}{3}$*

EXERCISES

PART A
Multiply.

1. $\frac{1}{4} \cdot \frac{2}{3} \cdot \frac{3}{4}$ *$\frac{6}{48}$*
2. $\frac{1}{5} \cdot \frac{4}{3} \cdot \frac{2}{5}$ *$\frac{8}{75}$*
3. $\left(\frac{2}{3}\right)\left(\frac{4}{5}\right)\left(-\frac{1}{3}\right)$ *$\frac{-8}{45}$*
4. $\left(\frac{2}{5}\right)\left(\frac{2}{3}\right)\left(-\frac{1}{2}\right)$

5. $\frac{2a^2}{3b^3} \cdot \frac{5a^3}{6b^6}$ *$\frac{10a^5}{18b^9}$*
6. $\frac{7x^2}{3y^4} \cdot \frac{4x^5}{5y^2}$ *$\frac{28x^7}{15y^6}$*
7. $-\frac{5a^2}{3b^5} \cdot \frac{4a^3}{3b^4}$ *$\frac{-20a^5}{9b^9}$*
8. $\frac{6x^3}{5y^2}\left(-\frac{3x^5}{2y^5}\right)$

9. $\frac{x^3}{y^7} \cdot \left(-\frac{x^2}{y^4}\right)$ *$\frac{-x^5}{y^{11}}$*
10. $\frac{a^2}{b^3} \cdot \frac{1}{b^4}$ *$\frac{a^2}{b^7}$*
11. $\frac{x^2}{y^3} \cdot \frac{x^4}{y^2} \cdot \frac{x^5}{y}$ *$\frac{x^{11}}{y^6}$*
12. $\frac{a^3}{b^2} \cdot \frac{a^2}{b^4} \cdot \frac{a}{b^5}$

13. $\frac{(x+1)}{(x+2)}\left(-\frac{2x-3}{2x+3}\right)$
14. $\left(\frac{x+2}{x+1}\right)\left(-\frac{3x-1}{3x+1}\right)$
15. $\left(\frac{x+3}{x+5}\right)\left(-\frac{2x-5}{2x+5}\right)$

16. $3\left(\frac{x-1}{x+5}\right)$ *$\frac{3x-3}{x+5}$*
17. $5\left(\frac{2x-1}{x+4}\right)$ *$\frac{10x-5}{x+4}$*
18. $6\left(\frac{x+2}{2x-5}\right)$ *$\frac{6x+12}{2x-5}$*

19. $(x-7)\left(\frac{2x+3}{x-4}\right)$
20. $\left(\frac{-a-4}{a+3}\right)(2a-1)$
21. $(2a-3)\left(\frac{a+5}{3a-7}\right)$

22. $a^3 \cdot \frac{a^7}{b^6}$ *$\frac{a^{10}}{b^6}$*
23. $\left(-\frac{x^2}{m^3}\right)(-x^5)$ *$\frac{x^7}{m^3}$*
24. $\left(-\frac{a-4}{a+3}\right)\left(-\frac{1}{2a-1}\right)$

PART B
Multiply.

25. $\left(\frac{a+b}{x-y}\right)\left(\frac{a-b}{x+2y}\right)$
26. $\left(\frac{2m-n}{m+3n}\right)\left(\frac{3m+n}{2m+n}\right)$ *$\frac{6m^2 - mn - n^2}{2m^2 + 7mn + 3n^2}$*
27. $\left(\frac{3r-t}{r+t}\right)\left(\frac{4r+t}{r+2t}\right)$

28. $(x+2y)\left(\frac{x-y}{x+y}\right)$
29. $\left(\frac{a-2b}{x-y}\right)\left(-\frac{a+2b}{x+y}\right)$
30. $\left(\frac{2x+3y}{m+n}\right)^2$

31. $\left(-\frac{3a+b}{2a+b}\right)^2$
32. $\left(\frac{a+b}{2a-3b}\right)(a-b)$ *$\frac{a^2 - b^2}{2a-3b}$*
33. $\left(-\frac{4a-b}{a+b}\right)\left(\frac{a+3b}{2a-b}\right)$

PART C
Multiply.

34. $\left(\frac{2x-y}{x+4y}\right)^2$
35. $\left(\frac{x-5}{x+5}\right)^2\left(\frac{x+2}{x-4}\right)$
36. $\left(\frac{3a-b}{a+b}\right)^2\left(\frac{2a-b}{a+b}\right)$

Rewriting Fractions in Simplest Form

▶ REVIEW CAPSULE

$$\frac{3}{5} \cdot \frac{4}{7} = \frac{3 \cdot 4}{5 \cdot 7}, \quad \text{or} \quad \frac{12}{35} \longleftarrow \frac{a}{b} \cdot \frac{c}{d} = \frac{ac}{bd}$$

$$\frac{5}{5} = 5 \cdot \frac{1}{5}, \text{ or } 1 \longleftarrow \frac{a}{a} = 1$$

EXAMPLE 1 Write $\frac{6}{15}$ as a product of two fractions.

Factor 6. ⟶
Factor 15. ⟶

$$\frac{6}{15} = \frac{3 \cdot 2}{5 \cdot 3} \qquad \text{or} \qquad \frac{6}{15} = \frac{2 \cdot 3}{5 \cdot 3}$$

$$= \frac{3}{5} \cdot \frac{2}{3} \qquad\qquad\qquad = \frac{2}{5} \cdot \frac{3}{3}$$

We can use the second product to rewrite $\frac{6}{15}$ in a different form.

$\frac{3}{3} = 1$ ⟶

$$\frac{2}{5} \cdot \frac{3}{3} = \frac{2}{5} \cdot 1, \text{ or } \frac{2}{5} \qquad \textbf{Thus, } \frac{6}{15} = \frac{2}{5}.$$

EXAMPLE 2 Write $\frac{20}{30}$ in simplest form.

Factor 20 into primes. ⟶
Factor 30 into primes. ⟶

Rearrange so like factors are over each other.

$$\frac{a}{b} \cdot \frac{c}{d} \cdot \frac{e}{f} = \frac{ace}{bdf}$$

$$\frac{2}{2} = 1 \qquad \frac{5}{5} = 1$$

$$\frac{20}{30} = \frac{2 \cdot 2 \cdot 5}{5 \cdot 3 \cdot 2}$$

$$= \frac{2 \cdot 2 \cdot 5}{3 \cdot 2 \cdot 5}$$

$$= \frac{2}{3} \cdot \frac{2}{2} \cdot \frac{5}{5}$$

$$= \frac{2}{3} \cdot 1 \cdot 1$$

$$= \frac{2}{3}$$

More Compact Form

$$\frac{20}{30} = \frac{2 \cdot 2 \cdot 5}{5 \cdot 3 \cdot 2}$$

$$= \frac{2 \cdot \overset{1}{\cancel{2}} \cdot \overset{1}{\cancel{5}}}{\underset{1}{\cancel{5}} \cdot 3 \cdot \underset{1}{\cancel{2}}} \longleftarrow \frac{2}{2} = \frac{1}{1} \quad \frac{5}{5} = \frac{1}{1}$$

$$= \frac{2 \cdot 1 \cdot 1}{1 \cdot 3 \cdot 1}$$

$$= \frac{2}{3}$$

The GCF of 2 and 3 is 1, so 2 and 3 are relatively prime.

$\frac{2}{3}$ is in simplest form, or lowest terms.

EXAMPLE 3 Simplify. (Write in simplest form.)

$$\frac{x^2 - 7x + 12}{2x^2 - 9x + 9}$$

$x^2 - 7x + 12$ | $2x^2 - 9x - 9$

$$\frac{(x - 3)(x - 4)}{(2x - 3)(x - 3)} \left\{ \begin{array}{l} \text{Factor numerator} \\ \text{and denominator.} \end{array} \right.$$

$$\frac{x - 3}{x - 3} = \frac{1}{1}$$

$$\frac{(x \overset{1}{\cancel{- 3)}}(x - 4)}{(2x - 3)\underset{1}{\cancel{(x - 3)}}} \left\{ \begin{array}{l} \text{Divide out} \\ \text{common factors.} \end{array} \right.$$

$1(x - 4) = x - 4$

$(2x - 3)1 = 2x - 3$

$$\frac{x - 4}{2x - 3}$$

EXAMPLE 4 Simplify $\dfrac{a - 4}{2a - 8}$.

$a - 4$ is not factorable.

$2a - 8 = 2(a - 4)$

$$\frac{a - 4}{2a - 8} = \frac{\overset{1}{\cancel{a - 4}}}{2\underset{1}{\cancel{(a - 4)}}} \left\{ \begin{array}{l} \text{Factor and divide} \\ \text{out common factors.} \end{array} \right.$$

The remaining factor 2 is in the denominator.

$$= \frac{1}{2 \cdot 1}, \text{ or } \frac{1}{2}$$

EXAMPLE 5 Show that $\dfrac{x + 3}{x + 4}$ cannot be simplified to $\dfrac{3}{4}$.

Let $x = 2$ in $\dfrac{x + 3}{x + 4}$.

$$\frac{2 + 3}{2 + 4} = \frac{5}{6}$$

But $\quad \dfrac{5}{6} \neq \dfrac{3}{4}$

Thus, $\dfrac{x + 3}{x + 4}$ cannot be simplified to $\dfrac{3}{4}$.

$\dfrac{x + 3}{x + 4} \neq \dfrac{3}{4}$

$\dfrac{x + 3}{x + 4}$ is already in simplest form.

EXAMPLE 6 Simplify $-\dfrac{3x^3 - 27x}{2x^2 - 6x}$.

Look for the GCF.

$3x^3 - 27x = 3(x^3 - 9x) = 3 \cdot x(x^2 - 9)$

$2x^2 - 6x = 2(x^2 - 3x) = 2 \cdot x(x - 3)$

$$-\frac{3x^3 - 27x}{2x^2 - 6x} = -\frac{3x(x^2 - 9)}{2x(x - 3)}$$

Factor $x^2 - 9$. Then divide out common factors.

$$= -\frac{3 \cdot \overset{1}{\cancel{x}}\overset{1}{\cancel{(x - 3)}}(x + 3)}{2 \cdot \underset{1}{\cancel{x}} \quad \underset{1}{\cancel{(x - 3)}}}$$

$3(x + 3) = 3x + 9$

$$= -\frac{3(x + 3)}{2}, \text{ or } -\frac{3x + 9}{2}$$

EXERCISES

PART A

Simplify.

1. $\dfrac{4}{12}$ *$\dfrac{1}{3}$*

2. $\dfrac{8}{16}$ *$\dfrac{1}{2}$*

3. $-\dfrac{15}{36}$ *$\dfrac{-5}{12}$*

4. $-\dfrac{8}{30}$ *$\dfrac{-4}{15}$*

5. $\dfrac{a^2 - 8a + 15}{2a^2 - 7a + 3}$

6. $\dfrac{m^2 - 3m - 10}{2m^2 - 9m - 5}$

7. $\dfrac{b^2 - 25}{b^2 - 7b + 10}$

8. $-\dfrac{x^2 - 9x + 14}{x^2 - 5x - 14}$

9. $\dfrac{x - 4}{4x - 16}$ *$\dfrac{1}{4}$*

10. $\dfrac{a - 8}{a^2 - 8a}$ *$\dfrac{1}{a}$*

11. $\dfrac{3b - 15}{b^2 - 7b + 10}$

12. $-\dfrac{x^2 - 5x + 4}{2x - 8}$

13. $\dfrac{4b - 12}{b^2 - 9}$

14. $\dfrac{a^2 - 7a + 12}{2a - 8}$

15. $\dfrac{y^2 + 3y - 28}{y^2 + 7y}$

16. $\dfrac{m^2 + 6m - 16}{m^2 + 8m}$

17. $\dfrac{3x^3 - 12x}{2x^2 - 4x}$

18. $\dfrac{2x^3 - 50x}{3x^2 - 15x}$

19. $\dfrac{b^2 - 7b}{b^2 - 49}$ *$\dfrac{b}{b + 7}$*

20. $\dfrac{2x^2 + 3x - 20}{8x - 20}$

21. $\dfrac{3p^2 + 5p - 2}{5p + 10}$

22. $\dfrac{2n^2 + 3n - 2}{n^2 - 4}$ ⟩ *$\dfrac{2n - 1}{n - 2}$*

23. $\dfrac{x^2 + 8x + 16}{x^2 - 16}$ ⟩ *$\dfrac{x + 4}{x - 4}$*

24. $\dfrac{a^2 + 2a}{a^2 - 5a - 14}$ ⟩ *$\dfrac{a}{a - 7}$*

PART B

EXAMPLE   Find the quotient $(x^2 + 7x + 12) \div (x + 4)$.

$\dfrac{a}{b}$ means $a \div b$ ⟶

$$(x^2 + 7x + 12) \div (x + 4) = \frac{x^2 + 7x + 12}{x + 4}$$

Factor. Then divide out common factors.

$$= \frac{\overset{1}{(\cancel{x + 4})}(x + 3)}{\underset{1}{\cancel{x + 4}}}$$

$$= \frac{x + 3}{1}, \text{ or } x + 3$$

Thus, the quotient is $x + 3$.

Find the quotient when the first polynomial is divided by the second.

25. $x^2 + x - 12$; $x - 3$ *$x + 4$*

26. $z^2 - 3z - 40$; $z + 5$ *$z - 8$*

27. $2x^2 + 9x - 5$; $2x - 1$ *$x + 5$*

28. $2a^2 - ab - 3b^2$; $2a - 3b$ *$a + b$*

29. $6a^2 - 11a + 3$; $2a - 3$ *$3a - 1$*

30. $10x^2 + 17x - 63$; $5x - 9$ *$2x + 7$*

31. $-11x^2 - 58x - 15$; $x + 5$ *$-11x - 3$*

32. $-21x^2 - 22x + 63$; $-7x + 9$ *$3x + 7$*

PART C

Find the quotient when the first polynomial is divided by the second.

33. $a^4 - 5a^2 + 4$; $a^2 + a - 2$

34. $a^4 - 8a^2 - 9$; $a^2 - 2a - 3$

The Great Airplane Mystery

On an airplane, three passengers got into a conversation with a stewardess. The following facts evolved.

1. The names of the passengers were Miller, Adams, and Baker.

2. The stewardess said that these were the names of the flight crew, which consisted of a pilot, a copilot, and a navigator.

3. Mr. Adams said that he earned $14,000 a year.

4. Mr. Baker said that he lived in Cleveland.

5. The stewardess said that the pilot lived halfway between Cleveland and St. Louis.

6. One of the passengers lived next door to the pilot and received exactly three times as much salary as the navigator.

7. The stewardess said that the copilot often played bridge with Miller, one of the crew members.

8. The pilot had the same name as the passenger who lived in St. Louis.

What is the navigator's name? Prove your answer.

Using The −1 Technique

 REVIEW CAPSULE

Rewrite each polynomial in descending order of exponents.

$-2 + 3x$	$-3x - 2 - x^2$	$-4 + x^2$
↓	↓	↓
$3x - 2$	$-x^2 - 3x - 2$	$x^2 - 4$

EXAMPLE 1   Rewrite $5x - x^2 + 4$ as a polynomial in descending order of exponents and whose first coefficient is positive.

Descending order ⟶
$-x^2 = -1x^2$ ⟶
Factor out −1. ⟶

$$5x - x^2 + 4$$
$$-x^2 + 5x + 4$$
$$-1x^2 + 5x + 4$$
$$-1(x^2 - 5x - 4)$$

This form is useful when factoring polynomials and simplifying fractions.

Convenient Form of a Polynomial
$$5x - x^2 + 4$$
$$-1(\underbrace{1x^2 - 5x - 4})$$
first coefficient positive   descending order

EXAMPLE 2   Simplify $\dfrac{x - 3}{9 - x^2}$.

Descending order ⟶

Convenient form ⟶

Factor $x^2 - 9$. Then divide out common factors.

$$\frac{x - 3}{9 - x^2} = \frac{x - 3}{-x^2 + 9}$$
$$= \frac{x - 3}{-1(x^2 - 9)}$$
$$= \frac{\overset{1}{\cancel{x - 3}}}{-1(\underset{1}{\cancel{x - 3}})(x + 3)}$$
$$= \frac{1}{-1(x + 3)}$$

EXAMPLE 3 Show that $-\dfrac{12}{3} = \dfrac{-1(12)}{3} = \dfrac{12}{-1(3)}$.

$$
\begin{array}{c|c|c}
-\dfrac{12}{3} & \dfrac{-1(12)}{3} & \dfrac{12}{-1(3)} \\[2mm]
-(12 \div 3) & \dfrac{-12}{3} & \dfrac{12}{-3} \\[2mm]
\end{array}
$$

Same answers ⟶ $\quad -4 \qquad\qquad -4 \qquad\qquad -4$

Thus, $-\dfrac{12}{3} = \dfrac{-1(12)}{3} = \dfrac{12}{-1(3)}$.

Example 3 suggests this. ⟶

$$-\frac{a}{b} = \frac{-1(a)}{b} = \frac{a}{-1(b)}, \quad b \neq 0$$

EXAMPLE 4 Rewrite $\dfrac{1}{-1(x+3)}$ in two other ways.

$\dfrac{a}{-1(b)} = -\dfrac{a}{b} = \dfrac{-1(a)}{b}$ ⟶

$$\frac{1}{-1(x+3)} = -\frac{1}{x+3} = \frac{-1(1)}{x+3}$$

Any one of the three is acceptable. Generally, we use the form $-\dfrac{a}{b}$.

EXAMPLE 5 Simplify $\dfrac{-3x^2 - 5x + 2}{2 - 6x}$.

Rewrite denominator in descending order.

$-3x^2 - 5x + 2$
$= -1(3x^2 + 5x - 2)$ $\quad$ $-6x + 2$
$= -1(6x - 2)$

2 is the GCF of $6x - 2$: $2(3x - 1)$.

$$\frac{-3x^2 - 5x + 2}{-6x + 2}$$

$$\frac{-1(3x^2 + 5x - 2)}{-1(6x - 2)}$$

$$\frac{-1(3x - 1)(x + 2)}{-1(2)(3x - 1)}$$

Divide out common factors.

$$\frac{\overset{1}{\cancel{-1}}(\overset{1}{\cancel{3x - 1}})(x + 2)}{\underset{1}{\cancel{-1}}(2)(\underset{1}{\cancel{3x - 1}})}$$

$$\frac{x + 2}{2}$$

EXAMPLE 6 Simplify $\dfrac{b^2 - 2b - 15}{30 - b - b^2}$.

$30 - b - b^2 = -b^2 - b + 30$
$\qquad\qquad\quad = -1(b^2 + b - 30)$

Factor. Then divide out common factors.

$\dfrac{a}{-1(b)} = -\dfrac{a}{b}$

$\dfrac{b^2 - 2b - 15}{-1(b^2 + b - 30)}$

$\dfrac{\overset{1}{(b-5)}(b+3)}{-1(b+6)(b-5)_{\,1}}$

$\dfrac{b+3}{-1(b+6)}$, or $-\dfrac{b+3}{b+6}$

EXERCISES

PART A

Simplify.

1. $\dfrac{x-4}{16-x^2} \quad -\dfrac{1}{x+4}$

2. $\dfrac{a+5}{25-a^2} \quad -\dfrac{1}{a-5}$

3. $\dfrac{5-b}{2b-10} \quad -\dfrac{1}{2}$

4. $\dfrac{8-b}{2b-16} \quad -\dfrac{1}{2}$

5. $\dfrac{-a^2 - 2a + 15}{12 - 4a}$

6. $\dfrac{-m^2 + m + 20}{2m - 10}$

7. $\dfrac{x^2 - 7x + 12}{3 - x}$

8. $\dfrac{p^2 - 2p - 15}{5 - p}$

9. $\dfrac{2m-8}{4-m} \quad -2$

10. $\dfrac{14-2x}{x^2-49} \quad -\dfrac{2}{x+7}$

11. $\dfrac{3-c}{c^2-5c+6}$

12. $\dfrac{6-2b}{b^2-6b+9}$

13. $\dfrac{a^2-2a-8}{4-a}$

14. $\dfrac{16+6m-m^2}{m^2+5m+6}$

15. $\dfrac{9-a^2}{a^2+5a-24}$

16. $\dfrac{c^2+8c-20}{16-8c}$

17. $\dfrac{y^2-y-42}{14+5y-y^2} \quad -\dfrac{y+6}{y+2}$

18. $\dfrac{a^2+10a+25}{40+3a-a^2} \quad -\dfrac{a+5}{a-8}$

19. $\dfrac{x^2-8x-20}{-x^2+14x-40} \quad -\dfrac{x+2}{x-4}$

20. $\dfrac{36-m^2}{2m^2-8m-24} \quad -\dfrac{m+6}{2(m+2)}$

PART B

Simplify.

21. $\dfrac{12+n-n^2}{2n^2-18} \quad -\dfrac{n-4}{2(n-3)}$

22. $\dfrac{2x^2-6x}{24-2x-2x^2} \quad -\dfrac{x}{x+4}$

23. $\dfrac{-a^2+b^2}{a^2+3ab+2b^2}$

24. $\dfrac{2x^2+xy-y^2}{-2x-2y} \quad -\dfrac{2x-y}{2}$

25. $\dfrac{a^2-b^2}{-2a^2-ab+b^2} \quad -\dfrac{a-b}{2a-b}$

26. $\dfrac{-10+22a-4a^2}{3a^2-16a+5} \quad -\dfrac{2(2a-1)}{3a-1}$

PART C

Simplify.

27. $\dfrac{-a^4+b^4}{a^3+ab^2}$

28. $\dfrac{a^6-a^2b^6}{a^2b^2-b^5}$

29. $\dfrac{x^4-8x^2+15}{3x-x^3}$

30. $\dfrac{a^2-a^3}{a^2-a}$

31. $\dfrac{-36+13b^2-b^4}{b^2-5b+6}$

32. $\dfrac{5+4m-m^2}{m^4-26m^2+25}$

Fractions with Common Monomial Factors

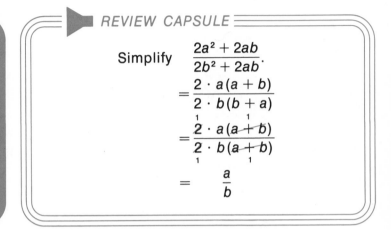

▶ REVIEW CAPSULE

Simplify $\dfrac{2a^2 + 2ab}{2b^2 + 2ab}$.

$$= \frac{2 \cdot a(a + b)}{2 \cdot b(b + a)}$$

$$= \frac{\overset{1}{2} \cdot a(a \overset{1}{+} b)}{\underset{1}{2} \cdot b(a \underset{1}{+} b)}$$

$$= \frac{a}{b}$$

EXAMPLE 1 Simplify $\dfrac{a^3}{a^7}$.

Write numerator and denominator in factored form. Then divide out common factors.

$a \cdot a \cdot a \cdot a = a^4 \longrightarrow$

$$\frac{a^3}{a^7} = \frac{\overset{1}{a} \cdot \overset{1}{a} \cdot \overset{1}{a}}{\underset{1}{a} \cdot \underset{1}{a} \cdot \underset{1}{a} \cdot a \cdot a \cdot a \cdot a}$$

$$= \frac{1}{a^4}$$

EXAMPLE 2 Simplify $\dfrac{x^5}{x^7}$.

Shorten the work by thinking of factored form in your head.

$\dfrac{\overset{1}{x} \cdot \overset{1}{x} \cdot \overset{1}{x} \cdot \overset{1}{x} \cdot \overset{1}{x}}{\underset{1}{x} \cdot \underset{1}{x} \cdot \underset{1}{x} \cdot \underset{1}{x} \cdot \underset{1}{x} \cdot x \cdot x}$

$$\frac{x^5}{x^7} = \frac{\overset{1}{x^5}}{\underset{x^2}{x^7}}$$

$$= \frac{1}{x^2}$$

EXAMPLE 3 Simplify $\dfrac{b^5}{b^2}$.

b is a factor two times in both numerator and denominator.

$\dfrac{\overbrace{b \cdot b \cdot b \cdot b \cdot b}}{\underbrace{b \cdot b}}$

$$\frac{b^5}{b^2} = \frac{\overset{b^3}{b^5}}{\underset{1}{b^2}}$$

$$= \frac{b^3}{1}, \text{ or } b^3$$

EXAMPLE 4 Simplify $\dfrac{x^7}{x}$.

x is a factor one time in both numerator and denominator.

$$\frac{x^7}{x^1} = \frac{\overset{x^6}{\cancel{x^7}}}{\underset{1}{\cancel{x^1}}}$$

$$= \frac{x^6}{1}, \text{ or } x^6$$

EXAMPLE 5 Simplify $\dfrac{12a^3b^5}{18ab^7}$.

Factor 12 and 18 into primes. a means a^1.

$\dfrac{a^3}{a^1} = \dfrac{a^2}{1}; \dfrac{b^5}{b^7} = \dfrac{1}{b^2}$

$2 \cdot 1 \cdot 1 \cdot a^2 \cdot 1 = 2a^2$
$3 \cdot 1 \cdot 1 \cdot 1 \cdot b^2 = 3b^2$

$$\frac{12a^3b^5}{18ab^7} = \frac{2 \cdot 2 \cdot 3 \cdot a^3 \cdot b^5}{3 \cdot 3 \cdot 2 \cdot a^1 \cdot b^7}$$

$$= \frac{2 \cdot 2 \cdot 3 \cdot \overset{a^2}{\cancel{a^3}} \cdot \cancel{b^5}}{3 \cdot 3 \cdot 2 \cdot \cancel{a^1} \cdot \underset{b^2}{\cancel{b^7}}}$$

$$= \frac{2a^2}{3b^2}$$

EXAMPLE 6 Simplify $\dfrac{a^3b^4(y^2 + 7y + 10)}{a^6b^2(-5 - y)}$.

Write $-5 - y$ in convenient form.
$-5 - y = -y - 5$
Factor out -1.
$-y - 5 = -1(y + 5)$

$$\frac{a^3b^4(y^2 + 7y + 10)}{a^6b^2(-y - 5)} \leftarrow \text{Descending order}$$

$$\frac{a^3b^4(y^2 + 7y + 10)}{a^6b^2(-1)(y + 5)}$$

Factor $y^2 + 7y + 10$.
Divide out common factors.

$\dfrac{a}{-1(b)} = -\dfrac{a}{b}$

$$\frac{\overset{1}{\cancel{a^3}}\overset{b^2}{\cancel{b^4}}(y + 2)(\cancel{y + 5})}{\underset{a^3}{\cancel{a^6}}\cancel{b^2}(-1)(\underset{1}{\cancel{y + 5}})}$$

$$\frac{b^2(y + 2)}{-1(a^3)}, \text{ or } -\frac{b^2(y + 2)}{a^3}$$

EXAMPLE 7 Simplify $\dfrac{a^2b(3x^2 - 12x + 9)}{ab^2(6x - 18)}$.

Look for common monomial factors.
$3x^2 - 12x + 9 = 3(x^2 - 4x + 3)$
$6x - 18 = 6(x - 3)$

$$\frac{a^2b(3)(x^2 - 4x + 3)}{ab^2(6)(x - 3)}$$

Factor $x^2 - 4x + 3$.
Divide out common factors.

$$\frac{\overset{a}{\cancel{a^2}}\overset{1}{\cancel{b}}(\overset{1}{\cancel{3}})(\cancel{x - 3})(x - 1)}{\underset{1}{\cancel{a}}\underset{b}{\cancel{b^2}}(\underset{2}{\cancel{6}})(\underset{1}{\cancel{x - 3}})}$$

$$\frac{a(x - 1)}{2b}$$

ORAL EXERCISES

Simplify.

$\overset{\frac{1}{a^3}}{}$ $\quad\overset{\frac{m^6}{1}}{}$ $\quad\overset{\frac{1}{a^2}}{}$ $\quad\overset{\frac{b^1}{1}}{}$ $\quad\overset{\frac{1}{b^1}}{}$ $\quad\overset{\frac{1}{a^2 b^4}}{}$ $\quad\overset{\frac{x^2 y^1}{1}}{}$ $\quad\overset{\frac{m^2 n^3}{1}}{}$

1. $\dfrac{a^4}{a^7}$ **2.** $\dfrac{m^9}{m^3}$ **3.** $\dfrac{a^{10}}{a^{12}}$ **4.** $\dfrac{b^6}{b^5}$ **5.** $\dfrac{b^8}{b^9}$ **6.** $\dfrac{a^2 b^3}{a^4 b^7}$ **7.** $\dfrac{x^3 y^3}{xy^2}$ **8.** $\dfrac{m^4 n^6}{m^2 n^3}$

EXERCISES

PART A

Simplify.

1. $\dfrac{4m^5 n^7}{6m^2 n^9}\dfrac{2m^3}{3n^2}$

2. $\dfrac{10x^6 y^4}{15x^3 y^8}\dfrac{2x^3}{3y^4}$

3. $\dfrac{4a^9 b^5}{8a^4 b^6}\dfrac{a^5}{2b}$

4. $\dfrac{x^2 y^3 (a^2 + 7a + 10)}{xy^5(-2 - a)}$

5. $\dfrac{m^2 n^4 (n^2 - 2n + 1)}{m^7 n^2 (1 - n)}$

6. $\dfrac{3a^2 b^3 (x^2 + 6x - 16)}{9ab^5 (2 - x)}$

7. $\dfrac{a^8 b^5 (6x^2 - 30x + 36)}{a^5 b^3 (3x - 9)}$

8. $\dfrac{m^6 (4x^2 - 64)}{m^9 (2x - 8)}\dfrac{2(x + 4)}{m^3}$

9. $\dfrac{x^3 (5b^2 - 20)}{x^4 (10b + 20)}$

10. $\dfrac{y^4 (a + 1)}{y^3 (a^2 + 6a + 5)}\dfrac{y}{a + 5}$

11. $\dfrac{k^4 (a - 8)}{k^5 (a^2 - 4a - 32)}$

12. $\dfrac{m^5 (y^2 - 8y - 20)}{m^2 (y - 10)}$

13. $\dfrac{n^4 (a^2 - 4)}{n^5 (a^2 - 3a + 2)}\dfrac{a + 2}{n(a - 1)}$

14. $\dfrac{c^2 (y^2 - 7y + 12)}{c^3 (2y - 8)}$

15. $\dfrac{b^5 (x^2 - 9)}{b^2 (x^2 - 4x + 3)}$

16. $\dfrac{a^3 b^5 (c^2 - 49)}{a^4 b^7 (c - 7)}$

17. $\dfrac{a^3 b^7 (2x^2 + 9x - 5)}{a^2 b^9 (2x^2 + 7x - 15)}$ $\searrow$

$\dfrac{a(2x - 1)}{b^2 (2x - 3)}$ $\swarrow$

18. $\dfrac{a^7 (3 - x)}{a^5 (x^2 - 9)}\dfrac{-a^2}{x + 3}$

PART B

EXAMPLE Simplify $\dfrac{a^2 b - a^2}{a^5}$.

$$\dfrac{a^2 b - a^2}{a^5} = \dfrac{a^2 (b - 1)}{a^5}$$

$$= \dfrac{\overset{1}{a^2}(b - 1)}{\underset{a^3}{a^5}}$$

$$= \dfrac{b - 1}{a^3}$$

Simplify.

19. $\dfrac{x^2 y - x^2}{x^6}\dfrac{y - 1}{x^4}$

20. $\dfrac{a^4}{a^3 b - a^3}\dfrac{a}{b - 1}$

21. $\dfrac{x^7}{x^2 b + x^2 y}\dfrac{x^5}{b + y}$

22. $\dfrac{a^2 (x - 3)}{a^4 x^2 - 9a^4}\dfrac{1}{a^2 (x + 3)}$

23. $\dfrac{b^2 x^2 - b^2 x - 2b^2}{b^5 (x + 1)}\dfrac{x - 2}{b^3}$

24. $\dfrac{a^4 (5 - m)}{a^4 m^2 - 7a^4 m + 10a^4}$

Simplifying Products of Fractions

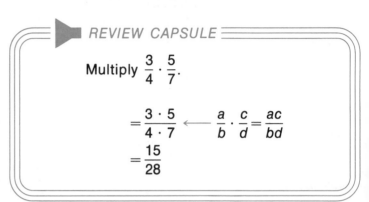

▶ REVIEW CAPSULE

Multiply $\frac{3}{4} \cdot \frac{5}{7}$.

$$= \frac{3 \cdot 5}{4 \cdot 7} \longleftarrow \frac{a}{b} \cdot \frac{c}{d} = \frac{ac}{bd}$$

$$= \frac{15}{28}$$

EXAMPLE 1 Multiply $\dfrac{x^2 - 3x + 2}{x + 5} \cdot \dfrac{2x + 10}{x - 2}$.

$\dfrac{a}{b} \cdot \dfrac{c}{d} = \dfrac{ac}{bd}$ $\longrightarrow$

Look for common monomial factors.
$2x + 10 = 2(x + 5)$

$x^2 - 3x + 2 = (x - 2)(x - 1)$ $\longrightarrow$

Divide out common factors.

Multiply remaining factors.

$2\overparen{(x - 1)} = 2x - 2$

$$\frac{(x^2 - 3x + 2)(2x + 10)}{(x + 5)(x - 2)}$$

$$\frac{(x^2 - 3x + 2)(2)(x + 5)}{(x + 5)(x - 2)}$$

$$\frac{(x - 2)(x - 1)(2)(x + 5)}{(x + 5)(x - 2)}$$

$$\frac{(\overset{1}{\cancel{x - 2}})(x - 1)(2)(\overset{1}{\cancel{x + 5}})}{(\underset{1}{\cancel{x + 5}})(\underset{1}{\cancel{x - 2}})}$$

$$\frac{2(x - 1)}{1}$$

$$\frac{2x - 2}{1}, \text{ or } 2x - 2$$

EXAMPLE 2 Multiply $(b + 5)\left(\dfrac{2b + 14}{4b^2 + 12b - 40}\right)$.

Rewrite $(b + 5)$ as $\left(\dfrac{b + 5}{1}\right)$.

$\dfrac{a}{b} \cdot \dfrac{c}{d} = \dfrac{ac}{bd}$ $\longrightarrow$

$2b + 14 = 2(b + 7)$
$4b^2 + 12b - 40 = 4(b^2 + 3b - 10)$
$4 = 2 \cdot 2$
$b^2 + 3b - 10 = (b + 5)(b - 2)$
Divide out common factors.

$$\left(\frac{b + 5}{1}\right)\left(\frac{2b + 14}{4b^2 + 12b - 40}\right)$$

$$\frac{(b + 5)(2b + 14)}{1(4b^2 + 12b - 40)}$$

$$\frac{(b + 5)(2)(b + 7)}{1(4)(b^2 + 3b - 10)}$$

$$\frac{(\overset{1}{\cancel{b + 5}})(\overset{1}{\cancel{2}})(b + 7)}{1 \cdot \underset{1}{\cancel{2}} \cdot 2(\underset{1}{\cancel{b + 5}})(b - 2)}, \text{ or } \frac{b + 7}{2(b - 2)}$$

EXAMPLE 3 Multiply $\dfrac{4x^6b^5}{5} \cdot \dfrac{15}{8x^7b^4}.$

Factor 4, 15, and 8 into primes. Then divide out common factors.

$\dfrac{x^6}{x^7} = \dfrac{1}{x^1} = \dfrac{1}{x} \Bigm| \dfrac{b^5}{b^4} = \dfrac{b^1}{1} = \dfrac{b}{1}$

$$\dfrac{4x^6b^5 \cdot 15}{5 \cdot 8x^7b^4}$$

$$\dfrac{\overset{1}{2} \cdot \overset{1}{2} \cdot \overset{1}{x^6} \cdot \overset{b^1}{b^5} \cdot 3 \cdot \overset{1}{5}}{\underset{1}{5} \cdot \underset{1}{2} \cdot \underset{1}{2} \cdot 2 \cdot \underset{x^1}{x^7} \cdot \underset{1}{b^4}}$$

$$\dfrac{3b}{2x}$$

EXAMPLE 4 Multiply $\dfrac{y^2 - 3y + 2}{3x^2y^5} \cdot \dfrac{12xy^3}{6 - 6y}.$

$\dfrac{a}{b} \cdot \dfrac{c}{d} = \dfrac{ac}{bd}$ ⟶

$$\dfrac{(y^2 - 3y + 2) \cdot 12xy^3}{3x^2y^5(6 - 6y)}$$

Write $6 - 6y$ in convenient form.
$(6 - 6y) = (-6y + 6) = -1(6y - 6)$

$$\dfrac{(y^2 - 3y + 2) \cdot 12 \cdot x \cdot y^3}{3 \cdot x^2 \cdot y^5(-1)(6y - 6)}$$

$\begin{cases} 12\,xy^3 = 12 \cdot x \cdot y^3 \\ 3x^2y^5 = 3 \cdot x^2 \cdot y^5 \end{cases}$

Factor.
$6y - 6 = 6(y - 1)$
$12 = 2 \cdot 2 \cdot 3$
$6 = 2 \cdot 3$
$y^2 - 3y + 2 = (y - 2)(y - 1).$

$$\dfrac{(y^2 - 3y + 2) \cdot 12 \cdot x \cdot y^3}{3 \cdot x^2 \cdot y^5(-1)(6)(y - 1)}$$

$$\dfrac{(y^2 - 3y + 2) \cdot 2 \cdot 2 \cdot 3 \cdot x \cdot y^3}{3 \cdot x^2 \cdot y^5(-1) \cdot 2 \cdot 3(y - 1)}$$

$$\dfrac{(y - 2)(y - 1) \cdot 2 \cdot 2 \cdot 3 \cdot x \cdot y^3}{3 \cdot x^2 \cdot y^5(-1) \cdot 2 \cdot 3(y - 1)}$$

Divide out common factors.

$\dfrac{x}{x^2} = \dfrac{x^1}{x^2} = \dfrac{1}{x}; \dfrac{y^3}{y^5} = \dfrac{1}{y^2}; \dfrac{y - 1}{y - 1} = 1$

$\dfrac{a}{-1(b)} = -\dfrac{a}{b}$

$$\dfrac{(y - 2)\,\overset{1}{(y - 1)} \cdot \overset{1}{2} \cdot 2 \cdot \overset{1}{3}\overset{1}{x}\overset{1}{y^3}}{\underset{1}{3} \cdot \underset{x^1}{x^2} \cdot \underset{y^2}{y^5}(-1) \cdot \underset{1}{2} \cdot 3\overset{1}{(y - 1)}}$$

$$\dfrac{2(y - 2)}{3 \cdot x \cdot y^2(-1)}, \text{ or } -\dfrac{2(y - 2)}{3xy^2}$$

ORAL EXERCISES

Give in simplest form.

1. $\dfrac{2x + 5}{x - 2} \cdot \dfrac{x - 2}{3x + 4}$ $\dfrac{2x + 5}{3x + 4}$

2. $\dfrac{a - 5}{2x - 3} \cdot \dfrac{2x - 3}{7}$ $\dfrac{a - 5}{7}$

3. $(b + 3)\left(\dfrac{x}{b + 3}\right)$

4. $\dfrac{a^3}{a^7} \cdot \dfrac{x - 2}{x + 5}$ $\dfrac{x - 2}{a^4(x + 5)}$

5. $\dfrac{b^3}{2x - 5} \cdot \dfrac{3x + 2}{b^7}$

6. $\dfrac{3x + 4}{m^4} \cdot \dfrac{m^6}{2x + 5}$

7. $\dfrac{-1(x - 3)}{5} \cdot \dfrac{4}{x - 3}$ $-\dfrac{4}{5}$

8. $\dfrac{c - 3}{a^3} \cdot \dfrac{a^5}{c - 3}$ a^2

9. $\dfrac{a - 5}{x^7} \cdot \dfrac{x^5}{a - 5}$ $\dfrac{1}{x^2}$

10. $\dfrac{2x - 3}{15} \cdot \dfrac{10}{3x + 2}$ $\dfrac{4x - 6}{9x + 6}$

11. $\left(\dfrac{2a - 5}{4a + 3}\right)(4a + 3)$

12. $\dfrac{x^7}{y^9} \cdot \dfrac{y^4}{x^5}$ $\dfrac{x^2}{y^5}$

EXERCISES

PART A

Multiply.

1. $\dfrac{x^2 - 7x + 10}{x + 7} \cdot \dfrac{3x + 21}{x - 5}$

2. $\dfrac{a - 10}{a - 3} \cdot \dfrac{a^2 - 8a + 15}{3a - 30}$ $\dfrac{a-5}{3}$

3. $\dfrac{3n + 18}{n^2 - 2n - 8} \cdot \dfrac{n - 4}{n + 6}$ $\dfrac{3}{n+2}$

4. $(x - 4)\left(\dfrac{3x - 3}{x^2 - 5x + 4}\right)$ 3

5. $\left(\dfrac{2\,b + 8}{4b^2 - 16b - 48}\right)(b - 6)$

6. $(m - 4)\left(\dfrac{6m + 30}{3m^2 - 48}\right)$

7. $\dfrac{3x^6 b^5}{7} \cdot \dfrac{14}{15x^7 b^3}$ $\dfrac{2b^2}{5x}$

8. $\dfrac{9}{5m^3 n^8} \cdot \dfrac{10m^5 n^4}{27}$ $\dfrac{2m^2}{3n^4}$

9. $\dfrac{5x^9 y^5}{6} \cdot \dfrac{18}{25x^7 y^6}$ $\dfrac{3x^2}{5y}$

10. $\dfrac{a^2 - 8a + 15}{7x^4 y} \cdot \dfrac{10x^2 y^4}{15 - 5a}$

11. $\dfrac{x^2 - 36}{2a^3 b^5} \cdot \dfrac{9a^4 b}{18 - 3x}$

12. $\dfrac{14 - 7x}{28x^3 y^6} \cdot \dfrac{5x^2 y^8}{x^2 - 4x + 4}$

13. $\dfrac{b^2 - 7b + 12}{b^2 - 7b + 10} \cdot \dfrac{4b - 20}{2b - 6}$

14. $\dfrac{x^2 - 2x - 15}{x - 6} \cdot \dfrac{3x - 18}{x^2 + 10x + 21}$

15. $\dfrac{b^2 - b - 20}{b^2 - 49} \cdot \dfrac{2b + 14}{2b + 8}$

16. $\dfrac{m^2 - m - 6}{m^2 + 6m + 8} \cdot \dfrac{m + 4}{3m - 9}$ $\dfrac{1}{3}$

17. $\dfrac{a - 2}{a - 5} \cdot \dfrac{a^2 - 25}{2a - 4}$ $\dfrac{a+5}{2}$

18. $\dfrac{6a - 9}{a - 1} \cdot \dfrac{a^2 - 1}{2a - 3}$

19. $\dfrac{7x^3 y^4}{2a^2 + 5a + 3} \cdot \dfrac{4a + 4}{21x^2 y^7}$

20. $\dfrac{4x^2 - 25}{x^2 + 10x + 16} \cdot \dfrac{6x + 12}{4x - 10}$

21. $\dfrac{2a^2 + 5a + 2}{a + 5} \cdot \dfrac{3a + 15}{2a^2 + 7a + 3}$

22. $\dfrac{6a^2 + 15a + 6}{6a + 30} \cdot \dfrac{6a + 30}{6a^2 + 21a + 9}$ $\dfrac{a+2}{a+3}$

23. $\dfrac{12x^2 - 75}{2x^2 + 20x + 32} \cdot \dfrac{24x + 48}{12x - 30}$

PART B

Multiply.

24. $\dfrac{5 - x}{x^2 - x - 20} \cdot \dfrac{x^2 + 8x + 16}{x^2 + 7x + 12}$

25. $\dfrac{c^2 - 5c - 6}{c^2 + 3c} \cdot \dfrac{4c + 12}{12 - 2c}$ $-\dfrac{2(c+1)}{c}$

26. $\dfrac{2n^2 - 13n - 7}{n} \cdot \dfrac{6n}{21 - 3n}$ $-2(2n+1)$

27. $\dfrac{2a^2 - 4a - 16}{a^2 - a - 12} \cdot \dfrac{a^2 + a - 6}{a^2 - 6a + 8}$ $\dfrac{2(a+2)}{a-4}$

28. $\dfrac{a^2 - 5a + 6}{a^2 - 7a + 10} \cdot \dfrac{5 + 4a - a^2}{a^2 - 2a - 3}$ -1

29. $\dfrac{c + d}{c} \cdot \dfrac{c^2}{c^2 + 2cd + d^2}$ $\dfrac{c}{c+d}$

30. $\dfrac{35 - 2x - x^2}{x^3 - 9x} \cdot \dfrac{x^2 + 3x}{x + 7}$ $-\dfrac{x-5}{x-3}$

31. $\dfrac{x^2 + 5xy + 6y^2}{a^5 b^2} \cdot \dfrac{4a^3 b}{2x + 6y}$ $\dfrac{2(x + 2y)}{a^2 b}$

32. $\dfrac{4m^2 - n^2}{2m^2 + 3m - 35} \cdot \dfrac{m + 5}{n - 2m}$ $-\dfrac{2m + n}{2m - 7}$

33. $\dfrac{a^2 - 7ab - 18b^2}{-a + 9b} \cdot \dfrac{3a + 9b}{a^2 - 4b^2}$ $-\dfrac{3(a + 3b)}{a - 2b}$

34. $\dfrac{2c^2 - 10cd + 12d^2}{3c^2 - 21cd + 30d^2} \cdot \dfrac{15c^2 + 12cd - 3d^2}{4c^2 - 8cd - 12d^2}$ $\dfrac{5c - d}{2(c - 5d)}$

PART C

Multiply.

35. $\dfrac{10 + m - 2m^2}{4m^2 - 1} \cdot \dfrac{2m^2 - 3m + 1}{2m^2 - 7m + 5}$

36. $\dfrac{10 - 16a - 8a^2}{2a^2 - 3a - 20} \cdot \dfrac{3a^2 - 12a}{12a^2 - 6a}$

37. $\dfrac{m^4 - 50m^2 + 49}{m^2 + 6m - 7} \cdot \dfrac{2}{28 - 4m}$

38. $\dfrac{x^6 - y^6}{x^6 - 3x^3 y^3 - 4y^6} \cdot \dfrac{4x^3 - 16y^3}{4x^3 - 4y^3}$

Puzzlers

PUZZLE 1.

Fill in the missing numbers for
this multiplication problem.

```
1.           *  *  3
             2  *  *
         ─────────────
          *  1  *  7
          *  *  *
       *  1  4  *
      ─────────────────
       *  *  *  *  *  *
```

PUZZLE 2.

Division puzzlers are even harder.
Fill in the numbers.

```
2.               1  *  *
         ┌──────────────
    2 1 5 │ *  *  *  *  *
           *  *  *
         ─────────
           *  *  *  *
           *  5  *  *
         ───────────
              *  4  *
              *  *  *
            ──────────
```

```
3.               *  8  *
           ┌──────────────
    2 * │ *  *  *  8  *
           *  8
         ───────
           *  *  *
           *  *  8
         ─────────
              *  *  *
              *  *  *
            ──────────
```

197

Dividing Fractions

▶ REVIEW CAPSULE

$$\frac{2}{3} \div \frac{5}{7} = \frac{2}{3} \cdot \frac{7}{5}$$

$$= \frac{2 \cdot 7}{3 \cdot 5}, \text{ or } \frac{14}{15}$$

$$\frac{a}{b} \div \frac{c}{d} = \frac{a}{b} \cdot \frac{d}{c}, \ b \neq 0, \ c \neq 0, \ d \neq 0.$$

EXAMPLE 1 Divide $\dfrac{x^2 - 7x + 12}{x^2 - 25} \div \dfrac{2x - 8}{x - 5}$.

$\dfrac{a}{b} \div \dfrac{c}{d} = \dfrac{a}{b} \cdot \dfrac{d}{c}$ ⟶

$\dfrac{a}{b} \cdot \dfrac{d}{c} = \dfrac{ad}{bc}$ ⟶

Look for common monomial factors. ⎱
$2x - 8 = 2(x - 4)$ ⎰

Factor $x^2 - 7x + 12$ and $x^2 - 25$. ⎱
Then divide out common factors. ⎰

$$\frac{x^2 - 7x + 12}{x^2 - 25} \cdot \frac{x - 5}{2x - 8}$$

$$\frac{(x^2 - 7x + 12)(x - 5)}{(x^2 - 25)(2x - 8)}$$

$$\frac{(x^2 - 7x + 12)(x - 5)}{(x^2 - 25)(2)(x - 4)}$$

$$\frac{(x - 3)(x \!\!-\!\! 4)(x \!\!-\!\! 5)}{(x \!\!-\!\! 5)(x + 5)(2)(x \!\!-\!\! 4)}$$

$$\frac{x - 3}{2(x + 5)}$$

EXAMPLE 2 Divide $\dfrac{k^2 - 7k - 18}{k^5} \div \dfrac{2k^2 - 18k}{6k^3}$.

$\dfrac{a}{b} \div \dfrac{c}{d} = \dfrac{a}{b} \cdot \dfrac{d}{c}$ ⟶

$\dfrac{a}{b} \cdot \dfrac{d}{c} = \dfrac{ad}{bc}$ ⟶

$k^2 - 7k - 18 = (k - 9)(k + 2),$ ⎱
$6 = 2 \cdot 3, \ 2k^2 - 18k = 2 \cdot k(k - 9)$ ⎰
Divide out common factors.

$$\frac{k^2 - 7k - 18}{k^5} \cdot \frac{6k^3}{2k^2 - 18k}$$

$$\frac{(k^2 - 7k - 18)(6k^3)}{k^5(2k^2 - 18k)}$$

$$\frac{(k \!\!-\!\! 9)(k + 2) \cdot 2 \cdot 3 \cdot k^3}{k^5 \cdot 2 \cdot k(k \!\!-\!\! 9)}$$

$$\frac{3(k + 2)}{k^3}$$

EXAMPLE 3 Divide $\dfrac{3a^2b^3}{6a - 2a^2} \div \dfrac{ab^4}{4a - 12}$.

$\dfrac{a}{b} \div \dfrac{c}{d} = \dfrac{a}{b} \cdot \dfrac{d}{c}$ ⟶

$\dfrac{a}{b} \cdot \dfrac{d}{c} = \dfrac{ad}{bc}$ ⟶

$6a - 2a^2 = -2a^2 + 6a = -1(2a^2 - 6a)$ ⟶

Look for common monomial factors.
$4a - 12 = 4(a - 3)$; $2a^2 - 6a = 2a(a - 3)$

Factor 4 into primes. Multiplication can
be done in any order. Divide out
common factors.

$\dfrac{a}{-1(b)} = -\dfrac{a}{b}$

$\dfrac{3a^2b^3}{6a - 2a^2} \cdot \dfrac{4a - 12}{ab^4}$

$\dfrac{3a^2b^3(4a - 12)}{(6a - 2a^2)ab^4}$

$\dfrac{3 \cdot a^2 \cdot b^3(4a - 12)}{-1(2a^2 - 6a)ab^4}$

$\dfrac{3 \cdot a^2 \cdot b^3 \cdot 4(a - 3)}{-1 \cdot 2 \cdot a(a - 3)ab^4}$

$\dfrac{3 \cdot \overset{1}{\cancel{a^2}} \cdot b^3 \cdot 2 \cdot \overset{1}{\cancel{2}}\overset{1}{\cancel{(a - 3)}}}{-1 \cdot \cancel{2} \cdot \cancel{a} \cdot \cancel{a} \cdot \underset{b}{\cancel{b^4}}\overset{1}{\cancel{(a - 3)}}}$

$\dfrac{6}{-1(b)}$, or $-\dfrac{6}{b}$

EXERCISES

PART A

Divide.

1. $\dfrac{x^2 - 6x + 8}{x^2 - 36} \div \dfrac{3x - 12}{x - 6}$

2. $\dfrac{4a - 28}{6} \div \dfrac{a^2 - 49}{3a - 21}$ $\dfrac{2(a - 7)}{a + 7}$ ↗

3. $\dfrac{a^2 - 25}{a + 1} \div \dfrac{2a + 10}{4a + 4}$ $2(a - 5)$ ↗

4. $\dfrac{k^2 - 6k - 16}{k^7} \div \dfrac{2k^2 - 16k}{8k^5}$

5. $\dfrac{5a^4}{a^2 - 5a - 14} \div \dfrac{9a^7}{3a^2 - 21a}$

6. $\dfrac{x^2 - 5x + 4}{5x^8} \div \dfrac{3x^2 - 12x}{6x^3}$

7. $\dfrac{7a^3b^5}{9a - 3a^2} \div \dfrac{a^8b}{5a - 15}$

8. $\dfrac{16 - 2x}{xy^4} \div \dfrac{x^2 - 8x}{7x^3y^2}$

9. $\dfrac{25 - m^2}{mn^5} \div \dfrac{3m^2 - 15m}{18m^3n^4}$

10. $\dfrac{m^2 - 4m + 3}{m^2 - 1} \div \dfrac{2m - 6}{m^2 + 2m + 1}$

11. $\dfrac{5b^2 - 20}{b^2 - 5b + 6} \div \dfrac{6b + 12}{3b - 6}$

12. $\dfrac{m}{m^2 + 6m + 9} \div \dfrac{1}{m + 3}$

13. $\dfrac{x^2 - 3x + 2}{x^2 - 1} \div \dfrac{2 - x}{x - 1}$ $\dfrac{x - 1}{x + 1}$

14. $\dfrac{y}{5 - y} \div \dfrac{y^3}{2y - 10}$ $\dfrac{2}{y^2}$

15. $\dfrac{3 - m}{m - 6} \div \dfrac{m^2 + 2m - 15}{m^2 - m - 30}$

16. $\dfrac{4a^3b^2}{3a^2 + 5a} \div \dfrac{6a^5b^7}{3a^2 + 17a + 20}$ $\dfrac{2(a + 4)}{3a^3b^5}$

17. $\dfrac{8x^7y^5}{5x^2 - 10x} \div \dfrac{4x^8y^4}{5x^2 + 15x - 50}$

PART B

Divide.

18. $\dfrac{4m^2 + 8m + 3}{6m^3 + 3m^2} \div \dfrac{4m^2 - 9}{2m^2 + m}$

19. $\dfrac{m^3 - m}{4m^2} \div \dfrac{2 - 2m}{m^8}$

20. $\dfrac{b^2 + 3b - 4}{b^2 + 6b + 8} \div \dfrac{b^2 + 4b + 3}{b^2 + 3b + 2}$ $\dfrac{b - 1}{b + 3}$

21. $\dfrac{a^2 + 3a - 10}{a^2 + 9a + 20} \div \dfrac{a^2 + 2a - 8}{a^2 + 7a + 12}$

Chapter Seven Review

Give the coordinate of point A. $[p.\ 175]$

1.

2.

3.

Find the missing factor. $[p.\ 175]$

4. $(7)\,(?) = \dfrac{7}{12}$

5. $(a-3)\,(?) = \dfrac{a-3}{a+7}$

6. $(?)\left(\dfrac{1}{3m+2}\right) = \dfrac{m}{3m+2}$

7. Find the reciprocal of 4, 0, -5, and $-\frac{1}{3}$.

Find the value(s) of x for which the fraction is undefined. $[p.\ 175]$

8. $\dfrac{7}{x-5}$

9. $\dfrac{3x+5}{2x-8}$

10. $\dfrac{7x-8}{x^2-10x+24}$

Multiply. $[p.\ 180]$

11. $\dfrac{4}{9}\cdot\dfrac{5}{7}$

12. $\left(\dfrac{3a^2}{5b^2}\right)\left(\dfrac{2a^3}{7b^7}\right)$

13. $(x-3)\left(\dfrac{x+5}{2x-3}\right)$

14. $\left(-\dfrac{a-2b}{a+b}\right)\left(\dfrac{a+2b}{a+3b}\right)$

Simplify. $[p.\ 184]$

15. $\dfrac{8}{20}$

16. $\dfrac{3a-15}{4a-20}$

17. $\dfrac{b^2-b}{2b-2}$

18. $\dfrac{12p^2+26p-10}{3p^2+11p-4}$

Find the quotient when the first polynomial is divided by the second. $[p.\ 184]$

19. $x^2-8x+12;\ x-6$

20. $z^2-3z-10;\ z-5$

Simplify. $[p.\ 188,\ 191]$

21. $\dfrac{3m-12}{4-m}$

22. $\dfrac{16-y^2}{y^2-8y+16}$

23. $\dfrac{10+a-3a^2}{a^2+5a-14}$

24. $\dfrac{8a^5b^9}{20a^7b^6}$

25. $\dfrac{x^3b-x^3}{x^4}$

26. $\dfrac{6x^2y^7(a^2-3a-40)}{14xy^8(16+6a-a^2)}$

Multiply or divide as indicated. $[p.\ 194,\ 198]$

27. $\dfrac{x^2-9x+14}{x+8}\cdot\dfrac{5x+40}{x-7}$

28. $(x-3)\left(\dfrac{3x+7}{x^2+3x-28}\right)$

29. $\dfrac{7x^9y^8}{5}\cdot\dfrac{15}{21x^6y^9}$

30. $\dfrac{a^2-10a+21}{x^7y^2}\cdot\dfrac{6x^3y^4}{21-3a}$

31. $\dfrac{a^2-13a+36}{a^2-49}\div\dfrac{5a-20}{a-7}$

32. $\dfrac{k^2-12k+27}{k^8}\div\dfrac{2k^2-18k}{14k^5}$

33. $\dfrac{3a^4b^6}{20a-5a^2}\div\dfrac{a^9b}{7a-28}$

34. $\dfrac{x^3-49x}{6x^3}\div\dfrac{21-3x}{12x^7}$

Chapter Seven Test

Give the coordinate of point _A_.

1.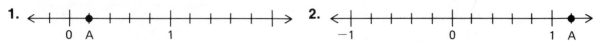

2.

Find the missing factor.

3. $(x - 2)(?) = \dfrac{x - 2}{3x + 1}$

4. $(?)\left(\dfrac{1}{5x - 1}\right) = \dfrac{2x - 9}{5x - 1}$

5. Find the reciprocal of $3, -7, 0,$ and $-\dfrac{1}{9}$.

Find the value(s) of _m_ for which the fraction is undefined.

6. $\dfrac{3}{2m - 8}$

7. $\dfrac{2m - 3}{m^2 - 7m + 12}$

Multiply.

8. $\dfrac{5}{7} \cdot \dfrac{3}{2}$

9. $\left(\dfrac{4m^3}{7b^6}\right)\left(\dfrac{3m^9}{5b^4}\right)$

10. $\left(\dfrac{m - 4}{2m - 7}\right)(m + 3)$

Simplify.

11. $\dfrac{12}{20}$

12. $\dfrac{5p - 35}{4p - 28}$

13. $\dfrac{6p^2 + 20p - 50}{3p^2 + 13p - 10}$

14. $\dfrac{9 - y^2}{y^2 - 10y + 21}$

15. $\dfrac{y^3 - y^3 a}{y^7}$

16. $\dfrac{4x^3 y^3 (t^2 - 13t + 42)}{12xy^7(28 + 3t - t^2)}$

Find the quotient when the first polynomial is divided by the second.

17. $a^2 + 7a + 10; \ a + 5$

18. $m^2 - 6m - 16; \ m - 8$

Multiply or divide as indicated.

19. $\dfrac{m^2 - 8m + 12}{m + 9} \cdot \dfrac{5m + 45}{m - 6}$

20. $(x - 8)\left(\dfrac{2x + 5}{x^2 - 2x - 48}\right)$

21. $\dfrac{a^2 - 7a - 8}{x^8 y^9} \cdot \dfrac{15x^7 y^5}{24 - 3a}$

22. $\dfrac{a^2 + 4a - 12}{4 - 2a} \div \dfrac{a^2 + 8a + 12}{2}$

23. $\dfrac{a^2 - 3ab + 2b^2}{a^2 - ab} \div \dfrac{2b - a}{a^3}$

24. $\dfrac{x^3 - 36x}{14x^4} \div \dfrac{30 - 5x}{12x^6}$

8 COMBINING FRACTIONS

Mathematics in the Trades

Several trades, such as the three pictured here, involve computing areas by first making accurate measurements.

Painters must measure walls in order to calculate the amount of paint needed to cover a room.

Tile setters must calculate the number of tiles that are needed in order to cover the floor.

Carpet layers must measure and cut precisely in order to cover the required area.

Adding Fractions: Same Denominator

REVIEW CAPSULE

$$\left. \begin{array}{c} 3\left(\dfrac{1}{7}\right) = \dfrac{3}{7} \\[2mm] 2\left(\dfrac{1}{5}\right) = \dfrac{2}{5} \end{array} \right\} \quad a\left(\dfrac{1}{b}\right) = \dfrac{a}{b}$$

EXAMPLE 1 Add $\dfrac{3}{7} + \dfrac{2}{7}$. | Add $\dfrac{4}{x} + \dfrac{5}{x}$.

$\dfrac{a}{b} = a\left(\dfrac{1}{b}\right)$ ────────────►

Use the distributive property. $\left.\begin{array}{c} \\ \\ \end{array}\right.$
$ac + bc = (a + b)c$

$$\frac{3}{7} + \frac{2}{7} = 3\left(\frac{1}{7}\right) + 2\left(\frac{1}{7}\right) \qquad \frac{4}{x} + \frac{5}{x} = 4\left(\frac{1}{x}\right) + 5\left(\frac{1}{x}\right)$$

$$= (3 + 2)\left(\frac{1}{7}\right) \qquad\qquad = (4 + 5)\left(\frac{1}{x}\right)$$

$$= 5\left(\frac{1}{7}\right) \qquad\qquad\qquad = 9\left(\frac{1}{x}\right)$$

$a\left(\dfrac{1}{b}\right) = \dfrac{a}{b}$ ────────────►

$$= \frac{5}{7} \qquad\qquad\qquad\qquad = \frac{9}{x}$$

Example 1 suggests this. ────────►

$$\frac{a}{b} + \frac{c}{b} = \frac{a + c}{b}, \; b \neq 0.$$

EXAMPLE 2 Add $\dfrac{5}{18} + \dfrac{1}{18}$. | Add $\dfrac{7}{3m} + \dfrac{2}{3m}$.

$\dfrac{a}{b} + \dfrac{c}{b} = \dfrac{a + c}{b}$ ────────────►

$$\frac{5}{18} + \frac{1}{18} = \frac{5 + 1}{18} \qquad \frac{7}{3m} + \frac{2}{3m} = \frac{7 + 2}{3m}$$

$$= \frac{6}{18} \qquad\qquad\qquad = \frac{9}{3m}$$

Factor into primes. $\left.\begin{array}{c} \\ \\ \end{array}\right.$
Divide out common factors.

$$= \frac{\overset{1}{3} \cdot \overset{1}{2}}{3 \cdot 3 \cdot 2} \qquad\qquad = \frac{\overset{1}{3} \cdot 3}{3 \cdot m}$$
$$\phantom{=\frac{}{3 \cdot 3 \cdot 2}}_{11} \qquad\qquad\phantom{=\frac{}{3 \cdot m}}_{1}$$

Simplest form ────────────►

$$= \frac{1}{3} \qquad\qquad\qquad = \frac{3}{m}$$

EXAMPLE 3   Add $\dfrac{2y}{y-4}+\dfrac{3y}{y-4}$.

$\dfrac{a}{b}+\dfrac{c}{b}=\dfrac{a+c}{b}$ ⟶

$\dfrac{2y}{y-4}+\dfrac{3y}{y-4}=\dfrac{2y+3y}{y-4}$

Combine like terms. ⟶
The result is in simplest form.

$=\dfrac{5y}{y-4}$

EXAMPLE 4   Add $\dfrac{x^2}{2x+14}+\dfrac{-49}{2x+14}$.

$\dfrac{a}{b}+\dfrac{c}{b}=\dfrac{a+c}{b}$ ⟶

$\dfrac{x^2}{2x+14}+\dfrac{-49}{2x+14}=\dfrac{x^2-49}{2x+14}$

Factor. $x^2-49=(x+7)(x-7)$ ⟶
$\qquad 2x+14=2(x+7)$ ⟶

$=\dfrac{(\overset{1}{\cancel{x+7}})(x-7)}{2(\underset{1}{\cancel{x+7}})}$

Simplest form ⟶

$=\dfrac{x-7}{2}$

EXAMPLE 5   Add $\dfrac{-3}{x^2-7x+12}+\dfrac{x}{x^2-7x+12}+\dfrac{-1}{x^2-7x+12}$.

$\dfrac{a}{b}+\dfrac{c}{b}+\dfrac{d}{b}=\dfrac{a+c+d}{b}$ ⟶

$\dfrac{-3+x-1}{x^2-7x+12}$

$\dfrac{x-4}{x^2-7x+12}$

Factor the denominator. ⎫
Divide out common factors. ⎭

$\dfrac{\overset{1}{\cancel{x-4}}}{(\underset{1}{\cancel{x-4}})(x-3)}$

Simplest form ⟶

$\dfrac{1}{x-3}$

ORAL EXERCISES

Add.

1. $\dfrac{3}{5}+\dfrac{1}{5}$ $\dfrac{4}{5}$

2. $\dfrac{5}{9}+\dfrac{3}{9}$ $\dfrac{8}{9}$

3. $\dfrac{3}{13}+\dfrac{7}{13}$ $\dfrac{10}{13}$

4. $\dfrac{5}{14}+\dfrac{4}{14}$ $\dfrac{9}{14}$

5. $\dfrac{3}{m}+\dfrac{2}{m}$ $\dfrac{5}{m}$

6. $\dfrac{3}{a}+\dfrac{-7}{a}$ $\dfrac{-4}{a}$

7. $\dfrac{x}{5}+\dfrac{3}{5}+\dfrac{2x}{5}$

8. $\dfrac{7m}{2}+\dfrac{5}{2}+\dfrac{-9m}{2}$

EXERCISES

PART A

Add.

1. $\dfrac{5}{9} + \dfrac{1}{9}$

2. $\dfrac{3}{18} + \dfrac{6}{18}$

3. $\dfrac{4}{7a} + \dfrac{3}{7a}$

4. $\dfrac{3}{10x} + \dfrac{5}{10x}$

5. $\dfrac{5y}{y-3} + \dfrac{2y}{y-3}$

6. $\dfrac{7x}{x-6} + \dfrac{6x}{x-6}$

7. $\dfrac{3m}{m+7} + \dfrac{14m}{m+7}$

8. $\dfrac{x^2}{3x-18} + \dfrac{-36}{3x-18}$

9. $\dfrac{a}{6a-18} + \dfrac{-3}{6a-18}$

10. $\dfrac{a}{7a+28} + \dfrac{4}{7a+28}$

11. $\dfrac{6}{m^2+m-30} + \dfrac{m}{m^2+m-30}$

12. $\dfrac{-15}{x^2-36} + \dfrac{x}{x^2-36} + \dfrac{9}{x^2-36}$

13. $\dfrac{-10}{a^2+7a} + \dfrac{a+17}{a^2+7a}$

14. $\dfrac{a}{a^2-a-20} + \dfrac{-5}{a^2-a-20}$ $\quad\dfrac{1}{a+4}$

15. $\dfrac{2a}{2a^2-5a-3} + \dfrac{1}{2a^2-5a-3}$ $\quad\dfrac{1}{a-3}$

16. $\dfrac{x}{x^2-5x} + \dfrac{-5}{x^2-5x}$ $\quad\dfrac{1}{x}$

PART B

Add.

17. $\dfrac{3}{26} + \dfrac{5}{26} + \dfrac{5}{26}$ $\quad\dfrac{1}{2}$

18. $\dfrac{2}{21} + \dfrac{7}{21} + \dfrac{5}{21}$ $\quad\dfrac{2}{3}$

19. $\dfrac{3a}{28} + \dfrac{5b}{28} + \dfrac{9a}{28} + \dfrac{3b}{28}$ $\quad\dfrac{3a+2b}{7}$

20. $\dfrac{5a}{32} + \dfrac{3b}{32} + \dfrac{7a}{32} + \dfrac{7b}{32}$ $\quad\dfrac{6a+5b}{16}$

21. $\dfrac{2x}{2x^2+13x+15} + \dfrac{3}{2x^2+13x+15}$

22. $\dfrac{3a}{6a^2+a-12} + \dfrac{-4}{6a^2+a-12}$ $\quad\dfrac{1}{2a+3}$

23. $\dfrac{2a^2}{6a^2-5a-25} + \dfrac{a-15}{6a^2-5a-25}$ $\quad\dfrac{a+3}{3a+5}$

24. $\dfrac{4b}{6b^2+11b-35} + \dfrac{-15}{6b^2+11b-35} + \dfrac{3b^2}{6b^2+11b-35}$ $\quad\dfrac{b+3}{2b+7}$

PART C

Add.

25. $\dfrac{a^3}{a^2+a} + \dfrac{4a^2}{a^2+a} + \dfrac{3a}{a^2+a}$

26. $\dfrac{4b^3+14b^2}{8b^2-12b} + \dfrac{-30b}{8b^2-12b}$

27. $\dfrac{8x^2-15y^2}{2x-5y} + \dfrac{-14xy}{2x-5y}$

28. $\dfrac{2x^2}{3x+6y} + \dfrac{7xy}{3x+6y} + \dfrac{6y^2}{3x+6y}$

Age Problems *(optional)*

<table>
<tr><td rowspan="2">

OBJECTIVE

■ To solve problems about ages
</td></tr>
</table>

EXAMPLE 1 Geri's age now is $x + 2$. Write algebraic expressions for Geri's age 3 years from now and 5 years ago.

Add 3 to the age now. ⟶

Subtract 5 from the age now. ⟶

Geri's age now $= x + 2$

Geri's age 3 years from now $= (x + 2) + 3$, or $x + 5$

Geri's age 5 years ago $= (x + 2) - 5$, or $x - 3$

Thus, $x + 5$ represents Geri's age 3 years from now and $x - 3$ represents Geri's age 5 years ago.

EXAMPLE 2 Amy is 4 years older than Mario. Write an algebraic expression for each of their ages 6 years from now.

Represent their ages now algebraically. ⟶

Let $x =$ Mario's age now

$x + 4 =$ Amy's age now

Make a chart. ⟶

	Now	6 Years from Now
Mario's age	x	$x + 6$
Amy's age	$x + 4$	$(x + 4) + 6$, or $x + 10$

Thus, $x + 6$ represents Mario's age 6 years from now and $x + 10$ represents Amy's age 6 years from now.

EXAMPLE 3 Dave is 5 years older than Grace. Write an algebraic expression for each of their ages 7 years ago.

Represent their ages now algebraically. ⟶

Let $x =$ Grace's age now

$x + 5 =$ Dave's age now

Make a chart. ⟶

	Now	7 Years Ago
Grace	x	$x - 7$
Dave	$x + 5$	$(x + 5) - 7$, or $x - 2$

Thus, $x - 7$ represents Grace's age 7 years ago and $x - 2$ represents Dave's age 7 years ago.

EXAMPLE 4 Fumiko is 3 years older than Omari. The sum of their ages is 25. Find their ages.

Represent the ages algebraically. ⟶ Let x = Omari's age
$x + 3$ = Fumiko's age

Write an equation. ⟶

Substitute. ⟶

Solve the equation.

Omari's age ⟶

Fumiko's age ⟶

$$\text{Sum of their ages} = 25$$
$$x + (x + 3) = 25$$
$$2x + 3 = 25$$
$$2x = 22$$
$$x = 11$$
$$x + 3 = 14$$

Thus, Omari is 11 and Fumiko is 14.

EXAMPLE 5 Ralph is 3 times as old as Peg. In 6 years Ralph will be only twice as old as Peg will be then. Find their ages now.

Represent the ages algebraically. ⟶ Let x = Peg's age now
$3x$ = Ralph's age now

Make a chart. ⟶

	Now	6 Years from Now
Peg's age	x	$x + 6$
Ralph's age	$3x$	$3x + 6$

Write an equation. ⟶

$$\left(\begin{array}{c}\text{Ralph's age}\\\text{in 6 yr}\end{array}\right) = \text{twice}\left(\begin{array}{c}\text{Peg's age}\\\text{in 6 yr}\end{array}\right)$$

Substitute. ⟶

Solve the equation.

$$3x + 6 = 2 \cdot (x + 6)$$
$$3x + 6 = 2x + 12$$
$$x = 6$$
$$3x = 3(6), \text{ or } 18$$

Check.

Ralph's age is 3 times Peg's age.

18	3(6)
	18

Ralph's age in 6 yr is twice Peg's age in 6 yr.

18 + 6	2(6 + 6)
24	2(12)
	24

Thus, Peg is 6 and Ralph is 18.

EXAMPLE 6   Mrs. Schrader is 36 and her son is 9. In how many years will Mrs. Schrader be exactly twice as old as her son?

Represent the number of years algebraically.

Let x = number of years until Mrs. Schrader is exactly twice as old as her son

Make a chart. ————————▶

	Now	x Years from Now
Mrs. Schrader's age	36	$36 + x$
Son's age	9	$9 + x$

Write an equation. ————————▶

$$\left(\begin{array}{c}\text{Mrs. Schrader's age} \\ \text{in } x \text{ yr}\end{array}\right) = \text{twice} \left(\begin{array}{c}\text{Son's age} \\ \text{in } x \text{ yr}\end{array}\right)$$

Substitute. ————————▶
Solve the equation.

$$36 + x = 2 \cdot (9 + x)$$
$$36 + x = 18 + 2x$$
$$36 = 18 + x$$
$$18 = x$$

Thus, in 18 years Mrs. Schrader will be exactly twice as old as her son.

EXAMPLE 7   Rhoda is 8 years younger than Irving. Two years ago, Irving was 3 times as old as Rhoda was then. Find their ages now.

Represent the ages algebraically. ————▶

Let x = Irving's age now
$x - 8$ = Rhoda's age now

Make a chart. ————————▶

	Now	2 Years Ago
Irving's age	x	$x - 2$
Rhoda's age	$x - 8$	$(x - 8) - 2$, or $x - 10$

Write an equation. ————————▶

$$\left(\begin{array}{c}\text{Irving's age} \\ \text{2 yr ago}\end{array}\right) = 3 \text{ times} \left(\begin{array}{c}\text{Rhoda's age} \\ \text{2 yr ago}\end{array}\right)$$

Substitute. ————————▶
Solve the equation.

$$x - 2 = 3 \cdot (x - 10)$$
$$x - 2 = 3x - 30$$
$$-2x - 2 = -30$$
$$-2x = -28$$

Irving's age ————————▶
Rhoda's age ————————▶

$$x = 14$$
$$x - 8 = 14 - 8, \text{ or } 6$$

Thus, Rhoda is 6 and Irving is 14.

EXERCISES

1. Tom is 7 years older than Joe. The sum of their ages is 37. Find their ages.

2. Beth is twice as old as Donna. The sum of their ages is 54. Find their ages.

3. Dorothy is 4 times as old as Louis. In 6 years Dorothy will be twice as old as Louis will be then. Find their ages now.

4. Steve is 16 years older than Denise. In 3 years he will be exactly 3 times as old as Denise will be then. Find their ages now.

5. Sylvia is 16 years younger than Martin. In 5 years Martin will be twice as old as Sylvia will be then. Find their ages now.

6. Andrew is 40 years younger than Sarah. In 10 years Sarah will be 3 times as old as Andrew will be then. Find their ages now.

7. Mrs. Wang is 29 and her daughter is 7. In how many years will Mrs. Wang be exactly 3 times as old as as her daughter?

8. Mr. Kickingbird is 39 and his son is 11. In how many years will Mr. Kickingbird be exactly 3 times as old as his son?

9. Debbie is 20 and Rita is 13. How many years ago was Debbie exactly twice as old as Rita?

10. John is 29 and Dianna is 18. How many years ago was John exactly twice as old as Dianna?

11. Pedro is twice as old as Mona. Four years ago, Pedro was 4 times as old as Mona was then. Find their ages now.

12. Lee is 7 years older than Phil. Eleven years ago, Lee was twice as old as Phil was then. Find their ages now.

13. Ruby is 37 and Eva is 21. How many years ago was Ruby exactly 3 times as old as Eva?

14. Ms. Ford is 75 and Ms. Garcia is 50. How many years ago was Ms. Ford exactly twice as old as Ms. Garcia?

15. Marge is 16 and her grandfather is 60. In how many years will Marge's grandfather be 3 times as old as she?

16. Sue and Jeff are twins. Their brother, Harry is 5 years older. The sum of their ages is 23. Find their ages.

Adding: Different Denominators

REVIEW CAPSULE

$$\frac{2a}{5} + \frac{7a}{5} = \frac{2a+7a}{5}$$

same denominator $= \frac{9a}{5}$

To add fractions with the same denominator, add the numerators.

EXAMPLE 1 Show that $\dfrac{2}{5} = \dfrac{2 \cdot 3}{5 \cdot 3}$.

$$
\begin{array}{c|c}
\dfrac{2}{5} & \dfrac{2 \cdot 3}{5 \cdot 3} \\[2ex]
\dfrac{2}{5} & \dfrac{2}{5} \cdot \dfrac{3}{3} \\[2ex]
\dfrac{3}{3} = 1 \qquad & \dfrac{2}{5} \cdot 1 \\[2ex]
& \dfrac{2}{5}
\end{array}
$$

Thus, $\dfrac{2}{5} = \dfrac{2 \cdot 3}{5 \cdot 3}$.

Example 1 suggests this. ⟶

$$\frac{a}{b} = \frac{a \cdot c}{b \cdot c}, \ c \neq 0.$$
Multiplying both numerator and denominator of a fraction by the same number does not change its value.

EXAMPLE 2 Add $\dfrac{5}{6} + \dfrac{1}{3}$.

Denominators are not the same. Factor 6 into primes, $6 = 2 \cdot 3$.

Multiply both numerator and denominator of $\frac{1}{3}$ by 2.

$$\frac{5}{6} + \frac{2}{6} = \frac{5+2}{6}, \text{ or } \frac{7}{6} \longrightarrow$$

$$\frac{5}{2 \cdot 3} + \frac{1}{3} \longleftarrow \left\{ \begin{array}{l} \text{This denominator needs the} \\ \text{factor 2 to be like } 2 \cdot 3. \end{array} \right.$$

$$\frac{5}{2 \cdot 3} + \frac{1 \cdot 2}{3 \cdot 2} = \frac{5}{6} + \frac{2}{6}$$

Thus, $\dfrac{5}{6} + \dfrac{1}{3} = \dfrac{7}{6}$.

In Example 2, $3 \cdot 2$ is the *least common denominator* (LCD).

EXAMPLE 3 Add $\dfrac{7}{12} + \dfrac{2}{3} + \dfrac{1}{6}$.

First find the LCD.

Factor the denominators. ──────────→ $\dfrac{7}{2 \cdot 2 \cdot 3} + \dfrac{2}{3} + \dfrac{1}{3 \cdot 2}$

The only factors present are 2 and 3. To have a common denominator, we must have exactly the same factors in each denominator.

$$\underset{\substack{\uparrow \quad \uparrow \\ \text{two 2's, one 3}}}{2 \cdot 2 \cdot 3} \qquad \underset{\substack{\uparrow \\ \text{one 3}}}{3} \qquad \underset{\substack{\nearrow \quad \nwarrow \\ \text{one 3, one 2}}}{3 \cdot 2}$$

$$\text{LCD} = \underset{\substack{\nearrow \quad \nwarrow \\ \text{two 2's, one 3}}}{2 \cdot 2 \cdot 3}$$

In each denominator, there are at most } two 2's and one 3.

$$\underset{\substack{\text{has two 2's,} \\ \text{one 3}}}{\dfrac{7}{2 \cdot 2 \cdot 3}} + \underset{\substack{\text{needs} \\ \text{two 2's}}}{\dfrac{2}{3}} + \underset{\substack{\text{needs} \\ \text{one 2}}}{\dfrac{1}{3 \cdot 2}}$$

In each fraction, multiply by the missing } factors.

$$\dfrac{7}{2 \cdot 2 \cdot 3} + \dfrac{2 \cdot 2 \cdot 2}{3 \cdot 2 \cdot 2} + \dfrac{1 \cdot 2}{3 \cdot 2 \cdot 2}$$

The denominators are the same. ──────→ $\dfrac{7}{12} + \dfrac{8}{12} + \dfrac{2}{12}$
Add the numerators. ──────────→

$$\dfrac{7 + 8 + 2}{12}$$

$$\dfrac{17}{12}$$

EXAMPLE 4 Add $\dfrac{5a}{6} + \dfrac{a}{3}$.

Denominators are not the same. Factor 6. $\dfrac{5a}{2 \cdot 3} + \dfrac{a}{3}$ ←── { This denominator needs the factor 2 to be like 6.

Rewrite each fraction with the LCD, $2 \cdot 3$. $\dfrac{5a}{2 \cdot 3} + \dfrac{a \cdot 2}{3 \cdot 2}$

The denominators are the same. Add the } numerators. $\dfrac{5a}{6} + \dfrac{2a}{6}$

$$\dfrac{7a}{6}$$

EXAMPLE 5 Add $\dfrac{7a}{18} + \dfrac{5a}{6} + \dfrac{7}{2}$.

Find the LCD.
Factor the denominators. $\Big\}$

$$\dfrac{7a}{3 \cdot 3 \cdot 2} + \dfrac{5a}{3 \cdot 2} + \dfrac{7}{2}$$

$\Big\{$ At most two 3's, one 2

$$\text{LCD} = 3 \cdot 3 \cdot 2 \longleftarrow \Big\{ \text{in any denominator}$$

In each fraction, multiply
by the missing factors. $\Big\}$

$$\dfrac{7a}{3 \cdot 3 \cdot 2} + \dfrac{5a \cdot 3}{3 \cdot 2 \cdot 3} + \dfrac{7 \cdot 3 \cdot 3}{2 \cdot 3 \cdot 3}$$

needed one 3   needed two 3's

$5a \cdot 3 = 5 \cdot 3 \cdot a$, or $15a$

$$\dfrac{7a}{18} + \dfrac{15a}{18} + \dfrac{63}{18}$$

Combine numerators. $\longrightarrow$

$$\dfrac{7a + 15a + 63}{18}$$

$7a + 15a = 22a$ $\longrightarrow$

$$\dfrac{22a + 63}{18}$$

EXAMPLE 6 Add $\dfrac{2b + 3}{8b} + \dfrac{3b + 5}{2b}$.

Find the LCD.
Factor the denominators. $\Big\}$

$$\dfrac{2b + 3}{2 \cdot 2 \cdot 2 \cdot b} + \dfrac{3b + 5}{2 \cdot b}$$

$\Big\{$ At most three 2's, one b

$$\text{LCD} = 2 \cdot 2 \cdot 2 \cdot b \longleftarrow \Big\{ \text{in any denominator}$$

In each fraction, multiply
by the missing factors. $\Big\}$

$$\dfrac{2b + 3}{2 \cdot 2 \cdot 2 \cdot b} + \dfrac{(3b + 5) \cdot 2 \cdot 2}{2 \cdot b \cdot 2 \cdot 2} \longleftarrow \text{needed two 2's}$$

$$\dfrac{2b + 3}{8b} + \dfrac{(3b + 5)4}{8b}$$

$(3b + 5)4 = 12b + 20$ $\longrightarrow$

$$\dfrac{2b + 3}{8b} + \dfrac{12b + 20}{8b}$$

Combine numerators. $\longrightarrow$

$$\dfrac{14b + 23}{8b}$$

EXAMPLE 7 Add $\dfrac{2x - 3}{6x} + \dfrac{4x - 1}{2x}$.

Rewrite each fraction with
the LCD: $2 \cdot 3 \cdot x$. $\Big\}$

$$\dfrac{2x - 3}{2 \cdot 3 \cdot x} + \dfrac{(4x - 1) \cdot 3}{2 \cdot x \cdot 3}$$

$(4x - 1) \cdot 3 = 12x - 3$ $\longrightarrow$

$$\dfrac{2x - 3}{6x} + \dfrac{12x - 3}{6x}$$

Combine numerators. $\longrightarrow$

$$\dfrac{14x - 6}{6x}$$

Factor: $14x - 6 = 2(7x - 3)$.
Then divide out common factors. $\Big\}$

$$\dfrac{\overset{1}{2}(7x - 3)}{\underset{3}{6x}} = \dfrac{7x - 3}{3x}$$

ORAL EXERCISES

Find the LCD.

1. $\dfrac{2}{3} + \dfrac{5}{3 \cdot 2}$ *3 · 2*
   2 · 2 · 7

2. $\dfrac{3}{5} + \dfrac{7}{5 \cdot 2}$ *5 · 2*
   5 · 2 · 2 · 2

3. $\dfrac{7a}{3} + \dfrac{5a}{3 \cdot 2} + \dfrac{7a}{3 \cdot 3 \cdot 2}$ *3 · 3 · 2*

4. $\dfrac{3m}{2} + \dfrac{5m}{7 \cdot 2} + \dfrac{3m}{2 \cdot 7 \cdot 2}$

5. $\dfrac{3}{5 \cdot 2 \cdot 2} + \dfrac{3a}{2 \cdot 2 \cdot 2} + \dfrac{1}{2 \cdot 5}$

6. $\dfrac{3a}{2 \cdot 5 \cdot 7} + \dfrac{2a}{5 \cdot 5} + \dfrac{11a}{7 \cdot 2}$

7. $\dfrac{3k + 1}{2 \cdot 3 \cdot 3} + \dfrac{3k - 4}{3 \cdot 3 \cdot 3} + \dfrac{2k - 6}{2 \cdot 2}$ *3 · 3 · 3 · 2 · 2*

8. $\dfrac{7b + 5}{8a} + \dfrac{3b + 2}{4a}$ *2 · 2 · 2 · a*

9. $\dfrac{2m + 1}{3m} + \dfrac{3m + 2}{27m}$ *3 · 3 · 3 · m*

2 · 5 · 5 · 7

EXERCISES

PART A

Add.

1. $\dfrac{2}{3} + \dfrac{5}{6}$ *$\frac{3}{2}$*

2. $\dfrac{1}{8} + \dfrac{3}{4}$ *$\frac{7}{8}$*

3. $\dfrac{4}{5} + \dfrac{7}{10}$ *$\frac{3}{2}$*

4. $\dfrac{2}{3} + \dfrac{1}{2} + \dfrac{5}{6}$ *2*

5. $\dfrac{2b}{7} + \dfrac{3b}{14}$ *$\frac{b}{2}$*

6. $\dfrac{7m}{9} + \dfrac{2m}{3}$ *$\frac{13m}{9}$*

7. $\dfrac{3a}{8} + \dfrac{5a}{2}$ *$\frac{23a}{8}$*

8. $\dfrac{7k}{15} + \dfrac{3k}{5}$ *$\frac{16k}{15}$*

9. $\dfrac{5a}{12} + \dfrac{3a}{2} + \dfrac{5}{6}$ *$\frac{23a + 10}{12}$*

10. $\dfrac{5m}{3} + \dfrac{3}{2} + \dfrac{5m}{18}$ *$\frac{35m + 27}{18}$*

11. $\dfrac{3m}{28} + \dfrac{5m}{7} + \dfrac{3}{4}$

12. $\dfrac{3b - 1}{6b} + \dfrac{4b + 1}{2b}$ *$\frac{15b + 2}{6b}$*

13. $\dfrac{2m - 3}{5m} + \dfrac{4m - 1}{15m}$ *$\frac{2m - 2}{3m}$*

14. $\dfrac{m - 1}{8m} + \dfrac{3m - 1}{4m}$

15. $\dfrac{7a + 5}{12a} + \dfrac{2a + 1}{3a}$ *$\frac{5a + 3}{4a}$*

16. $\dfrac{3m - 2}{10m} + \dfrac{m + 6}{5m}$ *$\frac{m + 2}{2m}$*

17. $\dfrac{2b - 3}{6b} + \dfrac{4b + 1}{2b}$

$\frac{7}{3}$

PART B

Add.

18. $\dfrac{2a - 5}{6} + \dfrac{1}{3} + \dfrac{5a + 2}{2}$ *$\frac{17a + 3}{6}$*

19. $\dfrac{4x - 1}{3} + \dfrac{2x}{15} + \dfrac{3x - 2}{5}$ *$\frac{31x - 11}{15}$*

20. $\dfrac{t + 1}{2} + \dfrac{3t - 5}{14} + \dfrac{4t - 3}{21}$ *$\frac{19t}{21}$*

21. $\dfrac{4a + 1}{3a} + \dfrac{5}{6a} + \dfrac{7a - 3}{2a}$ *$\frac{29a - 2}{6a}$*

PART C

Add.

22. $\dfrac{2m^2 - 5m + 3}{2m} + \dfrac{3m - 1}{7m} + \dfrac{m^2}{4m}$

23. $\dfrac{2a^2 - a - 3}{3a} + \dfrac{5a + 4}{5a} + \dfrac{a^2 - 9}{10a}$

Adding: Polynomial Denominators

OBJECTIVE

■ To add fractions like

$$\frac{2}{x^2 - 12x + 27} + \frac{3}{x - 3}$$

$$+ \frac{5}{x - 9}$$

▶ *REVIEW CAPSULE*

Add $\dfrac{3a + 2}{5a} + \dfrac{2}{15a}$.

$$\frac{3a + 2}{5a} + \frac{2}{5 \cdot 3 \cdot a} \quad \text{LCD} =$$

$$\frac{(3a + 2) \cdot 3}{5a \cdot 3} + \frac{2}{5 \cdot 3 \cdot a} \quad 5 \cdot 3 \cdot a$$

$$\frac{9a + 6}{15a} + \frac{2}{15a}$$

$$\frac{9a + 8}{15a}$$

EXAMPLE 1   Add $\dfrac{3}{x - 3} + \dfrac{2}{x^2 - 9} + \dfrac{5}{x + 3}$

Factor $x^2 - 9$. ⟶
$$\frac{3}{x - 3} + \frac{2}{(x + 3)(x - 3)} + \frac{5}{x + 3}$$
$$\text{LCD} = (x + 3)(x - 3)$$

$$\frac{3(x + 3)}{(x - 3)(x + 3)} + \frac{2}{(x + 3)(x - 3)} + \frac{5(x - 3)}{(x + 3)(x - 3)}$$
$$\text{needed } (x + 3) \qquad \qquad \text{needed } (x - 3)$$

$\left. \begin{array}{l} 3(x + 3) = 3x + 9 \\ 5(x - 3) = 5x - 15 \end{array} \right\}$
$$\frac{3x + 9}{(x - 3)(x + 3)} + \frac{2}{(x + 3)(x - 3)} + \frac{5x - 15}{(x + 3)(x - 3)}$$

$\dfrac{a}{b} + \dfrac{c}{b} + \dfrac{d}{b} = \dfrac{a + c + d}{b}$ ⟶
$$\frac{3x + 9 + 2 + 5x - 15}{(x + 3)(x - 3)}$$

Combine like terms. ⟶
$$\frac{8x - 4}{(x + 3)(x - 3)}$$

Factor the numerator. See if the fraction can be simplified.
$$\frac{4(2x - 1)}{(x + 3)(x - 3)}$$

There are no common factors other than 1. ⟶ **Thus,** the sum is $\dfrac{4(2x - 1)}{(x + 3)(x - 3)}$ in simplest form.

EXAMPLE 2   Add $\dfrac{8x + 15}{x^2 + 5x} + \dfrac{x}{x + 5}$.

$x^2 + 5x = x(x + 5)$ $\longrightarrow$

$LCD = x(x + 5)$

$$\frac{8x + 15}{x(x + 5)} + \frac{x}{x + 5}$$

$\nwarrow$ needs x

$$\frac{8x + 15}{x(x + 5)} + \frac{x \cdot x}{(x + 5) \cdot x}$$

$x \cdot x = x^2$ $\longrightarrow$

$$\frac{8x + 15}{x(x + 5)} + \frac{x^2}{(x + 5)x}$$

Combine numerators.

Write in descending order. $\Big\}$

$$\frac{x^2 + 8x + 15}{x(x + 5)}$$

Factor the numerator.

$x^2 + 8x + 15 = (x + 5)(x + 3)$ $\Big\}$

$$\frac{(x + 5)(x + 3)}{x(x + 5)}$$

Divide out common factors. $\longrightarrow$

$$\frac{\overset{1}{\cancel{(x + 5)}}(x + 3)}{x\underset{1}{\cancel{(x + 5)}}}$$

Thus, the sum is $\dfrac{x + 3}{x}$ in simplest form.

EXAMPLE 3   Add $\dfrac{2}{x^2 - 12x + 27} + \dfrac{3}{x - 3} + \dfrac{5}{x - 9}$.

$x^2 - 12x + 27 = (x - 9)(x - 3)$ $\longrightarrow$

$LCD = (x - 9)(x - 3)$

$$\frac{2}{(x - 9)(x - 3)} + \frac{3}{x - 3} + \frac{5}{x - 9}$$

needs $(x - 9)$ $\nearrow$ $\nwarrow$ needs $(x - 3)$

$$\frac{2}{(x - 9)(x - 3)} + \frac{3(x - 9)}{(x - 3)(x - 9)} + \frac{5(x - 3)}{(x - 9)(x - 3)}$$

$3(x - 9) = 3x - 27$ $\Big\}$

$5(x - 3) = 5x - 15$

$$\frac{2}{(x - 9)(x - 3)} + \frac{3x - 27}{(x - 3)(x - 9)} + \frac{5x - 15}{(x - 9)(x - 3)}$$

Combine numerators. $\longrightarrow$

$$\frac{2 + 3x - 27 + 5x - 15}{(x - 9)(x - 3)}$$

Combine like terms. $\longrightarrow$

$$\frac{8x - 40}{(x - 9)(x - 3)}$$

Factor. See if the fraction can be simplified.

$$\frac{8(x - 5)}{(x - 9)(x - 3)}$$

There are no common factors $\longrightarrow$

other than 1.

Thus, the sum is $\dfrac{8(x - 5)}{(x - 9)(x - 3)}$ in simplest form.

EXERCISES

PART A

Add.

1. $\dfrac{7}{a-4}+\dfrac{3}{a^2-16}+\dfrac{2}{a+4}$ $\dfrac{9a+23}{(a-4)(a+4)}$

2. $\dfrac{5}{b+5}+\dfrac{2}{b^2-25}+\dfrac{4}{b-5}$ $\dfrac{9b-3}{(b-5)(b+5)}$

3. $\dfrac{9x+14}{x^2+7x}+\dfrac{x}{x+7}$ $\dfrac{x+2}{x}$

4. $\dfrac{a}{a-5}+\dfrac{-3a-10}{a^2-5a}$ $\dfrac{a+2}{a}$

5. $\dfrac{7}{x^2+5x}+\dfrac{3}{x}$ $\dfrac{3x+22}{x(x+5)}$

6. $\dfrac{4}{m}+\dfrac{3}{m^2-4m}$ $\dfrac{4m-13}{m(m-4)}$

7. $\dfrac{2}{x-3}+\dfrac{5}{x^2-9}$ $\dfrac{2x+11}{(x-3)(x+3)}$

8. $\dfrac{7}{m-4}+\dfrac{2}{m^2-m-12}$ $\dfrac{7m+23}{(m-4)(m+3)}$

9. $\dfrac{5}{x^2-6x-16}+\dfrac{3}{x-8}$ $\dfrac{3x+11}{(x-8)(x+2)}$

10. $\dfrac{7}{m-7}+\dfrac{3}{m^2-2m-35}$

11. $\dfrac{5}{a+1}+\dfrac{2}{a^2-1}+\dfrac{4}{a-1}$

12. $\dfrac{2}{a-5}+\dfrac{3}{a^2-7a+10}+\dfrac{4}{a-2}$

13. $\dfrac{2}{a+3}+\dfrac{4}{2a^2+a-15}+\dfrac{6}{2a-5}$ ↘

14. $\dfrac{4}{k^2-k-20}+\dfrac{2}{k-5}+\dfrac{3}{k+4}$

$$\dfrac{10a+12}{(2a-5)(a+3)}$$

PART B

EXAMPLE   Add $\dfrac{x+1}{x^2-5x+6}+\dfrac{x+4}{x-3}$.

LCD $=(x-3)(x-2)$.
Second fraction needs $(x-2)$. ——————→

$$\begin{array}{c} x \quad + \quad 4 \\ x \quad - \quad 2 \\ \hline x^2+2x-8 \end{array}$$

$$\dfrac{x+1}{(x-3)\,(x-2)}+\dfrac{x+4}{x-3}$$

$$\dfrac{x+1}{(x-3)\,(x-2)}+\dfrac{(x+4)\,(x-2)}{(x-3)\,(x-2)}$$

$$\dfrac{x+1}{(x-3)\,(x-2)}+\dfrac{x^2+2x-8}{(x-3)\,(x-2)}$$

$$\dfrac{x^2+3x-7}{(x-3)\,(x-2)}$$

Add.

15. $\dfrac{4k-3}{k^2-5k+6}+\dfrac{k+1}{k-3}$

16. $\dfrac{2a+1}{a^2+3a+2}+\dfrac{a-4}{a+2}$ ↗ $\dfrac{a^2-a-3}{(a+2)(a+1)}$

17. $\dfrac{4m-1}{2m^2+5m}+\dfrac{m-2}{m}$

Operations

Binary Operations on

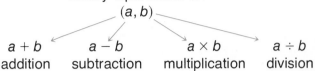

$a + b$	$a - b$	$a \times b$	$a \div b$
addition	subtraction	multiplication	division

> A *binary operation* is a rule which assigns one element to an ordered pair (a, b).

$(a, b) \longrightarrow a + b + 2$ is a binary operation.

Read: maps into.

$(2, 5) \longrightarrow 2 + 5 + 2$
$\qquad = 9$

$(3, 1) \longrightarrow 3 + 1 + 2$
$\qquad = 6$

PROBLEM

Does the operation $(a, b) \longrightarrow a + b + 2$ on $(4, 5)$ give the same number as on $(5, 4)$?

$(4, 5) \longrightarrow 4 + 5 + 2$
$\qquad = 11$

$(5, 4) \longrightarrow 5 + 4 + 2$
$\qquad = 11$

Yes

Since $a + b = b + a$ for all a and b,
the operation $(a, b) \longrightarrow a + b + 2$ is commutative.

PROJECT

Find the values of $(3, 2)$ and $(1, 4)$ for the following operations.

1. $(a, b) \longrightarrow ab + 3$
2. $(a, b) \longrightarrow 2a + 3b$
3. $(a, b) \longrightarrow (a + b)^2$
4. Do you think that $(a, b) \longrightarrow a + b + 2$ is associative?
   [Hint: Use 4, 3, 5 to check your guess.]
5. For the operations described in 1–3, which might be commutative? associative?

More on Adding Fractions

 REVIEW CAPSULE

Find the LCD.

$$\frac{5x+1}{2} + \frac{2x+1}{9} + \frac{2x+9}{8}$$

$$\frac{5x+1}{2} + \frac{2x+1}{3 \cdot 3} + \frac{2x+9}{2 \cdot 2 \cdot 2}$$

The LCD is $2 \cdot 2 \cdot 2 \cdot 3 \cdot 3$.

EXAMPLE 1   Add $4 + \dfrac{5}{3m}$.

Rewrite 4 as $\dfrac{4}{1}$. $3m$ means $3 \cdot m$. ⟶

$$\frac{4}{1} + \frac{5}{3 \cdot m}$$
$\hookleftarrow$ needs $3 \cdot m$

LCD $= 3 \cdot m$

Multiply by the needed missing factors. ⟶

$$\frac{4 \cdot 3 \cdot m}{1 \cdot 3 \cdot m} + \frac{5}{3 \cdot m}$$

$4 \cdot 3 \cdot m = 12m$ ⟶
$1 \cdot 3 \cdot m = 3m$ ⟶

$$\frac{12m}{3m} + \frac{5}{3m}$$

There are no common factors. ⟶ **Thus,** the sum is $\dfrac{12m+5}{3m}$ in simplest form.

EXAMPLE 2   Add $\dfrac{9}{y+4} + \dfrac{6}{y-4}$.

$\left.\begin{array}{l} y+4 \\ y-4 \end{array}\right\}$ cannot be factored. ⟶

$$\text{LCD} = (y+4)(y-4)$$

In each fraction, multiply by the missing factors. $\Big\}$

$$\frac{9(y-4)}{(y+4)(y-4)} + \frac{6(y+4)}{(y-4)(y+4)}$$

$\left.\begin{array}{l} 9(y-4) = 9y-36 \\ 6(y+4) = 6y+24 \end{array}\right\}$

$$\frac{9y-36}{(y+4)(y-4)} + \frac{6y+24}{(y-4)(y+4)}$$

$\dfrac{a}{b} + \dfrac{c}{b} = \dfrac{a+c}{b}$ ⟶

$$\frac{15y-12}{(y+4)(y-4)}$$

Factor $15y - 12$. See if the fraction can be simplified.

$$\frac{3(5y-4)}{(y+4)(y-4)}$$

There are no common factors, so the fraction cannot be simplified. $\Big\}$

Thus, the sum is $\dfrac{3(5y-4)}{(y+4)(y-4)}$ in simplest form.

EXAMPLE 3   Add $\dfrac{6}{5x^2} + \dfrac{-7}{3x} + \dfrac{2}{15x^3}$.

Find the LCD.
Factor the denominators.
At most one 3, one 5, three x's in
any denominator

$\dfrac{6}{5 \cdot x \cdot x} + \dfrac{-7}{3 \cdot x} + \dfrac{2}{3 \cdot 5 \cdot x \cdot x \cdot x}$
LCD $= 3 \cdot 5 \cdot x \cdot x \cdot x$, or $15x^3$

In each fraction, multiply by the
missing factors.

$\dfrac{6 \cdot 3 \cdot x}{5 \cdot x \cdot x \cdot 3 \cdot x} + \dfrac{-7 \cdot 5 \cdot x \cdot x}{3 \cdot x \cdot 5 \cdot x \cdot x} + \dfrac{2}{3 \cdot 5 \cdot x \cdot x \cdot x}$

$6 \cdot 3 \cdot x = 18x, -7 \cdot 5 \cdot x \cdot x = -35x^2 \longrightarrow$

$\dfrac{18x}{15x^3} \qquad + \qquad \dfrac{-35x^2}{15x^3} \qquad + \qquad \dfrac{2}{15x^3}$

Combine numerators.
Write in descending order.

$\dfrac{-35x^2 + 18x + 2}{15x^3}$

EXAMPLE 4   Add $\dfrac{2}{3y} + \dfrac{7 - 4y}{6y^3} + \dfrac{3 + 2y}{4y^2}$.

Find the LCD.
Factor the denominators.
At most two 2's, one 3, three y's in
any denominator.

$\dfrac{2}{3 \cdot y} + \dfrac{7 - 4y}{2 \cdot 3 \cdot y \cdot y \cdot y} + \dfrac{3 + 2y}{2 \cdot 2 \cdot y \cdot y}$
LCD $= 2 \cdot 2 \cdot 3 \cdot y \cdot y \cdot y$, or $12y^3$

In each fraction, multiply by the
missing factors.

$\dfrac{2 \cdot 2 \cdot 2 \cdot y \cdot y}{3 \cdot y \cdot 2 \cdot 2 \cdot y \cdot y} + \dfrac{(7 - 4y) \cdot 2}{2 \cdot 3 \cdot y \cdot y \cdot y \cdot 2} + \dfrac{(3 + 2y) \cdot 3 \cdot y}{2 \cdot 2 \cdot y \cdot y \cdot 3 \cdot y}$

$(7 - 4y)2 = 14 - 8y$
$(3 + 2y)3 = 9y + 6y^2$

$\dfrac{8y^2}{12y^3} \qquad + \qquad \dfrac{14 - 8y}{12y^3} \qquad + \qquad \dfrac{9y + 6y^2}{12y^3}$

$\dfrac{a}{b} + \dfrac{c}{b} + \dfrac{d}{b} = \dfrac{a + c + d}{b}$

$\dfrac{8y^2 + 14 - 8y + 9y + 6y^2}{12y^3}$

Combine like terms. $\longrightarrow$

$\dfrac{14y^2 + y + 14}{12y^3}$

ORAL EXERCISES

Find the LCD.

1. $\dfrac{3}{y^2} + \dfrac{7}{y} + \dfrac{8}{y^3}$ $y \cdot y \cdot y, \ or \ y^3$ **2.** $\dfrac{7}{a^2} + \dfrac{2}{a^3} + \dfrac{4}{a}$ $a \cdot a \cdot a, \ or \ a^3$ **3.** $\dfrac{3}{p^2} + \dfrac{4}{p} + \dfrac{2}{p^5}$ ↘

$p \cdot p \cdot p \cdot p \cdot p, \ or \ p^5$

EXERCISES

PART A

Add.

1. $\dfrac{3}{m} + 2$ $\dfrac{2m + 3}{m}$ **2.** $8 + \dfrac{3}{7b}$ $\dfrac{56b + 3}{7b}$ **3.** $3 + \dfrac{2}{m}$ $\dfrac{3m + 2}{m}$

4. $\dfrac{7}{a-1} + \dfrac{4}{a+2}$ $\quad \dfrac{11a+10}{(a-1)(a+2)}$

5. $\dfrac{4}{x+2} + \dfrac{3}{x-4}$ $\quad \dfrac{7x-10}{(x+2)(x-4)}$

6. $\dfrac{2}{3a-1} + \dfrac{4}{2a+5}$

7. $\dfrac{5}{a-3} + \dfrac{7}{2a+5}$

8. $\dfrac{3}{b-7} + \dfrac{-2}{2b+3}$

9. $\dfrac{8}{x^2} + \dfrac{7}{x} + \dfrac{3}{x^3}$

10. $\dfrac{7}{15y} + \dfrac{-3}{5y^3} + \dfrac{2}{3y^2}$

11. $\dfrac{3}{2a^2} + \dfrac{5}{3a^3} + \dfrac{7}{6a}$

12. $\dfrac{5}{x} + \dfrac{3}{x^2} + \dfrac{2}{x^3}$

13. $\dfrac{3}{m} + \dfrac{2}{m^2} + 5$

14. $6k + \dfrac{5}{3k}$ $\quad \dfrac{18k^2+5}{3k}$

15. $\dfrac{3}{a^2} + \dfrac{2}{a} + 1$

16. $\dfrac{7}{2a} + \dfrac{2-a}{3a^2} + \dfrac{3+5a}{6a^3}$ $\quad \dfrac{19a^2+9a+3}{6a^3}$

17. $\dfrac{2}{5b} + \dfrac{4-3b}{3b^2} + \dfrac{2b-3}{b^3}$ $\quad \dfrac{-9b^2+50b-45}{15b^3}$

18. $\dfrac{7-x}{2x^2} + \dfrac{3+2x}{10x^3} + \dfrac{2-5x}{5x}$ $\quad \dfrac{-10x^3-x^2+37x+3}{10x^3}$

19. $\dfrac{2a+5}{4a} + \dfrac{a-1}{6a^3} + \dfrac{3-a}{3a^2}$ $\quad \dfrac{6a^3+11a^2+14a-2}{12a^3}$

PART B

EXAMPLE   Add $x + 3 + \dfrac{7}{x-2}$.

$$\dfrac{x+3}{1} + \dfrac{7}{x-2}$$

$$\dfrac{(x+3)(x-2)}{1 \cdot (x-2)} + \dfrac{7}{x-2}$$

LCD $= 1 \cdot (x-2)$, or $x-2$.

$(x+3)(x-2) = x^2 + x - 6$ $\longrightarrow$

$$\dfrac{x^2+x-6}{x-2} + \dfrac{7}{x-2}$$

Combine numerators.

$$\dfrac{x^2+x+1}{x-2}$$

Add.

20. $a - 2 + \dfrac{4}{a+5}$

21. $2m - 1 + \dfrac{3}{m+5}$ $\quad \dfrac{2m^2+9m-2}{m+5}$

22. $\dfrac{5}{3a+1} + a - 4$ $\quad \dfrac{3a^2-11a+1}{3a+1}$

23. $2x - 1 + \dfrac{x-7}{2x-1}$

24. $\dfrac{a-5}{2a+3} + a - 2$ $\quad \dfrac{2a^2-11}{2a+3}$

25. $x - 5 + \dfrac{7}{3x+2}$ $\quad \dfrac{3x^2-13x-3}{3x+2}$

PART C

Add.

26. $\dfrac{7}{x-3} + \dfrac{x+4}{x-5} + \dfrac{x}{x+2}$

27. $x^2 + 3x + 1 + \dfrac{4}{x-5}$

Subtracting Fractions

OBJECTIVES
- To rewrite fractions like
$$-\frac{2x + 1}{x - 3}$$
- To simplify expressions like
$$\frac{2x - 3}{x^2 - 7x + 12} - \frac{x - 1}{x - 4}$$

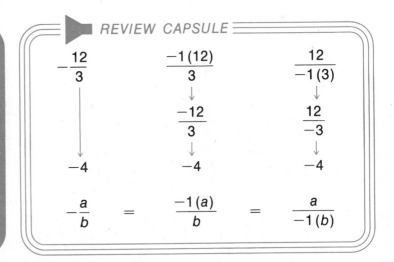

▶ REVIEW CAPSULE

$$-\frac{12}{3} \qquad \frac{-1(12)}{3} \qquad \frac{12}{-1(3)}$$

$$\downarrow \qquad\qquad \downarrow \qquad\qquad \downarrow$$

$$\qquad\qquad \frac{-12}{3} \qquad \frac{12}{-3}$$

$$\downarrow \qquad\qquad \downarrow \qquad\qquad \downarrow$$

$$-4 \qquad\qquad -4 \qquad\qquad -4$$

$$-\frac{a}{b} = \frac{-1(a)}{b} = \frac{a}{-1(b)}$$

EXAMPLE 1 Rewrite $-\dfrac{2x - 3}{x + 5}$.

$$-\frac{a}{b} = \frac{-1(a)}{b} \longrightarrow \qquad -\frac{2x - 3}{x + 5} = \frac{-1(2x - 3)}{x + 5}$$

$$-1(2x - 3) = -1(2x) + (-1)(-3) \qquad\qquad = \frac{-2x + 3}{x + 5}$$

EXAMPLE 2 Simplify $\dfrac{x}{x^2 - 4x + 3} - \dfrac{2}{x - 3}$.

Rewrite as addition.
$$-\frac{2}{x - 3} = \frac{-1(2)}{x - 3} \longrightarrow \qquad \frac{x}{x^2 - 4x + 3} + \frac{-1(2)}{x - 3}$$

Factor: $x^2 - 4x + 3 = (x - 3)(x - 1)$.
LCD $= (x - 3)(x - 1)$
$$\frac{x}{(x - 3)(x - 1)} + \frac{-2}{x - 3}$$

needs $(x - 1)$

$$\frac{x}{(x - 3)(x - 1)} + \frac{-2(x - 1)}{(x - 3)(x - 1)}$$

$$-2(x - 1) = -2x + 2 \longrightarrow \qquad \frac{x}{(x - 3)(x - 1)} + \frac{-2x + 2}{(x - 3)(x - 1)}$$

$$\frac{a}{b} + \frac{c}{b} = \frac{a + c}{b} \longrightarrow \qquad \frac{x - 2x + 2}{(x - 3)(x - 1)}$$

$$x - 2x = 1x - 2x = -1x, \text{ or } -x \qquad \frac{-x + 2}{(x - 3)(x - 1)}$$

EXAMPLE 3 Simplify $3 - \dfrac{3x - 1}{2x}$.

Rewrite as addition.

$-\dfrac{3x - 1}{2x} = \dfrac{-1(3x - 1)}{2x}$ ⟶ $\dfrac{3}{1} + \dfrac{-1(3x - 1)}{2x}$

$-1(3x - 1) = -3x + 1$ ⟶ $\dfrac{3}{1} + \dfrac{-3x + 1}{2x}$

$\qquad\qquad\qquad\qquad\qquad$ ↖ needs $2 \cdot x$

LCD $= 2 \cdot x$, or $2x$

$\qquad\qquad\qquad\qquad \dfrac{3 \cdot 2 \cdot x}{1 \cdot 2 \cdot x} + \dfrac{-3x + 1}{2 \cdot x}$

$3 \cdot 2 \cdot x = 6x$ ⟶ $\dfrac{6x}{2x} + \dfrac{-3x + 1}{2x}$

$1 \cdot 2 \cdot x = 2x$ ⟶

$\dfrac{a}{b} + \dfrac{c}{b} = \dfrac{a + c}{b}$ ⟶ $\dfrac{6x - 3x + 1}{2x}$

Thus, the result is $\dfrac{3x + 1}{2x}$.

EXAMPLE 4 Simplify $\dfrac{x^2 + 2}{x^2 - 5x + 4} - \dfrac{x - 2}{x - 1}$.

Rewrite as addition.

$\qquad\qquad\qquad\qquad \dfrac{x^2 + 2}{x^2 - 5x + 4} + \dfrac{-1(x - 2)}{x - 1}$

$-1(x - 2) = -1x + 2$ ⟶ $\dfrac{x^2 + 2}{x^2 - 5x + 4} + \dfrac{-1x + 2}{x - 1}$

Find the LCD.
$x^2 - 5x + 4 = (x - 4)(x - 1)$
LCD $= (x - 4)(x - 1)$

$\qquad\qquad\qquad\qquad \dfrac{x^2 + 2}{(x - 4)(x - 1)} + \dfrac{-1x + 2}{x - 1}$

$\qquad\qquad\qquad\qquad\qquad\qquad$ ↖ needs $x - 4$

$\dfrac{-1x \ + \ 2}{1x \ - \ 4}$

$-1x^2 + 6x - 8$ ⟶ $\dfrac{x^2 + 2}{(x - 4)(x - 1)} + \dfrac{(-1x + 2)(x - 4)}{(x - 1)(x - 4)}$

$\qquad\qquad\qquad\qquad \dfrac{x^2 + 2}{(x - 4)(x - 1)} + \dfrac{-1x^2 + 6x - 8}{(x - 1)(x - 4)}$

$\dfrac{a}{b} + \dfrac{c}{b} = \dfrac{a + c}{b}$ ⟶ $\dfrac{x^2 + 2 - 1x^2 + 6x - 8}{(x - 4)(x - 1)}$

Combine like terms. ⟶ $\dfrac{6x - 6}{(x - 4)(x - 1)}$

Factor the numerator:
$6x - 6 = 6(x - 1)$.
Divide out common factors.

$\dfrac{6(x - 1)^1}{(x - 4)(x - 1)_1}$

$\dfrac{6}{x - 4}$

Thus, the result is $\dfrac{6}{x - 4}$.

EXERCISES

Rewrite.

1. $-\dfrac{2}{a+5}$ $\dfrac{-2}{a+5}$

2. $-\dfrac{2a+5}{a^2-9}$ $\dfrac{-2a-5}{a^2-9}$

3. $-\dfrac{x^2-3x}{x^2+5x+1}$

Simplify. $\dfrac{-2x+1}{(x-2)(x+2)}$

4. $\dfrac{5}{x^2-4}-\dfrac{2}{x-2}$

5. $\dfrac{7}{a^2-7a+10}-\dfrac{3}{a-5}$ $\dfrac{-3a+13}{(a-5)(a-2)}$

6. $\dfrac{4}{b^2+4b+3}-\dfrac{3}{b+3}$

7. $5-\dfrac{3}{2x}$ $\dfrac{10x-3}{2x}$

8. $8-\dfrac{7}{5x}$ $\dfrac{40x-7}{5x}$

9. $4-\dfrac{2a+3}{a-2}$ $\dfrac{2a-11}{a-2}$

10. $\dfrac{5}{x-7}-\dfrac{x+3}{x^2-49}$

11. $\dfrac{3}{x-2}-\dfrac{2x-3}{x^2-6x+8}$

12. $\dfrac{2}{b-4}-\dfrac{b+5}{b^2-3b-4}$

13. $\dfrac{5}{3b-1}-\dfrac{4}{2b+7}$

14. $\dfrac{3}{5x-2}-\dfrac{2}{3x+4}$ $\dfrac{-x+16}{(5x-2)(3x+4)}$

15. $\dfrac{3}{8y^2}-\dfrac{5}{12y^3}$ $\dfrac{9y-10}{24y^3}$

Simplify.

16. $\dfrac{m^2-8}{m^2-8m+12}-\dfrac{m+1}{m-6}$

17. $\dfrac{a^2-22}{a^2-9a+20}-\dfrac{a-2}{a-5}$ $\dfrac{6}{a-4}$

18. $\dfrac{m^2-5}{m^2-5m}-\dfrac{m+3}{m}$

19. $\dfrac{5}{a+3}-\dfrac{2a+1}{a+2}$

20. $\dfrac{2a-3}{a^2-4}-\dfrac{a+1}{a-2}$

21. $\dfrac{3a^2}{2a^2-7a-15}-\dfrac{2a-5}{2a+3}$

22. $\dfrac{y+3}{y-6}-\dfrac{y+1}{y^2-4y-12}$ $\dfrac{y^2+4y+5}{(y-6)(y+2)}$

23. $\dfrac{2a+1}{a}-\dfrac{3a+1}{a^2-5a}$ $\dfrac{2a^2-12a-6}{a(a-5)}$

24. $\dfrac{4}{y-4}-\dfrac{2y-1}{y-2}$

Simplify.

25. $\dfrac{a-2}{a+4}-\dfrac{a-3}{2a-5}$

26. $\dfrac{x-5}{2x-5}-\dfrac{2x+1}{x-7}$

27. $\dfrac{3}{2y^2-5y-12}-\dfrac{y+1}{2y+3}+\dfrac{y-5}{y-4}$

28. $\dfrac{2m^2-5}{4m^3-9m}-\dfrac{3}{2m-3}+\dfrac{2m-1}{2m^2+3m}$

Simplifying Fractions: -1 Technique

OBJECTIVE

■ To simplify fractions like
$$\frac{7}{x^2 - 4x + 4} - \frac{2}{2 - x}$$

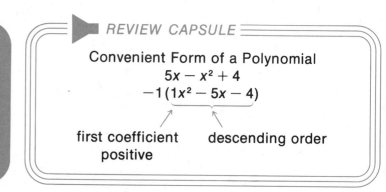

▶ *REVIEW CAPSULE*

Convenient Form of a Polynomial
$$5x - x^2 + 4$$
$$-1(1x^2 - 5x - 4)$$

first coefficient positive   descending order

EXAMPLE 1   Simplify $\dfrac{4x}{x^2 - 4} + \dfrac{2}{2 - x}$.

Get $2 - x$ in convenient form.
Arrange in descending order.
$$\frac{4x}{x^2 - 4} + \frac{2}{-x + 2}$$

Factor out -1: $-x + 2 = -1(x - 2)$.
$2 - x$ is now in convenient form.
$$\frac{4x}{x^2 - 4} + \frac{2}{-1(x - 2)}$$

$\dfrac{a}{-1(b)} = \dfrac{-1(a)}{b}$ ⟶
$$\frac{4x}{x^2 - 4} + \frac{-1(2)}{x - 2}$$
$$\frac{4x}{x^2 - 4} + \frac{-2}{x - 2}$$

Find the LCD.
Factor: $x^2 - 4 = (x - 2)(x + 2)$.
LCD $= (x - 2)(x + 2)$
$$\frac{4x}{(x - 2)(x + 2)} + \frac{-2}{x - 2}$$
$$\text{needs } x + 2$$

$$\frac{4x}{(x - 2)(x + 2)} + \frac{-2(x + 2)}{(x - 2)(x + 2)}$$

Use the distributive property. ⟶
$-2(x + 2) = -2x - 4$
$$\frac{4x}{(x - 2)(x + 2)} + \frac{-2x - 4}{(x - 2)(x + 2)}$$

$\dfrac{a}{b} + \dfrac{c}{b} = \dfrac{a + c}{b}$ ⟶
$$\frac{4x - 2x - 4}{(x - 2)(x + 2)}$$

Combine like terms. ⟶
$$\frac{2x - 4}{(x - 2)(x + 2)}$$

Factor: $2x - 4 = 2(x - 2)$.
Divide out common factors.
$$\frac{2(\overset{1}{\cancel{x - 2}})}{\underset{1}{\cancel{(x - 2)}}(x + 2)}$$

The result is in simplest form. ⟶
$$\frac{2}{x + 2}$$

EXAMPLE 2   Simplify $\dfrac{3}{m-1}+\dfrac{3m+2}{m-m^2}+\dfrac{3}{m}$.

Get $m-m^2$ in convenient form.
$m-m^2=-m^2+m=-1(m^2-m)$ }

$\dfrac{3m+2}{-1(m^2-m)}=\dfrac{-1(3m+2)}{m^2-m}=\dfrac{-3m-2}{m^2-m}\longrightarrow$

Factor: $m^2-m=m(m-1)$ —————→

LCD $=m(m-1)$ —————————→
$3(m-1)=3m-3$ —————————→

$\dfrac{a}{b}+\dfrac{c}{b}=\dfrac{a+c}{b}$ ——————————

The result is in simplest form. ————→

$$\dfrac{3}{m-1}+\dfrac{3m+2}{-1(m^2-m)}+\dfrac{3}{m}$$

$$\dfrac{3}{m-1}+\dfrac{-3m-2}{m^2-m}+\dfrac{3}{m}$$

$$\dfrac{3}{m-1}+\dfrac{-3m-2}{m(m-1)}+\dfrac{3}{m}$$

$$\dfrac{3\cdot m}{(m-1)\cdot m}+\dfrac{-3m-2}{m(m-1)}+\dfrac{3(m-1)}{m(m-1)}$$

$$\dfrac{3m}{(m-1)m}+\dfrac{-3m-2}{m(m-1)}+\dfrac{3m-3}{m(m-1)}$$

$$\dfrac{3m-3m-2+3m-3}{m(m-1)}$$

$$\dfrac{3m-5}{m(m-1)}$$

EXAMPLE 3   Simplify $\dfrac{-6}{x^2-7x+12}-\dfrac{x+2}{4-x}$.

Rewrite as addition:
$-\dfrac{x+2}{4-x}=\dfrac{-1(x+2)}{4-x}$

$4-x=-x+4=-1(x-4)$ ————→

$\dfrac{\overset{1}{\cancel{-1}}(x+2)}{\underset{1}{\cancel{-1}}(x-4)}=\dfrac{x+2}{x-4}$ ——————

LCD $=(x-3)(x-4)$

$\overset{\curvearrowright}{x}\overset{+}{\underset{}{\times}}\overset{2}{\underset{\curvearrowleft}{}}$
$\underset{x}{}\quad -\quad 3$
——————
x^2-x-6 ———————————→

Combine numerators.
Write in descending order. }

Factor: $x^2-x-12=(x-4)(x+3)$
Divide out common factors.

$$\dfrac{-6}{x^2-7x+12}+\dfrac{-1(x+2)}{4-x}$$

$$\dfrac{-6}{x^2-7x+12}+\dfrac{-1(x+2)}{-1(x-4)}$$

$$\dfrac{-6}{x^2-7x+12}+\dfrac{x+2}{x-4}$$

$$\dfrac{-6}{(x-3)(x-4)}+\dfrac{x+2}{x-4}$$
$\text{needs } (x-3)$

$$\dfrac{-6}{(x-3)(x-4)}+\dfrac{(x+2)(x-3)}{(x-4)(x-3)}$$

$$\dfrac{-6}{(x-3)(x-4)}+\dfrac{x^2-x-6}{(x-4)(x-3)}$$

$$\dfrac{x^2-x-12}{(x-3)(x-4)}$$

$$\dfrac{(\overset{1}{\cancel{x-4}})(x+3)}{(x-3)(\underset{1}{\cancel{x-4}})}$$

$$\dfrac{x+3}{x-3}$$

EXERCISES

Simplify.

1. $\dfrac{6x}{x^2 - 49} + \dfrac{3}{7 - x}$ $\dfrac{3}{x + 7}$

2. $\dfrac{8x}{x^2 - 25} + \dfrac{4}{5 - x}$ $\dfrac{4}{x + 5}$

3. $\dfrac{7b - 9}{b^2 - 3b + 2} + \dfrac{5}{2 - b}$ $\dfrac{2}{b - 1}$

4. $\dfrac{3a + 6}{4a - 8} + \dfrac{3}{2 - a}$ $\dfrac{3}{4}$

5. $\dfrac{3b - 1}{b^2 - b - 2} + \dfrac{4}{2 - b}$ $\dfrac{-b - 5}{(b - 2)(b + 1)}$

6. $\dfrac{3a - 5}{7a - 21} + \dfrac{2a - 5}{3 - a}$ $\dfrac{-11a + 30}{7(a - 3)}$

7. $\dfrac{2a}{a^2 - 6a + 8} - \dfrac{a}{2 - a}$ $\dfrac{a}{a - 4}$

8. $\dfrac{-5x}{x^2 - 9x + 14} - \dfrac{x}{7 - x}$ $\dfrac{x}{x - 2}$

9. $\dfrac{-7a}{a^2 - 3a - 10} - \dfrac{a}{5 - a}$ $\dfrac{a}{a + 2}$

10. $\dfrac{-2a}{a^2 - 12a + 35} - \dfrac{a}{7 - a}$ $\dfrac{a}{a - 5}$

11. $\dfrac{7}{m - 1} + \dfrac{4m - 6}{m - m^2} + \dfrac{5}{m}$ $\dfrac{8m + 1}{m(m - 1)}$

12. $\dfrac{5}{a - 4} + \dfrac{2a - 1}{4a - a^2} + \dfrac{7}{a}$ $\dfrac{10a - 27}{a(a - 4)}$

13. $\dfrac{k + 2}{k^2 - 8k + 12} + \dfrac{k}{6 - k}$ $\dfrac{-k^2 + 3k + 2}{(k - 6)(k - 2)}$

14. $\dfrac{2}{a + 2} - \dfrac{3}{8 - a} + \dfrac{2a}{a^2 - 6a - 16}$

15. $\dfrac{-2m}{m^2 - 12m + 35} - \dfrac{m}{7 - m}$ $\dfrac{m}{m - 5}$

16. $\dfrac{x^2 + 3x + 15}{x^2 + 5x - 24} + \dfrac{-2}{3 - x} + \dfrac{5}{x + 8}$ $\dfrac{x + 2}{x - 3}$

PART B

Simplify.

17. $\dfrac{2m}{m^2 - 7m + 10} + \dfrac{2m - 1}{5 - m}$ $\dfrac{-2m^2 + 7m - 2}{(m - 5)(m - 2)}$

18. $\dfrac{3a + 1}{a^2 - 25} - \dfrac{2a + 1}{5 - a}$ $\dfrac{2a^2 + 14a + 6}{(a - 5)(a + 5)}$

19. $\dfrac{2n - 1}{n + 3} - \dfrac{4n^2}{9 - n^2} + \dfrac{2}{n - 3}$ $\dfrac{6n^2 - 5n + 9}{(n - 3)(n + 3)}$

20. $\dfrac{2m + 1}{4 - m} - \dfrac{3m^2}{m^2 - 16} + \dfrac{7}{m + 4}$

       $\dfrac{-5m^2 - 2m - 32}{(m + 4)(m - 4)}$

PART C

Simplify.

21. $\dfrac{7}{a^2 - b^2} - \dfrac{2}{b - a} + \dfrac{a + 3b}{a + b}$

22. $\dfrac{7}{a^2 - 2ab} - \dfrac{3a - 2b}{4b^2 - a^2}$

23. $\dfrac{b - c}{b + c} - \dfrac{3bc}{c^2 - b^2}$

24. $\dfrac{4b}{b + 1} - \dfrac{2 + b}{1 - b} - \dfrac{4}{1 - b^2}$

Groups

An operation on a set forms a group if
- the set is closed under the operation
- the operation is associative
- there is an identity element
- every element has an inverse

TEST CASE

Let the integers be the set and addition the operation.

Closure

$a + b = c$

$2 + -3 = -1$

All elements are in the set.

$4 + (-1 + 5) = (4 + -1) + 5$

Associative

$a + (b + c) = (a + b) + c$

Identity

$a + 0 = a$

$-7 + 0 = -7$

identity element

$36 + (-36) = 0$

Inverse

$a + (-a) = 0$

element   inverse   identity

We have not proved that the integers form a group under addition, but we can think of no case where the four conditions do not hold.

Note: For multiplication, the zero element does not have to have an inverse to form a group.

A group is a *commutative group* if the operation is commutative.

Which do you think form groups? commutative groups?

PROJECT

1. The odd numbers under addition
2. The even numbers under addition
3. The odd numbers under multiplication
4. The even numbers under multiplication

Chapter Eight Review

Add. $[p.\,203, 210, 214]$

1. $\dfrac{2}{15} + \dfrac{1}{15} + \dfrac{7}{15}$

2. $\dfrac{3a}{6a^2 - a - 15} + \dfrac{-5}{6a^2 - a - 15}$

3. $\dfrac{3}{8} + \dfrac{1}{4}$

4. $\dfrac{1}{3} + \dfrac{1}{2} + \dfrac{5}{6}$

5. $\dfrac{5m}{6} + \dfrac{3m}{2}$

6. $\dfrac{3m}{7} + \dfrac{1}{2} + \dfrac{3m}{14}$

7. $\dfrac{2b + 3}{3b} + \dfrac{2b + 9}{6b}$

8. $\dfrac{3x - 1}{2} + \dfrac{3x}{14} + \dfrac{2x - 5}{7}$

9. $\dfrac{8x + 12}{x^2 + 2x} + \dfrac{x}{x + 2}$

10. $\dfrac{5}{a - 3} + \dfrac{4}{a^2 - 9}$

11. $\dfrac{3}{a - 6} + \dfrac{4}{a^2 - 2a - 24} + \dfrac{2}{a + 4}$

12. $\dfrac{-3x + 6}{x^2 - 7x + 10} + \dfrac{x + 3}{x - 5}$

Simplify. $[p.\,218, 221, 224]$

13. $7 + \dfrac{4}{5m}$

14. $\dfrac{7}{y + 3} + \dfrac{4}{y - 3}$

15. $\dfrac{5}{2x^2} + \dfrac{-3}{7x} + \dfrac{3}{14x^3}$

16. $\dfrac{4}{3y} + \dfrac{6 - 3y}{2y^3} + \dfrac{5 + 2y}{9y^2}$

17. $x + 5 + \dfrac{4}{x - 3}$

18. $x + \dfrac{2}{x - 5}$

19. $\dfrac{x}{x^2 - 7x + 12} - \dfrac{5}{x - 4}$

20. $5 - \dfrac{2x - 7}{3x}$

21. $\dfrac{x^2 - 1}{x^2 - 7x + 10} - \dfrac{x - 3}{x - 2}$

22. $\dfrac{7}{x - 2} - \dfrac{x + 3}{x^2 - 4}$

23. $\dfrac{10x}{x^2 - 9} + \dfrac{5}{3 - x}$

24. $\dfrac{7}{x - 1} + \dfrac{5x + 3}{x - x^2} + \dfrac{4}{x}$

25. $\dfrac{6m}{m^2 - 12m + 27} - \dfrac{m}{3 - m}$

26. $\dfrac{3m}{m^2 - 8m + 12} + \dfrac{2m - 1}{6 - m}$

Chapter Eight Test

Add.

1. $\dfrac{1}{18} + \dfrac{7}{18} + \dfrac{5}{18}$

2. $\dfrac{3m}{5} + \dfrac{1}{3} + \dfrac{2m}{15}$

3. $\dfrac{4a + 2}{5a} + \dfrac{7a + 11}{10a}$

4. $\dfrac{2x - 1}{3} + \dfrac{5x}{21} + \dfrac{2x + 5}{7}$

5. $\dfrac{10x + 21}{x^2 + 3x} + \dfrac{x}{x + 3}$

6. $\dfrac{7}{a - 6} + \dfrac{4}{a^2 - 36}$

7. $\dfrac{4}{a - 5} + \dfrac{2}{a^2 - 3a - 10} + \dfrac{3}{a + 2}$

8. $\dfrac{-14m - 6}{m^2 - 7m - 18} + \dfrac{m + 3}{m - 9}$

Simplify.

9. $6 + \dfrac{7}{3m}$

10. $\dfrac{4}{y + 2} + \dfrac{3}{y - 6}$

11. $\dfrac{5}{3x^2} + \dfrac{-4}{7x} + \dfrac{2}{21x^3}$

12. $\dfrac{7}{5a} + \dfrac{3 - 2a}{2a^3} + \dfrac{4 + 3a}{20a^2}$

13. $x - 4 + \dfrac{2}{x + 3}$

14. $\dfrac{x}{x^2 - 11x + 28} - \dfrac{6}{x - 7}$

15. $7 - \dfrac{3x - 2}{2x}$

16. $\dfrac{y^2 - 22}{y^2 - 9y + 20} - \dfrac{y - 2}{y - 5}$

17. $\dfrac{8x}{x^2 - 64} + \dfrac{4}{8 - x}$

18. $\dfrac{5}{m - 1} + \dfrac{4m + 2}{m - m^2} + \dfrac{6}{m}$

19. $\dfrac{4a}{a^2 - 12a + 32} - \dfrac{a}{4 - a}$

20. $\dfrac{8x}{x^2 - 10x + 9} + \dfrac{3x - 2}{9 - x}$

ALGEBRA IN A PLANE

The Great Swami

A	B	C	D	E	F
1	2	3	6	9	18
4	5	4	7	10	19
7	8	5	8	11	20
10	11	12	15	12	21
13	14	13	16	13	22
16	17	14	17	14	23
19	20	21	24	15	24
22	23	22	25	16	25
25	26	23	26	17	26

PROJECT

Have a friend tell the letter of each column that contains his or her age. The sum of the first numbers in each column will give the age. For example, if your friend answers column B, C, and E, then your friend's age is 2 + 3 + 9, or 14.

Absolute Value

OBJECTIVES
- To find the absolute value of a number
- To evaluate expressions like $|3x - 2|$ if $x = -4$
- To solve equations like $|x| = 3$

▶ *REVIEW CAPSULE*

Points *A* and *B* are graphed on a number line.

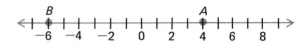

Point *A* is 4 units from the origin.
Point *B* is 6 units from the origin.

EXAMPLE 1 Find the distance between city *A* and city *D*.

$$80 + 100 + 150 = 330$$

Thus, the distance from *A* to *D* is 330 km, and the distance from *D* to *A* is 330 km.

EXAMPLE 2 Find the points on a number line whose distance is 4 units from the origin.

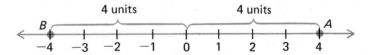

Points *A* and *B* are each 4 units from the origin.

Absolute values can be found by measuring distances on a number line.

We say that $\left.\begin{array}{l}\text{the absolute value of } 4 \\ \text{the absolute value of } -4\end{array}\right\}$ is 4.

An absolute value is associated with each number.

Number	3	−3	5	−5	0
Absolute value	3		5		0

EXAMPLE 3   Find the absolute value of 13 and of -13.

Say. $\longrightarrow$

The absolute value of 13 is 13.

$|13| = 13$

The absolute value of -13 is 13.

$|-13| = 13$

Write. $\longrightarrow$

Definition of absolute value $\longrightarrow$

$13 > 0 \quad |13| = 13$

$-13 < 0 \quad |-13| = -(-13) \text{ or } 13 \Big\}$

$$|x| \begin{cases} = x & \text{for } x \geq 0. \\ = -x & \text{for } x < 0. \end{cases}$$

EXAMPLE 4   Find $|7|$.   Find $|0|$.   Find $|-3|$.

Read $|7|$ as "absolute value of 7."

$|7| = 7$ $|0| = 0$ $|-3| = 3$

EXAMPLE 5   Find $|-8 + 4|$.   Find $|-7 + 9|$.

Simplify the expression inside the absolute value symbol first.

$|-8 + 4| = |-4|$
$\quad\quad\quad = 4$

$|-7 + 9| = |2|$
$\quad\quad\quad = 2$

EXAMPLE 6   Find $|3x - 2|$ if $x = -4$.

Substitute -4 for x. $\longrightarrow$
$3(-4) = -12 \longrightarrow$

$|3(-4) - 2|$
$|-12 - 2|$
$|-14|$

Absolute value of -14 is 14. $\longrightarrow$
14

EXAMPLE 7   Solve $|a| = 6$.

6 units   6 units

$-6 \quad\quad 0 \quad\quad 6$

Both -6 and 6 are 6 units from the origin; so $|-6| = 6$ and $|6| = 6$. $\longrightarrow$

We must find numbers with absolute value 6.

$|a| = 6$

$a = -6 \text{ or } a = 6$

Thus, the solutions are 6 and -6.

ORAL EXERCISES

Give the absolute value.

1. $|6|$ *6*   **2.** $|-5|$ *5*   **3.** $|-19|$ *19*   **4.** $|9|$ *9*

5. $|-8 + 2|$ *6*   **6.** $|4 - 3|$ *1*   **7.** $|7 - 9|$ *2*   **8.** $|3 - 4 - 1|$ *2*

EXERCISES

Find each.

1. $|x - 5|$ if $x = 2$ *3*
2. $|a - 7|$ if $a = -4$ *11*
3. $|m - 5|$ if $m = -1$ *6*
4. $|4x - 2|$ if $x = 5$ *18*
5. $|6k - 3|$ if $k = -2$ *15*
6. $|3y - 6|$ if $y = 1$ *3*
7. $|4 - 3a|$ if $a = -2$ *10*
8. $|2 - m|$ if $m = 3$ *1*
9. $|5 - 4m|$ if $m = 3$ *7*
10. $|5a - 3|$ if $a = -7$ *38*
11. $|6 - 4b|$ if $b = -3$ *18*
12. $|5 - 3t|$ if $t = -3$ *14*

Solve.

13. $|a| = 4$ *4, −4*
14. $|m| = 1$ *1, −1*
15. $|p| = 2$ *2, −2*
16. $|r| = 3$ *3, −3*

PART B

Find each.

17. $\left|\dfrac{3a}{2} - \dfrac{3}{5}\right|$ if $a = -2$ $\dfrac{18}{5}$

18. $\left|\dfrac{2m - 1}{3} + \dfrac{m}{2}\right|$ if $m = -3$ $\dfrac{23}{6}$

19. $\left|\dfrac{5}{a^2 - 4} + \dfrac{3}{a - 2}\right|$ if $a = -1$ $\dfrac{8}{3}$

20. $\left|\dfrac{1}{2} - \dfrac{3x}{x^2 - 3x + 1}\right|$ if $x = 0$ $\dfrac{1}{2}$

PART C

EXAMPLE Graph the solution set of $|x| < 3$ on a number line.

The solution set contains all numbers which are less than 3 units from the origin.

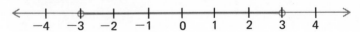

−3 and 3 are not solutions. The solutions are the numbers between −3 and 3. ⟶ The solution set is $\{x \mid -3 < x < 3\}$.

EXAMPLE Graph the solution set of $|x| > 3$.

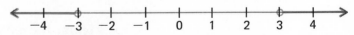

Numbers which are more than 3 units from the origin are solutions. ⟶ The solution set is $\{x \mid x < -3 \text{ or } x > 3\}$.

Find and graph the solution set.

21. $|x| < 2$
22. $|x| \le 4$
23. $|x| < 1$
24. $|x| > 0$
25. $|x| \ge 2$
26. $|x| > 5$

Equations with Absolute Value

OBJECTIVE
- To solve equations like $|3x - 2| = 4$

▶ *REVIEW CAPSULE*

Solve $|x| = 4$.

$x = -4$ or $x = 4$

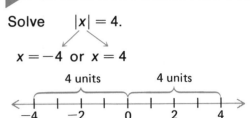

Both -4 and 4 are 4 units from origin.
Thus, -4 and 4 are the solutions.

EXAMPLE 1   Solve $|3x - 3| = 6$.

Think of $3x - 3$ as some number a.

$$|3x - 3| = 6$$
$$\downarrow$$
$$|a| = 6$$

$a = -6$ or $a = 6$

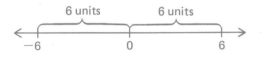

$|6| = 6$ or $|-6| = 6$

$3x - 3$ can be -6 or 6. ⟶   So, $3x - 3 = -6$ $3x - 3 = 6$

Add 3 to each side. $3x = -3$ $3x = 9$
Divide each side by 3. $x = -1$ $x = 3$

Check. ⟶

Let $x = -1$ $\dfrac{|3x - 3|}{|3(-1) - 3|} \; \dfrac{6}{6}$ │ Let $x = 3$ $\dfrac{|3x - 3|}{|3(3) - 3|} \; \dfrac{6}{6}$
$\qquad\qquad |-3 - 3|$ │ $\qquad\qquad |9 - 3|$
$\qquad\qquad |-6|$ │ $\qquad\qquad |6|$
$\qquad\qquad\; 6$ │ $\qquad\qquad\; 6$

Thus, the solutions are -1 and 3.

EXAMPLE 2   Solve $|x + 2| = 7$.

$x + 2$ can be -7 or 7. ⟶ $x + 2 = -7$ or $x + 2 = 7$
$\qquad\qquad\qquad\qquad x = -9 \qquad\qquad x = 5$

Thus, the solutions are -9 and 5.

EXAMPLE 3   Find the solution set of $|2 - 3x| = 10$.

$$|2 - 3x| = 10$$

Write two equations. $\longrightarrow$

Add -2 to each side. $\longrightarrow$

$$
\begin{array}{llll}
2 - 3x = -10 & \text{or} & 2 - 3x = 10 \\
\underline{-2 \qquad\quad -2} & & \underline{-2 \qquad\quad -2} \\
-3x = -12 & & -3x = \;\; 8 \\
\end{array}
$$

Divide each side by -3. $\longrightarrow$

$$
\begin{array}{ll}
x = \quad 4 \qquad\qquad\quad & x = \;\; \dfrac{8}{3} \\
 & \; -\dfrac{8}{3}
\end{array}
$$

Thus, the solution set is $\{-\frac{8}{3}, 4\}$.

EXERCISES

PART A

Solve and check.

1. $|x - 3| = 4$ $\;-1, 7$
4. $|2x - 5| = 7$ $\;6, -1$

2. $|4 - x| = 7$ $\;-3, 11$
5. $|2m + 1| = 5$ $\;-3, 2$

3. $|2m - 2| = 4$ $\;3, -1$
6. $|3x| = 12$ $\;4, -4$

Find the solution set.

7. $|2x - 6| = 4$ $\{1, 5\}$
10. $|3 - 7k| = 5$ $\{-\frac{2}{7}, \frac{8}{7}\}$
13. $|2m - 14| = 1$ $\{\frac{13}{2}, \frac{15}{2}\}$

8. $|4 - 3x| = 7$ $\{-1, \frac{11}{3}\}$
11. $|3x - 5| = 7$ $\{-\frac{2}{3}, 4\}$
14. $|7y - 13| = 2$ $\{\frac{11}{7}, \frac{15}{7}\}$

9. $|a + 4| = 7$ $\{3, -11\}$
12. $|5 - p| = 19$ $\{-14, 24\}$
15. $|2b - 7| = 5$ $\{1, 6\}$

PART B

EXAMPLE   Solve $3|x - 5| + 4 = 7$.

Add -4 to each side. $\longrightarrow$

Divide each side by 3.

$$
\begin{array}{rl}
3|x - 5| + 4 = & 7 \\
3|x - 5| = & 3 \\
|x - 5| = & 1
\end{array}
$$

$$x - 5 = -1 \quad \text{or} \quad x - 5 = 1$$

Add 5 to each side.

$$x = 4 \qquad\qquad x = 6$$

Thus, the solutions are 4 and 6.

Solve.

16. $2|a - 3| + 7 = 13$ $\;0, 6$

17. $3|2x - 7| - 4 = 17$ $\;0, 7$

18. $6 - |2x - 5| = 1$

PART C

Solve.

19. $|3x - 2| = |6 - x|$

20. $|x - 5| - |2x + 3| = -18$

Directed Distance on a Number Line

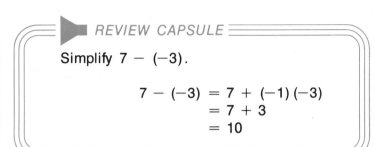

▶ *REVIEW CAPSULE*

Simplify $7 - (-3)$.

$$7 - (-3) = 7 + (-1)(-3)$$
$$= 7 + 3$$
$$= 10$$

No direction is indicated. ──────→

$$\overbrace{50 \text{ kilometers}}$$
↑
distance

Distance and direction
↓   ↓
50 km   right

$$\overbrace{50 \text{ kilometers to the right}}$$
↑
directed distance

EXAMPLE 1   Find the directed distance *from A to B*.

The coordinate of *A* is 6.
The coordinate of *B* is 8.

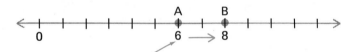

Start at *A*. Move 2 units to the *right* to *B*.

$\vec{d}(AB)$ means directed distance *from A to B*. ──────→   **Thus, $\vec{d}(AB) = +2$.**

Example 1 suggests this. ──────→   A directed distance to the right is positive.

EXAMPLE 2   Find $\vec{d}(QP)$.

$\vec{d}(QP)$ means directed distance *from Q to P*. ──────→

Start at *Q*. Move 3 units to the *left* to *P*.

left   distance
-3

Thus, $\vec{d}(QP) = -3$.

Example 2 suggests this. ──────→   A directed distance to the left is negative.

We now look for a formula to find directed distances.

EXAMPLE 3 Find $\vec{d}(RS)$.

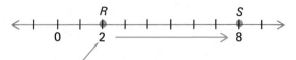

Start at R. Move 6 units to the *right* to S.

Directed distance to the right is positive. ———————→ **Thus, $\vec{d}(RS) = +6$.**

Notice that

$8 - 2 = 6$

$$\vec{d}(RS) = \text{coordinate of } S - \text{coordinate of } R$$
$$8 \qquad\qquad - \qquad\qquad 2$$

Example 3 suggests this. ———————→

Directed distance from P to Q

$$\vec{d}(PQ) = \text{coordinate of } Q - \text{coordinate of } P$$

EXAMPLE 4 Find $\vec{d}(MN)$ and $\vec{d}(NM)$.

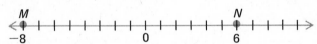

$\vec{d}(MN)$ $\vec{d}(NM)$

N coord. $- M$ coord. | M coord. $- N$ coord.

$\vec{d}(MN)$		$\vec{d}(NM)$
N coord.	$- \quad M$ coord.	M coord. $- \quad N$ coord.
6	$- \quad (-8)$	$-8 \quad - \quad 6$
6	$+(-1)(-8)$	-14
6	$+ \quad 8$	
$+14$, or 14		

$a - b$ means $a + (-1)(b)$. ———————→
$\vec{d}(MN)$ is to the right.
$\vec{d}(NM)$ is to the left.

Thus, $\vec{d}(MN) = 14$ and $\vec{d}(NM) = -14$.

$+14 = -(-14)$ ———————→ Observe that $\vec{d}(MN) = -\vec{d}(NM)$.

EXAMPLE 5 Find $\vec{d}(PQ)$.

coordinate of P: -3
coordinate of Q: -5

$\vec{d}(PQ)$

Q coord. $- P$ coord.

$a - b$ means $a + (-1)(b)$. ———————→

$$\begin{aligned}
\vec{d}(PQ) &= Q \text{ coord.} \quad - \quad P \text{ coord.}\\
&= \quad -5 \quad\quad - \quad\quad (-3)\\
&= \quad -5 \quad\quad + (-1)(-3)\\
&= \quad -5 \quad\quad +3\\
&= \quad -2
\end{aligned}$$

ORAL EXERCISES

Tell whether the directed distance is positive or negative.

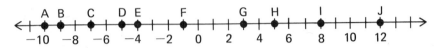

1. $\vec{d}(CE)$ *pos.*
2. $\vec{d}(BA)$ *neg.*
3. $\vec{d}(JB)$ *neg.*
4. $\vec{d}(FE)$ *neg.*
5. $\vec{d}(FC)$ *neg.*
6. $\vec{d}(AD)$ *pos.*
7. $\vec{d}(IG)$ *neg.*
8. $\vec{d}(HF)$ *neg.*
9. $\vec{d}(AE)$ *pos.*
10. $\vec{d}(FJ)$ *pos.*
11. $\vec{d}(DB)$ *neg.*
12. $\vec{d}(EJ)$ *pos.*

Use the number line above to find each directed distance.

13. $\vec{d}(CE)$ *3*
14. $\vec{d}(BA)$ *−1*
15. $\vec{d}(JB)$ *−21*
16. $\vec{d}(FE)$ *−3*
17. $\vec{d}(FC)$ *−6*
18. $\vec{d}(AD)$ *5*
19. $\vec{d}(IG)$ *−5*
20. $\vec{d}(HF)$ *−6*

EXERCISES

PART A

Find $\vec{d}(PQ)$.

1. coordinate of P: 4
   coordinate of Q: 8 *4*

2. coordinate of P: −8
   coordinate of Q: −4 *4*

3. coordinate of P: −6
   coordinate of Q: 4 *10*

4. coordinate of P: −8
   coordinate of Q: 10 *18*

5. coordinate of P: −2
   coordinate of Q: 4 *6*

6. coordinate of P: 7
   coordinate of Q: 18 *11*

7. coordinate of P: −16
   coordinate of Q: 2 *18*

8. coordinate of P: −8
   coordinate of Q: −3 *5*

9. coordinate of P: −18
   coordinate of Q: −14

PART B

Find $\vec{d}(AB)$.

10. coordinate of A: $-3\frac{1}{2}$ *$\frac{31}{4}$*

    coordinate of B: $4\frac{1}{4}$

11. coordinate of A: $-\frac{1}{3}$ *$\frac{5}{6}$*

    coordinate of B: $\frac{1}{2}$

12. coordinate of A: $-\frac{2}{3}$

    coordinate of B: $\frac{5}{9}$

PART C

Find each. Use the number line at the top of the page.

13. $\vec{d}(AB) + \vec{d}(BC)$

14. $\vec{d}(BD) + \vec{d}(DC)$

15. $\vec{d}(GF) + \vec{d}(GH)$

Fun for Philatelists

A philatelist (fi·lat′e·list) is a stamp collector. The two stamps illustrated are from a group of ten stamps issued by Nicaragua in 1971. The series gives the ten equations that changed the face of the earth. Each represents a major turning point in mathematics or science. On the back of each stamp is a brief history of the equation.

$$1 + 1 = 2$$

By counting on his fingers, an ancient man worked out the elementary equation, $1 + 1 = 2$. This equation brought an end to inexact tallying. It is the basis of our system of counting.

$$A^2 + B^2 = C^2$$

This geometric theorem, named after Pythagoras, compares the squares of the lengths of sides of a right triangle.

PROJECT

1. If anyone you know is a stamp collector, see if he or she has these stamps. Prepare a report on the history of the equations.

2. Prepare a display on other stamps which pertain to mathematics. Consult stamp collections, magazines, newspapers, and reference sources in the library.

Designed and printed by Thos De La Rue & Co. Ltd. Each stamp is 48 × 32 mm in sheets of 50 stamps.
Reprinted by permission of Oficina de Control de Especies, Postales y Filatella, Managua, Nicaragua.

Locating Points in a Plane

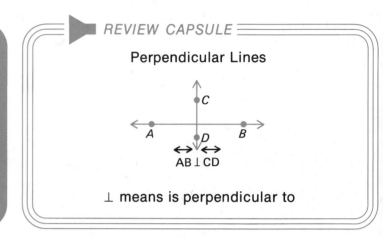

REVIEW CAPSULE

Perpendicular Lines

$AB \perp CD$

$\perp$ means is perpendicular to

A plane is a flat surface.

Points are located in a plane by using two perpendicular number lines.

EXAMPLE 1 Describe the location of point P.

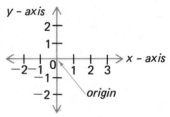

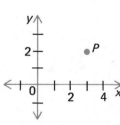

The position of P is described by an ordered pair.

x-coordinate   y-coordinate

(3,   2)

The x-coordinate is always first.

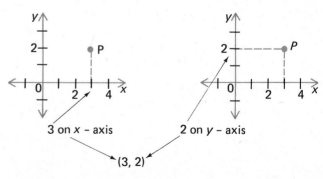

3 on x – axis

2 on y – axis

(3, 2)

EXAMPLE 2   Give the ordered pair for P, Q, R, and S.

For *P*: Read 4 on *x*-axis. }
        Read 2 on *y*-axis. }
For *Q*: Read −3 on *x*-axis. }
        Read −2 on *y*-axis. }

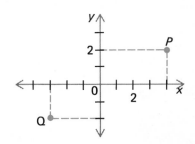
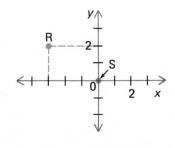

Point *S* is the origin. The coordinates are (0, 0).

$$P(4, 2) \qquad Q(-3, -2) \qquad R(-3, 2) \qquad S(0, 0)$$

EXERCISES

PART A

Give the ordered pair for each point.

1. *A* (1, 3)
2. *B* (2, 2)
3. *C* (1, 1)
4. *D* (3, −2)
5. *E* (−2, −3)
6. *F* (−1, 4)
7. *G* (−2, 2)
8. *H* (−2, −2)
9. *I* (2, −1)
10. *J* (3, −2)
11. *K* (4, −3)
12. *L* (3, −1)
13. *M* (3, 4)
14. *N* (−1, 3)
15. *P* (−3, 1)

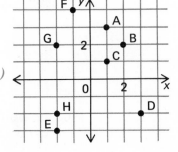
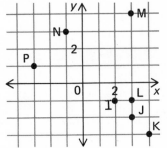

PART B

Each point except the origin is located in one of the quadrants or on one of the axes. The origin is on both axes.

The axes divide the plane into four quadrants.

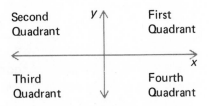

Second Quadrant		First Quadrant
Third Quadrant		Fourth Quadrant

Give the quadrant in which each point lies.

16. (−1, −5) *3*
17. (6, 10) *1*
18. (2, −8) *4*
19. (−7, −3) *3*
20. (1, −8) *4*
21. (−6, 5) *2*
22. Describe the coordinates of all points in the second quadrant.
        x-coord. neg.; y-coord. pos. ✓

Plotting Points in a Plane

OBJECTIVE
■ To plot points in a plane

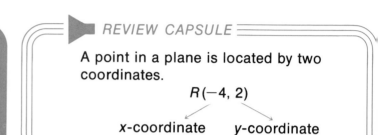

▶ *REVIEW CAPSULE*

A point in a plane is located by two coordinates.

$$R(-4, 2)$$

x-coordinate   *y*-coordinate

EXAMPLE 1   Plot the point (2, 3).

Draw and mark axes on graph paper.

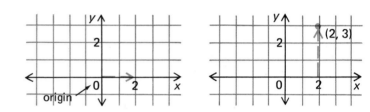

Start at the origin. ──────────────────→

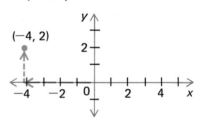

(2, 3)

First move to the right 2.   Then move up 3.

EXAMPLE 2   Plot the point (−4, 2).

Start at the origin.
(−4, 2)

Move left 4.   Move up 2.

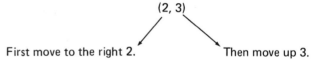

Examples 1 and 2 show that the signs of the coordinates tell in which directions to move from the origin.

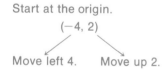

(*x*   ,   *y*)

right or left   up or down
  +   −   +   −

(2, 3)	(−4, 2)	(−1, −3)	(4, −3)
(+, +)	(−, +)	(−, −)	(+, −)
↓ ↓	↓ ↓	↓ ↓	↓ ↓
right up	left up	left down	right down

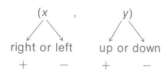

EXAMPLE 3 Plot the points.
$A(-2,-1), B(-1,3), C(3,-3), D(-2,-4)$

Draw and mark axes on graph paper.

$A(-2,-1)$

left 2   down 1

$B(-1,3)$

left 1   up 3

EXAMPLE 4   Plot $(-4,0)$.   Plot $(0,-2)$.

Begin at the origin.   Begin at the origin.
$(-4, \quad 0)$ $(0, \quad -2)$

left 4   neither up   neither right   down 2
nor down   nor left

$(-4,0)$ lies on the x-axis.
$(0,-2)$ lies on the y-axis.

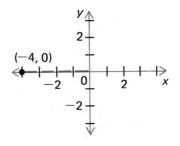 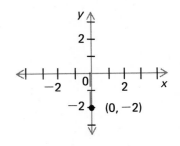

Any point on the   Any point on the
x-axis has y-axis has
y-coordinate 0. x-coordinate 0.

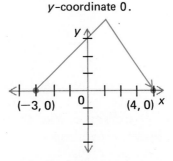 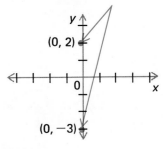

ORAL EXERCISES

Tell in which directions to move in order to plot each point. *left 8, up 2*

1. $A(3, 4)$ **2.** $B(2, -5)$ *right*   **3.** $C(-3, 7)$ **4.** $D(-2, -5)$ **5.** $E(-8, 2)$

6. $M(0, 2)$ *up 2*   **7.** $N(4, 0)$ **8.** $P(-5, 0)$ *left 5* **9.** $Q(0, -4)$ **10.** $R(-1, -3)$

down 4

EXERCISES

PART A

Plot each point.   *left 4, up 1*   *left 3, down 1*   *right 2, down 3*   *right 3*

1. $A(2, 3)$ **2.** $B(-4, 1)$ **3.** $C(-3, -1)$ **4.** $D(2, -3)$ **5.** $E(3, 0)$

6. $F(0, 0)$ *origin* **7.** $G(-3, 0)$ *left 3* **8.** $H(0, -4)$ **9.** $I(0, -7)$ **10.** $J(-5, 2)$

11. $K(4, -1)$ **12.** $L(-5, 1)$ **13.** $M(0, 3)$ *up 3* **14.** $N(6, 0)$ **15.** $P(-8, 0)$

PART B

Plot each point.

16. $Q(3\frac{1}{2}, 4\frac{1}{2})$ **17.** $R(-2\frac{1}{2}, 4\frac{1}{2})$ **18.** $S(4.5, -3.5)$ **19.** $T(-1\frac{1}{4}, 0)$

PART C

EXAMPLE A, B, and C are 3 vertices of a rectangle. Plot the points. Find the coordinates of the fourth point, D, to complete the rectangle.

$$A(2, 1), \ B(6, 1), \ C(6, 4)$$

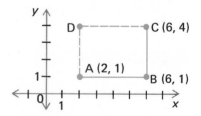

D has the same x-coord. as A and the same y-coord. as C. ⟶ **Thus,** $D(2, 4)$ **is the fourth point.**

A, B, and C are 3 vertices of a rectangle. Plot the points. Find the coordinates of the fourth point, D, to complete the rectangle.

20. $A(2, 3), B(7, 3), C(7, 5)$ *(2, 5)*   **21.** $A(-4, 2), B(7, 2), C(7, 8)$ *(−4, 8)*

Pascal's Triangle

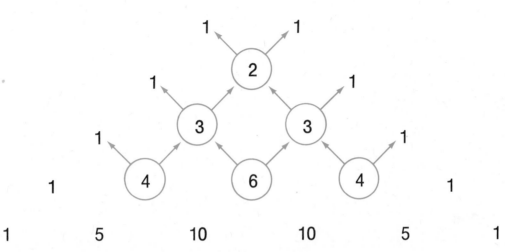

1

1   1

1   2   1

1   3   3   1

1   4   6   4   1

1   5   10   10   5   1

Pascal's triangle is an arrangement of numbers. Each number is the sum of the two numbers just above it. Each row begins and ends with 1.

This list shows the powers of $(a + b)$.

$$(a + b)^0 = \qquad\qquad\qquad 1$$
$$(a + b)^1 = \qquad\qquad\qquad 1a + 1b$$
$$(a + b)^2 = \qquad\qquad 1a^2 + 2ab + 1b^2$$
$$(a + b)^3 = \qquad 1a^3 + 3a^2b + 3ab^2 + 1b^3$$
$$(a + b)^4 = \qquad 1a^4 + 4a^3b + 6a^2b^2 + 4ab^3 + 1b^4$$
$$(a + b)^5 = 1a^5 + 5a^4b + 10a^3b^2 + 10a^2b^3 + 5ab^4 + 1b^5$$

Do you see Pascal's triangle?

PROJECT

1. What do the numerals of Pascal's triangle represent?

2. Write the next two rows of Pascal's triangle.

3. Write the expansions for $(a + b)^6$ and $(a + b)^7$.

Lines Parallel to the Axes

OBJECTIVES

■ To determine to which axis a horizontal or vertical line is parallel, given coordinates of points on the line
■ To find a missing coordinate for a point on a line parallel to an axis

▶ REVIEW CAPSULE

Give the coordinates of points A, B, and C.

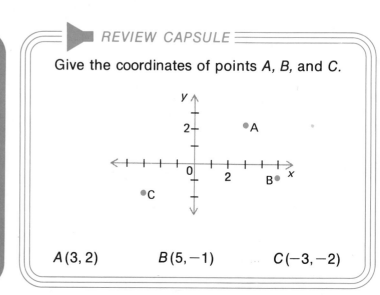

$A(3, 2)$ $B(5, -1)$ $C(-3, -2)$

EXAMPLE 1 The line containing A, B, and C is horizontal. The line containing D, E, and F is vertical. Give the coordinates for each point A, B, C, D, E, F.

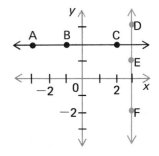

$A(-3, 2)$, $B(-1, 2)$, $C(2, 2)$

same y-coordinate

$D(3, 3)$, $E(3, 1)$, $F(3, -2)$

same x-coordinate

Example 1 suggests this. ————————→

Every point on a horizontal line has the same y-coordinate.

Every point on a vertical line has the same x-coordinate.

EXAMPLE 2   Determine to which axis the line joining
$M(-3, 5)$ and $N(7, 5)$ is parallel.

$$M(-3, 5) \qquad N(7, 5)$$

same *y*-coordinate

MN is a horizontal line.

Thus, $\overleftrightarrow{MN}$ is parallel to the *x*-axis.

EXAMPLE 3   Determine to which axis the line joining
$R(2, -5)$ and $S(2, 3)$ is parallel.

$$R(2, -5) \qquad S(2, 3)$$

same *x*-coordinate

RS is a vertical line.

Thus, $\overleftrightarrow{RS}$ is parallel to the *y*-axis.

EXERCISES

PART A

Determine, without sketching, to which axis the line joining *M* and *N* is parallel. Then sketch to check.

1. $M(3, 7)$, $N(-2, 7)$ *x-axis*   2. $M(-2, 4)$, $N(-2, -1)$ *y-axis*   3. $M(3, -5)$, $N(4, -5)$
4. $M(-2, 4)$, $N(-2, -4)$ *y-axis*   5. $M(-3, 3)$, $N(-3, 2)$ *y-axis*   6. $M(-5, -3)$, $N(-1, -3)$
7. $M(-6, -2)$, $N(6, -2)$ *x-axis*   8. $M(5, 1)$, $N(5, -8)$ *y-axis*   9. $M(-7, 3)$, $N(-7, -3)$

PART B

For what value of *b* will the line joining *P* and *Q* be parallel to the indicated axis?

10. $P(-4, 3)$, $Q(b, 1)$; *y*-axis -4
11. $P(-5, 2)$, $Q(7, b)$; *x*-axis 2
12. $P(5, 12)$, $Q(-4, 3b)$; *x*-axis 4
13. $P(8, 5)$, $Q(2b, 4)$; *y*-axis 4
14. $P(3b - 1, 5)$, $Q(8, 4)$; *y*-axis 3
15. $P(-6, 2b + 1)$, $Q(2, 7)$; *x*-axis 3

PART C

For what value of *b* will the line joining *P* and *Q* be parallel to the indicated axis?

16. $P(4b + 6, 7)$, $Q(3 + 4b, 5)$; *y*-axis
17. $P(8, b^2 - 7b)$, $Q(7, -12)$; *x*-axis

Directed Distances

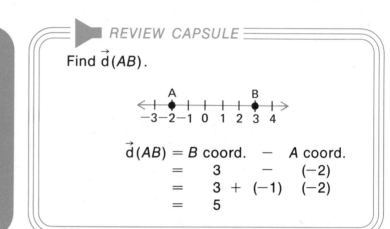
EXAMPLE 1 Find $\vec{d}(PQ)$.

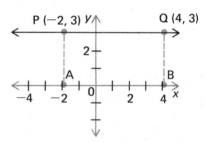

Use points directly below P and Q on the x-axis.

A and B are points on a number line. ⟶

$\vec{d}(AB) = B$ coord. $\quad - \quad A$ coord.
$= \quad 4 \quad - \quad (-2)$
$= \quad 4 \quad + (-1)(-2)$

$a - b = a + (-1)b.$ ⟶
A and B are directly below P and Q.

$= \quad 4 \quad + \quad 2 \quad$ or 6.

But, $\vec{d}(PQ) = \vec{d}(AB)$.

Thus, $\vec{d}(PQ) = 6$.

$\left. \begin{array}{l} P(-2,3) \quad Q(4,3) \\ \vec{d}(PQ) = 4 - (-2) \end{array} \right\}$

$\vec{d}(PQ)$ is determined only by the x-coordinates of P and Q.

Example 1 suggests this. ⟶

If $\overleftrightarrow{PQ}$ is a horizontal line,
$\vec{d}(PQ) = (x\text{-coord. of } Q) - (x\text{-coord. of } P)$.

EXAMPLE 2   Find $\vec{d}(ST)$ for $S(2,5)$ and $T(-7,5)$.

Both y-coord. are the same.
$S(2,5), T(-7,5)$

$\overleftrightarrow{ST}$ is a horizontal line.
So, $\vec{d}(ST) = (x\text{-coord. of } T) - (x\text{-coord. of } S)$
$$= \quad -7 \quad - \quad 2$$
$$= \quad -9$$

Thus, $\vec{d}(ST) = -9$.

EXAMPLE 3   Find $\vec{d}(RS)$.

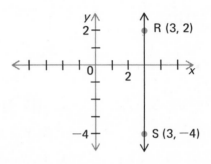

$\overleftrightarrow{RS}$ is a vertical line, since the x-coordinates of R and S are the same.
$R(3,2), S(3,-4)$

Find points directly across from R and S on the y-axis.

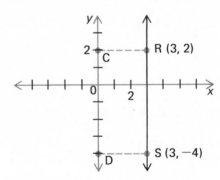

C and D are points on a number line. ⟶

$\vec{d}(CD) = D \text{ coord.} - C \text{ coord.}$
$$= \quad -4 \quad - \quad 2$$
$$= \quad -6$$
But, $\vec{d}(RS) = \vec{d}(CD)$.

$\vec{d}(RS)$ is determined only by the y-coord. of R and S.

Thus, $\vec{d}(RS) = -6$.

Example 3 suggests this. ⟶

If $\overleftrightarrow{PQ}$ is a vertical line,
$\quad \vec{d}(PQ) = (y\text{-coord. of } Q) - (y\text{-coord. of } P)$.

EXAMPLE 4 Find $\vec{d}(GH)$ for $G(-3,-4)$ and $H(-3,7)$.

Both x-coord. are the same.
$G(-3,-4)$, $H(-3,7)$

$\overleftrightarrow{GH}$ is a vertical line.
So, $\vec{d}(GH) = (y\text{-coord. of } H) - (y\text{-coord. of } G)$
$$7 \quad - \quad (-4)$$
$$= 7 + (-1)(-4)$$
$$= 11$$
Thus, $\vec{d}(GH) = 11$.

EXERCISES

PART A

Find $\vec{d}(MN)$.

1. $M(2,-7)$, $N(-5,-7)$ -7 **2.** $M(1,4)$, $N(1,-3)$ -7 **3.** $M(2,-6)$, $N(3,-6)$ 1

4. $M(-1,5)$, $N(-1,-3)$ -8 **5.** $M(6,-4)$, $N(-2,-4)$ -8 **6.** $M(-8,-2)$, $N(-8,-5)$

7. $M(-2,-3)$, $N(-5,-3)$ -3 **8.** $M(0,-4)$, $N(3,-4)$ 3 **9.** $M(1,2)$, $N(1,-9)$ -11

10. $M(0,-8)$, $N(-3,-8)$ -3 **11.** $M(-3,0)$, $N(-3,8)$ 8 **12.** $M(4,0)$, $N(4,-3)$ -3

13. $M(4,0)$, $N(4,-6)$ -6 **14.** $M(-3,-3)$, $N(5,-3)$ 8 **15.** $M(-4,6)$, $N(-4,-17)$

16. $M(-5,3)$, $N(42,3)$ 47 **17.** $M(0,-15)$, $N(0,14)$ 29 **18.** $M(-17,0)$, $N(6,0)$ 23

PART B

Find $\vec{d}(PQ)$.

19. $P(3\frac{1}{2},-5)$, $Q(2\frac{1}{4},-5)$ $-\frac{5}{4}$ **20.** $P(\frac{5}{6},4)$, $Q(-\frac{2}{3},4)$ $-\frac{3}{2}$

21. $P(6,-\frac{4}{3})$, $Q(6,\frac{5}{6})$ $\frac{13}{6}$ **22.** $P(3\frac{1}{8},-\frac{3}{4})$, $Q(3\frac{1}{8},\frac{5}{12})$ $\frac{7}{6}$

23. $P(-\frac{4}{5},5)$, $Q(\frac{7}{15},5)$ $\frac{19}{15}$ **24.** $P(3.8,2)$, $Q(-1.7,2)$ -5.5

25. $P(-4,1.6)$, $Q(-3.2,1.6)$ $.8$ **26.** $P(7,-5.3)$, $Q(7,4.9)$ 10.2

27. $P(1\frac{1}{8},4)$, $Q(-1\frac{3}{4},4)$ $-\frac{23}{8}$ **28.** $P(-\frac{4}{9},5)$, $Q(\frac{1}{27},5)$ $\frac{13}{27}$

PART C

Express $\vec{d}(RT)$ in terms of variables.

29. $R(3a,2b)$, $T(-5a,2b)$ **30.** $R(2m,5n)$, $T(2m,-7n)$

31. $R(3m,-2k)$, $T(3m,-5k)$ **32.** $R(2a-3,b)$, $T(-4a+3,b)$

33. $R(\frac{3m}{2},5)$, $T(\frac{2m}{3},5)$ **34.** $R(-4,\frac{5}{m^2})$, $T(-4,\frac{3}{m^2})$

Slopes of Line Segments

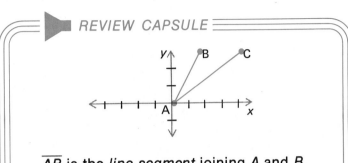

$\overline{AB}$ is the *line segment* joining *A* and *B*.
$\overline{AC}$ is the line segment joining *A* and *C*.

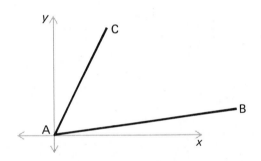

$\overline{AC}$ and $\overline{AB}$ are not parallel to either axis.

If the *x*-axis represents level ground and $\overline{AB}$ and $\overline{AC}$ represent paths up a hill, $\overline{AC}$ would be more difficult to climb than $\overline{AB}$.

Think of slope of a hill.

We say that $\overline{AC}$ has greater *slope* than $\overline{AB}$.

EXAMPLE 1 Find $\dfrac{\vec{d}(AE)}{\vec{d}(EB)}$.

$\vec{d}(AE)$ measures the vertical, or rise. ⟶ $\vec{d}(AE) = 5 - 1$
$$= 4$$

$\vec{d}(EB)$ measures the horizontal, or run. ⟶ $\vec{d}(EB) = 7 - 2$
$$= 5$$

$\dfrac{\text{Vertical directed distance}}{\text{Horizontal directed distance}}$ ⟶ **Thus,** $\dfrac{\vec{d}(AE)}{\vec{d}(EB)} = \dfrac{4}{5}$.

$\text{Slope} = \dfrac{\text{rise}}{\text{run}}$. ⟶ We say that the slope of $\overline{AB}$ is $\frac{4}{5}$.

EXAMPLE 2 Find the slopes of $\overline{AB}$ and $\overline{AC}$. Compare the slopes.

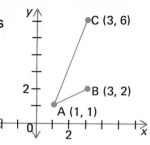

Draw the graph of each line segment separately.

Form a right triangle. ──────────→

Slope $= \dfrac{\text{rise}}{\text{run}}$. ──────────→ Slope of $\overline{AB} = \dfrac{\vec{d}(AD)}{\vec{d}(DB)}$

Vertical directed distance ──────→

Horizontal directed distance ──────→ $= \dfrac{2-1}{3-1}$, or $\dfrac{1}{2}$

Slope of $\overline{AC} = \dfrac{\vec{d}(AE)}{\vec{d}(EC)}$

$= \dfrac{6-1}{3-1}$, or $\dfrac{5}{2}$

Thus, the slope of $\overline{AC}$ is greater than the slope of $\overline{AB}$.

EXAMPLE 3 Find the slope of the line segment joining $A(2, 1)$ and $B(5, 3)$.

Draw a diagram.

Build a right triangle by drawing a vertical line segment through A and a horizontal line segment through B.

Slope $= \dfrac{\text{rise}}{\text{run}}$. ──────────→ Slope of $\overline{AB} = \dfrac{\vec{d}(AC)}{\vec{d}(CB)}$

$= \dfrac{3-1}{5-2}$, or $\dfrac{2}{3}$

Thus, the slope of $\overline{AB}$ is $\frac{2}{3}$.

In Example 3, for $A(2, 1)$ and $B(5, 3)$ we found:

Difference of *y*-coordinates / Difference of *x*-coordinates

$$\text{Slope of } \overline{AB} = \frac{\overset{\substack{y\text{-coord.} \\ \text{of } B}}{3} - \overset{\substack{y\text{-coord.} \\ \text{of } A}}{1}}{\underset{\substack{x\text{-coord.} \\ \text{of } B}}{5} - \underset{\substack{x\text{-coord.} \\ \text{of } A}}{2}}$$

We can find the slope of a segment directly from the coordinates of its endpoints.

$$\text{Slope} = \frac{\text{difference of the } y\text{-coordinates}}{\text{difference of the } x\text{-coordinates}}.$$

EXAMPLE 4 Find the slope of $\overline{AB}$ for $A(6, 3)$, $B(-1, -4)$.

First way

Difference of *y*-coordinates / Difference of *x*-coordinates $\longrightarrow$

$A(6, 3)$, $B(-1, -4)$

$$\text{Slope} = \frac{y\text{-coord. of } B - y\text{-coord. of } A}{x\text{-coord. of } B - x\text{-coord. of } A}$$

$$= \frac{-4 - 3}{-1 - 6}$$

$$= \frac{-7}{-7}$$

$$= 1$$

Second way

Difference of *y*-coordinates / Difference of *x*-coordinates $\longrightarrow$

$A(6, 3)$, $B(-1, -4)$

$$\text{Slope} = \frac{y\text{-coord. of } A - y\text{-coord. of } B}{x\text{-coord. of } A - x\text{-coord. of } B}$$

$$= \frac{3 - (-4)}{6 - (-1)}$$

$$= \frac{3 + (-1)(-4)}{6 + (-1)(-1)}$$

$$= \frac{3 + 4}{6 + 1}$$

$$= \frac{7}{7}, \text{ or } 1$$

Both ways give the same slope. $\longrightarrow$ **Thus,** the slope of $\overline{AB}$ is 1.

EXAMPLE 5 Find the slope of $\overline{CD}$ for $C(8, 2)$ and $D(-2, 6)$.

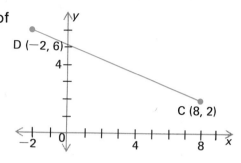

Also, $\frac{2-6}{8-(-2)} = \frac{-4}{10}$.

The slope of a line segment can be negative. ———————→

Slope of $\overline{CD} = \frac{6-2}{-2-8}$, or $\frac{4}{-10}$.

Thus, the slope of $\overline{CD}$ is $-\frac{4}{10}$, or $-\frac{2}{5}$.

EXAMPLE 6 Find the slope of $\overline{AB}$ for $A(3, 5)$ and $B(6, 5)$.

$\overline{AB}$ is a horizontal line segment.

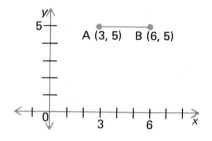

Also, $\frac{5-5}{3-6} = \frac{0}{-3} = 0$.

The slope of a line segment can be zero. ———————→

Slope of $\overline{AB} = \frac{5-5}{6-3}$, or $\frac{0}{3}$.

Thus, the slope of $\overline{AB}$ is 0.

EXERCISES

PART A

Find the slope of $\overline{AB}$.

1. $A(0, 0)$, $B(4, 3)$ $\frac{3}{4}$
2. $A(3, 5)$, $B(7, 6)$ $\frac{1}{4}$
3. $A(2, 5)$, $B(5, 7)$ $\frac{2}{3}$
4. $A(-3, -4)$, $B(8, 2)$ $\frac{6}{11}$
5. $A(-4, -1)$, $B(6, 2)$ $\frac{3}{10}$
6. $A(5, 3)$, $B(1, 8)$ $-\frac{5}{4}$
7. $A(-8, 3)$, $B(7, -1)$ $-\frac{4}{15}$
8. $A(-1, 1)$, $B(7, 4)$ $\frac{3}{8}$
9. $A(0, 4)$, $B(7, 4)$ 0

PART B

Express the slope of $\overline{AB}$ in terms of variables.

10. $A(2b, 5k)$, $B(4b, 8k)$ $\frac{3k}{2b}$
11. $A(3i, 5t)$, $B(-4i, 7t)$ $-\frac{2t}{7i}$
12. $A(2c, -4d)$, $B(-5c, 7d)$ $-\frac{11d}{7c}$
13. $A(-3b, 5k)$, $B(b, k)$ $-\frac{k}{b}$

Slope of Lines

OBJECTIVES
- To find the slope of a line
- To determine if lines are parallel from their slopes
- To determine the slant of a line from its slope

REVIEW CAPSULE

Find the slope of $\overline{PQ}$ for $P(-4, -2)$ and $Q(7, 6)$.

$$\frac{y\text{-coord. of } Q - y\text{-coord. of } P}{x\text{-coord. of } Q - x\text{-coord. of } P}$$

$$\frac{6 \quad - \quad (-2)}{7 \quad - \quad (-4)}$$

$$\frac{6 + (-1)(-2)}{7 + (-1)(-4)}, \text{ or } \frac{8}{11}$$

EXAMPLE 1

$A, B, C,$ and D are points on the same line. Find the slopes of $\overline{AB}$ and $\overline{CD}$.

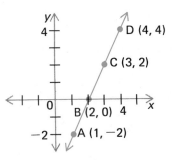

$A(1, -2), B(2, 0); C(3, 2), D(4, 4)$

The slope of both segments is the same. ⟶

Slope of $\overline{AB} = \dfrac{0 - (-2)}{2 - 1}$ Slope of $\overline{CD} = \dfrac{4 - 2}{4 - 3}$

$\qquad\qquad = \dfrac{2}{1}, \text{ or } 2$ $\qquad\qquad = \dfrac{2}{1}, \text{ or } 2$

We say that the slope of $\overleftrightarrow{AB}$ is 2.

Use any two points on the line to find the slope.

> The slope of a line is the slope of any line segment on the line.

EXAMPLE 2

Find the slope of $\overleftrightarrow{PQ}$ for $P(4, 1)$ and $Q(1, 3)$.

Slope of $\overleftrightarrow{PQ} = \dfrac{3 - 1}{1 - 4}$

$\dfrac{\text{diff. of } y\text{-coords.}}{\text{diff. of } x\text{-coords.}}$ ⟶

$\qquad\qquad = \dfrac{2}{-3}, \text{ or } -\dfrac{2}{3}$

EXAMPLE 3   Find the slope of $\overleftrightarrow{AB}$.

$\overleftrightarrow{AB}$ is a horizontal line.

$$\text{Slope of } \overleftrightarrow{AB} = \frac{2-2}{4-(-1)}$$
$$= \frac{0}{5}, \text{ or } 0$$

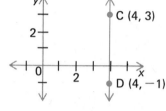

EXAMPLE 4   Find the slope of $\overleftrightarrow{CD}$.

$$\text{Slope of } \overleftrightarrow{CD} = \frac{3-(-1)}{4-4}$$

A fraction cannot have 0 in the denominator.

$$= \frac{4}{0}$$
$\llcorner$ undefined

Thus, the slope of the vertical line $\overleftrightarrow{CD}$ is undefined.

Examples 3 and 4 suggest this. ⟶

The slope of a horizontal line is zero.
The slope of a vertical line is undefined.

See Examples 1–4. ⟶ The slope of a line determines its slant.

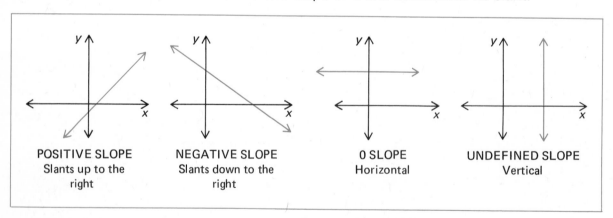

POSITIVE SLOPE	NEGATIVE SLOPE	0 SLOPE	UNDEFINED SLOPE
Slants up to the right	Slants down to the right	Horizontal	Vertical

EXAMPLE 5   Find the slope of $\overleftrightarrow{CD}$ for $C(-2,-4)$ and $D(5,8)$.
Then describe the slant of $\overleftrightarrow{CD}$.

Difference of y-coordinates
Difference of x-coordinates

$$\text{Slope of } \overleftrightarrow{CD} = \frac{8-(-4)}{5-(-2)} = \frac{12}{7}.$$

Thus, the slope of $\overleftrightarrow{CD}$ is $\frac{12}{7}$.

The slope of $\overleftrightarrow{CD}$ is positive. ⟶ $\overleftrightarrow{CD}$ slants up to the right.

EXAMPLE 6 $\overleftrightarrow{PQ}$ is parallel to $\overleftrightarrow{AB}$.
Find the slope of each.

Difference of y-coordinates ⟶
Difference of x-coordinates ⟶

$$\text{Slope of } \overleftrightarrow{AB} \qquad \text{Slope of } \overleftrightarrow{PQ}$$

$$\frac{2-0}{3-0} \quad \bigg| \quad \frac{4-2}{3-0}$$

$$\frac{2}{3} \quad \bigg| \quad \frac{2}{3}$$

Thus, the slope of each line is $\frac{2}{3}$.

Example 6 suggests this. ⟶ | Parallel lines have the same slope.

ORAL EXERCISES

Describe the slant of the line whose slope is given.

1. $\frac{2}{3}$ ↘ **2.** $-\frac{4}{5}$ ↘ **3.** $\frac{0}{4}$ ↘ **4.** $\frac{5}{0}$ ↘ **5.** $-\frac{1}{2}$ ↘

slants up to the right   slants down to the right   horizontal   vertical   slants down to the right

EXERCISES

PART A

Find the slope of $\overleftrightarrow{PQ}$ and describe its slant. $-\frac{3}{5}$; *down to the right   0; horizontal*

1. $P(3,4)$, $Q(3,7)$ **2.** $P(3,2)$, $Q(-2,5)$ ↗   **3.** $P(2,5)$, $Q(3,5)$
4. $P(-5,-3)$, $Q(7,-4)$ **5.** $P(0,0)$, $Q(-8,-5)$ **6.** $P(-6,5)$, $Q(7,5)$
7. $P(-3,-4)$, $Q(-3,6)$ ↘   **8.** $P(-6,1)$, $Q(7,5)$ ↘   **9.** $P(1,-2)$, $Q(-5,-2)$ ↘

undefined; vertical $\frac{4}{13}$; *up to the right*   *0; horizontal*

Determine whether $\overleftrightarrow{PQ}$ is parallel to $\overleftrightarrow{RS}$.

10. $P(2,5)$, $Q(3,7)$ *no*   **11.** $P(3,7)$, $Q(6,9)$ *yes*   **12.** $P(1,3)$, $Q(2,5)$ *no*
    $R(2,7)$, $S(0,5)$ $R(3,1)$, $Q(9,5)$ $R(0,1)$, $S(2,11)$

PART B

Determine whether A, B, and C lie on the same line. [Hint: Check if the slope of $\overline{AB}$ = the slope of $\overline{BC}$.]

13. $A(1,1)$, $B(-3,-7)$, $C(5,9)$ *yes*   **14.** $A(0,3)$, $B(-2,5)$, $C(1,0)$ *no*
15. $A(2,-3)$, $B(-2,-7)$, $C(0,-3)$ *no*   **16.** $A(4,3)$, $B(-6,-2)$, $C(8,5)$ *yes*
17. $A(0,0)$, $B(1,-3)$, $C(-2,4)$ *no*   **18.** $A(3,-3)$, $B(-1,2)$, $C(6,-2)$ *no*
19. $A(10,5)$, $B(-5,-1)$, $C(0,1)$ *yes*   **20.** $A(2,1)$, $B(-4,-8)$, $C(6,7)$ *yes*

Chapter Nine Review

Find each. $[p.\ 231]$

1. $|-6|$ **2.** $|-7+5|$ **3.** $|3a-2|$ if $a=-4$ **4.** $|\frac{2a}{3}-\frac{1}{5}|$ if $a=-2$

Solve. $[p.\ 231,\ 234]$

5. $|x|=7$ **6.** $|5-2x|=1$ **7.** $|3x-5|=2$ **8.** $2|x-4|+3=9$

Find $\vec{d}(MN)$. $[p.\ 236]$

9. coordinate of M: -5
   coordinate of N: 4

10. coordinate of M: 6
   coordinate of N: -3

11. coordinate of M: $\frac{5}{6}$
   coordinate of N: $-\frac{2}{3}$

Give the ordered pair for each point. $[p.\ 240]$

12. A	**17.** F
13. B	**18.** G
14. C	**19.** H
15. D	**20.** I
16. E	**21.** J

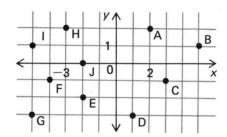

Give the quadrant in which each point lies. Then plot the point. $[p.\ 240,\ 242]$

22. $A(3,5)$ **23.** $B(-3,2)$ **24.** $C(-5,0)$ **25.** $D(0,3)$

$[p.\ 246]$

Determine, without sketching, to which axis the line joining P and Q is parallel.

26. $P(3,5)$, $Q(-7,5)$ **27.** $P(4,8)$, $Q(4,-8)$ **28.** $P(a,b)$, $Q(c,b)$

$[p.\ 246]$

For what value of b will the line joining P and Q be parallel to the indicated axis?

29. $P(-5,2)$, $Q(b,1)$; y-axis   **30.** $P(6,3b+1)$, $Q(2,4)$; x-axis

Find $\vec{d}(MN)$. $[p.\ 248]$

31. $M(-4,3)$, $N(7,3)$ **32.** $M(2,-6)$, $N(2,8)$ **33.** $M(-1,-5)$, $N(4,-5)$

Find the slope of $\overleftrightarrow{PQ}$. Then describe its slant. $[p.\ 251,\ 255]$

34. $P(1,5)$, $Q(2,9)$ **35.** $P(4,3)$, $Q(7,3)$
36. $P(2,5)$, $Q(5,-2)$ **37.** $P(3,4)$, $Q(3,1)$

Determine whether $\overleftrightarrow{PQ}$ is parallel to $\overleftrightarrow{RS}$. $[p.\ 255]$

38. $P(1,-5)$, $Q(4,1)$
   $R(6,13)$, $S(-4,-7)$

39. $P(5,2)$, $Q(-5,-4)$
   $R(10,7)$, $S(-15,-8)$

40. $P(3,1)$, $Q(-6,-2)$
   $R(9,5)$, $S(6,2)$

Chapter Nine Test

Find each.

1. $|-4|$ **2.** $|2-8|$ **3.** $|3a-5|$ if $a=-4$ **4.** $|\frac{3a}{5}-\frac{1}{2}|$ if $a=-2$

Solve.

5. $|x|=6$ **6.** $|3x-4|=7$ **7.** $3|x-2|+5=14$

Find $\vec{d}(MN)$.

8. coordinate of M: -6
coordinate of N: 1

9. coordinate of M: $\frac{1}{8}$
coordinate of N: $-\frac{3}{4}$

Give the ordered pair for each point.

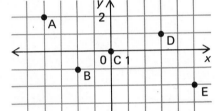

10. A
11. B
12. C
13. D
14. E

Give the quadrant in which each point lies. Then plot each point.

15. $A(5,2)$ **16.** $B(-3,-6)$ **17.** $C(0,-4)$

Determine, without sketching, to which axis the line joining P and Q is parallel.

18. $P(-2,4)$, $Q(8,4)$ **19.** $P(-3,-4)$, $Q(-3,2)$

For what value of b will the line joining P and Q be parallel to the indicated axis?

20. $P(-6,3)$, $Q(b,4)$; y-axis   **21.** $P(5,6)$, $Q(12,2b+1)$; x-axis

Find $\vec{d}(MN)$.

22. $M(-5,3)$, $N(7,3)$ **23.** $M(5,2\frac{1}{2})$, $N(5,3\frac{3}{4})$

Find the slope of $\overleftrightarrow{PQ}$. Then describe its slant.

24. $P(2,3)$, $Q(7,9)$ **25.** $P(-4,2)$, $Q(3,2)$
26. $P(5,1)$, $Q(7,1)$ **27.** $P(3,4)$, $Q(3,8)$

Determine whether $\overleftrightarrow{PQ}$ is parallel to $\overleftrightarrow{RS}$.

28. $P(6,3)$, $Q(-3,-3)$ **29.** $P(0,0)$, $Q(-6,-15)$
$R(0,4)$, $S(3,6)$ $R(2,6)$, $S(4,9)$

Mathematics in Construction

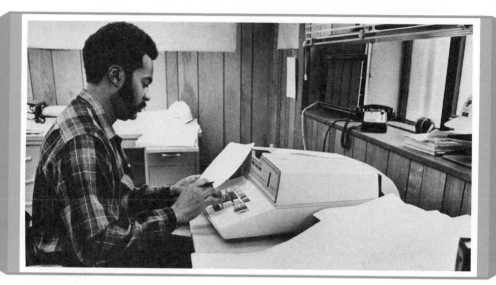

Construction workers must make careful plans in the form of cost budgets, time schedules, and blueprints (scale drawing of project). Pictured above is a foreman preparing a time schedule.

PROJECT Find the perimeter of the room shown on the scale drawing.

Scale: 1 cm → 5 m

Ratio and Proportion

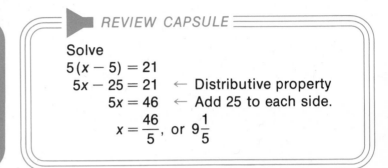

▶ REVIEW CAPSULE

Solve

$5(x - 5) = 21$

$5x - 25 = 21$ ← Distributive property

$5x = 46$ ← Add 25 to each side.

$x = \dfrac{46}{5}$, or $9\dfrac{1}{5}$

EXAMPLE 1

John can paint a house in 4 days. He works 3 days. Write a fraction which compares the number of days actually worked with the number of days needed to do the entire job.

$\dfrac{3}{4}$ is a *ratio*.

$$\frac{\text{Number of days worked}}{\text{Number of days to do entire job}} = \frac{3}{4}$$

Numbers being compared should represent the same units. In Example 1, 3 and 4 represent days.

The comparison of two numbers by division is a *ratio*.

Two ways to write the ratio 3 to 4

$$\frac{3}{4} \qquad 3:4$$

EXAMPLE 2

Write the ratio 5 to 7 in two ways.

Compare 5 to 7. ⟶ $\dfrac{5}{7}$, or 5:7

EXAMPLE 3

Write an equation.

The ratio is the same as the ratio

3 to 4   a to 16

The ratios are equal.
The equation is a proportion.

$$\frac{3}{4} = \frac{a}{16}$$

or 3:4   =   a:16

A *proportion* is an equation which states that two ratios are equal.

$$\frac{a}{b} = \frac{c}{d} \qquad \text{or} \qquad a:b = c:d$$

extremes

means

a and d are *extremes*.
b and c are *means*.

EXAMPLE 4 Identify the extremes and means.
$$\frac{7}{10} = \frac{14}{20}$$

$7:10 = 14:20$

means

extremes

Extremes are 7 and 20. Means are 10 and 14.

EXAMPLE 5 Solve the proportion $\frac{3}{4} = \frac{x}{16}$.

Multiply each side by the product of the denominators: $4 \cdot 16 = 64$.

$$\overset{16}{\cancel{64}} \cdot \frac{3}{\underset{1}{\cancel{4}}} = \frac{x}{\underset{1}{\cancel{16}}} \cdot \overset{4}{\cancel{64}}$$

$$3 \cdot 16 = 4 \cdot x$$
$$48 = 4x$$
$$12 = x$$

$\frac{3}{4} = \frac{12}{16}.$ ⟶ **Thus,** the solution is 12.

Example 4 suggests this. ⟶

$\left. \begin{array}{c} \frac{3}{4} = \frac{12}{16} \\ 3 \cdot 16 = 4 \cdot 12 \end{array} \right\}$

In a proportion $\frac{a}{b} = \frac{c}{d}$,
$$ad = bc$$
product of extremes = product of means

EXAMPLE 6 Solve the proportion $\frac{x}{3} = \frac{2}{5}$.

$\frac{a}{b} = \frac{c}{d}$ ⟶

$a \cdot d = b \cdot c$ ⟶

$$\frac{x}{3} = \frac{2}{5}$$
$$x \cdot 5 = 3 \cdot 2$$
$$5x = 6$$

Thus, $x = \frac{6}{5}$ and the solution is $\frac{6}{5}$, or $1\frac{1}{5}$.

EXAMPLE 7   Solve $\dfrac{x-5}{7}=\dfrac{3}{5}$.

Use
prod. of extremes = prod. of means.
$5(x-5)=5\cdot x+5\cdot-5$, or $5x-25$

$$5(x-5)=7\cdot 3$$
$$5x-25=21$$
$$5x=46$$

Divide each side by 5.

Thus, $\qquad x=\dfrac{46}{5}$ and the solution is $\dfrac{46}{5}$, or $9\dfrac{1}{5}$.

EXAMPLE 8   If one out of five people use Cavity Toothpaste, how many people can be expected to use this brand in a city of 30,000 population?

Let $t=$ number of people using Cavity

Write a proportion by setting the ratios equal.

$$\dfrac{t}{30,000}=\dfrac{\text{Cavity users}}{\text{total population}}$$

1 out of $5=\dfrac{1}{5}$ $\longrightarrow$

But, $\qquad \dfrac{1}{5}=\dfrac{\text{Cavity users}}{\text{total population}}$

$$\dfrac{t}{30,000}=\dfrac{1}{5}$$

$t\cdot 5=30,000\cdot 1$ $\longrightarrow$
$$5t=30,000$$
$$t=6,000$$

Thus, 6,000 people use Cavity Toothpaste.

EXAMPLE 9   Solve $\dfrac{m}{3}=\dfrac{2}{m+5}$.

Prod. of extremes = prod. of means.
$m(m+5)=m^2+5m$ $\longrightarrow$
Add -6 to each side. $\longrightarrow$
Factor. $\longrightarrow$
Set each factor equal to 0. $\longrightarrow$
$m=-6$ or $m=1$ $\longrightarrow$

$$m(m+5)=3\cdot 2$$
$$m^2+5m=6$$
$$m^2+5m-6=0$$
$$(m+6)(m-1)=0$$
$$m+6=0 \quad\text{or}\quad m-1=0$$
Thus, the solutions are -6 and 1.

ORAL EXERCISES

Identify the means and extremes of each proportion.

1. $\dfrac{3}{5}=\dfrac{6}{10}$ *means: 5, 6*
   ext: 3, 10

2. $7:14=21:42$

3. $\dfrac{a}{b}=\dfrac{m}{n}$

4. $\dfrac{3}{5}=\dfrac{x}{4}$

5. $2:5=7:5a$

6. $\dfrac{5}{9}=\dfrac{2m}{3}$

7. $\dfrac{3m}{2b}=\dfrac{7x}{5y}$

8. $x:b=2y:t$

EXERCISES

PART A

Solve.

1. $\dfrac{5}{3} = \dfrac{a}{2}$ *10 3*

2. $\dfrac{3}{10} = \dfrac{x}{4}$ *6 5*

3. $\dfrac{7}{14} = \dfrac{m}{21}$ *21 2*

4. $\dfrac{2}{m} = \dfrac{3}{7}$ *14 3*

5. $\dfrac{3}{x} = \dfrac{7}{x+5}$ *15 4*

6. $\dfrac{m+4}{2} = \dfrac{m-3}{5}$ *26 3*

7. $\dfrac{a+3}{5} = \dfrac{14}{10}$ *4*

8. $\dfrac{x-2}{3} = \dfrac{2x+7}{5}$ *31*

9. $\dfrac{5}{2m+5} = \dfrac{2}{4m-1}$ *15 16*

10. In Centerville, 3 out of 5 people belong to a union. How many union members can we find if the population is 70,000?

11. Pat's batting average is .385 (385 : 1,000). How many hits should Pat get in 6,000 times at bat?

12. One out of 4 people earns less than $2,000 per year. How many people in a city of 40,000 earn less than $2,000 per year? *10,000*

13. Four out of 5 freshmen study algebra. How many study algebra in a freshman class of 400? *320*

Solve.

14. $\dfrac{4}{x} = \dfrac{x}{9}$ *6, −6*

15. $\dfrac{a}{2} = \dfrac{32}{a}$ *8, −8*

16. $\dfrac{x}{2} = \dfrac{2}{x+3}$ *1, −4*

17. $\dfrac{y-4}{1} = \dfrac{2}{y-3}$ *2, 5*

PART B

EXAMPLE   Find two numbers in the ratio 2 : 3 whose sum is 15.

$$\dfrac{2x}{3x} = \dfrac{\overset{1}{\cancel{2x}}}{\underset{1}{\cancel{3x}}} = \dfrac{2}{3} \longrightarrow$$

Let $2x$ = one of the numbers
$3x$ = the other number
$$2x + 3x = 15$$
$$5x = 15$$
$$x = 3$$

Check: $\dfrac{6}{9} = \dfrac{2}{3}$ and $6 + 9 = 15.$

Thus, first number, $2x$, is $2 \cdot 3$, or 6
and   second number, $3x$, is $3 \cdot 3$, or 9.

18. Find two numbers whose ratio is 3 : 5 and whose sum is 24. *9, 15*

19. Find two numbers whose ratio is 3 : 8 and whose sum is 33. *9, 24*

PART C

20. Find three numbers whose ratio is 2 : 3 : 5 and whose sum is 30.

21. Find two numbers whose ratio is 7 : 3 and whose difference is 28.

Equation of a Line

OBJECTIVES

■ To write an equation of a line given two points on it
■ To show that a point lies on a line if an equation of the line is given

▶ REVIEW CAPSULE

Find the slope of $\overleftrightarrow{PQ}$.
$$P(3, 4), \quad Q(7, 9)$$

Slope of $\overleftrightarrow{PQ} = \dfrac{9 - 4}{7 - 3}$

$$= \dfrac{5}{4}$$

Given two points, only one line can be drawn through them.

The line through the points $R(-2, -7)$ and $S(3, 8)$ is shown. $G(x, y)$ represents any other point on the same line.

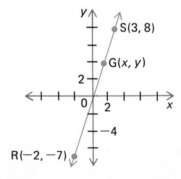

(x, y) represents the coordinates of a general point (G) on the line.

$\overleftrightarrow{RS}$, $\overleftrightarrow{RG}$, and $\overleftrightarrow{SG}$ are different names for the same line. The slope of the line is the slope of any segment on it.

EXAMPLE 1 Write an equation of the line through $R(-2, -7)$ and $S(3, 8)$.

Slope $= \dfrac{\text{diff. of } y\text{-coordinates}}{\text{diff. of } x\text{-coordinates}}$

Slope of $\overline{RS} = \dfrac{8 - (-7)}{3 - (-2)} = \dfrac{8 + 7}{3 + 2} = \dfrac{15}{5} = \dfrac{3}{1}$.

We could have found slope of $\overline{GR}$ instead.

Slope of $\overline{SG} = \dfrac{y - 8}{x - 3}$.

R, S, and G are on the same line. ⟶ But, slope of $\overline{SG}$ = slope of $\overline{RS}$.

Set the two slopes equal. ⟶ **Thus,** $\dfrac{y - 8}{x - 3} = \dfrac{3}{1}$ is an equation of the line.

EXAMPLE 2   Solve the equation $\dfrac{y-8}{x-3}=\dfrac{3}{1}$ for y
(from Example 1).

The equation is a proportion.

$$\dfrac{y-8}{x-3}=\dfrac{3}{1}$$

Prod. of extremes = prod. of means. ────→ $1(y-8)=3(x-3)$
$3(x-3)=3x-9$ ─────────────→ $y-8=3x-9$
Add 8 to each side. ─────────────→ $y=3x-1$

An equation of the line in Example 1 is $y=3x-1$.
It describes every point on the line.

EXAMPLE 3   Show that the point $P(-5,-16)$ lies on the line $\overleftrightarrow{RS}$ in Example 1.

To show that a point is on a line, we show that its coordinates satisfy an equation of the line.

Substitute in the equation.

Let $\begin{array}{l}x=-5 \\ y=-16\end{array}\Big\}$

y	$3x-1$
-16	$3(-5)-1$
	$-15-1$
	-16

Thus, $P(-5,-16)$ lies on $\overleftrightarrow{RS}$.

EXAMPLE 4   Write an equation for $\overleftrightarrow{PQ}$ given $P(-1,4)$ and $Q(2,-5)$.

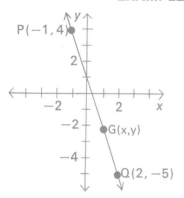

Let $G(x,y)$ represent any point on the line.

Slope of $\overline{PG}$ = Slope of $\overline{QP}$

$$\dfrac{y-4}{x-(-1)}=\dfrac{4-(-5)}{-1-2}$$

$$\dfrac{y-4}{x+1}=\dfrac{9}{-3}$$

Solve the proportion.
$-3(y-4)=-3y+12$ ─────────────→

$$-3(y-4)=9(x+1)$$
$$-3y+12=9x+9$$
$$\underline{-12-12}$$
$$-3y=9x-3$$

Divide each side by -3. ─────────────→
$\dfrac{9x-3}{-3}=\dfrac{9}{-3}x+\dfrac{-3}{-3}$ ─────────────→

$$y=\dfrac{9x-3}{-3}$$
$$y=-3x+1$$

Thus, an equation of $\overleftrightarrow{PQ}$ is $y=-3x+1$.

EXAMPLE 5 Show that $R(5, -14)$ is on $\overleftrightarrow{PQ}$ of Example 4.

See if the coordinates of R satisfy an equation of $\overleftrightarrow{PQ}$.

Let $\left. \begin{array}{l} x = 5 \\ y = -14 \end{array} \right\}$

y	$-3x + 1$
-14	$-3(5) + 1$
	$-15 + 1$
	-14

Thus, $R(5, -14)$ is on $\overleftrightarrow{PQ}$.

ORAL EXERCISES

Give an expression for the slope of $\overleftrightarrow{PG}$.

1. $P(1, 3)$, $G(x, y)$

2. $P(4, 3)$, $G(x, y)$

3. $P(-3, 1)$, $G(x, y)$

4. $P(-3, -5)$, $G(x, y)$

5. $P(1, -2)$, $G(x, y)$

6. $P(-1, -1)$, $G(x, y)$

EXERCISES

PART A

Write an equation for $\overleftrightarrow{PQ}$.

$y = 2x - 5$

1. $P(1, 1)$, $Q(2, 3)$ $y = 2x - 1$
2. $P(1, 5)$, $Q(3, 11)$ $y = 3x + 2$
3. $P(3, 1)$, $Q(4, 3)$

4. $P(2, -1)$, $Q(5, 2)$ $y = x - 3$
5. $P(-1, 3)$, $Q(1, 5)$ $y = x + 4$
6. $P(-2, -6)$, $Q(5, 8)$

7. $P(-2, -10)$, $Q(1, 2)$
8. $P(-1, 15)$, $Q(2, 6)$
9. $P(-1, 0)$, $Q(3, -8)$

10. $P(-3, 8)$, $Q(2, -7)$
11. $P(1, 7)$, $Q(-2, -2)$
12. $P(-3, -13)$, $Q(4, 1)$

13. $P(0, 4)$, $Q(2, -2)$ ↘
14. $P(0, 1)$, $Q(2, -9)$ ↘
15. $P(4, 0)$, $Q(3, -2)$ ↘

$y = -3x + 4$
$y = -5x + 1$
$y = 2x - 8$

Show that P lies on the line with the given equation.

16. $P(-1, -1)$ $y = 2x + 1$ ↘
$-1 = 2(-1) + 1$

17. $P(-3, 1)$ $y = -2x - 5$ ↘
$-2(-3) - 5 = 1$

18. $P(-3, -1)$ $y = -x - 4$
$-(-3) - 4 = -1$

PART B

Write an equation for $\overleftrightarrow{PQ}$. Show that R lies on $\overleftrightarrow{PQ}$.

$y = -3x + 4$

19. $P(1, 4)$, $Q(2, 8)$, $R(3, 12)$ $y = 4x;\ 12 = 4(3)$
20. $P(0, 4)$, $Q(2, -2)$, $R(3, -5)$

21. $P(0, -5)$, $Q(2, 1)$, $R(3, 4)$ ↘
22. $P(-1, 5)$, $Q(1, 1)$, $R(3, -3)$ ↘

$y = 3x - 5;\ 4 = 3(3) - 5$
$y = -2x + 3;\ -3 = -2(3) + 3$

PART C

Write an equation of the line through the given point and having the given slope.

23. $P(-2, 1)$; slope 2

24. $P(0, 5)$; slope -3

25. $P(0, 0)$; slope 1

26. $P(1, 6)$; slope 0

More Difficult Equations

OBJECTIVES

- To write an equation of a line
- To find the *y*-coordinate of a point on a line given the *x*-coordinate and an equation
- To set up a table of values

REVIEW CAPSULE

Write an equation of the line through $P(2, 7)$ and $Q(4, 13)$.

Let $G(x, y)$ represent any point on the line.

Slope of $\overline{QG}$ = Slope of $\overline{PQ}$

$$\frac{y - 13}{x - 4} = \frac{13 - 7}{4 - 2}$$

$$\frac{y - 13}{x - 4} = \frac{6}{2}$$

$$2(y - 13) = 6(x - 4)$$

$$2y - 26 = 6x - 24$$

$$y = 3x + 1$$

EXAMPLE 1 Write an equation for $\overleftrightarrow{AB}$ given $A(1, -1)$ and $B(7, 3)$.

$G(x, y)$ represents any point on the line. ⟶

Slope of $\overline{BG}$ = Slope of $\overline{AB}$

$$\frac{y - 3}{x - 7} = \frac{3 - (-1)}{7 - 1}$$

$3 - (-1) = 3 + (-1)(-1) = 3 + 1$

$$\frac{y - 3}{x - 7} = \frac{4}{6}$$

Prod. of extremes = prod. of means. ⟶
Use the distributive property. ⟶
Add 18 to each side. ⟶

$$6(y - 3) = 4(x - 7)$$

$$6y - 18 = 4x - 28$$

$$6y = 4x - 10$$

Divide each side by 6. ⟶

$$y = \frac{4x - 10}{6}$$

$$y = \frac{4}{6}x - \frac{10}{6}$$

Rewrite each fraction in simplest form. ⟶

$$y = \frac{2}{3}x - \frac{5}{3}$$

EXAMPLE 2 Write an equation for $\overleftrightarrow{AB}$ given $A(3,3)$ and $B(0,5)$.

Let $G(x,y)$ represent any point on the line.

Slope of $\overline{AG}$ = Slope of $\overline{AB}$

Find the slope of each segment. ──────→
$$\frac{y-3}{x-3}=\frac{5-3}{0-3}$$
$$\frac{y-3}{x-3}=\frac{2}{-3}$$

Prod. of means = prod. of extremes ──────→
$$-3(y-3)=2(x-3)$$
$$-3y+9=2x-6$$

Add -9 to each side. ──────→
$$-3y=2x-15$$

Divide each side by -3. ──────→
$$y=\frac{2x-15}{-3}$$

$\dfrac{2x-15}{-3}=\dfrac{2}{-3}x+\dfrac{-15}{-3}$ ──────→
$$y=-\frac{2}{3}x+5$$

EXAMPLE 3 $C(6,y)$ lies on $\overleftrightarrow{AB}$ of Example 2. Find y.

$C(6,y)$

$\uparrow$

x

Use the equation of $\overleftrightarrow{AB}$.

$$y=-\frac{2}{3}x+5$$

Let $x=6$ in the equation. ──────→
$$y=-\frac{2}{3}(6)+5$$

$-\dfrac{2}{3}(6)=\dfrac{-2}{3}\cdot\dfrac{6}{1}$

$=\dfrac{-2\cdot 3\cdot 2}{3\cdot 1}=-4$

$$y=-4+5$$
$$y=1$$

The point $C(6,1)$ lies on $\overleftrightarrow{AB}$.

Check by drawing the line joining $A(3,3)$ and $B(0,5)$.

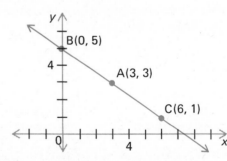

ORAL EXERCISES
Rename each.

1. $\dfrac{3x-5}{2}\quad \dfrac{3x}{2}+\dfrac{-5}{2}$

2. $\dfrac{-2x+5}{7}\quad \dfrac{-2x}{7}+\dfrac{5}{7}$

3. $\dfrac{4x-8}{5}\quad \dfrac{4}{5}x+\dfrac{-8}{5}$

4. $\dfrac{-3x+5}{2}$

EXERCISES

PART A

Write an equation for $\overleftrightarrow{PQ}$.

1. $P(1, 2)$, $Q(3, 5)$ $y = \frac{3}{2}x + \frac{1}{2}$ **2.** $P(3, 5)$, $Q(8, 7)$ $y = \frac{2}{5}x + \frac{19}{5}$ **3.** $P(2, 5)$, $Q(6, 6)$ $y = \frac{1}{4}x + \frac{9}{2}$

4. $P(0, 5)$, $Q(4, 6)$ $y = \frac{1}{4}x + 5$ **5.** $P(3, 3)$, $Q(-2, 5)$ **6.** $P(-2, -3)$, $Q(-7, -5)$

7. $P(-2, 0)$, $Q(3, 4)$ **8.** $P(0, 8)$, $Q(3, 0)$ **9.** $P(-2, 0)$, $Q(0, 5)$

$y = \frac{4}{5}x + \frac{8}{5}$ $y = -\frac{8}{3}x + 8$ $y = \frac{5}{2}x + 5$

Write an equation for $\overleftrightarrow{AB}$. Then use the equation to find the y-coordinate of point C on $\overleftrightarrow{AB}$.

10. $A(0, 2)$, $B(-4, -1)$, $C(4, y)$ **11.** $A(-3, -5)$, $B(3, -1)$, $C(6, y)$

12. $A(0, 1)$, $B(-3, -1)$, $C(-6, y)$ **13.** $A(2, 5)$, $B(6, 11)$, $C(-2, y)$

PART B

EXAMPLE   An equation of $\overleftrightarrow{MN}$ is $y = 3x - 2$. Write a table of values and give the coordinates of three points on the line.

Choose any three numbers for x. Use numbers that will make the arithmetic easy.

x	$3x - 2$	y
1	$3(1) - 2$	1
0	$3(0) - 2$	-2
-1	$3(-1) - 2$	-5

Thus, $(1, 1)$, $(0, -2)$, and $(-1, -5)$ are three points on $\overleftrightarrow{MN}$.

Write a table of values and give the coordinates of three points on the line whose equation is given.

14. $y = x + 1$ **15.** $y = 2x - 3$ **16.** $y = -3x + 4$

17. $y = \frac{1}{2}x - 2$ **18.** $y = \frac{2}{3}x + 3$ **19.** $y = -\frac{1}{4}x - 1$

Write an equation for $\overleftrightarrow{PQ}$. Then use the equation to set up a table of values and give the coordinates of three other points on the line.

20. $P(0, 1)$, $Q(2, 7)$ $y = 3x + 1$ **21.** $P(6, 8)$, $Q(12, 11)$ **22.** $P(-9, -11)$, $Q(15, 5)$

23. $P(0, -6)$, $Q(10, -1)$ **24.** $P(-16, 10)$, $Q(0, 6)$ **25.** $P(0, 1)$, $Q(12, 9)$

$y = \frac{1}{2}x - 6$ $y = -\frac{1}{4}x + 6$ $y = \frac{2}{3}x + 1$

PART C

Find the value of b so that the given point lies on the line.

26. $y = bx - 3$; $(3, -1)$ **27.** $y = bx + 1$; $(4, -1)$

28. $y = bx + 4$; $(10, 8)$ **29.** $y = bx - \frac{1}{2}$; $(12, -2)$

Ratio and Proportion Applied to Travel

In recent years we have become concerned with two problems in travel: the rising costs of fuel and the increasing shortage of fuel. These problems have caused the automobile industry to produce cars that will average more kilometers per liter of gas.

PROBLEM

Anita's car averages 15 km/L. How many liters of gas will she need for a 500-km trip? How much will the gas cost if gas sells at $.20/L?

Let n = number of liters of gas needed

Write the ratio: total km to total L.	$\dfrac{500}{n} = \dfrac{\text{number of km}}{\text{number of liters of gas}}$
Write 15 km/L as a ratio. ⟶	$\dfrac{15}{1} = \dfrac{\text{number of km}}{\text{number of liters of gas}}$
Set the ratios equal. ⟶	$\dfrac{500}{n} = \dfrac{15}{1}$
If $\dfrac{a}{b} = \dfrac{c}{d}$, then $ad = bc$. ⟶	$15n = 500$
Divide each side by 15. ⟶	$n = 33\dfrac{1}{3}$

For practicality, round off to the next whole number. She needs 34L of gas.

Find the cost. ⟶ Cost = (.20) (34) = 6.80

Thus, the trip will cost $6.80.

PROJECT

1. A sales representative's car averages 12 km/L. How much will the gas for a 1,000-km trip cost if gas sells at $.25/L?

2. An insurance agent travels 70,000 km in a year. The car averages 10 km/L. Find the agent's yearly gas expense if gas sells at $.22/L.

$y = mx + b$

 REVIEW CAPSULE

Write an equation of the line passing through points $P(5, 6)$ and $Q(10, 4)$.

Let $G(x, y)$ represent any point on the line.

Slope of $\overline{QG}$ = Slope of $\overline{PQ}$

$$\frac{y - 4}{x - 10} = \frac{4 - 6}{10 - 5}$$

$$\frac{y - 4}{x - 10} = \frac{-2}{5}$$

$$5y - 20 = -2x + 20$$

$$5y = -2x + 40$$

$$y = -\frac{2}{5}x + 8$$

Notice this pattern from the Review Capsule.

Slope of $\overleftrightarrow{PQ} = -\frac{2}{5}$

Equation of $\overleftrightarrow{PQ}$ is $y = -\frac{2}{5}x + 8$.

The slope is the coefficient of x.

EXAMPLE 1   Give the slope of each line.

$y = \frac{4}{7}x - 3$ $y = -\frac{3}{5}x + 8$

The slope is the coefficient of x.

Slope is $\frac{4}{7}$.   Slope is $-\frac{3}{5}$.

Graphing $\overleftrightarrow{PQ}$ reveals another pattern.

The x-coordinate of any point on the y-axis is 0.

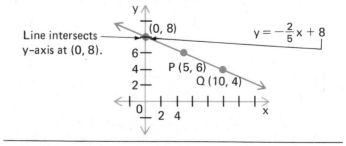

Line intersects y-axis at $(0, 8)$.

Definition of y-intercept. →
The x-coordinate is 0.

> The y-coordinate of the point of intersection of a line with the y-axis is the y-intercept.

EXAMPLE 2 Find the y-intercept.

$y = \frac{4}{7}x - 3$ | $y = -\frac{3}{5}x + 8$

$$y = \frac{4}{7}x - 3$$

Let $x = 0$ to find y. →

$$y = \frac{4}{7}(0) - 3$$
$$y = -3$$

$$y = -\frac{3}{5}x + 8$$
$$y = -\frac{3}{5}(0) + 8$$
$$y = 8$$

Examples 1 and 2 suggest this. →

> If $y = mx + b$ is an equation of a line, then
> slope is m and y-intercept is b.

EXAMPLE 3 Give the slope and the y-intercept.

$$y = \frac{4}{5}x - 12$$

The line crosses the y-axis at $(0, -12)$.

Slope is $\frac{4}{5}$. y-intercept is -12.

EXAMPLE 4 Write an equation for the line whose slope is m and whose y-intercept is b.

b is the y-intercept, $x = 0$. → $P(0, b)$ is a point on the line.

Let $G(x, y)$ represent any point on the line.

The slope of a line is the slope of any segment on it. → Slope of $\overline{PG} = m$

$$\frac{y - b}{x - 0} = \frac{m}{1}$$

Prod. of extremes = prod. of means. → $1(y - b) = mx$

Get y alone on one side. Add b to each side.

$$y - b = mx$$
$$y = mx + b$$

> A line with slope m and y-intercept b has equation $y = mx + b$.

EXAMPLE 5 Write an equation for the line whose slope is -5 and whose y-intercept is -3.

m is the slope.
b is the y-intercept.

$$m = -5 \qquad b = -3$$

$$y = mx + b$$

Thus, $y = -5x - 3$ is the equation.

EXAMPLE 6 Graph $y = \dfrac{2}{3}x + 1$.

The y-intercept is 1. $\longrightarrow$ Plot $P(0, 1)$.

Use the slope to locate another point Q.

Slope $= \dfrac{2}{3} \begin{array}{l} \longleftarrow \text{ up 2} \\ \longleftarrow \text{ right 3} \end{array}$

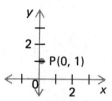

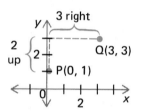

Connect P and Q.

Graph of $y = \dfrac{2}{3}x + 1$ $\longrightarrow$

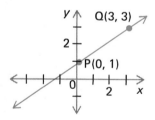

Read: the set of points (x, y) such $\longrightarrow$ that $y = \dfrac{2}{3}x + 1$.

The graph shows $\left\{ (x, y) \mid y = \dfrac{2}{3}x + 1 \right\}$.

Each point on a line satisfies its equation. For example, $(-3, -1)$ is on $\overleftrightarrow{PQ}$,

See the graph. $\longrightarrow$

y	$\dfrac{2}{3}x + 1$
-1	$\dfrac{2}{3}(-3) + 1$
	$-2 + 1$
	-1

Plot $(0, 1)$, $(3, 3)$, and $(-3, -1)$ to check that all three points are on the same line.

since $(-3, -1)$ satisfies the equation.

EXAMPLE 7   Graph $\left\{(x,y) \mid y = -\frac{2}{5}x + 3\right\}$.

Rewrite $-\frac{2}{5}$ as $\frac{-2}{5}$. ⟶
$$y = \frac{-2}{5}x + 3$$

slope   y-intercept

The y-intercept is 3. ⟶ Plot $(0, 3)$.
Then use the slope.   Draw $\overleftrightarrow{PQ}$.

Slope $= \frac{-2}{5}$ ⟵ down 2
⟵ right 5

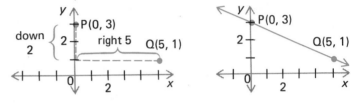
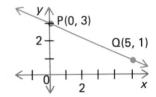

EXERCISES

PART A

Give the slope and y-intercept.

1. $y = \frac{1}{2}x - 7$ $\frac{1}{2}; -7$ **2.** $y = \frac{2}{3}x + 4$ $\frac{2}{3}; 4$ **3.** $y = -\frac{4}{5}x + 7$ $-\frac{4}{5}; 7$ **4.** $y = 2x$ $2; 0$

Write an equation for the line.

5. slope $= 2$ $y = 2x + 4$ **6.** slope $= -3$ $y = -3x - 5$ **7.** slope $= 5$ $y = 5x$
y-intercept $= 4$ y-intercept $= -5$ y-intercept $= 0$

Graph.

$(-4, 5), (4, -1)$

8. $y = \frac{2}{3}x + 1$ $(-3, -1), (3, 3)$ **9.** $y = -\frac{3}{4}x + 2$ $(-5, -2), (5, -6)$
10. $y = -\frac{2}{5}x - 4$
11. $y = 3x + 1$ (Hint: Write the slope as $\frac{3}{1}$.)   **12.** $y = 4x - 3$ $(1, 1), (2, 5)$
13. $y = -2x + 4$ $(1, 2), (2, 0)$ **14.** $y = -3x - 1$ **15.** $y = -4x + 5$
16. $\{(x, y) \mid y = \frac{2}{3}x + 6\}$ **17.** $\{(x, y) \mid y = -\frac{5}{3}x + 2\}$ **18.** $\{(x, y) \mid y = \frac{3}{4}x - 2\}$
$(3, 8), (-3, 4)$ $(-3, 7), (3, -3)$ $(4, 1), (-4, -5)$ $(1, 1), (2, -3)$

PART B

Graph.

$(-1, -3), (1, 3)$ $(-3, 9), (3, -9)$
19. $y = 2x$ (Hint: Crosses y-axis at $(0, 0)$.)   **20.** $y = 3x$ **21.** $y = -3x$

PART C

Graph. [Hint: Parallel lines have the same slope.]

22. The line with y-intercept 3   **23.** The line with y-intercept -2
and parallel to $y = \frac{2}{3}x + 5$.   and parallel to $y = -\frac{4}{5}x + 8$.

$y = mx + b$ **275**

Graphing A Line

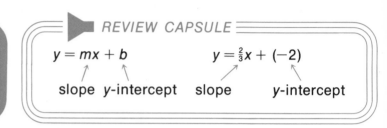

REVIEW CAPSULE

$y = mx + b$ $y = \frac{2}{3}x + (-2)$

↑ slope ↑ y-intercept   ↗ slope   ↖ y-intercept

EXAMPLE 1 Give the slope and y-intercept of $3x - 2y = 10$.

Put the equation in $y = mx + b$ form.

Get y alone on one side. ⎫
Add $-3x$ to each side. ⎬
Divide each side by -2. ⎭

$\dfrac{-3x + 10}{-2} = \dfrac{-3}{-2}x + \dfrac{10}{-2}$ ⟶

Solve for y.

$$3x - 2y = 10$$
$$\underline{-3x \qquad\quad -3x}$$
$$-2y = -3x + 10$$
$$y = \dfrac{-3x + 10}{-2}$$
$$y = \dfrac{3}{2}x - 5$$

Thus, the slope is $\frac{3}{2}$ and the y-intercept is -5.

EXAMPLE 2 Graph $\{(x, y) | -y - x = 2\}$.

$$-1y - 1x = 2$$
$$\underline{+ 1x \quad +1x}$$
$$-1y = +1x + 2$$
$$1y = -1x - 2$$
$$y = -\dfrac{1}{1}x - 2$$

Slope is $-\frac{1}{1}$; y-intercept is -2.

Plot $(0, -2)$.
Then use the slope.   Draw $\overleftrightarrow{PQ}$.

Slope $= \dfrac{-1}{1}$ ← down 1
              ← right 1

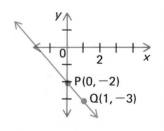

P(0, −2)
Q(1, −3)

EXAMPLE 3 Graph $x + 3y = 0$.

Solve for y.
Add $-1x$ to each side.
Divide each side by 3.

$$1x + 3y = 0$$
$$3y = -1x$$
$$y = \tfrac{-1}{3}x, \text{ or } y = \tfrac{-1}{3}x + 0$$

Slope is $\tfrac{-1}{3}$. y-intercept is 0.

Since the y-intercept is 0, the line passes through the origin. ⟶ Plot $(0, 0)$.
Then use the slope.   Draw $\overleftrightarrow{PQ}$.

Slope $= \dfrac{-1}{3}$ ⟵ down 1
⟵ right 3

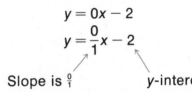

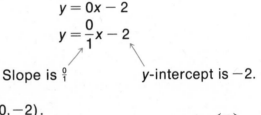

EXAMPLE 4 Graph $\{(x, y) \mid y = -2\}$.

Rewrite: $0x = 0 \cdot x = 0$ ⟶

$$y = 0x - 2$$
$$y = \frac{0}{1}x - 2$$

Slope is $\frac{0}{1}$ y-intercept is -2.

Plot $(0, -2)$.
Then use the slope.   Draw $\overleftrightarrow{PQ}$.

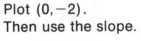

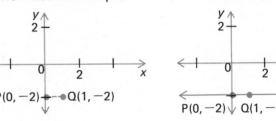

Slope $= \dfrac{0}{1}$ ⟵ neither up nor down
⟵ right 1

A horizontal line has 0 slope. ⟶ $\overleftrightarrow{PQ}$ is a horizontal line.

$y = -2$ represents a horizontal line.
$P(0, -2)$ $Q(1, -2)$

Same y-coordinate

Instead of the method shown in Example 4, we can graph a horizontal line like this.

First plot the y-intercept.
Then plot any other point with the same y-coordinate and draw the line through these points.

EXAMPLE 5   Graph $3y - 9 = 0$.

Solve for y.
Add 9 to each side.
Divide each side by 3.

$$3y - 9 = 0$$
$$3y = 9$$
$$y = 3, \text{ or } y = 0x + 3$$

The y-intercept is 3. ⟶ Plot $P(0, 3)$.

Then, use any other point with y-coordinate 3 like $Q(4, 3)$.

Draw the horizontal line. ⟶

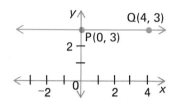

EXERCISES

PART A

Graph.

1. $3x - 2y = 3$ $(2, \frac{3}{2}), (4, \frac{9}{2})$
2. $4y + 3x = 8$ $(-4, 5), (4, -1)$
3. $5y + 2x = -10$ $(-5, 0), (5, -4)$
4. $y - 1 = x$ $(-1, 0), (1, 2)$
5. $y = 6$ $(0, 6), (2, 6)$
6. $2y + 6 = 0$ $(0, -3), (-2, -3)$

Graph.

7. $\{(x, y) \mid 3y - 2x = 12\}$ $(-3, 2), (3, 6)$
8. $\{(x, y) \mid y - 2x = 0\}$ $(-1, -2), (1, 2)$
9. $\{(x, y) \mid 4x + 2y = 8\}$ $(-1, 6), (1, 2)$
10. $\{(x, y) \mid y = 4\}$ $(-1, 4), (1, 4)$
11. $\{(x, y) \mid 2y - 5x = 10\}$ $(2, 10), (4, 15)$
12. $\{(x, y) \mid x + y = 2\}$ $(-1, 3), (1, 1)$

PART B

EXAMPLE   Graph $y = 2x - 1$. Use a table of values.

Choose any 3 numbers for x.
Find the y-coordinates.
Plot the 3 points.
Draw the line.

x	$2x - 1$	y
1	$2(1) - 1$	1
0	$2(0) - 1$	-1
-1	$2(-1) - 1$	-3

Graph. Use a table of values.

13. $y = x + 3$ $(-1, 2), (1, 4)$
14. $y = -3x + 1$ $(-1, 4), (1, -2)$
15. $y = -2x$ $(-1, 2), (1, -2)$
16. $2x + y = 1$ $(-1, 3), (1, -1)$
17. $2x - 3y = 4$ $(-3, \frac{-10}{3}), (3, \frac{2}{3})$
18. $6x - y = 1$ $(-1, -7), (1, 5)$

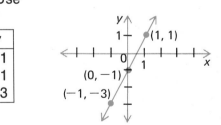

Vertical Lines

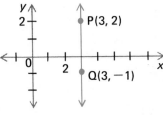

▶ REVIEW CAPSULE

Find the slope of $\overleftrightarrow{PQ}$ for $P(3, 2)$, $Q(3, -1)$.

$$\text{Slope of } \overleftrightarrow{PQ} = \frac{2 - (-1)}{3 - 3}$$

$$= \frac{3}{0} \leftarrow \begin{array}{l}\text{Division by 0} \\ \text{is undefined.}\end{array}$$

Thus, the slope of $\overleftrightarrow{PQ}$ is undefined.

EXAMPLE 1 Graph $\overleftrightarrow{PQ}$ for $P(3, 2)$, $Q(3, -1)$. Identify the slope and the y-intercept.

See the Review Capsule. ———————→ The slope of $\overleftrightarrow{PQ}$ is undefined.

It does not cross the y-axis.———→ $\overleftrightarrow{PQ}$ has no y-intercept.
It is parallel to the y-axis.

$\overleftrightarrow{PQ}$ in Example 1 is a vertical line.
A vertical line does not have an equation of the form.

A vertical line (other than the y-axis) has no y-intercept.

$$y = mx + b.$$
undefined slope —↑   ↑— no y-intercept

EXAMPLE 2 Write an equation for $\overleftrightarrow{PQ}$ in Example 1.

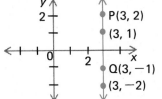

$\overleftrightarrow{PQ}$ is parallel to the y-axis and 3 units to the right of the y-axis.

Observe that every point on $\overleftrightarrow{PQ}$ has x-coordinate 3.

$\overleftrightarrow{PQ}$ is the set of all points (x, y) such that $x = 3$.
$$\{(x, y) \mid x = 3\}$$

y is not mentioned in the equation. It can be any number. But x is always 3. ———→ **Thus,** an equation is $x = 3$.

EXAMPLE 3   Graph $\{(x, y) \mid x = -6\}$.

y is not mentioned in $x = -6$. ⟶ The graph is a vertical line.
y is any number. x is −6. ⟶ The line is the set of all points with x-coordinate −6.

Use any two points with x-coordinate −6 to graph.
For example, $P(-6, 0)$ and $Q(-6, 2)$.

Draw a line through the points P and Q.

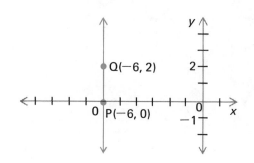

EXAMPLE 4   Graph $x = 5$.

y is not mentioned in $x = 5$.
The graph is a vertical line.

The line will be the set of all points whose x-coordinate is 5.

y can be any number.
x is always 5.

Use any two points with x-coordinate 5 like $P(5, 2)$ and $Q(5, -1)$ to draw the graph.

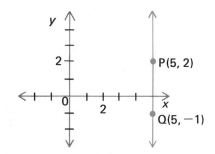

EXERCISES

PART A

Graph.

$(-2, -1), (-2, 0), (-2, 1)$

$(1, -1), (1, 0), (1, 1)$ $(-3, -1), (-3, 0), (-3, 1)$ $(9, -1), (9, 0), (9, 1)$

1. $x = -2$ **2.** $x = 1$ **3.** $x = -3$ **4.** $x = 9$

5. $\{(x, y) \mid x = 3\}$ **6.** $\{(x, y) \mid x = -4\}$ **7.** $\{(x, y) \mid x = 7\}$ **8.** $\{(x, y) \mid 8 = x\}$

$(3, -1), (3, 0), (3, 1)$ $(-4, -1), (-4, 0), (-4, 1)$ $(7, -1), (7, 0), (7, 1)$

PART B

$(8, -1), (8, 0), (8, 1)$

Graph. (Hint: Solve for x.)

$(3, -1), (3, 0), (3, 1)$

9. $\{(x, y) \mid 3x - 9 = 0\}$ **10.** $\{(x, y) \mid 8 + 2x = 0\}$ **11.** $\{(x, y) \mid 6 - x = 0\}$

280   VERTICAL LINES

$(-4, -1), (-4, 0), (-4, 1)$ $(6, -1), (6, 0), (6, 1)$

Graphing Inequalities in Two Variables

 REVIEW CAPSULE

Inequalities in one variable can be
graphed on a number line.

$$-2x + 4 \leq 10$$

Add −4 to each side. ⟶ $-2x \leq 6$
Divide each side by −2.
Reverse the order. ⟶ $x \geq -3$

Graph. ⟶

```
←+++++●++++→
 −6−5−4−3−2−1 0
```

EXAMPLE 1 Graph $y < 2$ on a plane.

First graph $y = 2$ with a dashed line.

Graph of $y = 2$ is a horizontal line. The
y-coordinate of every point is 2.

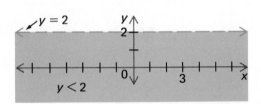

The y-coordinate of every point below
the line is less than 2. ⟶ The graph of $y < 2$ is *below* the line. The shaded
region is the graph of $y < 2$.

EXAMPLE 2 Graph $y > 2$ on a plane.

First graph $y = 2$ with a dashed line.

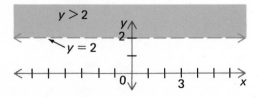

The y-coordinate of every point above
the line is greater than 2.

The graph of $y > 2$ is the shaded region *above*
the line.

EXAMPLE 3 Graph $y = 2x - 1$ with a dashed line. Show that $(-2, 1)$ satisfies the inequality $y > 2x - 1$. Show that $(3, -4)$ satisfies the inequality $y < 2x - 1$.

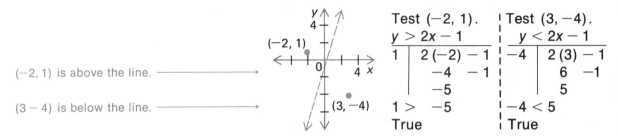

Test $(-2, 1)$.

y	$> 2x - 1$
1	$2(-2) - 1$
	$-4 \quad - 1$
	-5
$1 >$	-5

True

Test $(3, -4)$.

y	$< 2x - 1$
-4	$2(3) - 1$
	$6 \quad -1$
	5
$-4 < 5$	

True

$(-2, 1)$ is above the line. ⟶

$(3 - 4)$ is below the line. ⟶

Example 3 suggests this. ⟶

The graph of $y = mx + b$ is a line.
The graph of $y > mx + b$ is the region *above* the line.
The graph of $y < mx + b$ is the region *below* the line.

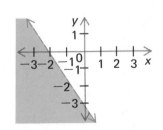

EXAMPLE 4 Graph $-3x - 2y > 6$.

Solve for y.
Add $3x$ to each side. ⟶
Divide each side by -2.
Reverse the order.

$$-3x - 2y > 6$$
$$-2y > 3x + 6$$
$$y < \frac{3x + 6}{-2}$$
$$y < -\frac{3}{2}x - 3$$

Graph $y = -\frac{3}{2}x - 3$ with a dashed line.

$$y = -\frac{3}{2}x - 3$$

slope $-\frac{3}{2}$ y-intercept -3

To graph $y < -\frac{3}{2}x - 3$, shade the region

below the line. ⟶

Thus, the graph of $-3x - 2y > 6$ is the shaded region *below* the line.

EXAMPLE 5   Graph $\{(x, y) \mid y \geq 3x - 1\}$

Graph $y = 3x - 1$.

Slope $\dfrac{3}{1}$ y-intercept -1

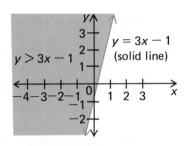

$y > 3x - 1$

$y = 3x - 1$
(solid line)

$\geq$ means is greater than or equal to. The graph must include the line $y = 3x - 1$. Draw a solid line.

Thus, the graph of $\{(x, y) \mid y \geq 3x - 1\}$ is the *line* and the shaded region *above* the line.

EXAMPLE 6   Graph $\{(x, y) \mid x > 3\}$. Then graph $\{(x, y) \mid x < 3\}$.

First graph $x = 3$ with a dashed line.

Graph of $x = 3$ is a vertical line. The x-coordinate of every point is 3.

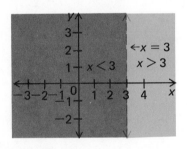

$x < 3$ $\leftarrow x = 3$
$x > 3$

The x-coordinate of every point to the *right* of the line is *greater* than 3.

The x-coordinate of every point to the *left* of the line is less than 3.

The graph of $\{(x, y) \mid x > 3\}$ is the shaded portion to the *right* of the line.
The graph of $\{(x, y) \mid x < 3\}$ is the shaded portion to the *left* of the line.

Example 6 suggests this. ———————→

The graph of $x = a$ is a vertical line.
The graph of $x > a$ is the region to the right of the line.
The graph of $x < a$ is the region to the left of the line.

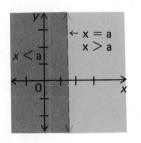

$x < a$ $\leftarrow x = a$
$x > a$

ORAL EXERCISES

Give the equation of the line which must be graphed in order to graph each inequality. Tell whether the shaded region will be above, below, to the left, or to the right of the line. Tell whether the line will be included in the graph.

1. $y \le 3x + 2$ 2. $y > x + 5$ 3. $y \le 4$ 4. $y < x + 3$ 5. $y \ge 2x - 1$ 6. $x \ge 5$
7. $x < 2$ 8. $y > 7$ 9. $y \le 4x + 1$ 10. $y > x$ 11. $x \le 3$ 12. $y < 3$

EXERCISES

PART A

Solve for y.

1. $x + y < 3$

2. $x - y > 8$ ↗ $y < x - 8$

3. $x + 3 > -y$ ↗ $y > -x - 3$

4. $2x - y \le 4$ ↗ $y \ge 2x - 4$

5. $3x + 2y > 0$ ↘ $y > -\frac{3}{2}x$

6. $4x + y \ge 6$ ↘ $y \ge -4x + 6$

7. $-3x + y < 4$ ↘ $y < 3x + 4$

8. $3y < x$ $y < \frac{1}{3}x$

Graph each inequality.

9. $y > 3$ 10. $x < -1$ 11. $y \le -4$ 12. $\{(x, y) \mid x \ge 2\}$

13. $y < 3x$ 14. $y > 2x$ 15. $y \le x$ 16. $\{(x, y) \mid y \ge -2x\}$

17. $y \le x + 5$ 18. $y \ge 2x - 3$ 19. $y < -x - 3$ 20. $\{(x, y) \mid y > 3x - 4\}$

21. $y \le 2x + 1$ 22. $y \ge 3x - 2$ 23. $x < 0$ 24. $\{(x, y) \mid y \ge 0\}$

25. $y < \frac{2}{3}x + 1$ ↘   26. $y \ge \frac{3}{5}x - 2$ ↘   27. $y \le \frac{1}{2}x + 1$ ↘   28. $\{(x, y) \mid y > \frac{2}{3}x - 2\}$)

below   *above and including*   *below and including*   *above*

Graph each inequality. Then determine which of the given points belong to the graph.

29. $y > 1$; (3, 1), (3, 7) *(3, 7)*   30. $x \le 4$; (−5, 3), (7, 3) *(−5, 3)*

31. $y > x - 6$; (3, −3), (3, 8) *(3, 8)*   32. $y \ge x - 6$; (8, 2), (8, 1) *(8, 2)*

33. $y \le 3x + 1$; (3, 11), (3, 0) *(3, 0)*   34. $y < 3x - 4$; (3, 5), (3, 2) *(3, 2)*

PART B

Graph each inequality.

35. $2y < 8$ 36. $-3x \le 9$ 37. $3x \ge 2y$ 38. $\{(x, y) \mid -4y \ge 8\}$

39. $3x - 2y \le 6$ 40. $2x - 3y \ge 9$ 41. $4x - 3y \ge 6$ 42. $\{(x, y) \mid 2x - 5y \ge 10\}$

43. $3x - 5y \le 15$ 44. $3x \le 4y + 12$ 45. $8x + 4y > 2$ 46. $\{(x, y) \mid 6x - 3y < 9\}$

PART C

Graph each.

47. $4x - 3(y - 2) \le y - (6 - x)$ 48. $3x - (6 - 2y) > x - (4 - y)$

49. $6 < y \le 9$ 50. $8 \le x < 10$

Diophantus

HERE YOU SEE THE TOMB CONTAINING THE REMAINS OF DIOPHANTUS. ONE SIXTH OF HIS LIFE GOD GRANTED HIM YOUTH. AFTER A TWELFTH MORE HIS CHEEKS WERE BEARDED. AFTER AN ADDITIONAL SEVENTH HE KINDLED THE LIGHT OF MARRIAGE AND IN THE FIFTH YEAR HE FATHERED A SON. ALAS THE UNFORTUNATE SON'S LIFE SPAN WAS ONLY HALF THAT OF HIS FATHER WHO CONSOLED HIS GRIEF IN THE REMAINING FOUR YEARS OF HIS LIFE. BY THIS DEVICE OF NUMBERS TELL THE EXTENT OF HIS LIFE...

According to legend the above is the inscription on Diophantus' tomb. He was a Greek mathematician who lived in Alexandria in the 3rd century A.D. Diophantus is thought to be one of the originators of algebra. He was probably the first to use symbols for unknowns and operations. He also developed analytical approaches to solve problems. Diophantus was dedicated to algebra, as his epitaph indicates.

PROJECT Can you find how old Diophantus was when he died?

Chapter Ten Review

Identify the means and extremes. Solve. $[p.\ 261]$

1. $\dfrac{x}{6} = \dfrac{4}{3}$

2. $\dfrac{2}{5} = \dfrac{x}{10}$

3. $\dfrac{x+2}{4} = \dfrac{x-5}{3}$

4. $\dfrac{3}{2x-1} = \dfrac{4}{x+4}$

5. $\dfrac{2x+1}{5} = \dfrac{x}{4}$

6. $\dfrac{3x+1}{2} = \dfrac{4x-3}{5}$

7. $\dfrac{x}{9} = \dfrac{1}{x}$

8. $\dfrac{x+5}{4} = \dfrac{-1}{x}$

Solve. $[p.\ 261]$

9. Two out of 9 people use Gum Tooth-brushes. How many use this brand in a town of 27,000 people?

10. Lee's batting average is .675. How many hits should Lee score in 5,000 times at bat?

Write an equation for $\overleftrightarrow{PQ}$. $[p.\ 265,\ 268]$

11. $P(3, 1)$, $Q(5, 5)$

12. $P(0, 1)$, $Q(2, 7)$

13. $P(1, 4)$, $Q(3, 0)$

14. $P(1, 1)$, $Q(5, 3)$

15. $P(-2, 3)$, $Q(1, 4)$

16. $P(-3, -2)$, $Q(1, 1)$

Write an equation for $\overleftrightarrow{PQ}$. Show that R lies on $\overleftrightarrow{PQ}$. $[p.\ 265]$

17. $P(2, 4)$, $Q(3, 6)$, $R(4, 8)$

18. $P(1, 2)$, $Q(2, 5)$, $R(3, 8)$

Write an equation for the line. $[p.\ 272]$

19. slope $= \dfrac{2}{3}$

y-intercept $= -5$

20. slope $= -\dfrac{3}{7}$

y-intercept $= 6$

21. slope $= 3$

y-intercept $= -1$

Give the slope and y-intercept. Graph the line. $[p.\ 272,\ 276]$

22. $y = \dfrac{2}{3}x - 4$

23. $y = -\dfrac{4}{5}x + 2$

24. $y = -2x$

25. $\{(x, y)\,|\,y = 2x + 1\}$

26. $\{(x, y)\,|\,x - 3y = 6\}$

27. $\{(x, y)\,|\,y = -6\}$

Graph. Use a table of values. $[p.\ 276]$

28. $y = 2x - 1$

29. $y = x + 4$

30. $2x - 3y = 15$

Graph. $[p.\ 279,\ 281]$

31. $x = 3$

32. $x = -4$

33. $\{(x, y)\,|\,2x + 4 = 0\}$

34. $\{(x, y)\,|\,y < x + 5\}$

35. $\{(x, y)\,|\,3x - 2y > 8\}$

36. $\{(x, y)\,|\,x \geq 2\}$

Chapter Ten Test

Identify the means and extremes. Solve.

1. $\dfrac{x}{14} = \dfrac{1}{7}$

2. $\dfrac{2x + 1}{3} = \dfrac{x - 4}{5}$

3. $\dfrac{x + 2}{6} = \dfrac{-2}{x - 5}$

Solve.

4. Two out of 5 people shave with Dull Blades. How many use this brand in a town of 20,000?

5. Pat's batting average is .125. How many hits should Pat expect in 2,000 times at bat?

Write an equation for $\overleftrightarrow{PQ}$.

6. $P(4, 9)$, $Q(6, 13)$

7. $P(0, 1)$, $Q(2, -3)$

8. $P(2, 3)$, $Q(5, 1)$

9. $P(0, 2)$, $Q(5, 0)$

Write an equation for $\overleftrightarrow{PQ}$. Show that R lies on $\overleftrightarrow{PQ}$.

10. $P(3, 4)$, $Q(5, 5)$, $R(7, 6)$

11. $P(0, 3)$, $Q(2, 10)$, $R(4, 17)$

Write an equation for the line.

12. slope $= \dfrac{3}{4}$

    y-intercept $= -7$

13. slope $= 2$

    y-intercept $= 3$

Give the slope and y-intercept. Graph the line.

14. $y = \dfrac{2}{3}x - 4$

15. $y = -\dfrac{4}{5}x + 2$

16. $y = 8$

17. $x + y = 5$

18. $\{(x, y) \mid y = 3x + 2)\}$

19. $\{(x, y) \mid 2x - 3y = 6\}$

Graph. Use a table of values.

20. $y = 2x - 7$

21. $x - 2y = -16$

Graph.

22. $x = -2$

23. $\{(x, y) \mid x = 3\}$

24. $\{(x, y) \mid 5x + 20 = 0\}$

25. $\{(x, y) \mid y > x + 2\}$

26. $\{(x, y) \mid 4x - 3y \le 15\}$

27. $\{(x, y) \mid x < 3\}$

Linear Programming

The shaded region of the graph below is called a polygonal region. It represents the intersection of the solution of the system of inequalities listed below.

$x \geq 0$
$y \geq 0$
$x \leq 4$
$x + y \leq 8$

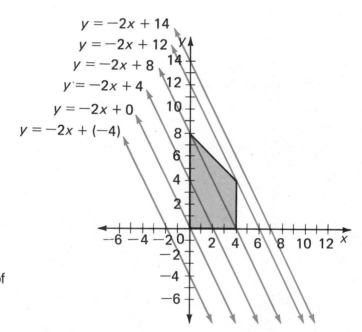

The lines are the graphs of
$y = -2x + k$ for
$k = \{-4, 0, 4, 8, 12, 14\}$.

The graphs of inequalities and equations as shown above are useful in solving problems in industry. This technique is called linear programming. The graph tells us the maximum (12) and minimum (0) values of k that the equation may use and still have a solution in the polygonal region.

PROJECT

Graph $y = -x + k$ for $k = \{-6, -3, 0, 3, 6, 9, 12\}$ and $x \geq -3$, $y \geq 0$, $x \leq 2$, $y \leq x + 5$.
Find the maximum and minimum values of k in the polygonal region.

Systems of Equations: Graphing

 REVIEW CAPSULE

The intersection of two sets is the set of all elements common to both sets.

$$\{3, 4, 5, 6\} \cap \{2, 4, 5, 8\} = \{4, 5\}$$

The graph of $\{(x, y) \,|\, y = 3x + 2\}$ is the line whose equation is $y = 3x + 2$.

EXAMPLE 1 Graph $\{(x, y) \,|\, y = 3x - 9\}$ and $\{(x, y) \,|\, y = -4x + 5\}$ on the same set of axes.

Use the slope-intercept method to graph each line:

$y = 3x - 9$

slope $\dfrac{3}{1}$ y-intercept -9

$y = -4x + 5$

slope $\dfrac{-4}{1}$ y-intercept 5

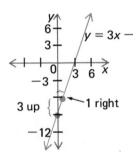

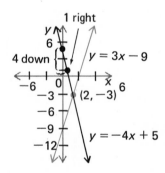

From the graph, $(2, -3)$ is a point common to both lines.

EXAMPLE 2 Find $\{(x, y) \,|\, y = 3x - 9\} \cap \{(x, y) \,|\, y = -4x + 5\}$.

Each set of points is graphed in Example 1. $(2, -3)$ is in both sets.

Intersection is the set of points in common. ────────→ **Thus, $\{(2, -3)\}$ is the intersection of the two sets.**

The two equations in Example 1 form a *system* of equations. ────→

A System of Equations

$$y = 3x - 9$$
$$y = -4x + 5$$

$(2, -3)$ satisfies both equations. ────→ $(2, -3)$ is a solution of the system.

EXAMPLE 3 Verify that $(2, -3)$ satisfies both $y = 3x - 9$ and $y = -4x + 5$ in Example 1.

(2, −3)   (x, y)
Let $x = 2$ and $y = -3$.

y	$3x - 9$
-3	$3(2) - 9$
	$6 \;-9$
	-3

y	$-4x + 5$
-3	$-4(2) + 5$
	$-8 \;+5$
	-3

Thus, $(2, -3)$ satisfies both equations.

EXAMPLE 4 Solve the system by graphing.
$$3x - 2y = 4$$
$$y = -2x + 5$$

Put $3x - 2y = 4$ in $y = mx + b$ form;
solve for y.
Add $-3x$ to each side.
Divide each side by -2.

$$3x - 2y = 4$$
$$-2y = -3x + 4$$
$$y = \frac{3}{2}x - 2$$

slope   y-intercept

$y = -2x + 5$ is already in $y = mx + b$ form.

$$y = -2x + 5$$

$$y = \frac{-2}{1}x + 5$$

slope

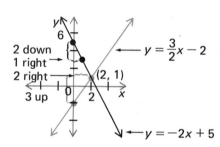

2 down
1 right
2 right
3 up

$y = \frac{3}{2}x - 2$

$(2, 1)$

$y = -2x + 5$

From the graph, find the solution.
The two lines intersect at $(2, 1)$. ⟶ $(2, 1)$ is a solution of the system.

Check by letting $x = 2$ and $y = 1$ in each ⟶ **Thus,** $(2, 1)$ is a solution of both $3x - 2y = 4$
equation. and $y = -2x + 5$.

SUMMARY   **To solve a system of equations by graphing:**

Graph each equation on the same set of axes.   **Then read the coordinates of the point of intersection from the graph.**

EXERCISES

PART A

Find the intersection. Verify that its coordinates satisfy both equations.

1. $\{(x, y) \mid y = -2x + 1\} \cap \{(x, y) \mid y = \frac{1}{2}x - 4\}$ *(2, -3)*
2. $\{(x, y) \mid y = \frac{1}{2}x + 6\} \cap \{(x, y) \mid y = -2x + 11\}$ *(2, 7)*
3. $\{(x, y) \mid y = -2x + 4\} \cap \{(x, y) \mid y = 3x + 4\}$ *(0, 4)*
4. $\{(x, y) \mid y = 3x - 6\} \cap \{(x, y) \mid y = -\frac{2}{3}x + 5\}$ *(3, 3)*
5. $\{(x, y) \mid y = x + 4\} \cap \{(x, y) \mid y = -\frac{3}{2}x + 9\}$ *(2, 6)*
6. $\{(x, y) \mid 3x - 2y = 4\} \cap \{(x, y) \mid 3x + 2y = 8\}$ *(2, 1)*

Solve each system by graphing.

7. $y = 2x + 1$
   $y = -\frac{3}{2}x + 8$ *(2, 5)*

8. $3x - 2y = 6$
   $x - y = 2$ *(2, 0)*

9. $y = 2x$
   $x + y = 9$ *(3, 6)*

10. $x = 3y + 6$
   $x + 3y = 6$ *(6, 0)*

PART B

EXAMPLE Find $\{(x, y) \mid y = 3x + 5\} \cap \{(x, y) \mid y = 3x - 2\}$.

The lines are parallel. They never intersect.

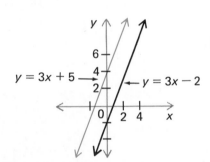

The lines have no points in common.

$y = 3x + 5$
$y = 3x - 2$

$\{(x, y) \mid y = 3x + 5\} \cap \{(x, y) \mid y = 3x - 2\} = \phi$

We call this an *inconsistent system.*
A *consistent system* is one which has a solution.

Determine whether each system is consistent or inconsistent.

inconsistent

11. $3x - 2y = 14$
   $6x - 4y = 8$
   inconsistent

12. $x + y = 8$
   $x - y = 10$
   consistent

13. $y = 3x - 2$
   $y - 3x = 4$
   inconsistent

14. $y = 4$
   $y = -2$

PART C

For what value of *m* will the system be inconsistent?

15. $3x - 2y = 8$
   $mx - 2y = 10$

16. $5x + 2y = 4$
   $mx + 4y = 8$

17. $mx - 4y = 10$
   $5x - 2y = 4$

18. $mx + 4y = 8$
   $2x + 8y = 16$

Systems of Inequalities: Graphing *(optional)*

OBJECTIVE
■ To solve a system of inequalities by graphing

▶ *REVIEW CAPSULE*

Graph $y > 3x + 2$.

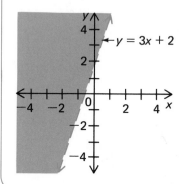

Graph $y = 3x + 2$ with a dashed line. Then shade the region above the line.

Thus, the graph of $y > 3x + 2$ is the shaded region above the line.

EXAMPLE 1 Find $\{(x, y) \mid y \leq 3\} \cap \{(x, y) \mid x < 4\}$ by graphing.

Graph $y \leq 3$.

Graph $x < 4$ on the same set of axes.

Graph $y = 3$ with a solid line. The y-coord. is always 3. Shade the region below the line.

Graph $x = 4$ with a dashed line. The x-coord. is always 4. Shade the region to the left of the line. The two shadings overlap each other.

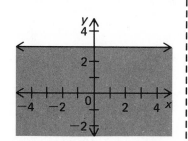
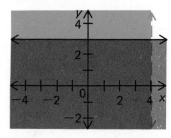

The double shaded region contains all points common to both sets.

Thus, $\{(x, y) \mid y \leq 3\} \cap \{(x, y) \mid x < 4\}$ is the double shaded region.

EXAMPLE 2 Verify that (1, 2) satisfies both $y \leq 3$ and $x < 4$.

Test (1, 2).

y	3
2	3
$2 \leq 3$	

x	r
1	4
$1 < 4$	

$2 \leq 3$ is true and $1 < 4$ is true.

Thus, (1, 2) satisfies both $y \leq 3$ and $x < 4$.

EXAMPLE 3   Solve the system by graphing.

$$3x - 2y < 2$$
$$y < -\frac{3}{5}x - 2$$

Solve $3x - 2y < 2$ for y.

Add $-3x$ to each side. ————————→

Divide each side by -2. Reverse the order from $<$ to $>$.

$$3x - 2y < 2$$
$$-2y < -3x + 2$$
$$y > \frac{3}{2}x - 1$$

Graph $y = \frac{3}{2}x - 1$ with a dashed line.

slope $\frac{3}{2}$ y-intercept -1

Shade the region above the line.

Graph $y = -\frac{3}{5}x - 2$ with a dashed line.

Shade the region below the line.

Graph $y > \frac{3}{2}x - 1$.

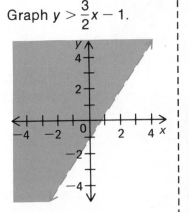

Graph $y < -\frac{3}{5}x - 2$ on the same set of axes.

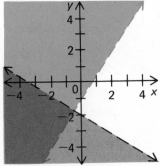

The double shaded region contains all points common to both inequalities.

Thus, the solution of the system is the double shaded region.

EXERCISES

Find the intersection. Pick a point in each intersection and check algebraically.

1. $\{(x, y) \mid x < 4\} \cap \{(x, y) \mid y \geq -2\}$

2. $\{(x, y) \mid y > x + 4\} \cap (x, y) \mid y < -2x - 5\}$

Solve each system by graphing.

3. $y \geq 2$
$\quad x < -5$

4. $x < 4$
$\quad y \geq -5$

5. $y > x + 5$
$\quad x \leq 2$

6. $2x - y \leq 8$
$\quad y < 6$

7. $y < x$
$\quad y \geq \frac{2}{3}x - 5$

8. $y \leq 3x - 2$
$\quad y > x + 4$

9. $y > 2x - 3$
$\quad x - 3y < 9$

10. $3x - 2y \leq 8$
$\quad x - y > 4$

Systems of Equations: Substitution

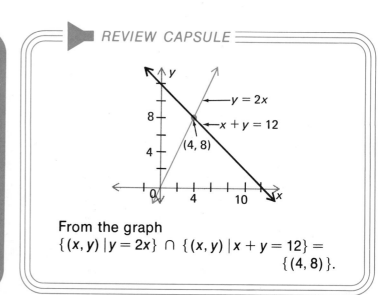

▶ REVIEW CAPSULE

From the graph
$$\{(x, y) \mid y = 2x\} \cap \{(x, y) \mid x + y = 12\} = \{(4, 8)\}.$$

EXAMPLE 1 Solve the system algebraically.
$$y = 2x$$
$$x + y = 12$$

We want values of x and y that satisfy both equations. y must be the same in both equations.

$$y = 2x$$

$$x + y = 12$$
$$\downarrow$$

Replace y by $2x$ in $x + y = 12$. ⟶
Solve the equation for x.

$$x + 2x = 12$$
$$3x = 12$$
$$x = 4$$

{ Substitute for y to get an equation with one variable.

To find y, let $x = 4$ in either equation.

Replace x by 4 in one of the equations. ⟶
Solve for y.

$y = 2x$	or	$x + y = 12$
$y = 2(4)$		$4 + y = 12$
$y = 8$		$y = 8$

So, $x = 4$ and $y = 8$.

Check. ⟶
Let $x = 4$ and $y = 8$ in each equation. ⟶

y	$2x$
8	$2(4)$
	8

$x + y$	12
$4 + 8$	12
12	

Thus, $(4, 8)$ is a solution of the system.

EXAMPLE 2   Solve.

$$3x + 2y = 13$$
$$2x - y = 4$$

Choose a variable whose coefficient
is 1 or −1. ─────────────────→ First solve $2x - y = 4$ for y.

$-y = -1y$ ─────────────────→
Add $-2x$ to each side. ──────────→

$$2x - 1y = 4$$
$$-1y = -2x + 4$$

Divide each side by −1. $\dfrac{-2}{-1} = 2$;

$\dfrac{+4}{-1} = -4$

$$y = \frac{-2x + 4}{-1}, \text{ or } \frac{-2}{-1}x + \frac{4}{-1}$$
$$y = 2x - 4$$

The other equation ──────────────→

$$3x + 2y = 13$$

Replace y by $2x - 4$. ──────────→
$2(2x - 4) = 4x - 8$ ──────────→
Combine like terms. ──────────────→
Add 8 to each side. ──────────────→

$$3x + 2(2x - 4) = 13$$
$$3x + 4x - 8 = 13$$
$$7x - 8 = 13$$
$$\underline{8 \quad 8}$$
$$7x = 21$$

Divide each side by 7. ──────────→

$$x = 3$$

Any of the equations could be used.
$y = 2x - 4$ is easiest to use, since it
is already solved for y.

To find y, let $x = 3$ in $y = 2x - 4$.

$$y = 2x - 4$$
$$y = 2 \cdot 3 - 4$$
$$y = 6 - 4$$
$$y = 2$$

So, $x = 3$ and $y = 2$.

Check by letting $x = 3$ and $y = 2$ in both
equations. ──────────────────→

Thus, $(3, 2)$ is a solution of the system.

$2x - y = 4$, or
$2x - 1y = 4$
coefficient is −1

The method of substitution is easy to use when one
equation contains a variable with a coefficient of
1 or −1.

SUMMARY   **To solve a system of equations by substitution:**

| **Solve one equation for one of its variables.** | **Then substitute for that variable in the other equation.** |

ORAL EXERCISES

Identify the variable for which it is easier to solve.

1. $2x - y = 7$ y
  $3x + 7y = 8$

2. $3x - 4y = 6$
  $x + 2y = 8$ x

3. $x + 3y = 9$ x
  $2x - 5y = 6$

4. $3x - 7y = 1$
  $2x - y = 4$ y

EXERCISES

PART A

Solve.

1. $y = 2x$
  $x + y = 9$ $(3, 6)$

2. $x + y = 6$
  $y = x - 4$ $(5, 1)$

3. $y = 2x - 5$
  $x - y = 2$ $(3, 1)$

4. $x + y = 7$
  $y = x + 1$ $(3, 4)$

5. $3x - 2y = 9$
  $x + 2y = 3$ $(3, 0)$

6. $2x - 3y = 8$
  $x + y = 4$ $(4, 0)$

7. $x - 3y = 2$
  $3x - 2y = 6$ $(2, 0)$

8. $x - 2y = 6$
  $x + 2y = 2$ $(4, -1)$

PART B

Solve.

9. $x - y = 6$
  $x + y = 5$ $(\frac{11}{2}, -\frac{1}{2})$

10. $x + y = 8$
  $2x - y = -6$ $(\frac{2}{3}, \frac{22}{3})$

11. $y = 2x$
  $2x + y = 10$ $(\frac{5}{2}, 5)$

12. $x + y = 1$
  $y = x$ $(\frac{1}{2}, \frac{1}{2})$

PART C

EXAMPLE   Solve by substitution.

$$3y = 5 - 2x$$
$$4x + 3y = 11$$

Replace $3y$ by $5 - 2x$. $\longrightarrow$

Combine like terms. $\longrightarrow$

$$4x + 3y = 11$$
$$4x + (5 - 2x) = 11$$
$$2x + 5 = 11$$
$$x = 3$$

Use $3y = 5 - 2x$ and find y. $\longrightarrow$

Let $x = 3$. $\longrightarrow$

$$3y = 5 - 2x$$
$$3y = 5 - 2 \cdot 3$$
$$y = -\frac{1}{3}$$

Thus, $(3, -\frac{1}{3})$ is a solution.

Solve.

13. $5y = x - 1$
  $2x = 5y$

14. $4x = 2y - 5$
  $2y - 5 + 3x = 14$

15. $2x - 5y = 2$
  $5y = 3x + 1$

16. $7y = 3x - 2$
  $2x + 7y = 13$

Systems of Equations: $ax + by = c$ $dx - by = e$

 REVIEW CAPSULE

The addition property for equations

$3 + 1 = 4$	$x - 5 = 3x$	$3x = 12$
$5 + 2 = 7$	$-x = -x$	$2x = 18$
$8 + 3 = 11$	$-5 = 2x$	$5x = 30$

EXAMPLE 1 Add the equations.
$$5x + 2y = 12$$
$$3x - 2y = 4$$
Solve the resulting equation.

+2y ⟵ ⎤
−2y ⟵ ⎦ opposites

Equation with only one variable

Divide each side by 2. ⟶

$$5x + 2y = 12 \longleftarrow \text{first equation (1)}$$
$$3x - 2y = 4 \longleftarrow \text{second equation (2)}$$
$$\overline{8x + 0 = 16} \longleftarrow \text{third, or resulting equation (3)}$$
$$x = 2$$

EXAMPLE 2 Let $x = 2$ in $5x + 2y = 12$ in Example 1. Solve for the corresponding value of y.

Replace x with 2. ⟶
Solve for y.
Add −10 to each side.
Divide each side by 2.

$$5x + 2y = 12$$
$$5 \cdot 2 + 2y = 12$$
$$10 + 2y = 12$$
$$2y = 2$$
$$y = 1$$

Show that (2, 1) is a solution of the system.
$$5x + 2y = 12$$
$$3x - 2y = 4$$

Check in both equations.
Let $x = 2$ and $y = 1$. ⟶

$5x + 2y$	12	$3x - 2y$	4
$5 \cdot 2 + 2 \cdot 1$	12	$3 \cdot 2 - 2 \cdot 1$	4
$10 + 2$		$6 - 2$	
12		4	

Thus, (2, 1) is a solution of the system.

EXAMPLE 3   Solve.

$$4x - 3y = 6$$
$$2x + 3y = 12$$

Get an equation with one variable. ⎤
Add the two equations.   ⎬
An equation with only one variable ⎦
Solve $6x = 18$ for x. ————————————→

$$
\begin{array}{ll}
4x - 3y = 6 & (1)\\
2x + 3y = 12 & (2)\\
\hline
6x \quad\;\; = 18 & (3)\\
x = 3
\end{array}
$$

To find y, let $x = 3$ in either equation (1) or (2).

Replace x with 3. ————————————→

Solve for y. ⎤
Add -12 to each side. ⎬
Divide each side by -3. ⎦

$$
\begin{array}{c|c}
\begin{aligned}
4x - 3y &= 6\\
4 \cdot 3 - 3y &= 6\\
12 - 3y &= 6\\
-3y &= -6\\
y &= 2
\end{aligned}
&
\begin{aligned}
2x + 3y &= 12\\
2 \cdot 3 + 3y &= 12\\
6 + 3y &= 12\\
3y &= 6\\
y &= 2
\end{aligned}
\end{array}
$$

So, $x = 3$ and $y = 2$.

Check in both equations. ————————→ **Thus,** $(3, 2)$ is a solution of the system.

$-3y$ ⟵⎤
      opposites
$3y$ ⟵⎦

> A system of equations like
> $$4x - 3y = 6$$
> $$2x + 3y = 12$$
> can be solved by addition.

EXAMPLE 4   Solve by addition.

$$x + 3y = -7$$
$$-x - 7y = 19$$

x ⟵⎤
   opposites
$-x$ ⟵⎦

Equation with only one variable y

$$
\begin{array}{ll}
x + 3y = -7 & (1)\\
-x - 7y = 19 & (2)\\
\hline
-4y = 12 & (3)\\
y = -3
\end{array}
$$

To find x, let $y = -3$ in either equation (1) or (2).

$$x + 3y = -7 \quad (1)$$

Replace y with -3. ————————————→

$$x + 3(-3) = -7$$

Add 9 to each side. ————————————→

$$x - 9 = -7$$
$$x = 2$$

So, $x = 2$ and $y = -3$.

Check in both equations. ————————→ **Thus,** $(2, -3)$ is a solution of the system.

EXERCISES

PART A

Solve.

1. $x + y = 8$
   $x - y = 4$ $(6, 2)$

2. $-2x + y = 6$ $(-1, 4)$
   $2x + 3y = 10$

3. $3x - 2y = 2$
   $5x + 2y = 14$ $(2, 2)$

4. $-7x + y = 1$
   $7x + 3y = 3$ $(0, 1)$

5. $3x - y = 5$
   $2x + y = 5$ $(2, 1)$

6. $2x - 3y = 3$
   $x + 3y = 3$ $(2, \frac{1}{3})$

7. $5x - 2y = 6$
   $x + 2y = 6$ $(2, 2)$

8. $-2x + 5y = -3$
   $2x + 3y = 11$
   $(4, 1)$

PART B

EXAMPLE Solve.

$$4x - 3y = 14 \quad (1)$$
$$5x = -3y + 31 \quad (2)$$

The variables are not on one side in $5x = -3y + 31$.

Add $3y$ to each side. The variables are now on one side. ⟶

Add the two equations. ⟶

Substitute 5 for x. ⟶

Add -31 to each side. ⟶

Check $(5, 2)$ in both equations. ⟶

The addition method works best if both variables are on one side in each equation.

$$5x = -3y + 31 \quad (2)$$
$$5x + 3y = 31 \quad (2)$$
$$\underline{4x - 3y = 14 \quad (1)}$$
$$9x \quad\;\; = 45 \quad (3)$$
$$x = 5$$

To find y, let $x = 5$ in either equation (1) or (2).
$$5x = -3y + 31 \quad (2)$$
$$5 \cdot 5 = -3y + 31$$
$$25 = -3y + 31$$
$$-6 = -3y$$
$$2 = y$$

So, $x = 5$ and $y = 2$.
Thus, $(5, 2)$ is a solution of the system.

Solve.

9. $5x + 8y = 31$
   $4y = 5x - 7$ $(3, 2)$

10. $x - 4y = 5$
    $2x = -4y - 2$ $(1, -1)$

11. $2x = -9y + 24$
    $-9y + 4x = -6$ $(3, 2)$

12. $3x + 2y = 13$
    $5x = 2y + 11$ $(3, 2)$

PART C

Solve.

13. $2x - (4 - y) = 8$
    $5x - y = 9$

14. $.05x - .23y = -.13$
    $-.05x + .46y = .36$

15. $\frac{2}{3}x - \frac{1}{5}y = 8$
    $\frac{1}{3}x + \frac{1}{5}y = 7$

Systems of Equations: $\begin{array}{l} ax + by = c \\ dx + ey = f \end{array}$

OBJECTIVE

■ To solve systems like

$3x + 2y = 13$
$2x + 5y = 16$

by addition

 REVIEW CAPSULE

Transform $3x + 2y = 8$ into another equation by multiplying each side by 2.

$$2(3x + 2y) = 2 \cdot 8$$
$$6x + 4y = 16$$

Both $3x + 2y = 8$ and $6x + 4y = 16$ have the same solutions.

EXAMPLE 1   Solve by addition.

$$3x + 2y = 13 \quad (1)$$
$$2x + 5y = 16 \quad (2)$$

Adding (1) and (2) does not give an equation in one variable.

$3x + 2y = 13$ (1)
$2x + 5y = 16$ (2)
$\overline{5x + 7y = 29}$ (3)

Transform each equation so that adding them gives an equation in one variable.

Multiply each side by 5. ───────→

Multiply each side by −2. ──────→

$+10y$ ← opposites
$-10y$ ←

An equation in one variable ──────→

$$5(3x + 2y) = 5 \cdot 13$$

$$-2(2x + 5y) = -2 \cdot 16$$
$$15x + 10y = 65$$
$$\underline{-4x - 10y = -32}$$
$$11x \qquad = 33$$
$$x = 3$$

To find y, let $x = 3$ in either equation (1) or (2).

$$3x + 2y = 13 \quad (1)$$
$$3 \cdot 3 + 2y = 13$$
$$9 + 2y = 13$$
$$2y = 4$$
$$y = 2$$

Replace x with 3. ───────→
Solve for y.
Add −9 to each side.
Divide each side by 2.

So, $x = 3$ and $y = 2$.

Check (3, 2) in both equations. ──────→   **Thus,** (3, 2) is a solution of the system.

EXAMPLE 2   Solve.

$$3x - 2y = 6 \quad (1)$$
$$5x + 7y = 41 \quad (2)$$

↙ Two ways ↘

Make the coefficients of y opposites.	Make the coefficients of x opposites.
$7(3x - 2y) = 7 \cdot 6$	$5(3x - 2y) = 5 \cdot 6$
$2(5x + 7y) = 2 \cdot 41$	$-3(5x + 7y) = -3 \cdot 41$

$-14y$ ↖ opposites ↗ $+15x$
$+14y$ ↙ ↘ $-15x$

$21x - 14y = 42$	$15x - 10y = 30$
$\underline{10x + 14y = 82}$	$\underline{-15x - 21y = -123}$
$31x \qquad = 124$	$-31y = -93$
$x = 4$	$y = 3$

We can solve for the other variable by using either equation.

To find y, let $x = 4$ in either (1) or (2).	To find x, let $y = 3$ in either (1) or (2).
$5x + 7y = 41 \quad (2)$	$3x - 2y = 6 \quad (1)$
$5 \cdot 4 + 7y = 41$	$3x - 2 \cdot 3 = 6$
$20 + 7y = 41$	$3x - 6 = 6$
$7y = 21$	$3x = 12$
$y = 3$	$x = 4$

Both ways give the same solution. ⟶ **Thus, $(4, 3)$ is a solution of the system.**

EXAMPLE 3   Solve.

$$x + y = -2 \quad (1)$$
$$x - 2y = 7 \quad (2)$$

Make the coefficients of x opposites.
Multiply each side of equation (1) by -1.
Leave equation (2) alone.

$$-1(x + y) = -1(-2)$$
$$-1x - 1y = 2$$

$-1x$ ↖ opposites
$+1x$ ↙

$$-1x - 1y = 2$$
$$\underline{1x - 2y = 7}$$
$$-3y = 9$$

Divide each side by -3. ⟶ $\qquad y = -3$

To find x, let $y = -3$ in either equation (1) or (2).

$$x + y = -2 \quad (1)$$

Replace y by -3. ⟶ $\qquad x + (-3) = -2$
$$x - 3 = -2$$
$$x = 1$$

Check $(1, -3)$ in both equations. ⟶ **Thus, $(1, -3)$ is a solution of the system.**

ORAL EXERCISES

Select a multiplier for each equation so that addition leads to an equation in one variable.

1. $3x + 2y = 8$
   $2x + 5y = 9$ $2, -3$

2. $5x - 2y = 3$
   $2x + 7y = 9$ $7, 2$

3. $2x + 2y = 8$
   $5x - 3y = 4$ $3, 2$

4. $5x - 3y = 2$
   $4x + 2y = 6$ $2, 3$

5. $5x + 4y = 29$
   $3x - 2y = 13$ $1, 2$

6. $3x - 5y = 1$
   $2x + 10y = 14$ $2, 1$

7. $7x + 2y = 9$
   $3x + 8y = 11$ $-4, 1$

8. $4x - 7y = 5$
   $2x + 8y = 14$ $1, -2$

9. $8x - 6y = 10$
   $4x - 5y = 3$ $1, -2$

10. $-12x + y = 14$
    $-7x + y = -11$

11. $11x - 3y = 16$
    $4x + 2y = 12$ $2, 3$

12. $7x + 5y = 31$
    $-14x + 6y = -30$

13. $x + y = 4$
    $2x + y = 2$ $-1, 1$

14. $x - 7y = 4$
    $x + 7y = 16$ $1, 1$

15. $6x - 2y = -7$
    $13x - 2y = 0$ $-1, 1$

16. $5x - y = 13$
    $x - y = -1$ $1, -1$

EXERCISES

PART A

Solve each system in Exercises 1–16 above.

PART B

     EXAMPLE   Solve.

$$3x - 2y = 6$$
$$5x = -7y + 41$$

Add $7y$ to each side to get both variables on one side. $\longrightarrow$

$$5x = -7y + 41$$
$$5x + 7y = 41$$

Solve as in Example 2.

$$3x - 2y = 6$$
$$5x + 7y = 41$$

Thus, $(4, 3)$ is a solution of the system.

Solve.

17. $3x - 2y = 5$
    $2x = 5y - 4$ $(3, 2)$

18. $2x - 5y = 1$
    $3x = 4y - 2$ $(-2, -1)$

19. $3x = -7y + 2$
    $2x + 5y = 4$
             $(-18, 8)$

20. $3y = -2x + 7$
    $4x + 3y = 1$
           $(-3, \frac{13}{3})$

PART C

Solve.

21. $8x - 3(y - x) = 2x + 19$
    $y - (2y - x) = 7x - 13$

22. $\frac{1}{2}x - y = 3\frac{1}{2}$
    $x + 2y = 3$

23. $\frac{4}{5}x - y = \frac{4}{5}$
    $\frac{9}{5}x + 4y = \frac{4}{5}$

Mathematics in Pharmacy

As drugs are manufactured, their quality is constantly checked. Results of such tests are known immediately through the use of computer-video systems as shown above. Other aspects of a pharmacist's job are the development of new drugs and the careful preparation of doctors' prescriptions.

PROJECT A prescription for 120 cm³ of cough syrup called for 7% alcohol. Find the amount of alcohol in the prescription.

Dry Mixtures: Representing Costs

 REVIEW CAPSULE

Find the cost in cents of 5 kg of gumdrops at $1.25 per kg.

$1.25 = 125$ cents $5(125) = 625$ cents

$$\begin{pmatrix} \text{number} \\ \text{of kg} \end{pmatrix}\begin{pmatrix} \text{cost in cents} \\ \text{of 1 kg} \end{pmatrix} = \begin{pmatrix} \text{cost} \\ \text{in cents} \end{pmatrix}$$

EXAMPLE 1

Cheese costs 89¢ per kg. Find the cost in cents of 4 kg. Find the cost in cents of x kg.

$$\begin{pmatrix} \text{number} \\ \text{of kg} \end{pmatrix}\begin{pmatrix} \text{cost in cents} \\ \text{of 1 kg} \end{pmatrix} = \begin{pmatrix} \text{cost} \\ \text{in cents} \end{pmatrix}$$

$4 \cdot 89 = 356$ cents $x \cdot 89 = 89x$ cents

EXAMPLE 2

Find the cost in cents of a mixture of 3 kg of coffee at $3.25 per kg and 5 kg of coffee at $2.95 per kg.

Use $\begin{pmatrix} \text{number} \\ \text{of kg} \end{pmatrix}\begin{pmatrix} \text{cost in cents} \\ \text{of 1 kg} \end{pmatrix}$ twice. ⟶

$3(325) + 5(295) = 975 + 1{,}475$, or $2{,}450$
Thus, the cost of the mixture is 2,450 cents.

EXAMPLE 3

Find the cost in cents of a mixture of x kg of candy at $1.35 per kg and y kg of candy at $.85 per kg.

Use $\begin{pmatrix} \text{number} \\ \text{of kg} \end{pmatrix}\begin{pmatrix} \text{cost in cents} \\ \text{of 1 kg} \end{pmatrix}$ twice. ⟶

$x(135) + y(85)$
Thus, the cost of the mixture is $(135x + 85y)$ cents.

EXAMPLE 4

Complete the chart.

	Number of kg	Cost per kg	Cost in Cents
Brand A	x	$1.45	?
Brand B	y	$1.95	?
	Total cost in cents		

$\left.\begin{array}{l} \$1.45 = 145 \text{ cents} \\ \$1.95 = 195 \text{ cents} \end{array}\right\}$

	Number of kg	Cost per kg	Cost in Cents
Brand A	x	$1.45	$145x$
Brand B	y	$1.95	$195y$
	Total cost in cents		$145x + 195y$

EXAMPLE 5 Three kg of candy at $1.70 per kg are to be mixed with 5 kg of candy at $1.10 per kg to form an 8-kg box. Find the cost of the 8-kg box.

Use a chart to display the information.
Then use
$\left(\begin{matrix}\text{number}\\\text{of kg}\end{matrix}\right)\left(\begin{matrix}\text{cost in cents}\\\text{of 1 kg}\end{matrix}\right)=\left(\begin{matrix}\text{cost}\\\text{in cents}\end{matrix}\right).$

	Number of kg	Cost per kg	Cost in Cents
1st Brand	3	170	$3 \cdot 170 = 510$
2nd Brand	5	110	$5 \cdot 110 = 550$
		Total cost in cents	1,060

1,060 cents = $10.60 ⟶ **Thus,** $10.60 is the cost of the 8-kg box.

EXAMPLE 6 x kg of candy at $.75 per kg are to be mixed with y kg of candy at $.95 per kg. Find the number of kg in the mixture and the total cost.

Use a chart to display the information.
Then use
$\left(\begin{matrix}\text{number}\\\text{of kg}\end{matrix}\right)\left(\begin{matrix}\text{cost in cents}\\\text{of 1 kg}\end{matrix}\right)=\left(\begin{matrix}\text{cost}\\\text{in cents}\end{matrix}\right).$

	Number of kg	Cost per kg	Cost in Cents
1st Brand	x	75	$x \cdot 75 = 75x$
2nd Brand	y	95	$y \cdot 95 = 95y$
		Total cost in cents	$75x + 95y$

Thus, $(x + y)$ kg cost $(75x + 95y)$ cents.

ORAL EXERCISES

Give the cost in cents.

1. 5 kg at 45¢ per kg *225¢*   **2.** 6 kg at $2.00 per kg *1,200¢* **3.** x kg at 85¢ per kg
85x¢

EXERCISES

PART A

Find the number of kilograms and the total cost in cents of the combined mixture.

1. 5 kg at $.90 per kg
6 kg at $1.35 per kg

2. 7 kg at $.85 per kg
9 kg at $1.35 per kg

3. x kg at $1.58 per kg
y kg at $2.10 per kg

4. x kg at $2.15 per kg
y kg at $3.35 per kg

5. x kg at $.04 per kg
y kg at $.78 per kg

6. x kg at $1.41 per kg
y kg at $2.10 per kg

11 kg; 1,260¢   *(x + y) kg; (215x + 335y) ¢*   *16 kg; 1,810¢*

PART B

Find the number of kilograms and the total cost in cents of the combined mixture.

7. x kg at $1.35 per kg
y kg at m¢ per kg

8. x kg at $1.40 per kg
(y + 3) kg at $.75 per kg

9. x kg at p¢ per kg
y kg at q¢ per kg

(x + y) kg; (135x + my)¢

Solving Dry Mixture Problems

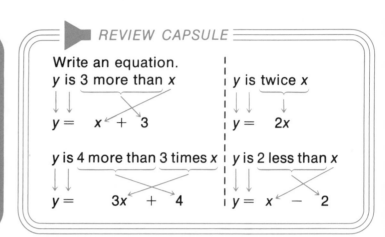

EXAMPLE 1

One brand of candy costs $1.70 per kg. Another costs $1.50 per kg. The two brands are to be mixed to form a 5-kg gift box that will cost $8.10. How many kg of each should be included?

Use a chart to display the information. Then use
$$\binom{\text{number}}{\text{of kg}}\binom{\text{cost in cents}}{\text{of 1 kg}} = \binom{\text{cost}}{\text{in cents}}.$$

	Number of kg	Cost per kg	Cost in Cents
1st Brand	x	170	$x \cdot 170 = 170x$
2nd Brand	y	150	$y \cdot 150 = 150y$
		Total cost in cents	$170x + 150y$

The total number of kilograms is 5. Write an equation. The total cost is 810 cents. Write an equation.

total kg: $x + y = 5$
cost in cents: $170x + 150y = 810$

Solve the system by substitution.
Solve for x in $x + y = 5$.
Replace x by $-y + 5$. ⟶
Distribute the 170. ⟶

Add -850 to each side. ⟶

$x = -y + 5$ (1)
$170x + 150y = 810$ (2)

{ The two equations form a system.

$170(-y + 5) + 150y = 810$
$-170y + 850 + 150y = 810$
$\qquad -20y + 850 = 810$
$\qquad\qquad -20y = -40$
$\qquad\qquad\qquad y = 2$

To find x, let $y = 2$ in equation (1).
$$x = -y + 5$$
$$x = -2 + 5$$
$$x = 3$$

Thus, 3 kg at $1.70 per kg and 2 kg at $1.50 per kg should be included in the mixture.

EXAMPLE 2 Juan wants to make up packs of $.25 comic books mixed with $.15 comic books to sell at $2.45 per pack. The number of $.15 books is 3 more than the number of $.25 books. Write a system of equations which can be used to find the number of each type in a pack.

Use a chart to display the information.
Then use
$\left(\begin{matrix}\text{no. of}\\\text{books}\end{matrix}\right)\left(\begin{matrix}\text{cost in cents}\\\text{of 1 book}\end{matrix}\right) = \left(\begin{matrix}\text{cost}\\\text{in cents}\end{matrix}\right).$

No. of Books	Cost per Book	Cost in Cents
x	25	$x \cdot 25 = 25x$
y	15	$y \cdot 15 = 15y$
	Total cost in cents	$25x + 15y$

No. of 15¢ books is 3 more than no. of 25¢ books.

Write an equation.
$2.45 = 245$ cents

$$y = x + 3$$

Total cost is 245 cents.

Write an equation.

$$25x + 15y = 245$$

The two equations form a system.
Solve the system on your own.

Thus, a system which can be used is $y = x + 3$
$$25x + 15y = 245.$$

EXAMPLE 3 A wholesaler wants to mix pencils costing $.05 each with those costing $.04 each. She wants to make a single pack of pencils that will cost $1.04. How many of each type should be in the pack if the number at $.04 is twice the number at $.05?

Use a chart to display the information.
Then use
$\left(\begin{matrix}\text{no. of}\\\text{pencils}\end{matrix}\right)\left(\begin{matrix}\text{cost in cents}\\\text{of 1 pencil}\end{matrix}\right) = \left(\begin{matrix}\text{cost}\\\text{in cents}\end{matrix}\right).$

No. of Pencils	Cost per Pencil	Cost in Cents
x	5	$x(5) = 5x$
y	4	$y(4) = 4y$
	Total cost in cents	$5x + 4y$

No. of 4¢ pencils is twice no. of 5¢ pencils.

$$y = 2 \cdot x$$

Total cost is 104 cents.

Write an equation.
$1.04 = 104$ cents

$$5x + 4y = 104$$

Write an equation.

Solve the system by substitution.
Replace y by $2x$.
$5x + 8x = 104$
$13x = 104$
$x = 8$

$y = 2x \quad (1)$ { The two equations
$5x + 4y = 104 \quad (2)$ { form a system.
$5x + 4(2x) = 104$
$5x + 8x = 104$
$x = 8$

To find y, let $x = 8$ in equation (1).
$$y = 2x = 2 \cdot 8, \text{ or } 16$$

Thus, no. of $.04 pencils is 16; no. of $.05 pencils is 8.

EXAMPLE 4   Show the check for Example 3.

No. of $.04 pencils is twice no. of $.05 pencils.

16	2(8)
	16

No. of $.04 pencils: 16 ⎫
No. of $.05 pencils: 8 ⎭

$\left(\begin{matrix}\text{No. of} \\ \text{pencils}\end{matrix}\right)\left(\begin{matrix}\text{Cost in cents} \\ \text{of 1 pencil}\end{matrix}\right) = \left(\begin{matrix}\text{cost} \\ \text{in cents}\end{matrix}\right).$

Cost of 4¢ pencils + cost of 5¢ pencils is 104¢.

16 (4)	+	8 (5)		104
64	+	40		
	104			

EXERCISES

PART A

Write a system of equations which can be used to solve the problem.

1. Ike wants to mix candy costing $.90 per kg with candy costing $1.30 per kg. He wants to make a 7-kg box that will cost $7.50. How many kg of each should he use?

2. Gina wants to mix candy costing $2.60 per kg with candy costing $2.90 per kg. She wants to make a 5-kg box that will cost $13.30. How many kg of each should she use?

3. Lois wants to mix pencils costing $.05 each with pencils costing $.15 each. The mixture will cost $1.30. The number of $.15 pencils is 2 more than the number of $.05 pencils. How many of each type should be included in the package?

4. Two varieties of cards are to be mixed. The assortment will cost $3.65. One kind costs $.45 each, the other $.25 each. The number of $.45 cards is 1 more than 3 times the number of $.25 cards. How many of each kind should be included?

5. Assorted creams cost $2.30 per kg. Caramels cost $1.70 per kg. The number of kg of creams is 2 less than the number of kg of caramels. How many kg of each type should be mixed to make a box that will cost $7.40? *x = y − 2; 230x + 170y = 740*

6. A $6.00 box of nuts contains two varieties. One type costs $1.40 per kg and the other $1.80 per kg. The number of kg at $1.40 per kg is 3 times the number of kg at $1.80 per kg. Find the number of kg of each. *x = 3y; 140x + 180y = 600*

Solve.   *5 kg at $.50; 4 kg at $.70*

7. Jan sold a 9-kg box of candy that contained two varieties. One sold at $.50 per kg and the other at $.70 per kg. The mixture sold at $5.30. How many kg of each type were included?

8. Two brands of candy were mixed in a 10-kg gift box. One cost $3.00 per kg and the other $2.70 per kg. The gift box cost $29.10. How many kg of each were included?

7kg at $3.00; 3kg at $2.70

9. Mr. Lead wants to mix pencils costing $.15 each with pencils costing $.35 each. The mixture will cost $3.45. The number of $.35 pencils is 7 more than the number of $.15 pencils. How many of each type should be included in the package?

11. A $20.80 gift box of candy contains two varieties. One type costs $1.60 per kg and the other costs $1.80 per kg. The number of kg at $1.80 per kg is twice the number of kg at $1.60 per kg. Find the number of kg of each. *4 kg at $1.60; 8 kg at $1.80*

2 at $.15; 9 at $.35

10. Cashews cost $2.50 per kg. Pecans cost $2.70 per kg. The number of kg of cashews is one less than the number of kg of pecans. How many kg of each should be mixed to make a box to sell at $28.70?

5 kg cashews; 6 kg pecans

12. Two types of gift-wrap paper are to be mixed. The assortment will cost $2.90. One type sells at $.25 per sheet, the other at $.30 per sheet. The number of sheets of $.30 paper is 2 more than 3 times the number of sheets of $.25 paper. How many of each type should be included?

2 sheets at $.25; 8 sheets at $.30

PART B

13. Ribbons costing $.20 each are to be mixed with ribbons costing $.15 each. The mixture will cost $1.20. The number of $.20 ribbons is $\frac{3}{4}$ the number of $.15 ribbons. Find the number of each type in the box.

3 at $.20; 4 at $.15

15. Meg wants to sell a box of candy which contains two varieties for $14.40. The number of kg at $1.60 per kg is 1 less than $\frac{3}{4}$ the number of kg at $.80 per kg. Find the number of kg of each kind. *8 kg at $.80; 5 kg at $1.60*

14. Party decorations costing $.20 each are to be mixed with decorations costing $.30 each. The assortment will cost $4.30. The number at $.30 each is 5 more than $\frac{1}{2}$ the number at $.20 each. Find the number of each type.

16. A $1.60 assortment of pads contains $.20 pads and $.15 pads. The number of $.20 pads is 2 less than $\frac{1}{2}$ the number of $.15 pads. Find the number of each type of pad.

2 pads at $.20; 8 pads at $.15

PART C

17. Ms. Garcia wants to sell a box of candy which contains two varieties for $9.60. One variety sells at $1.20 per kg, the other at $1.80 per kg. The total weight is 3 kg more than twice the weight of the $1.80 type. How many kg of each type are included in the box?

18. Mr. Weiss wants to sell a box of candy which contains two varieties for $6.70. One variety sells at $1.50 per kg, the other at $1.30 per kg. The total weight is 5 times the weight of the $1.50 variety. How many kg of each type are included in the box?

Solving Number Relation Problems

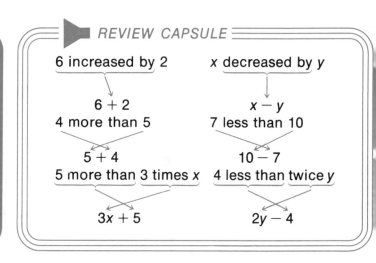

REVIEW CAPSULE

6 increased by 2   x decreased by y

6 + 2   x − y
4 more than 5   7 less than 10

5 + 4   10 − 7
5 more than 3 times x   4 less than twice y

3x + 5   2y − 4

EXAMPLE 1 The sum of two numbers is 42. One number is 5 times the other number. Find the numbers.

Write an equation.
Sum means add.

Let x = one number
   y = other number
The sum of the numbers is 42.

$x + y$ = 42
One number is 5 times the other number.

Write another equation. ——————→

$x = 5 \cdot y$
$x + y = 42$ (1)   The two equations
$x = 5y$ (2)   form a system.

Solve the system by substitution.
Replace x by $5y$ in equation (1).

$5y + y = 42$
$6y = 42$
$y = 7$

Use either equation to find x.
Equation (2) is already solved for x.

To find x, let $y = 7$ in equation (2).
$x = 5y$
$x = 5 \cdot 7$
$x = 35$

Check. ————————————→

Sum is 42.   One is 5 times the other.

$7 + 35$	42	35	$5 \cdot 7$
	42		35

Thus, the two numbers are 35 and 7.

EXAMPLE 2   One number is 5 times another number. Their difference is 8. Find the numbers.

The problem tells us that one number is larger than the other. ⟶ Let x = larger number

y = smaller number

One number is 5 times another number.

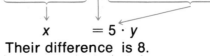

The larger is 5 times the smaller. ⟶

$$x \quad = 5 \cdot y$$

Their difference is 8.

$$\text{Larger} - \text{smaller} = 8.$$

$$x \quad - \quad y \quad = 8$$

$$x = 5y \qquad (1)$$

The two equations form a system.

Replace x by $5y$ in equation (2). ⟶

$$x - y = 8 \quad (2)$$
$$5y - y = 8$$
$$4y = 8$$
$$y = 2$$

To find x, let $y = 2$ in equation (1).

$$x = 5y$$
$$x = 5 \cdot 2$$
$$x = 10$$

Thus, the two numbers are 2 and 10.

EXAMPLE 3   The sum of two numbers is 50. One number is 5 less than 4 times the other number. Find the numbers.

Let x = one number

y = other number

Their sum is 50.

$$x + y \quad = 50$$

One number is 5 less than 4 times the other.

$$x \quad = \quad 4y \quad - \quad 5$$

$$x + y = 50 \quad (1)$$
$$x = 4y - 5 \quad (2)$$

Replace x by $4y - 5$ in equation (1). ⟶

$$4y - 5 + y = 50$$
$$5y - 5 = 50$$
$$5y = 55$$
$$y = 11$$

To find x, let $y = 11$ in (2).

$$x = 4y - 5$$
$$x = 4(11) - 5$$
$$x = 44 - 5, \text{ or } 39$$

Thus, the two numbers are 39 and 11.

EXAMPLE 4 One number is 3 less than another number. If twice the smaller number is increased by the larger number, the result is 18. Find the numbers.

The problem tells us that one number is smaller than the other. ⟶

Let x = smaller number
y = larger number

One number is 3 less than another.

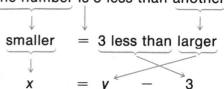

smaller $=$ 3 less than larger

$x = y - 3$

Twice smaller increased by larger is 18.

$2x + y = 18$

$$x = y - 3 \quad (1)$$
$$2x + y = 18 \quad (2)$$

Solve by substitution. Replace x by $y - 3$ in equation (2). ⟶
$2(y - 3) + 1y = 2y - 6 + 1y = 3y - 6$ ⟶

$$2(y - 3) + y = 18$$
$$3y - 6 = 18$$
$$3y = 24$$
$$y = 8$$

To find x, let $y = 8$ in equation (1).
$$x = y - 3$$
$$x = 8 - 3$$
$$x = 5$$

Check. ⟶

Smaller is 3 less than larger.

5	8 − 3
	5

Twice smaller increased by larger is 18.

2 · 5	+	8	18
10	+	8	
	18		

Thus, the two numbers are 5 and 8.

EXERCISES

PART A

Find the numbers.

1. The sum of two numbers is 50. One number is 4 times the other. *10, 40*

2. One number is 3 more than twice another. Their sum is 24. *7, 17*

3. The sum of two numbers is 18. Their difference is 6. *6, 12*

5. One number is 9 more than another. If the larger is increased by 7, the result is 5 times the smaller. *4, 13*

7. The sum of two numbers is 22. One number is 2 more than three times the other. *5, 17*

9. One number is 4 more than another. If twice the smaller is added to the larger, the result is 28. *8, 12*

4. The sum of two numbers is 72. One number is 8 more than the other. *32, 40*

6. One number is 3 less than another. If the larger is decreased by twice the smaller, the result is −7. *13, 10*

8. One number is 9 less than twice another. The sum of the numbers is 12. *5, 7*

10. One number is 2 less than another. If twice the larger is decreased by 3 times the smaller, the result is −10. *14, 16*

PART B

EXAMPLE The length of a rectangle is 5 meters more than the width. The perimeter is 38 meters. Find the length and width.

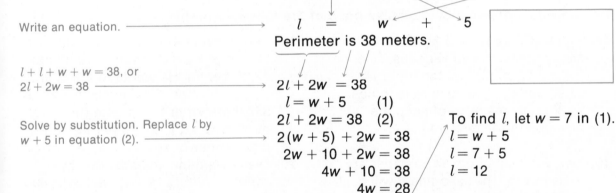

Length is 5 meters more than width.

Write an equation. ⟶ $l = w + 5$

Perimeter is 38 meters.

$l + l + w + w = 38$, or
$2l + 2w = 38$ ⟶ $2l + 2w = 38$
$l = w + 5$ (1)
$2l + 2w = 38$ (2)

Solve by substitution. Replace l by $w + 5$ in equation (2). ⟶
$2(w + 5) + 2w = 38$
$2w + 10 + 2w = 38$
$4w + 10 = 38$
$4w = 28$
$w = 7$

To find l, let $w = 7$ in (1).
$l = w + 5$
$l = 7 + 5$
$l = 12$

Thus, the length is 12 meters and the width is 7 meters.

Solve.

11. The length of a rectangle is twice the width. The perimeter is 42 meters. Find the length and width. *width 7 m; length 14 m*

13. The length of a rectangle is 8 kilometers more than 6 times the width. Find the length and width if the perimeter is 156 kilometers. *width 10 km; length 68 km*

12. The perimeter of a rectangle is 68 meters. The length is 2 meters less than 3 times the width. Find the length and width.

14. A rectangle is 4 times as long as it is wide. Find the length and width if the perimeter is 50 centimeters. *width 5 cm; length 20 cm*

Chapter Eleven Review

Find the intersection. Verify that its coordinates satisfy both equations. $[p.\,289]$

1. $\{(x, y)\,|\,x + y = 8\} \cap \{(x, y)\,|\,x - y = 2\}$
2. $\{(x, y)\,|\,y = 3x\} \cap \{(x, y)\,|\,x + y = 8\}$
3. $\{(x, y)\,|\,3x - 2y = 4\} \cap \{(x, y)\,|\,y = x\}$
4. $\{(x, y)\,|\,y = 3x + 2\} \cap \{(x, y)\,|\,y + x = 10\}$

Determine whether each system is consistent or inconsistent. $[p.\,289]$

5. $x + y = 4$
   $x + y = 6$

6. $2x - y = 5$
   $x + y = 4$

7. $x - y = 2$
   $3x + 3y = 4$

8. $3y = 2x - 15$
   $2x - 3y = -2$

Solve by addition. $[p.\,297,\,300]$

9. $x + y = 4$
   $x - y = 2$

10. $x - 5y = 6$
    $-x = y + 6$

11. $2x + 5y = 5$
    $3x + 3y = 12$

12. $3x = 4y + 5$
    $2x + 2y = 8$

Solve by substitution. $[p.\,294]$

13. $y = 2x$
    $x + y = 9$

14. $x - y = 8$
    $x + y = 12$

15. $x - 5y = 6$
    $x + y = 6$

16. $x + y = 1$
    $x - y = 4$

Use a system of equations to solve each of the following problems. $[p.\,306,\,310]$

17. Nan wants to sell a 5-kg box of candy containg two varieties. One sells at $1.50 per kg, the other at $1.90 per kg. The mixture is to cost $8.30. How many kg of each are included in the mixture?

18. Pedro wants to mix candy selling at $2.20 per kg with another selling at $2.40 per kg. He wants to make an $11.60 gift box. The number of kg at $2.20 per kg is 1 less than the number of kg at $2.40 per kg. Find the number of kg of each.

19. Two varieties of gift-wrap paper are to be mixed. The assortment will cost $2.00. One sells at $.40 per sheet, the other at $.30 per sheet. The number of sheets at $.30 per sheet is twice the number of sheets at $.40 per sheet. How many of each type should be included?

20. Diane wants to sell a box of two varieties of birthday cards for $5.80. The number of $.30 cards is 6 more than $\dfrac{1}{2}$ the number of $.35 cards. Find the number of cards of each type.

21. The sum of two numbers is 40. One number is 8 more than the other. Find the numbers.

22. The sum of two numbers is 24. Their difference is 8. Find the numbers.

23. One number is 3 more than twice another. If the larger is increased by the smaller, the result is 18. Find the numbers.

24. The perimeter of a rectangle is 36. The length is 6 more than twice the width. Find the length and width.

Chapter Eleven Test

Find the intersection. Verify that its coordinates satisfy both equations.

1. $\{(x, y) \mid x + y = 4\} \cap \{(x, y) \mid x - y = 6\}$
2. $\{(x, y) \mid y = 3x\} \cap \{(x, y) \mid 3x + y = 6\}$

Determine whether each system is consistent or inconsistent.

3. $x + y = 7$
   $x + y = 5$

4. $3x - y = 4$
   $x + y = 4$

5. $2x = y + 3$
   $2x - y = 6$

Solve by substitution.

6. $y = 3x$
   $x + y = 8$

7. $x - y = 8$
   $x + y = 4$

8. $2x + y = 3$
   $y = 2x + 1$

Solve by addition.

9. $2x + y = 4$
   $x - y = 8$

10. $2x - 3y = 1$
    $3x - 5y = 1$

11. $2x = 7y + 1$
    $5x + 3y = 23$

Use a system of equations to solve each of the following problems.

12. Ed wants to sell a 7-kg box of candy containing two varieties. One sells at $1.30 per kg, the other at $1.70 per kg. The mixture is to cost $10.30. How many kg of each are included in the mixture?

13. Tanya wants to mix candy selling at $2.80 per kg with another selling at $2.40 per kg. She wants to make a $26.40 gift box. The number of kg at $2.80 per kg is 2 more than the number of kg at $2.40 per kg. Find the number of kg of each.

14. The sum of two numbers is 60. One number is 20 less than the other. Find the numbers.

15. One number is 5 less than twice another. Their sum is 16. Find the numbers.

16. One number is 7 more than 3 times another. If the larger is decreased by twice the smaller, the result is 9. Find the numbers.

17. The perimeter of a rectangle is 28. The width is 2 less than the length. Find the length and the width of the rectangle.

Galileo and Free Fall

Galileo Galilei, the renowned Italian astronomer and physicist, made a remarkable discovery in 1585. He timed an object as it fell from a given height, discovering the "free fall" equation.

$$d = 4.9t^2$$

distance of the fall in meters

elapsed time in seconds after the start of the fall

According to legend, Galileo dropped small cannon balls from the colonnades of the Leaning Tower of Pisa, timing their fall.
Even though the cannon balls were of different sizes and weights, they all took the same number of seconds to hit the ground.

PROJECT

1. Stand on a chair and drop a book and a pencil at the same time. What do you notice?
2. Drop a pencil and a large piece of paper. What do you notice? Crumble the paper into a ball and drop it at the same time with a pencil. What do you notice?
3. Using Galileo's formula, compute how long it will take an object to fall 122.5 meters.

Relations and Functions

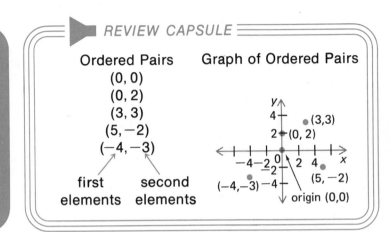

▶ REVIEW CAPSULE

Ordered Pairs	Graph of Ordered Pairs
(0, 0)	
(0, 2)	
(3, 3)	
(5, −2)	
(−4, −3)	

first elements   second elements

origin (0,0)

Set *C* is a relation. ──────────▶ $C = \{(-1, 3), (2, 4), (0, -2), (-1, -5)\}$.

Definition of relation ──────────▶ A *relation* is a set of ordered pairs.

List −1 only once. ──────────▶ Domain of relation $C = \{-1, 2, 0\}$.
Range of relation $C = \{3, 4, -2, -5\}$.

Definition of domain and range ──────▶ The set of all first elements of the ordered pairs in a relation is the *domain*. The set of all second elements is the *range*.

EXAMPLE 1   Graph $A = \{(5, 0), (-3, 4), (-3, -1), (-2, 4)\}$.
Then give the domain and the range of relation *A*.

Graph of relation *A* ──────────▶

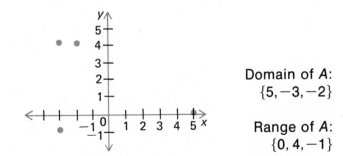

In the domain, list −3 only once.

In the range, list 4 only once.

Domain of *A*:
$\{5, -3, -2\}$

Range of *A*:
$\{0, 4, -1\}$

Set *S* is a function. $\longrightarrow$ $S = \{(4, 8), (2, -1), (-6, 7), (5, 7)\}$.

A function is a special kind of a relation.

No two first elements   Second elements
are the same.   may be the same.

Definition of function $\longrightarrow$

A *function* is a relation in which no two
ordered pairs have the same first element.

EXAMPLE 2

Graph
$$B = \{(0, -3), (3, 1), (4, -3), (-3, -5), (-6, 6)\}.$$
Give the domain and the range of relation *B*. Is *B*
a function?

Graph of relation *B* $\longrightarrow$

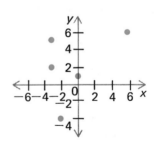

$\{(0, -3), (3, 1), (4, -3), (-3, -5), (-6, 6)\}$

No two first elements are the same in a
function.

Domain of *B*:
$\{0, 3, 4, -3, -6\}$

Range of *B*:
$\{-3, 1, -5, 6\}$

B is a function.

EXAMPLE 3

List the ordered pairs in relation *C* graphed below.
Give the domain and the range of *C*. Is *C* a
function?

Graph of relation *C* $\longrightarrow$

Ordered pairs in relation *C* $\longrightarrow$

$C = \{(-3, 2), (-3, 5), (-2, -4), (0, 1), (6, 6)\}$.
Domain of $C = \{-3, -2, 0, 6\}$.
Range of $C = \{2, 5, -4, 1, 6\}$.

Both $(-3, 2)$ and $(-3, 5)$ are in *C*. $\longrightarrow$

-3 is the first element in two of the ordered pairs
in *C*.

Two first elements are the same.

Thus, *C* is not a function.

EXERCISES

PART A

List the ordered pairs in each relation graphed below. Give the domain and the range of the relation. Is the relation a function?

1.

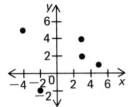

2.

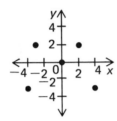

3.

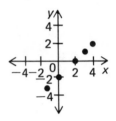

$\{(-4,5), (-2,-2), (3,2), (3,4), (5,1)\}; D = \{-4,-2,3,5\}; R = \{-2,1,2,4,5\}; no$

Graph each relation. Give the domain and the range. Is the relation a function?

4. $\{(0,1), (-1,1), (3,-2), (-4,4)\}$
5. $\{(3,2), (4,2), (-1,2), (0,2)\}$
6. $\{(2,-2), (2,-3), (2,-1), (2,0)\}$
7. $\{(3,0), (-3,0), (0,3), (0,-3)\}$
  $D = \{3,-3,0\}; R = \{0,3,-3\}; no$
8. $\{(-1,1), (-2,2), (0,0), (1,-1), (2,-2)\}$
9. $\{(-1,-1), (-2,-2), (0,0), (1,1), (2,2)\}$ $D = \{-1,-2,0,1,2\}; R = \{-1,-2,0,1,2\}; yes$
10. $\{(3,0), (-1,2), (2,4), (3,-4), (0,-2)\}$ $D = \{3,-1,2,0\}; R = \{0,2,4,-4,-2\}; no$

PART B

EXAMPLE

The inverse of relation A is relation B. ⟶

The first and second elements of the ordered pairs in A are interchanged to form B.

$A = \{(1,3), (2,0), (-1,3)\}$

$B = \{(3,1), (0,2), (3,-1)\}$

B is the inverse of A. Also, A is the inverse of B. Is A a function? Is B a function?

A is a function. B is not a function.

Give the inverse of each relation. Is the relation a function? Is its inverse a function?

11. $\{(-2,4), (-1,1), (0,4)\}$
12. $\{(2,3), (1,-2), (2,-4), (3,0)\}$
13. $\{(-1,1), (-2,1), (0,1), (1,1), (2,1)\}$
  $\{(3,2), (-2,1), (-4,2), (0,3)\}; no; yes$

PART C

For what value of k will each relation not be a function?

14. $\{(-12,4), (k^2 - 7k, 5)\}$
15. $\{(\frac{k}{4}, 7), (\frac{9}{k}, -3)\}$

Types of Functions

OBJECTIVES

■ To determine if a relation is a function by applying the vertical line test to its graph

■ To identify linear and constant functions

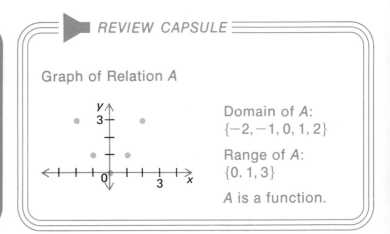

▶ REVIEW CAPSULE

Graph of Relation *A*

Domain of *A*:
$\{-2, -1, 0, 1, 2\}$

Range of *A*:
$\{0, 1, 3\}$

A is a function.

EXAMPLE 1   Is the following the graph of a function?

The dashed vertical line crosses the graph in two points:

$(4, 2)$ and $(4, -2)$.

same first element

Two ordered pairs have the same first element. ────────→ **Thus,** the graph is not the graph of a function.

This curve is a parabola.

$(4, 2)$

$(4, -2)$

Vertical Line Test

A *relation* is a function if no vertical line crosses its graph in more than one point.

EXAMPLE 2   Is $\{(x, y) \,|\, y = 2x + 1\}$ a function?

Use the slope-intercept method to graph $y = 2x + 1$.

Slope $\frac{2}{1}$ y-intercept 1

No vertical line will cross the graph in more than one point.

No two ordered pairs have the same first element. ────────→ **Thus,** $\{(x, y) \,|\, y = 2x + 1\}$ is a function.

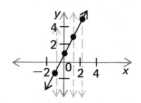

Definition of linear function ⟶ | A *linear function* is a function whose graph is a line or a subset of a line which is neither vertical nor horizontal.

EXAMPLE 3 Is $\{(x, y) \mid y = -3\}$ a function? If so, is it a linear function?

Plot $(0, -3)$, since the y-intercept is -3.
Then plot any other point with y-coord.
-3 like $(5, -3)$.
Draw the horizontal line.

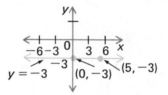

No two ordered pairs have the same first element. ⟶ **Thus,** $\{(x, y) \mid y = -3\}$ is a function.

Its graph is a horizontal line. ⟶ $\{(x, y \mid y = -3\}$ is not a linear function.

Definition of constant function ⟶ | A *constant function* is a function whose graph is a horizontal line or a subset of a horizontal line.

Example 3 shows a constant function.

EXAMPLE 4 Is $\{(x, y) \mid x = 5\}$ a function? If so, is it a linear function or a constant function?

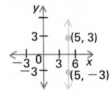

y is not mentioned in $x = 5$. The graph is a vertical line. Use any two points with x-coordinate 5 like $(5, 3)$ and $(5, -3)$.

The graph is a vertical line. ⟶ **Thus,** $\{(x, y) \mid x = 5\}$ is not a function.

ORAL EXERCISES

Which relations are functions? Which functions are linear functions? Which functions are constant functions?

function ↗

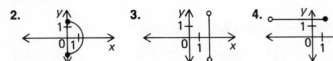

1. 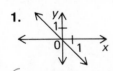 **2.** **3.** 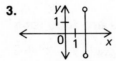 **4.** 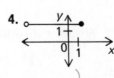 **5.**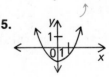

function; linear function   *function; constant function*

EXERCISES

PART A

Graph each relation. Which relations are functions? Which functions are linear functions? Which functions are constant functions?

1. $\{(x, y \mid y = 3x\}$ *(0,0), (1,3)*   2. $\{(x, y) \mid y = -2x\}$ 3. $\{(x, y) \mid y = x\}$
4. $\{(x, y) \mid y = 5\}$ *(0,5), (2,5)*   5. $\{(x, y) \mid x = -4\}$ 6. $\{(x, y) \mid -2 = y\}$
7. $\{(x, y) \mid 3 = x\}$ *(3,0), (3,2)*   8. $\{(x, y) \mid y = x + 1\}$ 9. $\{(x, y) \mid y = 2x - 3\}$
10. $\{(x, y) \mid x = 4y\}$ 11. $\{(x, y) \mid x = 3y - 1\}$ 12. $\{(x, y) \mid x = 0\}$
13. $\{(x, y) \mid y = 0\}$ *(0,0), (2,0)*   14. $\{(x, y) \mid y = -2x - 4\}$ 15. $\{(x, y) \mid y = 3x - 2\}$
16. $\{(x, y) \mid 2x + y = 3\}$ 17. $\{(x, y) \mid x + 2y = -1\}$ 18. $\{(x, y) \mid y = -x\}$
19. $\{(x, y) \mid x + y = 4\}$ 20. $\{(x, y) \mid x - y = -6\}$ 21. $\{(x, y) \mid x = 4\}$
22. $\{(x, y) \mid y = -3\}$ 23. $\{(x, y) \mid 2x + 4y = -1\}$ 24. $\{(x, y) \mid 3x = y - 1\}$
25. $\{(x, y) \mid 3y = 4 + x\}$ 26. $\{(x, y) \mid x + 1 = 0\}$ 27. $\{(x, y) \mid 3 + y = 0\}$
28. $\{(x, y) \mid 2x = y - 1\}$ *(0,1), (2,5)*   29. $\{(x, y) \mid -3x + y = 5\}$ *(0,5), (-1,2)*   30. $\{(x, y) \mid -y - x = -4\}$ *(0,4), (4,0)*

PART B

EXAMPLE   Graph $\{(x, y) \mid y = -x^2\}$. Is the relation a function?

Find some ordered pairs.
Choose any numbers for x.
Find the y-coordinates.
Draw a smooth curve through the points.

x	$-x^2$	y
0	$-(0)^2$	0
1	$-(1)^2$	-1
-1	$-(-1)^2$	-1
2	$-(2)^2$	-4
-2	$-(-2)^2$	-4
3	$-(3)^2$	-9
-3	$-(-3)^2$	-9

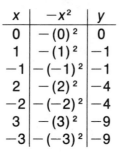

The curve is a parabola.

No vertical line will cross the graph in more than one point. ⟶ **Thus, $\{(x, y) \mid y = -x^2\}$ is a function.**

Graph each relation. Which relations are functions?

31. $\{(x, y) \mid y = x^2\}$ *function*   32. $\{(x, y) \mid y = x^2 + 1\}$ *function*   33. $\{(x, y) \mid y = x^2 - 3\}$ *function*
34. $\{(x, y) \mid y = 2x^2\}$ *function*   35. $\{(x, y) \mid y = -3x^2\}$ *function*   36. $\{(x, y) \mid 4x^2 = -2y\}$ *function*
37. $\{(x, y) \mid x = y^2\}$ *not f.*   38. $\{(x, y) \mid x = -1y^2\}$ *not f.*   39. $\{(x, y) \mid x = 3y^2\}$ *not f.*
40. $\{(x, y) \mid 2y^2 = -1x\}$ *not f.*   41. $\{(x, y) \mid x = y^2 + 2\}$ *not f.*   42. $\{(x, y) \mid x = y^2 - 1\}$ *not f.*

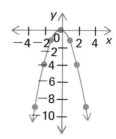

PART C

Graph each relation. Which relations are functions?

43. $\{(x, y) \mid y = x^3\}$ 44. $\{(x, y) \mid y = x^3 + 2\}$ 45. $\{(x, y) \mid y = 3x^3\}$
46. $\{(x, y) \mid y = -1x^3\}$ 47. $\{(x, y) \mid x = y^4\}$ 48. $\{(x, y) \mid y = -1x^4\}$

f(x) Notation

EXAMPLE 1 In the function above, what value of y is paired with each of these values of $x: 0, -4, 2$?

Examine each ordered pair:
$(0, 1), (-4, 3), (2, -3)$.

When x is 0, y is 1.
When x is -4, y is 3.
When x is 2, y is -3.

Definition of value of f at x ⟶
Read $f(x) = y$ as the value of f at x is y, or as f at x is y.

If (x, y) is an ordered pair in function f, then the value of f at x is y.
$$f(x) = y$$

For $(0, 1)$ | For $(-4, 3)$ | For $(2, -3)$
$f(0) = 1$ | $f(-4) = 3$ | $f(2) = -3$

For function f above,
$f(0) = 1$ $f(-4) = 3$ $f(2) = -3$.
f at 0 is 1. f at -4 is 3. f at 2 is -3.

EXAMPLE 2 $f = \{(x, y) \mid y = 2x - 1\}$. Find $f(2)$, $f(-1)$, and $f(20)$.

Find $f(2)$. | Find $f(-1)$. | Find $f(20)$.

Substitute 2, -1, and 20 for x.

$f(x) = 2x - 1$ | $f(x) = 2x - 1$ | $f(x) = 2x - 1$
$f(2) = 2 \cdot 2 - 1$ | $f(-1) = 2(-1) - 1$ | $f(20) = 2 \cdot 20 - 1$
$\quad = 4 - 1$ | $\quad = -2 - 1$ | $\quad = 40 - 1$
$\quad = 3$ | $\quad = -3$ | $\quad = 39$

f at 2 is 3. | f at -1 is -3. | f at 20 is 39.

EXAMPLE 3 $h(x) = x^2 - 2$, and the domain of h is $\{-1, 0, 1\}$.
Determine the range of h.

Substitute -1, 0, and 1 for x.

Find $h(-1)$. | Find $h(0)$. | Find $h(1)$.
$h(x) = x^2 - 2$ | $h(x) = x^2 - 2$ | $h(x) = x^2 - 2$
$h(-1) = (-1)^2 - 2$ | $h(0) = 0^2 - 2$ | $h(1) = 1^2 - 2$
$= 1 - 2$ | $= 0 - 2$ | $= 1 - 2$
$= -1$ | $= -2$ | $= -1$

List -1 only once. ⟶ **Thus,** the range of h is $\{-1, -2\}$.

EXERCISES

PART A

$f = \{(x, y) | y = 3x - 2\}$. **Find each.**

1. $f(0)$ -2 **2.** $f(4)$ 10 **3.** $f(-2)$ -8 **4.** $f(15)$ 43 **5.** $f(-22)$ -68

$g = \{(x, y) | y = -4x + 7\}$. **Find each.**

6. $g(-1)$ 11 **7.** $g(5)$ -13 **8.** $g(13)$ -45 **9.** $g(-7)$ 35 **10.** $g(30)$ -113

$h(x) = x^2 - 5$. **Find each.**

11. $h(0)$ -5 **12.** $h(-4)$ 11 **13.** $h(4)$ 11 **14.** $h(15)$ 220 **15.** $h(-20)$ 395

D **is the domain of each function. Determine the range.**

16. $f(x) = 4x - 3$ $D = \{0, 1, 2\}$
17. $h(x) = 6x + 2$ $D = \{-3, 1, 4\}$
18. $g(x) = -2x - 9$ $D = \{2, 4, 6\}$
19. $r(x) = -7x + 4$ $D = \{-2, -4, -6\}$
20. $f(x) = x^2 + 1$ $D = \{-3, 0, 9\}$
21. $g(x) = 2x^2 + 3$ $D = \{-8, -7, -6\}$
22. $k(x) = x^2 + x - 1$ $D = \{2, 1, 0\}$
$R = \{5, 1, -1\}$
23. $r(x) = 2x^2 - 3x - 2$ $D = \{1, 3, 6\}$
$R = \{-3, 7, 52\}$

PART B

D **is the domain of each function. Determine the range.**

24. $f(x) = 2x - 8$ $D = \{\frac{1}{2}, \frac{1}{4}, \frac{1}{3}\}$
25. $g(x) = -3x + 7$ $D = \{.5, .6, .7\}$
26. $f(x) = (x + 1)^2$ $D = \{0, 2, 4\}$
27. $k(x) = (2x - 3)^2$ $D = \{-1, -2, -3\}$
28. $r(x) = (x^2 - 2)^2$ $D = \{-2, 0, 2\}$
$\{4\}$
29. $j(x) = x^2 - 5$ $D = \{-\frac{1}{2}, \frac{1}{2}, \frac{1}{4}\}$
$\{-4\frac{3}{4}, -4\frac{15}{16}\}$

PART C

$f(x) = 4x - 5$ and $g(x) = x^2 + 3$. **Find each.**

30. $f(2) + g(2)$ **31.** $g(6) - f(6)$ **32.** $f(7) - g(-3)$ **33.** $g(-8) + f(-2)$
34. $g[f(1)]$ **35.** $g[f(-2)]$ **36.** $f[g(4)]$ **37.** $f[g(-6)]$

The Greatest Integer Function

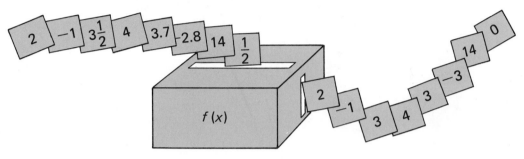

$f(x)$

PROBLEM

Can you see a pattern here?

x	$f(x)$
$35\dfrac{3}{4}$	35
21	21
3.2	3
$\dfrac{1}{3}$	0
0	0
$-2\dfrac{1}{4}$	−3
−7	−7

$$\left.\begin{array}{l} 13 \\ 13.1 \\ 13\dfrac{1}{2} \\ 13.23 \\ 13\dfrac{2}{7} \\ 13.99 \end{array}\right\} \longrightarrow 13$$

In each case, $f(x)$ is the nearest integer to x which is less than or equal to x. This is called the *greatest integer function* and is written $[x]$.

For any number n, $[n]$ is the greatest integer less than or equal to n.

$$[2.3] = 2 \qquad \left[34\dfrac{1}{2}\right] = 34 \qquad \left[-\dfrac{1}{4}\right] = -1$$

PROJECT   Draw the graph of the greatest integer function.

Digit Problems *(optional)*

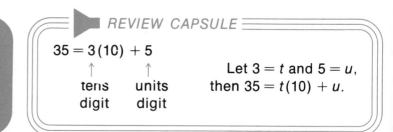

REVIEW CAPSULE

$$35 = 3(10) + 5$$

↑   ↑
tens   units
digit   digit

Let $3 = t$ and $5 = u$,
then $35 = t(10) + u$.

The Review Capsule suggests this. ⟶

> If t is the tens digit and u is the units digit of a two-digit number, then $10t + u$ is the number.

EXAMPLE 1 $10t + u$ represents a two-digit number. Express the sum of the digits in algebraic terms.

$10t + u$ is the number.

Let $t =$ tens digit
    $u =$ units digit

Thus, the sum of the digits is $t + u$.

EXAMPLE 2 $10t + u$ represents a two-digit number. Express 13 less than the number in algebraic terms.

13 less than the number

$$(10t + u) - 13$$

Thus, the expression is $(10t + u) - 13$.

EXAMPLE 3   Reverse the digits of 65.

$$65 = 6(10) + 5$$
$$56 = 5(10) + 6$$

Thus, 56 is the result of reversing the digits of 65.

EXAMPLE 4   Reverse the digits of $10t + u$.

$$10t + u$$
$$\diagdown\!\!\!\!\diagup$$
$$10u + t$$

Thus, $10u + t$ is the result of reversing the digits of $10t + u$.

EXAMPLE 5   The sum of the digits of a two-digit number is 10. If the digits of the number are reversed, the new number is 18 less than the original number. Find the original number.

Represent the digits algebraically. ⟶   Let $t =$ tens digit of the original number
$u =$ units digit of the original number
$10t + u =$ the original number
$10u + t =$ the number with its digits reversed

Write two equations.
First equation ⟶

Sum of the digits is 10.
$$t + u = 10$$

Second equation ⟶
Simplify.

New number is 18 less than original.
$$10u + t = (10t + u) - 18$$
$$-9t + 9u = -18$$
$$9t - 9u = 18$$

Solve the system. (Use substitution.)
$$t + u = 10$$
$$9t - 9u = 18$$

First solve $t + u = 10$ for t.
Subtract u from each side. ⟶
$$t = 10 - u.$$

Replace t with $10 - u$. ⟶
Solve the equation.

$$9(10 - u) - 9u = 18$$
$$90 - 9u - 9u = 18$$
$$90 - 18u = 18$$

Add -90 to each side. ⟶
Divide each side by -18. ⟶

$$-18u = -72$$
$$u = 4$$

Find t. Substitute for u in one of
the equations. ⟶

$$t + u = 10$$
$$t + 4 = 10$$
$$t = 6$$

$10t + u = 10(6) + 4$ ⟶   **Thus,** the original number is 64.

EXAMPLE 6 Three times the tens digit of a two-digit number, increased by the units digit, is 21. If the digits are reversed, the new number is 9 more than the original number. Find the original number.

Represent the digits algebraically. ⟶ Let t = tens digit of the original number
u = units digit of the original number
$10t + u$ = the original number
$10u + t$ = the number with its digits reversed

Write two equations.
First equation ⟶

3 times tens digit, increased by units digit, is 21.

$$3t \qquad + \qquad u \qquad = 21$$

Second equation ⟶
Simplify.

New number is 9 more than original number.
$$10u + t = (10t + u) + 9$$
$$9u - 9t = 9$$

Solve the system.
$$3t + u = 21 \qquad (1)$$
$$9u - 9t = 9 \qquad (2)$$

Divide each side of (2) by −1. ⟶
$$-u + t = -1 \qquad (3)$$

Rearrange the variables in (3). ⟶
$$t - u = -1$$

Add equations (1) and (3).
$$3t + u = 21$$
$$\underline{t - u = -1}$$
$$4t = 20$$

Divide each side by 4. ⟶
$$t = 5$$

Find u.
Substitute for t in (1). ⟶
$$3t + u = 21 \qquad (1)$$
$$3(5) + u = 21$$
$$15 + u = 21$$
$$u = 21 - 15$$
$$u = 6$$

Thus, the original number is 56.

EXERCISES

1. The sum of the digits of a two-digit number is 15. If the digits are reversed, the new number is 27 less than the original number. Find the original number.

2. The sum of the digits of a two-digit number is 6. If the digits are reversed, the new number is 18 more than the original number. Find the original number.

3. The tens digit of a two-digit number is twice the units digit. If the digits are reversed, the new number is 36 less than the original number. Find the original number.

4. The units digit of a two-digit number is twice the tens digit. If the digits are reversed, the new number is 18 more than the original number. Find the original number.

5. The tens digit of a two-digit number is 3 times the units digit. If the digits are reversed, the new number is 54 less than the original number. Find the original number.

6. The units digit of a two-digit number is 3 times the tens digit. If the digits are reversed, the new number is 36 more than the original number. Find the original number.

7. The sum of the digits of a two-digit number is 11. If the digits are reversed, the new number is 7 more than twice the original number. Find the original number.

8. The sum of the digits of a two-digit number is 6. If the digits are reversed, the new number is 9 less than 4 times the original number. Find the original number.

9. The sum of the digits of a two-digit number is 13. If the digits are reversed, the new number is 4 less than twice the original number. Find the original number.

10. The sum of the digits of a two-digit number is 8. If the digits are reversed, the new number is 3 more than 4 times the original number. Find the original number.

11. The units digit of a two-digit number is 1 more than 3 times the tens digit. If the digits are reversed, the new number is 9 less than 3 times the original number. Find the new number.

12. The tens digit of a two-digit number is 7. If the digits are reversed, the new number is 9 less than the original number. Find the new number.

Direct Variation

OBJECTIVES
- ■ To determine if a relation is a direct variation
- ■ To find the constant of proportionality in a direct variation
- ■ To solve direct variation problems

 REVIEW CAPSULE

Formula for the perimeter of an equilateral triangle:

$$p = 3s$$

If $s = 2$, then
$p = 3 \cdot 2 = 6$.

If $s = 5$, then
$p = 3 \cdot 5 = 15$.

EXAMPLE 1

Find the ratio $\dfrac{p}{s}$ for each pair of numbers in the table below.

The table shows ordered pairs, $(2, 6)$, $(4, 12)$, $(5, 15)$, etc.

s	p
2	6
4	12
5	15
6	18
10	30

$\dfrac{p}{s} = \dfrac{6}{2} = 3$

$\dfrac{p}{s} = \dfrac{12}{4} = 3$

$\dfrac{p}{s} = \dfrac{15}{5} = 3$

Thus, the ratio $\dfrac{p}{s} = 3$ in all cases.

$\{(s, p) \mid p = 3s\}$ is a function.

The formula $\dfrac{p}{s} = 3$ describes a direct variation.

Definition of direct variation ⟶

> A *direct variation* is a function in which the ratio y to x is always the same.

Table of values for graph of $y = 3x$

x	y
2	6
1	3
−1	−3
−2	−6

Slope is 3.

3 is the constant of variation.

For a direct variation,
$$\frac{y}{x} = k,$$
or $y = kx$, where k is a constant.

y varies directly as x

or

y is directly proportional to x.

k is the constant of variation, or constant of proportionality. $\longrightarrow$

We say. $\longrightarrow$

EXAMPLE 2 From the table, determine if y varies directly as x. If so, find the constant of proportionality.

x	y
2	-10
3	-15
-1	5
-4	20

See if $\frac{y}{x} = k$, a constant.

$$\frac{-10}{2} = -5 \qquad \frac{-15}{3} = -5$$

$$\frac{5}{-1} = -5 \qquad \frac{20}{-4} = -5$$

$\frac{y}{x} = -5$ for all pairs (x, y).

$\frac{y}{x} = k$, where $k = -5$. $\longrightarrow$ **Thus,** y varies directly as x. The constant of proportionality is -5.

EXAMPLE 3 y varies directly as x, and $y = 32$ when $x = 4$. Find y when $x = 9$.

(x_1, y_1)

x-sub-one, y-sub-one

$\frac{y}{x} = k$ for all (x, y). $\longrightarrow$

Let (x_1, y_1) and (x_2, y_2) be any two ordered pairs that satisfy $y = kx$.

$$\frac{y_1}{x_1} = k \qquad \frac{y_2}{x_2} = k$$

Therefore,

$$\frac{y_1}{x_1} = \frac{y_2}{x_2}$$

Let $(x_1, y_1) = (4, 32)$ and $(x_2, y_2) = (9, y_2)$.

Solve the proportion.

$$\frac{32}{4} = \frac{y_2}{9}$$

$$4 \cdot y_2 = 32 \cdot 9$$

$$4y_2 = 288$$

Divide each side by 4. $\longrightarrow$

$$\frac{4y_2}{4} = \frac{288}{4}$$

$$y_2 = 72$$

Thus, $y = 72$ when $x = 9$.

EXAMPLE 4   On a map, 50 km are represented by 3 cm.
How many km are represented by 2 cm?

The relationship between cm and km describes a direct variation.

$\dfrac{cm_1}{km_1} = \dfrac{cm_2}{km_2}$ ⟶

Use prod. of means = prod. ⎤
of extremes.   ⎦ ⟶

Let x = no. of km represented by 2 cm

$$\frac{3}{50} = \frac{2}{x}$$
$$3(x) = 50(2)$$
$$3x = 100$$
$$x = \frac{100}{3}, \text{ or } 33\frac{1}{3}$$

Thus, 2 cm represents $33\frac{1}{3}$ km.

EXAMPLE 5   The cost of a certain metal varies directly as its
weight. If 6 g cost \$9, find the cost of 15 g.

Cost varies directly as weight.

$\dfrac{c_1}{g_1} = \dfrac{c_2}{g_2} \;\bigg|\; \dfrac{9}{6} = \dfrac{x}{15}$

Prod. of extremes = prod. of means

Let x = cost of 15 g

$$\frac{9}{6} = \frac{x}{15}$$
$$9(15) = 6(x)$$
$$135 = 6x$$
$$\frac{135}{6} = x$$

Divide each side by 6. ⟶

$$\begin{array}{r} 22.50 \\ 6\overline{)135.00} \end{array}$$

Thus, the cost of 15 g is \$22.50.

EXERCISES

PART A

Which tables express direct variations? For each direct variation, give the constant of proportionality.

1. _6_

x	y
1	6
2	12
3	18
4	24

2.

x	y
1	2
3	4
5	6
7	8

3. _-4_

x	y
-2	8
-1	4
1	-4
2	-8

4.

x	y
5	20
10	15
15	10
20	5

5. _-2_

x	y
-1	2
-2	4
-3	6
-4	8

_y_ varies directly as _x_.

6. y is 24 when x is 3. Find y when x is 4. _32_

7. y is -12 when x is -6. Find y when x is 7. _14_

8. y is 3 when x is 21. Find y when x is 35. _5_

9. y is -4 when x is 36. Find x when y is 6. _-54_

PART B

10. On a map, 40 km are represented by 7 cm. How many km are represented by 14 cm? *80 km*

11. On a map, 250 km are represented by 4 cm. How many km are represented by 7 cm? *437.5 km*

12. The cost of a certain metal varies directly as its weight. If 5 kg cost $15, find the cost of 8 kg. *$24*

13. The cost of gold varies directly as its weight. If 3 g cost $125, find the cost of 5 g. *$208.33*

14. At a given time and place, the height of an object varies directly as the length of the shadow it casts. A building casts a 170-m shadow while a 6-m flagpole casts a 10-m shadow. How tall is the building? *102 m*

15. In a recipe, the amount of flour varies directly as the amount of sugar. Three cups of flour are used for every 2 cups of sugar. How much sugar is used with 15 cups of flour? *10 cups*

16. The ratio of an object's weight on Earth to its weight on Mars is 5:2. A rock weighs 60 kg on Earth. How much would it weigh on Mars? *24 kg*

17. On a blueprint, a 5-m hallway is represented by 3 cm. Find the dimensions of a room represented by a rectangle 8 cm by 10 cm. *$13\frac{1}{3}$ m by $16\frac{2}{3}$ m*

PART C

EXAMPLE y varies directly as the square of x.
$y = 25$ when $x = 3$. Find y when $x = 2$.

$$\frac{25}{3^2} = \frac{y}{2^2}$$

$$\frac{25}{9} = \frac{y}{4}$$

$$100 = 9y$$

$$\frac{100}{9} = y \qquad \textbf{Thus, } y = \frac{100}{9}.$$

18. y varies directly as the square of x. $y = 36$ when $x = 2$. Find y when $x = 10$.

19. y varies directly as the square of x. $y = 15$ when $x = 4$. Find y when $x = 6$.

20. The distance needed to stop a car varies directly as the square of its speed. It requires 190 m to stop a car at 75 km per hour. What distance is needed to stop a car at 90 km per hour? $\left[\text{Hint: } \dfrac{190}{75^2} = \dfrac{x}{90^2}\right]$

21. The distance which a freely falling body falls varies directly as the square of the time it falls. A brick falls 22 m in 2 seconds. How far will it fall in 10 seconds?

Inverse Variation

OBJECTIVES
- To determine if a relation is an inverse variation
- To find the constant of variation in an inverse variation
- To solve inverse variation problems

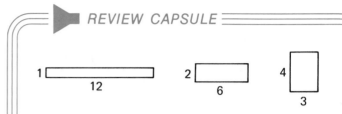

REVIEW CAPSULE

Area: $12 \cdot 1 = 12$ $6 \cdot 2 = 12$ $4 \cdot 3 = 12$

The area of each rectangle is 12.
$$lw = 12$$

EXAMPLE 1 Find the product lw for each pair of numbers in the table below.

The table shows ordered pairs, $(12, 1)$, $(6, 2)$, $(4, 3)$, etc.

l	w	
12	1	⟵ $12 \cdot 1 = 12$
6	2	⟵ $6 \cdot 2 = 12$
4	3	⟵ $4 \cdot 3 = 12$
24	$\frac{1}{2}$	⟵ $24 \cdot \frac{1}{2} = 12$

Thus, the product $lw = 12$ in all cases.

$\{(l, w) \mid lw = 12\}$ is a function.

The formula $lw = 12$ describes an inverse variation.

Definition of inverse function ⟶ An *inverse variation* is a function in which the product xy is always the same.

Table of values for graph of $xy = 12$

Other ordered pairs are $(3, 4)$, $(2, 6)$, $(1, 12)$.

x	y
12	1
6	2
4	3
−1	−12
−2	−6
−3	−4
−6	−2
−12	−1

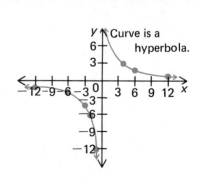

Curve is a hyperbola.

k is the constant of variation.

Also, $y = k \cdot \dfrac{1}{x}$.

We say.

For an inverse variation,
$$xy = k,$$
or $\quad y = \dfrac{k}{x},$ where k is a constant.

y varies inversely as x
or
y is inversely proportional to x.

EXAMPLE 2 From the table, determine if y varies inversely as x. If so, find the constant of variation.

x	y
2	9
6	3
−1	−18
−9	−2

See if $x \cdot y = k$, a constant.
$$2 \cdot 9 = 18$$
$$6 \cdot 3 = 18$$
$$-1\,(-18) = 18$$
$$-9\,(-2) = 18$$

$x \cdot y = 18$ for all pairs (x, y).

$x \cdot y = k$, where $k = 18$. ⟶ **Thus,** y varies inversely as x. The constant of variation is 18.

EXAMPLE 3 y varies inversely as x, and $y = 5$ *when* $x = 12$. Find x when $y = -4$.

Let $x \cdot y = k$ be the inverse variation.
Let (x_1, y_1) and (x_2, y_2) be any two ordered pairs that satisfy $x \cdot y = k$.

$x \cdot y = k$, for all (x, y). ⟶ $\qquad x_1 \cdot y_1 = k \qquad x_2 \cdot y_2 = k$

Let $(x_1, y_1) = (12, 5)$ and $(x_2, y_2) = (x_2, -4)$. ⟶

Therefore,
$$x_1 \cdot y_1 = x_2 \cdot y_2$$
$$12 \cdot 5 = x_2\,(-4)$$
$$60 = -4x_2$$

Divide each side by -4. ⟶
$$\frac{60}{-4} = \frac{-4x_2}{-4}$$
$$-15 = x_2$$

Thus, $x = -15$ when $y = -4$.

ORAL EXERCISES

Which formulas describe inverse variations? For each inverse variation, give the constant of variation.

1. $r \cdot t = 60$ *60*   **2.** $c = 3.14d$ **3.** $x \cdot y = -8$ *−8*   **4.** $36 = b \cdot h$ *36*   **5.** $x \cdot y = 1$ *1*

6. $\dfrac{20}{y} = x$ *20*   **7.** $r = \dfrac{s}{-6}$ **8.** $\dfrac{-22}{b} = a$ *−22*   **9.** $\dfrac{p}{4} = s$ **10.** $\dfrac{1}{5} \cdot y = x$

EXERCISES

PART A

Which tables express inverse variations? For each inverse variation, give the constant of variation.

1. *18*

x	y
3	6
−2	−9
36	$\frac{1}{2}$
−18	−1

2.

x	y
1	1
−1	−1
0	0
2	2

3.

x	y
3	6
6	12
−3	−6
−6	−12

4. *100*

x	y
5	20
−10	−10
−4	−25
$\frac{1}{2}$	200

5. *−1*

x	y
$\frac{1}{2}$	−2
−1	1
$-\frac{3}{4}$	$\frac{4}{3}$
1	−1

y varies inversely as x.

6. y is 24 when x is 8. Find y when x is 4. *48*
7. y is 30 when x is 2. Find y when x is 15. *4*
8. y is −7 when x is 8. Find y when x is 4. *−14*

PART B

EXAMPLE   Jane weighs 70 kg and is sitting 160 cm from the fulcrum of a seesaw. John weighs 56 kg. How far from the fulcrum must he sit to balance the seesaw?

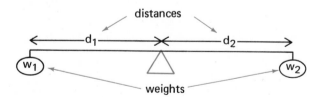

distances

weights

Law of the Lever

	Jane	John
weight	w_1	w_2
distance	d_1	d_2

The lever is in balance if $w_1 \cdot d_1 = w_2 \cdot d_2$.
$$70 \cdot 160 = 56 \cdot d_2$$
$$11{,}200 = 56 \cdot d_2$$
$$200 = d_2$$

Thus, John must sit 200 cm from the fulcrum.

9. Laurie weighs 60 kg and is sitting 165 cm from the fulcrum of a seesaw. Bill weighs 55 kg. How far from the fulcrum must Bill sit to balance the seesaw? *180 cm*

10. Jack is sitting 170 cm from the fulcrum of a seesaw. Mary weighs 65 kg and is sitting 210 cm from the fulcrum. How heavy is Jack if the seesaw is in balance? *80.3 kg*

11. The dimensions of a rectangle are 6 meters and 18 meters. Find the width of another rectangle with the same area and a length of 12 meters. *9 m*

12. The volume of a gas is 60 cubic meters under 6 kg of pressure. What is its volume at the same temperature under 9 kg of pressure? *40 m³*

13. A trip takes 5 hours at 50 km per hour. How long does it take at 60 km per hour? $4\frac{1}{6}$ *hr*

14. It takes 8 women 6 hours to do a job. How long will it take 12 women working at the same rate? *4 hr*

15. What amount invested at 6% yields the same yearly income as $1,000 invested at $4\frac{1}{2}$%? *$750*

16. At what rate does $15,000 yield the same annual income as $12,000 invested at 5%? *4%*

17. The base of a triangle is 16 centimeters and the altitude is 9 centimeters. Find the base of a triangle of equal area whose altitude is 6 centimeters. *24 cm*

18. Nancy weighs 72 kg and Bob weighs 60 kg. Nancy is sitting 2 m from the fulcrum of a seesaw. How far from Nancy should Bob sit to balance the seesaw? *4.4 m*

19. Sophia has enough money to buy 3 meters of fabric priced at $6.40 per meter. How many meters of fabric priced at $3.60 per meter can she buy with the same amount of money?

20. The current through a circuit is 25 amperes when the resistance is 16 ohms. What is the current when the resistance is increased to 20 ohms? *20 amps*

PART C

21. Tina and Wilt are sitting 4 meters apart on a seesaw. Tina weighs 65 kg, and Wilt weighs 80 kg. How far from the fulcrum must Tina be sitting if the seesaw is in balance?

22. Ruiz drove a round trip between cities A and B in $7\frac{1}{2}$ hours. From A to B he averaged 60 km/hr, and from B back to A he averaged 65 km/hr. How far apart are A and B?

23. Cylinders A and B have the same volume. Their altitudes vary inversely as the squares of the radii of the bases. The altitude of cylinder A is 8 m, and the radius of its base is 6 m. Find the altitude of cylinder B if the radius of its base is 4 m.

24. The weight of a body at or above the Earth's surface varies inversely as the square of the body's distance from the Earth's center. What does a 220-kg object weigh when it is 370 km above the Earth's surface? (Use 6,500 km as the Earth's radius.)

Chapter Twelve Review

List the ordered pairs in each relation graphed below. Give the domain and the range. Is the relation a function? $[p.\ 317]$

1.

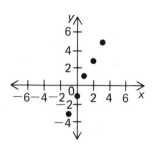

2.

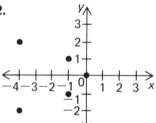

3.

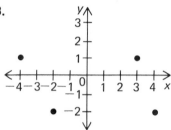

Graph each relation. Give the domain and range. Is the relation a function? $[p.\ 317]$

4. $\{(-1,-1),\ (-2,-2),\ (0,0),\ (-1,1),\ (-2,2)\}$
5. $\{(-2,1),\ (-1,1),\ (0,1),\ (1,1),\ (2,1)\}$

Graph each relation. Which relations are functions? Which functions are linear functions? Which functions are constant functions? $[p.\ 320]$

6. $\{(x,y)\,|\,y=2x\}$ **7.** $\{(x,y)\,|\,x=4\}$ **8.** $\{(x,y)\,|\,y=x+2\}$
9. $\{(x,y)\,|\,y-3x=-1\}$ **10.** $\{(x,y)\,|\,y=-1\}$ **11.** $\{(x,y)\,|\,y=2x^2+1\}$

$f=\{(x,y)\,|\,y=x^2+3\}$. **Find each.** $[p.\ 323]$

12. $f(0)$ **13.** $f(3)$ **14.** $f(-2)$ **15.** $f(6)$ **16.** $f(-12)$

D **is the domain of each function. Determine the range.** $[p.\ 323]$

17. $f(x)=3x-2\quad D=\{0,1,-1\}$ **18.** $g(x)=-x^2+3\quad D=\{-3,-2,-1\}$

Which tables express direct variations? Which express inverse variations? For each variation give the constant of variation. $[p.\ 330,\ 334]$

19.

x	y
-3	-9
-1	-3
1	3
2	6

20.

x	y
2	3
-1	-6
-3	-2
12	$\frac{1}{2}$

21.

x	y
-1	-3
0	-1
1	1
2	3

22.

x	y
-2	4
5	-10
-3	6
4	-8

23.

x	y
2	-6
-3	-4
-1	12
4	3

24. y varies directly as x, and $y=-4$ when x is 12. Find y when x is -18.
26. The cost of a metal varies directly as its weight. If 3 kg cost $10, what is the cost of 24 kg?

25. y varies inversely as x, and y is 5 when x is 4. Find x when y is -2.
27. Sheila weighs 50 kg and is sitting 180 cm from the fulcrum of a seesaw. Joan weighs 60 kg. How far from the fulcrum must Joan sit to balance the seesaw?

Chapter Twelve Test

List the ordered pairs in each relation graphed below. Give the domain and the range. Is the relation a function?

1.

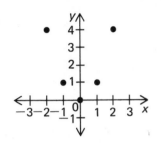

2.

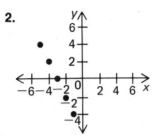

3.

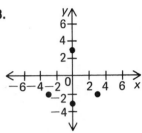

Graph each relation. Which relations are functions? Which functions are linear functions? Which functions are constant functions?

4. $\{(x, y) \mid x = -2\}$

5. $\{(x, y) \mid y = 3\}$

6. $\{(x, y) \mid y = x^2 + 1\}$

$f = \{(x, y) \mid y = 2x - 3\}$. **Find each.**

7. $f(3)$

8. $f(0)$

9. $f(-10)$

D is the domain of each function. Find the range.

10. $f(x) = 2x^2 - 1 \quad D = \{-1, 0, 1\}$

11. $h(x) = -3x + 4 \quad D = \{-2, 0, 2\}$

Which tables express direct variations? Which express inverse variations? For each variation, give the constant of variation.

12.

x	y
−1	4
0	3
1	2
2	1

13.

x	y
8	−8
−2	32
−4	16
−8	8

14.

x	y
2	−6
1	−3
−1	3
−2	6

15. y varies directly as x, and y is 24 when x is 6. Find y when x is −8.

16. y varies inversely as x, and y is 8 when x is −4. Find x when y is −2.

17. The cost of a metal varies directly as its weight. If 7 g cost $20, what is the cost of 35 g?

18. Moira weighs 45 kg and is sitting 2 m from the fulcrum of a seesaw. Juan weighs 50 kg. How far from the fulcrum must Juan sit to balance the seesaw?

Mathematics and Electricians

The electrician and his assistant are upgrading the existing wiring in this house from 60 amps to 150 amps.

An electrician must apply some basic algebraic and scientific formulas. One of these is Ohm's law.

$$V = IR \quad \text{or} \quad E = IR$$

voltage   current   resistance

If $R = 100$ *ohms* ($100\,\Omega$) and $I = 20$ amps,
the voltage V is $(100)(20)$, or $2{,}000$ *v*.

PROJECT Suppose the voltage is 400*v*. What will happen to I (the current) as the resistance (value of R) is steadily increased?

Solving Fractional Equations

 REVIEW CAPSULE

Find the least common denominator (LCD).

$$\frac{x}{10} + \frac{x}{4} + \frac{3x+1}{5}$$

$$\frac{x}{5 \cdot 2} + \frac{x}{2 \cdot 2} + \frac{3x+1}{5}$$

The LCD is $5 \cdot 2 \cdot 2$.

Two equations which have the same solution are equivalent equations.

We can use the equation properties to transform an equation into another equation which has the same solution.

$a = b$	$a = b$	$a = b$
$a + c = b + c$	$ac = bc$	$\dfrac{a}{c} = \dfrac{b}{c}$
↓	↓	↓
Add the same number to each side.	Multiply each side by the same number.	Divide each side by the same number.

EXAMPLE 1 Rewrite $\dfrac{x}{2} + \dfrac{2}{3} = \dfrac{x}{6}$ as an equation with no fractions.

Find the LCD by factoring the denominators. ⟶

$$\frac{x}{2} + \frac{2}{3} = \frac{x}{3 \cdot 2} \quad \text{The LCD is } 3 \cdot 2.$$

Multiply each side by the LCD, $3 \cdot 2$. ⟶

$$3 \cdot 2\left(\frac{x}{2} + \frac{2}{3}\right) = 3 \cdot 2 \cdot \frac{x}{3 \cdot 2}$$

Use the distributive property. ⟶

$$3 \cdot 2 \cdot \frac{x}{2} + 3 \cdot 2 \cdot \frac{2}{3} = 3 \cdot 2 \cdot \frac{x}{3 \cdot 2}$$

Do multiplications. ⟶

$$3 \cdot \overset{1}{2} \cdot \frac{x}{\underset{}{\cancel{2}}} + \overset{1}{3} \cdot 2 \cdot \frac{2}{\underset{1}{\cancel{3}}} = \overset{1}{\cancel{3}} \cdot \overset{1}{\cancel{2}} \cdot \frac{x}{\underset{1}{\cancel{3}} \cdot \underset{1}{\cancel{2}}}$$

This equation has no fractions. It is a simpler equation to solve. ⟶

$$3x + 4 = x$$

EXAMPLE 2 Solve $3x + 4 = x$, the resulting equation in Example 1. Then show that the solution also satisfies the original fractional equation $\dfrac{x}{2} + \dfrac{2}{3} = \dfrac{x}{6}$.

$x = 1x$ ⟶

Add $-3x$ to each side. ⟶

$$\begin{array}{r} 3x + 4 = 1x \\ -3x -3x \\ \hline 4 = -2x \end{array}$$

Divide each side by -2. ⟶

$$-2 = x$$

Check -2 in $\dfrac{x}{2} + \dfrac{2}{3} = \dfrac{x}{6}$.

Replace x by -2. ⟶

$$\begin{array}{c|c} \dfrac{x}{2} + \dfrac{2}{3} & \dfrac{x}{6} \\[2mm] \hline \dfrac{-2}{2} + \dfrac{2}{3} & \dfrac{-2}{6} \\[2mm] \dfrac{-1}{1} + \dfrac{2}{3} & -\dfrac{1}{3} \\[2mm] -\dfrac{1}{3} & \end{array}$$

$$\left.\begin{array}{c} \dfrac{-1}{1} + \dfrac{2}{3} = \dfrac{-3}{3} + \dfrac{2}{3} \\[2mm] = -\dfrac{1}{3} \end{array}\right\}$$

Thus, -2 is the solution of $\dfrac{x}{2} + \dfrac{2}{3} = \dfrac{x}{6}$.

To solve a fractional equation:
First, find the LCD for all fractions.
Next, multiply each side by the LCD.
Then, solve the resulting equation.

EXAMPLE 3 Find the solution set of $\dfrac{3a}{5} + \dfrac{3}{2} = \dfrac{7a}{10}$.

Find the LCD by factoring the denominators. ⟶

$$\dfrac{3a}{5} + \dfrac{3}{2} = \dfrac{7a}{5 \cdot 2} \quad \text{The LCD is } 5 \cdot 2.$$

Multiply each side by the LCD, $5 \cdot 2$.

$$5 \cdot 2\left(\dfrac{3a}{5} + \dfrac{3}{2}\right) = 5 \cdot 2 \cdot \dfrac{7a}{5 \cdot 2}$$

Distribute the $5 \cdot 2$: $5 \cdot 2\left(\dfrac{3a}{5} + \dfrac{3}{2}\right)$ ⟶

$$5 \cdot 2 \cdot \dfrac{3a}{5} + 5 \cdot 2 \cdot \dfrac{3}{2} = 5 \cdot 2 \cdot \dfrac{7a}{5 \cdot 2}$$

Do multiplications. ⟶

$$\overset{1}{5} \cdot 2 \cdot \dfrac{3a}{\underset{1}{5}} + 5 \cdot \overset{1}{2} \cdot \dfrac{3}{\underset{1}{2}} = \overset{1}{5} \cdot \overset{1}{2} \cdot \dfrac{7a}{\underset{1}{5} \cdot \underset{1}{2}}$$

$2 \cdot 3a = 6a$; $5 \cdot 3 = 15$ ⟶

$$6a + 15 = 7a$$

Add $-6a$ to each side. ⟶

$$15 = a$$

Check on your own. ⟶ **Thus,** the solution set is $\{15\}$.

EXAMPLE 4 Solve $\dfrac{3a}{4} - \dfrac{2a-1}{2} = \dfrac{a-7}{6}$.

$-\dfrac{2a-1}{2} = \dfrac{-1(2a-1)}{2}$ ────────────→

$-1(2a-1) = -2a+1$ ────────────→ The LCD is
                                    $3 \cdot 2 \cdot 2$.

Factor the denominators. ────────→

Multiply each side by the LCD. ──────→

Use the distributive property. ──────→

$$\dfrac{3a}{4} + \dfrac{-1(2a-1)}{2} = \dfrac{a-7}{6}$$

$$\dfrac{3a}{2 \cdot 2} + \dfrac{-2a+1}{2} = \dfrac{a-7}{2 \cdot 3}$$

$$3 \cdot 2 \cdot 2\left(\dfrac{3a}{2 \cdot 2} + \dfrac{-2a+1}{2}\right) = 3 \cdot 2 \cdot 2 \cdot \dfrac{a-7}{2 \cdot 3}$$

$$3 \cdot 2 \cdot 2 \cdot \dfrac{3a}{2 \cdot 2} + 3 \cdot 2 \cdot 2 \cdot \dfrac{-2a+1}{2} = 3 \cdot 2 \cdot 2 \cdot \dfrac{a-7}{2 \cdot 3}$$

$$3 \cdot \overset{1}{\cancel{2}} \cdot \overset{1}{\cancel{2}} \cdot \dfrac{3a}{\underset{1}{\cancel{2}} \cdot \underset{1}{\cancel{2}}} + 3 \cdot 2 \cdot \overset{1}{\cancel{2}} \cdot \dfrac{-2a+1}{\underset{1}{\cancel{2}}} = \overset{1}{\cancel{3}} \cdot \overset{1}{\cancel{2}} \cdot 2 \cdot \dfrac{a-7}{\underset{1}{\cancel{2}} \cdot \underset{1}{\cancel{3}}}$$

Simplify. ────────────────→

$\left.\begin{array}{l} 6(-2a+1) = -12a+6 \\ 2(a-7) = 2a-14 \end{array}\right\}$

Add $3a$ to each side. ────────→

Add 14 to each side. ────────→

Check by letting $a = 4$ in the original
equation. ────────────────→

$$3 \cdot 3a + 6(-2a+1) = 2(a-7)$$
$$9a \quad -12a+6 = 2a-14$$
$$-3a+6 = 2a-14$$
$$6 = 5a-14$$
$$20 = 5a$$
$$4 = a$$

Thus, the solution is 4.

EXAMPLE 5 Solve $\dfrac{4}{5} + \dfrac{3}{a} = 2$.

$2 = \dfrac{2}{1}$; the denominators are already

factored. ────────────────→

$$\dfrac{4}{5} + \dfrac{3}{a} = \dfrac{2}{1} \qquad \text{The LCD is } 5 \cdot a.$$

Multiply each side by the LCD, $5 \cdot a$.

$$5 \cdot a\left(\dfrac{4}{5} + \dfrac{3}{a}\right) = 5 \cdot a \cdot \dfrac{2}{1}$$

Distributive property: $5 \cdot a\left(\dfrac{4}{5} + \dfrac{3}{a}\right)$ ──────→

$$5 \cdot a \cdot \dfrac{4}{5} + 5 \cdot a \cdot \dfrac{3}{a} = 5 \cdot a \cdot \dfrac{2}{1}$$

$$\overset{1}{\cancel{5}} \cdot a \cdot \dfrac{4}{\underset{1}{\cancel{5}}} + 5 \cdot \overset{1}{\cancel{a}} \cdot \dfrac{3}{\underset{1}{\cancel{a}}} = 5 \cdot a \cdot 2$$

$a \cdot 4 = 4 \cdot a = 4a$;
$5 \cdot a \cdot 2 = 5 \cdot 2 \cdot a = 10a$ ────────→

Add $-4a$ to each side. ────────→

Divide each side by 6. ────────→

$\dfrac{15}{6} = \dfrac{5}{2}$ ────────────────→

$$4a + 15 = 10a$$
$$15 = 6a$$
$$\dfrac{15}{6} = a$$

Thus, the solution is $\dfrac{5}{2}$, or $2\dfrac{1}{2}$.

EXAMPLE 6 Solve the proportion $\dfrac{3x-1}{2}=\dfrac{5x+1}{4}$.

	First Method	Second Method

In a proportion, $\dfrac{a}{b}=\dfrac{c}{d}$, $a \cdot d = b \cdot c$;

prod. of extremes = prod. of means. $\longrightarrow$

or

In the second method multiply each side by the LCD.

First Method

$$\frac{3x-1}{2}=\frac{5x+1}{4}$$

$$4(3x-1)=2(5x+1)$$

$$\begin{array}{rcl} 12x-4 &=& 10x+2 \\ -10x & & -10x \\ \hline 2x-4 &=& 2 \\ 4 & & 4 \\ \hline 2x &=& 6 \\ x &=& 3 \end{array}$$

Second Method

$$\frac{3x-1}{2}=\frac{5x+1}{2 \cdot 2}$$

$$\overset{1}{2} \cdot 2 \cdot \frac{3x-1}{\underset{1}{2}} = \overset{1}{2} \cdot \overset{1}{2} \cdot \frac{5x+1}{\underset{1}{2} \cdot \underset{1}{2}}$$

$$\begin{array}{rcl} 2(3x-1) &=& 5x+1 \\ 6x-2 &=& 5x+1 \\ -5x & & -5x \\ \hline x-2 &=& 1 \\ x &=& 3 \end{array}$$

Both methods give the same solution.

A proportion can be solved in two ways:

One way $\longrightarrow$ Product of the extremes = product of the means.

Second way $\longrightarrow$ Multiply each side of the equation by the LCD.

EXERCISES

PART A

Solve.

1. $\dfrac{2a-3}{6}=\dfrac{2a}{3}+\dfrac{1}{2}$ *−3*

2. $\dfrac{3a}{5}+\dfrac{3}{2}=\dfrac{7a}{10}$ *15*

3. $\dfrac{3m}{2}+\dfrac{5}{4}=\dfrac{5m}{2}$ *5/4*

4. $\dfrac{5}{4x}+\dfrac{1}{x}=3$ *3/4*

5. $\dfrac{3}{5b}+\dfrac{7}{2b}=1$ *41/10*

6. $\dfrac{1}{m}+\dfrac{2}{3}=1$ *3*

7. $\dfrac{3r+4}{12}-\dfrac{5}{3}=\dfrac{2r-1}{2}$ *10/9*

8. $\dfrac{2x-3}{7}-\dfrac{x}{2}=\dfrac{x+3}{14}$ *9/4*

9. $\dfrac{a}{4}-\dfrac{a}{3}=7$ *−84*

Find the solution set.

10. $\dfrac{3a+2}{6}=\dfrac{2a+2}{3}$ *{−2}*

11. $\dfrac{2m-5}{3}=\dfrac{m+1}{2}$ *{13}*

12. $\dfrac{2a-3}{5}=\dfrac{3a+1}{7}$ *{−26}*

PART B

Find the solution set.

13. $\dfrac{2}{3}(x-2)+\dfrac{x+3}{2}=\dfrac{5x+3}{6}$ *{1}*

14. $\dfrac{3}{5}(a-3)+\dfrac{a+1}{15}=\dfrac{1}{3}$ *{31/10}*

15. $\dfrac{2}{3}b-\dfrac{5}{6}(3-b)=\dfrac{2b-5}{3}$ *{1}*

16. $\dfrac{3m}{5}+\dfrac{1-2m}{3}=\dfrac{m+1}{15}$ *{2}*

Percent of a Number

PROBLEM 1.

45% of freshmen study algebra. How many freshmen in a class of 400 study algebra?

Let t = number of freshmen taking algebra

Write a proportion. ⟶ $\dfrac{t}{400} = \dfrac{\text{number of algebra students}}{\text{total number of freshmen}}$

45% means $\dfrac{45}{100}$ or $\dfrac{.45}{1}$ ⟶ $\dfrac{.45}{1} = \dfrac{\text{number of algebra students}}{\text{total number of freshmen}}$

Set the ratios equal. ⟶ $\dfrac{t}{400} = \dfrac{.45}{1}$

If $\dfrac{a}{b} = \dfrac{c}{d}$, then $ad = bc$. ⟶ $t(1) = .45(400)$

$$\begin{array}{r} 400 \\ .45 \\ \hline 20\,00 \\ 160\,0 \\ \hline 180.00 \end{array}$$

To find 45% of 400, write 45% as a decimal, then multiply.

Thus, 180 students study algebra.

PROBLEM 2.

A $256.24 television is advertised at a 23% discount. How much is saved?

23% of 256.24 means .23(256.24).

$$\begin{array}{r} 2\,5\,6.2\,4 \\ .2\,3 \\ \hline 7\,6\,8\,7\,2 \\ 5\,1\,2\,4\,8 \\ \hline 5\,8.9\,3\,5\,2 \end{array}$$ ⟵ Move decimal point 4 places.

Sometimes with discounts, merchants round to the next lower penny.

Thus, the savings are $58.94.

PROJECT

1. Find 32% of 78. 2. Find 43% of $6,598. 3. Find 62% of 19.
4. Find the savings when buying a $243.65 washer at a 27% discount.
5. Find the savings when buying a $49.95 radio at a 6% discount.
   [Hint: 6%=.06.]

More Fractional Equations

OBJECTIVE

■ To solve equations like

$$\frac{6}{a+2}+\frac{3}{a^2-4}=\frac{2a-7}{a-2}$$

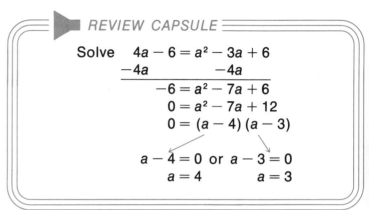

▶ REVIEW CAPSULE

Solve

$$4a - 6 = a^2 - 3a + 6$$
$$\underline{-4a \qquad\qquad -4a}$$
$$-6 = a^2 - 7a + 6$$
$$0 = a^2 - 7a + 12$$
$$0 = (a-4)(a-3)$$

$$a - 4 = 0 \text{ or } a - 3 = 0$$
$$a = 4 \qquad\qquad a = 3$$

EXAMPLE 1 Solve $\dfrac{3x}{x^2-5x+4}=\dfrac{2}{x-4}+\dfrac{3}{x-1}$.

Factor $x^2 - 5x + 4$; LCD is $(x-4)(x-1)$. →

$$\frac{3x}{(x-4)(x-1)}=\frac{2}{x-4}+\frac{3}{x-1}$$

Multiply each side by the LCD, $(x-4)(x-1)$.

$$(x-4)(x-1)\cdot\frac{3x}{(x-4)(x-1)}=$$
$$(x-4)(x-1)\left(\frac{2}{x-4}+\frac{3}{x-1}\right)$$

$$(x-4)(x-1)\left(\frac{2}{x-4}+\frac{3}{x-1}\right) \longrightarrow$$

$$(x-4)(x-1)\cdot\frac{3x}{(x-4)(x-1)}=$$
$$(x-4)(x-1)\cdot\frac{2}{x-4}+(x-4)(x-1)\cdot\frac{3}{x-1}$$

Do multiplications. ─────→

$$(x-4)(x-1)\cdot\frac{3x}{(x-4)(x-1)}=$$

$$(x-4)(x-1)\cdot\frac{2}{x-4}+(x-4)(x-1)\cdot\frac{3}{x-1}$$

$(x-1)2 = 2x - 2;$

$(x-4)3 = 3x - 12$ ─────→

Combine like terms. ─────→

Add $-5x$ to each side. ─────→

Divide each side by -2. ─────→

$$3x = (x-1)2 + (x-4)3$$
$$3x = 2x - 2 + 3x - 12$$
$$3x = 5x - 14$$
$$-2x = -14$$
$$x = 7$$

Thus, the solution is 7.

EXAMPLE 2 Show that 7 is the solution of

$$\frac{3x}{x^2 - 5x + 4} = \frac{2}{x - 4} + \frac{3}{x - 1}.$$

$\dfrac{3x}{x^2 - 5x + 4}$	$\dfrac{2}{x - 4} + \dfrac{3}{x - 1}$
$\dfrac{3 \cdot 7}{7^2 - 5 \cdot 7 + 4}$	$\dfrac{2}{7 - 4} + \dfrac{3}{7 - 1}$
$\dfrac{21}{18}$	$\dfrac{2}{3} + \dfrac{3}{6}$
$\dfrac{7}{6}$	$\dfrac{4}{6} + \dfrac{3}{6}$, or $\dfrac{7}{6}$

Replace x by 7.

$7^2 - 5 \cdot 7 + 4 = 49 - 35 + 4 = 18 \longrightarrow$

$\dfrac{21}{18} = \dfrac{7}{6}; \dfrac{2}{3} = \dfrac{4}{6}$ ————————

Thus, 7 is the solution of $\dfrac{3x}{x^2 - 5x + 4} = \dfrac{2}{x - 4} + \dfrac{3}{x - 1}.$

EXAMPLE 3 Find the solution set of $\dfrac{7}{m^2 - 5m} + \dfrac{3}{5 - m} = \dfrac{4}{m}.$

Put $5 - m$ in convenient form.
$5 - m = -1m + 5 = -1(m - 5)$ ————→
   descending order

$\dfrac{3}{-1(m - 5)} = \dfrac{-1 \cdot 3}{m - 5} = \dfrac{-3}{m - 5}$ ————→

Factor $m^2 - 5m$; LCD is $m(m - 5)$. ————→
Multiply each side by the LCD, $m(m - 5)$.

$$\dfrac{7}{m^2 - 5m} + \dfrac{3}{-1(m - 5)} = \dfrac{4}{m}$$

$$\dfrac{7}{m^2 - 5m} + \dfrac{-3}{m - 5} = \dfrac{4}{m}$$

$$\dfrac{7}{m(m - 5)} + \dfrac{-3}{m - 5} = \dfrac{4}{m}$$

$$m(m - 5)\left[\dfrac{7}{m(m - 5)} + \dfrac{-3}{m - 5}\right] = m(m - 5) \cdot \dfrac{4}{m}$$

Distribute $m(m - 5)$. Do multiplications.

$$\overset{1}{m}(m \overset{1}{-} 5) \cdot \dfrac{7}{\underset{1}{m}(m \underset{1}{-} 5)} + m(m \overset{1}{-} 5) \cdot \dfrac{-3}{m \underset{1}{-} 5} =$$

$$\overset{1}{m}(m - 5) \cdot \dfrac{4}{\underset{1}{m}}$$

$m(-3) = -3m;$
$(m - 5)4 = 4m - 20$ ————→
Add $3m$ to each side. ————→

Add 20 to each side. ————→

Divide each side by 7. ————→

$$7 + m(-3) = (m - 5)4$$
$$7 \quad -3m = 4m - 20$$
$$\underline{\quad 3m \qquad 3m \quad}$$
$$7 \quad = 7m - 20$$
$$\underline{20 \qquad\qquad 20}$$
$$27 \quad = 7m$$
$$\dfrac{27}{7} \quad = m$$

Thus, the solution set is $\{\frac{27}{7}\}$.

EXAMPLE 4   Solve $\dfrac{6}{a+2}+\dfrac{3}{a^2-4}=\dfrac{2a-7}{a-2}$.

Factor a^2-4; LCD is $(a-2)(a+2)$. ⟶ $\dfrac{6}{a+2}+\dfrac{3}{(a-2)(a+2)}=\dfrac{2a-7}{a-2}$

Multiply each side by the LCD, $(a-2)(a+2)$.

$$(a-2)(a+2)\left[\dfrac{6}{a+2}+\dfrac{3}{(a-2)(a+2)}\right]=$$

$$(a-2)(a+2)\cdot\dfrac{2a-7}{a-2}$$

Distribute $(a-2)(a+2)$. ⟶ $(a-2)(a+2)\cdot\dfrac{6}{a+2}+(a-2)(a+2)\cdot$

$$\dfrac{3}{(a-2)(a+2)}=(a-2)(a+2)\cdot\dfrac{2a-7}{a-2}$$

$$(a-2)\cancel{(a+2)}\cdot\dfrac{6}{\cancel{a+2}}+\cancel{(a-2)}\cancel{(a+2)}\cdot$$

$$\dfrac{3}{\cancel{(a-2)}\cancel{(a+2)}}=\cancel{(a-2)}(a+2)\cdot\dfrac{2a-7}{\cancel{a-2}}$$

$$(a-2)6+3=(a+2)(2a-7)$$
$$6a-12+3=(a+2)(2a-7)$$
$$6a-9=2a^2-3a-14$$

$\begin{array}{l}(a-2)6=6a-12\\[4pt]\quad a\quad\;+\;2\\ \quad 2a\quad-\;7\\ \hline 2a^2\;\;-3a\;\;-14\end{array}$

Put the quadratic equation in standard form.

$$6a-9=2a^2-3a-14$$

Coefficient of a^2 term is positive. Get polynomial $=0$. Add $-6a$, then 9 to each side.

$$-9=2a^2-9a-14\qquad\text{Terms are arranged in}$$
$$0=2a^2-9a-5\;\longleftarrow\;\text{descending order.}$$

Factor. ⟶ $0=(2a+1)(a-5)$

Set each factor $=0$. ⟶ $2a+1=0$ or $a-5=0$

Solve each equation for a. ⟶ $2a=-1$

$$a=-\tfrac{1}{2}\qquad\qquad\qquad a=5$$

Thus, the solutions are $-\tfrac{1}{2}$ and 5.

EXERCISES

PART A

Solve.

1. $\dfrac{3}{x^2-4}+\dfrac{5}{x-2}=\dfrac{7}{x+2}$ $\dfrac{27}{2}$

2. $\dfrac{8}{x^2-7x+12}=\dfrac{5}{x-3}+\dfrac{2}{x-4}$ $\dfrac{34}{7}$

3. $\dfrac{9}{a^2 - 5a} + \dfrac{3}{a - 5} = \dfrac{2}{a}$ -19

4. $\dfrac{4}{x - 5} = \dfrac{2x - 30}{x^2 - 25} + \dfrac{4}{x + 5}$ *35*

5. $\dfrac{5}{n^2 - 3n} - \dfrac{3}{n - 3} = \dfrac{2}{n}$ $\dfrac{11}{5}$

6. $\dfrac{2}{b^2 - 5b - 14} = \dfrac{3}{b - 7} - \dfrac{4}{b + 2}$ *32*

Find the solution set.

7. $\dfrac{4}{y + 5} - \dfrac{2}{y - 8} = \dfrac{3}{y^2 - 3y - 40}$ $\left\{\dfrac{45}{2}\right\}$

8. $\dfrac{7}{a^2 - 5a} - \dfrac{2}{a - 5} = \dfrac{4}{a}$ $\left\{\dfrac{9}{2}\right\}$

9. $\dfrac{8}{4 - x} + \dfrac{2x + 3}{x^2 - 2x - 8} = \dfrac{7}{x + 2}$ $\left\{\dfrac{15}{13}\right\}$

10. $\dfrac{7}{m^2 - 3m} - \dfrac{4}{m} = \dfrac{5}{3 - m}$ $\{-19\}$

11. $\dfrac{4}{a + 3} + \dfrac{2}{3 - a} = \dfrac{4}{a^2 - 9}$ $\{11\}$

12. $\dfrac{2x + 3}{x^2 - 5x + 6} = \dfrac{2}{x - 2} - \dfrac{5}{x - 3}$ $\left\{\dfrac{1}{5}\right\}$

13. $\dfrac{-7}{b^2 - 9b + 20} = \dfrac{b}{b - 4} + \dfrac{1}{b - 5}$ $\{1, 3\}$

14. $\dfrac{x + 3}{x + 5} + \dfrac{2}{x - 9} = \dfrac{-20}{x^2 - 4x - 45}$ $\{1, 3\}$

PART B

EXAMPLE   Solve $\dfrac{x + 1}{x - 3} = \dfrac{3}{x} + \dfrac{12}{x^2 - 3x}$.

Multiply each side by the LCD, $x(x - 3)$. ⟶

$$x(x - 3) \cdot \dfrac{x + 1}{x - 3} = x(x - 3) \cdot \dfrac{3}{x} + x(x - 3) \cdot \dfrac{12}{x(x - 3)}$$

$x(x + 1) = x^2 + x;$
$(x - 3)3 = 3x - 9$ ⟶

Write the equation in standard form.

$$x(x + 1) = (x - 3)3 + 12$$
$$x^2 + x = 3x - 9 + 12$$
$$x^2 - 2x - 3 = 0$$
$$(x - 3)(x + 1) = 0$$

$x - 3 = 0$ or $x + 1 = 0$
$x = 3$ $x = -1$

If we replace x with 3 in the original equation $\dfrac{x + 1}{x - 3} = \dfrac{3 + 1}{3 - 3}$, or $\dfrac{4}{0}$ which is undefined.

The fraction $\dfrac{x + 1}{x - 3}$ is undefined when $x = 3$.

So, 3 cannot be a solution.

Thus, the solution is -1.

In the example, 3 is an extraneous solution.

An *extraneous solution* of an equation is an apparent solution that does not check.

Solve and check for extraneous solutions.

15. $\dfrac{4}{y^2 - 8y + 12} = \dfrac{y}{y - 2} + \dfrac{1}{y - 6}$ -1

16. $\dfrac{2}{a + 2} - \dfrac{a}{a - 2} = \dfrac{-13}{a^2 - 4}$ *3, -3*

17. $x - \dfrac{5x}{x - 2} = \dfrac{-10}{x - 2}$ *5*

18. $\dfrac{x^2 + 7x}{x - 2} = 4 + \dfrac{36}{2x - 4}$ *-5*

Representing Amounts of Work

 REVIEW CAPSULE

Fractions are used to compare parts of an object with the whole.

What part of the diagram is shaded?

Four of the 5 squares are shaded.
Thus, $\frac{4}{5}$ of the diagram is shaded.

EXAMPLE 1   Sheila can mow a lawn in 3 hours. What part of the lawn can she mow in 1 hour?

Lawn

3 hours

1 hour
3 hours

In 1 hour, she can mow $\frac{1}{3}$ of the lawn.

EXAMPLE 2   Pedro can paint a house in 5 days. What part will he paint in 1 day? in 3 days? in 4 days? in x days?

He will have finished in

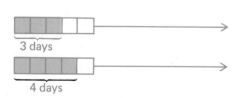

1 day	$\frac{1}{5}$ of the job.
3 days	$3 \cdot \frac{1}{5} = \frac{3}{5}$ of the job.
4 days	$4 \cdot \frac{1}{5} = \frac{4}{5}$ of the job.
x days	$x \cdot \frac{1}{5} = \frac{x}{5}$ of the job.

Example 2 shows this. ⟶

Number of hours to do the job	Part of job done in 1 hour	Part of job done in h hours
x	$\dfrac{1}{x}$	$h\left(\dfrac{1}{x}\right) = \dfrac{h}{x}$

EXAMPLE 3 Emma can mow a lawn in 8 hours. If John helps her they can finish in 5 hours. What part of the job will Emma do?

$a\left(\dfrac{1}{b}\right) = \dfrac{a}{b}$

Emma will do

in 1 hour } $\dfrac{1}{8}$ of the job. in 5 hours } $5 \cdot \dfrac{1}{8}$, or $\dfrac{5}{8}$ of the job.

EXAMPLE 4 Morris can build a fence in 5 days. Helen can build the same fence in x days. If they work together, they can finish in 3 days. What part of the fence is built by each if they work together?

Morris completes

in 1 day } $\dfrac{1}{5}$ of the work. in 3 days } $3 \cdot \dfrac{1}{5}$, or $\dfrac{3}{5}$ of the work.

Helen completes

in 1 day } $\dfrac{1}{x}$ of the work. in 3 days } $3 \cdot \dfrac{1}{x}$, or $\dfrac{3}{x}$ work.

Thus, in 3 days, Morris does $\dfrac{3}{5}$ of the work and

Helen does $\dfrac{3}{x}$ of the work.

EXAMPLE 5 Robert and Sandra sewed costumes for a school play. Working together, they completed a costume in 5 hours. By himself, Robert could sew the costume in 9 hours. Working together, what part of the job did Sandra complete?

Robert completes

in 1 hour } $\dfrac{1}{9}$ of the job. in 5 hours } $5\left(\dfrac{1}{9}\right)$, or $\dfrac{5}{9}$

$\dfrac{5}{9} + \dfrac{4}{9} = 1$ ⟶ **Thus,** Sandra completed $\dfrac{4}{9}$ of the job.

1 means the whole job.

ORAL EXERCISES

What fractional part of the work is completed by each?

		Hours for Entire Job	Hours Worked	
1.	Joel	5	1	$\frac{1}{5}$
2.	Peg	4	3	$\frac{3}{4}$
3.	Mary	7	5	$\frac{5}{7}$

		Hours for Entire Job	Hours Worked	
4.	José	7	2	$\frac{2}{7}$
5.	Linda	$5a$	4	$\frac{4}{5a}$
6.	Jeff	$3x + 1$	3	$\frac{3}{3x+1}$

EXERCISES

PART A

What fractional part of the job is completed by each when they work together?

1. It takes Jake 5 hours and Bill x hours to do a job. Working together, they finish in 3 hours. *Jake* $\frac{3}{5}$ *Bill* $\frac{3}{x}$

2. It takes Janet m hours and Paula 8 hours to wallpaper a room. Working together, they finish the job in 5 hours. *Paula* $\frac{5}{8}$ *Janet* $\frac{5}{m}$

3. It takes Maria x hours and Todd $2x$ hours to do a job. Working together, they finish in 12 hours. *Maria* $\frac{12}{x}$ *Todd* $\frac{6}{x}$

4. It takes Rudy $3x + 1$ hours and Jane $2x + 4$ hours to repair a radio. Working together, they complete the job in 6 hours. *Rudy* $\frac{6}{3x+1}$ *Jane* $\frac{6}{2x+4}$

5. It takes Lester $2m$ hours and Jim $m + 1$ hours to put up a shed. Working together, they finish in 14 hours. *Lester* $\frac{7}{m}$ *Jim* $\frac{14}{m+1}$

6. It takes Shirley $2x + 3$ days and Ruth x days to paint a kitchen. Working together, they finish the work in 2 days. *Shirley* $\frac{2}{2x+3}$ *Ruth* $\frac{2}{x}$

7. It takes Mark $3m + 1$ days and Stuart $m - 4$ days to plant a field. Working together, they finish in 3 days. *Mark* $\frac{3}{3m+1}$ *Stuart* $\frac{3}{m-4}$

8. It takes Joyce $a - 2$ hours and Lee $3a + 4$ hours to wax a floor. Working together, they complete the work in 3 hours. *Joyce* $\frac{3}{a-2}$ *Lee* $\frac{3}{3a+4}$

9. It takes Helene and Joan 5 days to complete a job if they work together. Joan can do it alone in 7 days.

10. Working together, it takes Mark and Tina 10 hours to clean a house. Mark can clean it in 30 hours.

PART B

What fractional part of the job is completed by each when they work together?

11. It takes Eleanor 5 hours and Ted twice as long to do a job. Working together, they complete the job in x hours. *Eleanor* $\frac{x}{5}$ *Ted* $\frac{x}{10}$

12. It takes Martha 4 days and Chris 3 days longer than Martha to do a job. Working together, they finish in x days. *Martha* $\frac{x}{4}$ *Chris* $\frac{x}{7}$

13. It takes Donald x hours and Merv 3 times as long to do a job. Working together, they finish in 5 hours. *Donald*, $\frac{5}{x}$; *Merv*, $\frac{5}{3x}$

14. It takes Hank x hours to do a job. It takes Sylvia 1 hour longer to do the job. Working together, they finish in 6 hours. *Hank*, $\frac{6}{x}$; *Sylvia*, $\frac{6}{x+1}$

Work Problems

 REVIEW CAPSULE

John can paint a house in 5 days.

Part of Job Done in 1 Day	Number of Days Worked	Part of Job Completed
$\dfrac{1}{5}$	x	$x \cdot \dfrac{1}{5} = \dfrac{x}{5}$

EXAMPLE 1   It takes Jack 5 hours and Joan 10 hours to paint a shed. How long will it take them to do the job if they work together?

	Part of Job Done in 1 Hour	Number Hours Working Together	Part of Job Completed
Jack	$\dfrac{1}{5}$	x	$x \cdot \dfrac{1}{5} = \dfrac{x}{5}$
Joan	$\dfrac{1}{10}$	x	$x \cdot \dfrac{1}{10} = \dfrac{x}{10}$

Let x = hours worked together.

The sum of the fractional parts of a job is 1 whole job.

$$\underbrace{\text{Part Jack did}} + \underbrace{\text{part Joan did}} = \underbrace{\text{whole job.}}$$

$$\frac{x}{5} \qquad + \qquad \frac{x}{10} \qquad = \qquad 1$$

$$\frac{x}{5} + \frac{x}{5 \cdot 2} = 1$$

Factor 10; LCD is $5 \cdot 2$.

Multiply each side by $5 \cdot 2$.

$$5 \cdot 2\left(\frac{x}{5} + \frac{x}{5 \cdot 2}\right) = 5 \cdot 2 \cdot \frac{1}{1}$$

Distribute $5 \cdot 2$; do multiplications.

$$\overset{1}{5} \cdot 2 \cdot \frac{x}{\underset{1}{5}} + \overset{1}{5} \cdot \overset{1}{2} \cdot \frac{x}{\underset{1}{5} \cdot \underset{1}{2}} = 5 \cdot 2 \cdot 1$$

$$2x + 1x = 10$$

$$3x = 10$$

$$x = \frac{10}{3}$$

Thus, it takes $3\frac{1}{3}$ hours if they work together.

EXAMPLE 2 Mike can build a fence in twice the time it would take Henry. Working together, they can build the fence in 7 hours. How long would it take each?

	Part of Job Done in 1 Hour	Number Hours Working Together	Part of Job Completed
Henry	$\dfrac{1}{x}$	7	$7 \cdot \dfrac{1}{x} = \dfrac{7}{x}$
Mike	$\dfrac{1}{2x}$	7	$7 \cdot \dfrac{1}{2x} = \dfrac{7}{2x}$

Let x = hours for Henry alone.

$2x$ = hours for Mike alone.

Part Henry did + part Mike did = 1.

$$\frac{7}{x} + \frac{7}{2x} = 1$$

Multiply each side by the LCD, $2 \cdot x$.

$$2 \cdot x\left(\frac{7}{x} + \frac{7}{2 \cdot x}\right) = 2 \cdot x \cdot \frac{1}{1}$$

Distribute $2 \cdot x$; do multiplications.

$$2 \cdot \overset{1}{\cancel{x}} \cdot \frac{7}{\cancel{x}} + \overset{1}{\cancel{2}} \cdot x \cdot \frac{7}{\underset{1}{\cancel{2}} \cdot \underset{1}{\cancel{x}}} = 2 \cdot x \cdot 1$$

$$14 + 7 = 2x$$

Hours for Mike alone

Hours for Henry alone

$$21 = 2x$$
$$10\tfrac{1}{2} = x$$

Thus, it would take Henry $10\tfrac{1}{2}$ hours and Mike 21 hours.

EXAMPLE 3 Working together, Pat and Pam can paint a house in 14 hours. If it takes Pam 30 hours alone, how long would it take Pat alone?

	Part of Job Done in 1 Hour	Number Hours Working Together	Part of Job Completed
Pam	$\dfrac{1}{30}$	14	$14 \cdot \dfrac{1}{30} = \dfrac{14}{30}$
Pat	$\dfrac{1}{x}$	14	$14 \cdot \dfrac{1}{x} = \dfrac{14}{x}$

Let x = hours for Pat alone.

Part Pam did + part Pat did = 1.

$$\frac{14}{30} + \frac{14}{x} = 1$$

Multiply each side by the LCD, $30 \cdot x$.

$$30 \cdot x\left(\frac{14}{30} + \frac{14}{x}\right) = 30 \cdot x \cdot \frac{1}{1}$$

Distribute $30 \cdot x$; do multiplications.

$$\overset{1}{\cancel{30}} \cdot x \cdot \frac{14}{\underset{1}{\cancel{30}}} + 30 \cdot \overset{1}{\cancel{x}} \cdot \frac{14}{\underset{1}{\cancel{x}}} = 30 \cdot x \cdot 1$$

$$14x + 420 = 30x$$

Add $-14x$ to each side.

$$420 = 16x$$

$\dfrac{420}{16} = \dfrac{105}{4}$, or $26\tfrac{1}{4}$

$$26\tfrac{1}{4} = x$$

Thus, it would take Pat $26\tfrac{1}{4}$ hours.

EXERCISES

PART A

1. Fay can prepare surgical equipment in 3 hours. Another nurse, Carlo, can do it in 4 hours. How long will it take if they work together? $1\frac{5}{7}$ hr.

2. A mason can put up a tile wall in 6 days. A helper can do it alone in 8 days. How long will it take them if they work together? $3\frac{3}{7}$ days

3. Together, Stanley and Elsie can mow a lawn in 3 hours. It would take Elsie 5 hours to do it alone. How long would it take Stanley? $7\frac{1}{2}$ hr.

4. Together, Pat and Pam can prepare a turkey dinner in 6 hours. It would take Pam 8 hours by herself. How long would it take Pat? 24 hr.

5. George can address envelopes in 4 hours. If Flora helps him, they can complete the job in 1 hour. How long would it take Flora alone? $1\frac{1}{3}$ hr.

6. Noah can deliver papers in twice the time it would take Jake. How long would it take each if they can do the job together in 3 hours? *Jake* $4\frac{1}{2}$,

7. Working together, Josephine and Lois can clean a house in 6 hours. It takes Lois 3 times longer than Josephine to do it alone. How long would it take each girl alone?

Josephine 8 hr.,
Lois 24 hr.

8. Working together, two carpenters can build a house in 5 months. It takes one of them twice as long as the other to do it alone. How long would it take each alone? $7\frac{1}{2}$ mo., 15 mo.   *Noah 9*

PART B

9. To do a job alone, it would take Rose 4 hours, Bill 3 hours, and Marc 5 hours. How long would it take if they all work together? $1\frac{13}{47}$ hr.

10. To do a job alone, it would take Jane 3 hours, Mary 5 hours, and Jerry 6 hours. How long would it take if they all work together? $1\frac{3}{7}$ hr.

11. Eva can mow a lawn in 4 hours. It would take Bob 3 hours. How long would it take Ted if, working together, all three can do the job in 1 hour? $2\frac{2}{5}$ hr.

12. Martha can build a desk in 3 weeks. It would take Joe 5 weeks. How long would it take Kim if, working together, all three can do the job in 1 week? $2\frac{1}{7}$ wk.

13. Mary can make a suit in 5 hours. It would take Jane twice as long as Jerome. How long would it take Jane if, working together, all three can do it in 2 hours? 10 hr.

14. Bill can repair a transmission in 8 hours. It would take Henry 3 times as long as Clara. How long would it take Clara if, working together, all three can do it in 4 hours? $10\frac{2}{3}$ hr.

Applying Percent

PROBLEM 1.

8 is what % of 14?

Let x = the %

8 is what % of 14?

x% of 14 means $x \cdot 14$. $8 = x \cdot 14$

$8 = 14x$

$\dfrac{8}{14} = x$

$.57 = x$

$$14\overline{)8.00}$$ $.57$

70

100

98

2

.57 means 57%.   Thus, 8 is 57% of 14.

PROBLEM 2.

A basketball team won 5 games and lost 3 games. What % of the games played did the team win?

Let x = % of games won

What % of games played are games won?

5 wins + 3 losses = 8 games $x \cdot 8 = 5$

$8x = 5$

$x = \dfrac{5}{8}$ or .63

.63 means 63%.   Thus, the team won 63% of their games.

PROJECT

1. 6 is what % of 30?   **2.** 14 is what % of 42?

3. A team won 7 games and lost 5. What % of the games are wins?   **4.** A class has 20 girls and 15 boys. What % of the class are boys?

PROBLEM 3.

60% of what number is 300?

Let n = number
60% of what number is 300?

60% of n = .60(n) $\Big\}$
    = .60n

60% of $\qquad$ n $\qquad$ = 300

.60n = 300

Multiply each side by 100. $\longrightarrow$

100 (.60n) = 100 (300)

60n = 30000

Divide each side by 60. $\longrightarrow$

n = 500

Thus, 60% of 500 is 300.

PROBLEM 4.

A store manager lists the selling price of a television at $156. If the profit is 30% of the cost, find the cost.

Let x = cost

Profit is 30% of cost $\Big\}$
    30% of x

30% of x: .30(x)

| cost | + | profit | = selling price |

x + 30% of x = 156

x + .30(x) = 156

1x + .30x = 156

Multiply each side by 100. $\longrightarrow$

100(1x + .30x) = 100 (156)

100x + 30x = 15600

130x = 15600

Divide each side by 130. $\longrightarrow$

x = 120

$\dfrac{120}{130)\overline{15600}}$

Thus, the cost of the T.V. is $120.

PROJECT

5. 40% of what number is 20?

6. 60% of what number is 24?

7. A merchant sells a camera for $250. Find the cost if the profit is 25% of the cost.

8. A couch is sold for $550. Find the cost if the profit is 40% of the cost.

Equations with Decimals

OBJECTIVE

■ To solve equations which contain decimals

► *REVIEW CAPSULE*

$10(.3782)$	$100(.3782)$	$1{,}000(.3782)$
3.782	37.82	378.2

Point moved 1 place to the right. | Point moved 2 places to the right. | Point moved 3 places to the right.

Multiplying a decimal by   moves the point

10	1	
100	2	place(s) to the right.
1,000	3	

EXAMPLE 1

Rewrite $.3x + .45 = .984$ as an equation which has only whole numbers.

First rewrite all decimals as fractions.
$$\frac{3}{10}x + \frac{45}{100} = \frac{984}{1{,}000} \leftarrow \text{LCD is 1,000.}$$

$.3 = \frac{3}{10}; .45 = \frac{45}{100}; .984 = \frac{984}{1{,}000}$

Multiply each side by 1,000. ⟶
$$1{,}000\left(\frac{3}{10}x + \frac{45}{100}\right) = 1{,}000\left(\frac{984}{1{,}000}\right)$$

Distribute 1,000; do multiplications. ⟶
$$\overset{100}{1{,}000}\left(\frac{3}{\underset{1}{10}}x\right) + \overset{10}{1{,}000}\left(\frac{45}{\underset{1}{100}}\right) = \overset{1}{1{,}000}\left(\frac{984}{\underset{1}{1{,}000}}\right)$$

Equation with only whole numbers
$$300x + 450 = 984$$

.3   .45   .984
↓   ↓   ↓   LCD = 1,000
$\frac{3}{10}$ $\frac{45}{100}$ $\frac{984}{1{,}000}$

$1{,}000(.3) = 300.$ $1{,}000(.45) = 450.$
$1{,}000(.984) = 984.$

Here is a more convenient technique.
$$.3x + .45 = .984$$

$$1{,}000(.3x + .45) = 1{,}000(.984)$$
$$1{,}000(.3x) + 1{,}000(.45) = 1{,}000(.984)$$
$$300x + 450 = 984$$

Notice that this is the same equation as the resulting equation in Example 1.

For the equation,

$$.3x \quad + \quad .45 \quad = \quad .984$$

one digit   two digits   three digits
past point   past point   past point

the LCD is 1,000.

three zeros

The greatest number of digits past any decimal point is three. LCD = 1,000.

EXAMPLE 2

Give the LCD for each equation.

$.03x - .004 = .72x + 1.8 \qquad .2x + .04 = 5x - .36$

Number of digits past decimal point

$.03x - .004 = .72x + 1.8 \mid .2x + .04 = 5(x) - .36$

two   three   two   one $\mid$ one   two   none   two

LCD is 1,000.   LCD is 100.

EXAMPLE 3

Solve $.5x - 1.2 = 6.4$.

The greatest number of digits past any decimal point is one. LCD = 10.

To multiply by 10, move the decimal point one place to the right. ⟶

Add 12 to each side. ⟶

Divide each side by 5. ⟶

$$10(.5x - 1.2) = 10(6.4)$$
$$10(.5x) - 10(1.2) = 10(6.4)$$
$$5x \quad - \quad 12 \quad = 64$$
$$5x = 76$$
$$x = \frac{76}{5}, \text{ or } 15\frac{1}{5}$$

$\frac{1}{5} = 1 \div 5 = .2$ ⟶ **Thus,** the solution is $15\frac{1}{5}$, or 15.2.

EXAMPLE 4

Solve $.15x - 7.2 = 8.5$.

$$.15x - 7.2 = 8.5$$

two   one   one

The greatest number of digits past any decimal point is two. LCD = 100.

Multiply each side by 100. ⟶

To multiply by 100, move the decimal point two places to the right. ⟶

Add 720 to each side. ⟶

Divide each side by 15. ⟶

$$100(.15x - 7.2) = 100(8.5)$$
$$100(.15x) - 100(7.2) = 100(8.5)$$
$$15x \quad - \quad 720 \quad = 850$$
$$15x = 1,570$$
$$x = \frac{1,570}{15}, \text{ or } 104\frac{2}{3}$$

Thus, the solution is $104\frac{2}{3}$.

EXERCISES

PART A

Solve. Answers may be written in fraction or decimal form.

1. $.03x = .2$ $\frac{20}{3}$

2. $.016 = .32x$ $.05$

3. $.004x - 7.1 = .12$ $1,805$

4. $.1x - 2.4 = 1.17$ 35.7

5. $.007 = .7x - .21$ $.31$

6. $2.1x = .72 + 1.8x$ 2.4

7. $.18x - 24 = .1x + .6$ $\frac{615}{2}$

8. $5 - .03x = .7x - .11$ 7

9. $.7x - .2 = .13x - 80$

10. $.012x - 4 = .112x + 1$ -50

11. $.7x - 1 = .6x + .002$ 10.02

12. $.5 - .08x = .004x + .2$ $\frac{25}{7}$

PART B

EXAMPLE   Solve $.02(4 - .3x) = .15x + 3.2$.

Distribute .02. $\longrightarrow$

$.02(.3) = \dfrac{2}{100}\left(\dfrac{3}{10}\right) = \dfrac{6}{1,000} = .006$

$.02(4) - .02(.3x) = .15x + 3.2$

$\underbrace{.08}_{\text{two}} - \underbrace{.006x}_{\text{three}} = \underbrace{.15x}_{\text{two}} + \underbrace{3.2}_{\text{one}}$

Multiply each side by the LCD, 1,000. $\longrightarrow$

$1,000(.08 - .006x) = 1,000(.15x + 3.2)$

$1,000(.08) - 1,000(.006x) = 1,000(.15x) + 1,000(3.2)$

$80 - 6x = 150x + 3,200$

$-156x = 3,120$

$x = \dfrac{3,120}{-156},\ \text{or} -20$

Thus, the solution is -20.

Solve. Answers may be written in fraction or decimal form.

13. $.03(4 - .2x) = .17x - 1.2$ $\frac{15}{2}$

14. $.01(5 - .2x) = .75 + .198x$ -3.5

15. $.3x + 2.91 = 5 - .2(3 - .01x)$ 5

16. $47.582 - .01(.2 + 3x) = 7.9x$ 6

17. $.04(.2 - .1x) = 7.12 + .02x$ $-296\frac{1}{3}$

18. $.1(2 - 7x) = 7.1 - 3x$ 3

PART C

Solve. Answers may be written in fraction or decimal form.

19. $.3x - .02[.7 - .1(5 - .04x)] = .006$

20. $7 - .04[6x - (2 - .01x)] = .005$

Rational Numbers

OBJECTIVES
- To identify rational numbers
- To write repeating decimals like .3$\overline{3}$ in fractional form

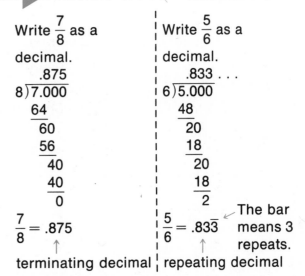

REVIEW CAPSULE

Write $\frac{7}{8}$ as a decimal.

$$\begin{array}{r} .875 \\ 8\overline{)7.000} \\ \underline{64} \\ 60 \\ \underline{56} \\ 40 \\ \underline{40} \\ 0 \end{array}$$

$\frac{7}{8} = .875$

↑ terminating decimal

Write $\frac{5}{6}$ as a decimal.

$$\begin{array}{r} .833 \ldots \\ 6\overline{)5.000} \\ \underline{48} \\ 20 \\ \underline{18} \\ 20 \\ \underline{18} \\ 2 \end{array}$$

$\frac{5}{6} = .83\overline{3}$

The bar means 3 repeats.

↑ repeating decimal

Definition of rational number ⟶

A *rational number* is a number which can be written in the form $\frac{a}{b}$, where a and b are integers and $b \neq 0$.

EXAMPLE 1　Show that the integers −16, 0, 1, and 23 are rational numbers.

Write each as $\frac{a}{b}$, where a is the integer itself and b is 1.

$-16 = \frac{-16}{1}$　$0 = \frac{0}{1}$　$1 = \frac{1}{1}$　$23 = \frac{23}{1}$

Thus, −16, 0, 1, and 23 are rational numbers.

Every integer is a rational number.

EXAMPLE 2　Show that $\frac{2}{3}$, $\frac{5}{2}$, and $-\frac{9}{16}$ are rational numbers.

$-\frac{9}{16} = \frac{-9}{16}$

All are in the form $\frac{a}{b}$, where a and b are integers.

$\frac{2}{3}$　$\frac{5}{2}$　$\frac{-9}{16}$

Thus, $\frac{2}{3}$, $\frac{5}{2}$, and $-\frac{9}{16}$ are rational numbers.

EXAMPLE 3 Show that these decimals are rational numbers.

.7 | −.06 | 2.591
↓ | ↓ | ↓

Write each as $\frac{a}{b}$, where b is 10, 100, and 1,000. ⟶ $\frac{7}{10}$ | $\frac{-6}{100}$ | $\frac{2{,}591}{1{,}000}$

Thus, .7, −.06, and 2.591 are rational numbers.

Every terminating decimal is a rational number.

EXAMPLE 4 Show that $.3\overline{3}$ is a rational number.

The bar means 3 repeats.
$.3\overline{3} = .3333\ldots$ ⟶ Let $n = .333\overline{3}$ (1)

Multiply each side by 10; the decimal point moves one place. ⟶

Multiply each side of equation (1) by −1. Add equations (2) and (3). ⟶

$$\begin{array}{rl} 10n = & 3.333\overline{3} \ (2) \\ -\ \ 1n = - & .333\overline{3} \ (3) \\ \hline 9n = & 3.0000 \end{array}$$

or $9n = 3$

Divide each side by 9. ⟶ $n = \frac{3}{9}$, or $\frac{1}{3}$

$\frac{3}{9} = \frac{1}{3}$ ⟵ integer ⟶ **Thus, $.3\overline{3}$ is the rational number $\frac{1}{3}$.**

EXAMPLE 5 Show that $.94\overline{4}$ is a rational number.

Let $n = .944\overline{4}$ (1)

Multiply each side by 10; the decimal point moves one place. ⟶

Multiply each side of equation (1) by −1. Add equations (2) and (3). ⟶

$$\begin{array}{rl} 10n = & 9.444\overline{4} \ (2) \\ -\ \ 1n = - & .944\overline{4} \ (3) \\ \hline 9n = & 8.5000 \end{array}$$

or $9n = 8.5$

Divide each side by 9. ⟶ $n = \frac{8.5}{9}$

$\frac{8.5}{9} = \frac{8.5(10)}{9(10)} = \frac{85}{90}$ ⟵ integer ⟶ $n = \frac{85}{90}$, or $\frac{17}{18}$

Check. $\begin{array}{r} .94\overline{4} \\ 18\overline{)17.000} \end{array}$ ⟶ **Thus, $.94\overline{4}$ is the rational number $\frac{17}{18}$.**

Every repeating decimal is a rational number.

EXAMPLE 6 Show that $2.6\overline{6}$ is a rational number.

Let $n = 2.666\overline{6}$ (1)

Multiply each side by 10; the decimal point moves one place. ⟶

Multiply each side of equation (1) by −1.

Add equations (2) and (3). ⟶

$$10n = 26.666\overline{6} \ (2)$$
$$- \ 1n = - 2.666\overline{6} \ (3)$$
$$\overline{9n = 24.0000}$$

or

$$9n = 24$$

Divide each side by 9. ⟶

$$n = \frac{24}{9}, \text{ or } \frac{8}{3}$$

Thus, $2.6\overline{6}$ is the rational number $\frac{8}{3}$.

EXERCISES

PART A

Show that each is a rational number.

1. $-1 \ \frac{-1}{1}$ **2.** $32 \ \frac{32}{1}$ **3.** $-16 \ \frac{-16}{1}$ **4.** $0 \ \frac{0}{1}$ **5.** $-\frac{24}{36} \ \frac{-24}{36}$ **6.** $.00706 \ \frac{706}{100,000}$ **7.** $-3.64 \ \frac{-364}{100}$

8. $.7\overline{7} \ \frac{7}{9}$ **9.** $.4\overline{4} \ \frac{4}{9}$ **10.** $.62\overline{2} \ \frac{28}{45}$ **11.** $.75\overline{5} \ \frac{34}{45}$ **12.** $1.2\overline{2} \ \frac{11}{9}$ **13.** $3.5\overline{5} \ \frac{32}{9}$ **14.** $.48\overline{8} \ \frac{22}{45}$

PART B

EXAMPLE   Show that $1.78\overline{78}$ is a rational number.

Let $n = 1.787878$ (1)

Multiply each side by 100; the decimal point moves two places. ⟶

Multiply each side of equation (1) by −1.

Add equations (2) and (3). ⟶

$$100n = 178.787\overline{878} \ (2)$$
$$- \ 1n = - 1.787\overline{878} \ (3)$$
$$\overline{99n = 177}$$

$$n = \frac{177}{99}, \text{ or } \frac{59}{33}$$

Divide each side by 99. ⟶

Thus, $1.78\overline{78}$ is the rational number $\frac{59}{33}$.

Show that each is a rational number.

15. $.16\overline{16} \ \frac{16}{99}$ **16.** $.24\overline{24} \ \frac{8}{33}$ **17.** $.83\overline{83} \ \frac{83}{99}$ **18.** $.75\overline{75} \ \frac{25}{33}$ **19.** $.98\overline{98} \ \frac{98}{99}$

PART C

Show that each is a rational number.

20. $5.781234\overline{234}$ **21.** $3.06789\overline{789}$ **22.** $214.5681428\overline{142}$

Investment and Loan Problems *(optional)*

<table>
<tr>
<td>

OBJECTIVE

■ To solve problems about investments and loans using the formula $i = prt$

</td>
<td>

 REVIEW CAPSULE

John invested $400 at 6% for 1 year. How much interest did he earn?

$i = ?$ $i = prt$
$p = \$400$ $= 400\,(.06)\,(1)$
$r = 6\%$ $= 24.$ ⌐__Change the
$t = 1$ yr   percent to
                    a decimal.

Thus, he earned $24 interest.

</td>
</tr>
</table>

i	=	p	×	r	×	t
↓		↓		↓		↓
Interest: Money paid to use money invested or loaned		Principal Money invested or loaned		Rate Percent paid per year to use money invested or loaned		Time Years money is invested or loaned

Interest formula ⟶

EXAMPLE 1   Marita borrowed x dollars at $7\frac{1}{2}\%$ interest for 1 year. Write an algebraic expression for the amount of interest she paid.

Use the formula. ⟶ $i = prt$
Substitute; $7\frac{1}{2}\% = .075$. ⟶ $= x\,(.075)\,(1)$
                                         $= .075x$

Thus, $.075x$ represents the interest Marita paid.

EXAMPLE 2   The Lees invested $1,000 for 1 year. They earned $60 interest. What was the rate of return?

Use the formula. ⟶ $i = prt$
Substitute. ⟶ $60 = 1,000\,(x)\,(1)$
                               $\dfrac{60}{1,000} = x$

$\dfrac{60}{1,000} = \dfrac{6}{100} = .06$, or 6%. ⟶ **Thus,** the rate of return was 6%.

EXAMPLE 3 Ellen invested one sum of money at $5\frac{1}{2}\%$ and another sum at 6%. She invested $300 more at the 6% rate than at the $5\frac{1}{2}\%$ rate. If her total interest for 1 year was $133, find the amount she invested at each rate.

Represent the amounts invested algebraically.

Let $x =$ amount (in dollars) invested at $5\frac{1}{2}\%$
$x + 300 =$ amount (in dollars) invested at 6%

Make a chart. ──────────────→

Principal	Rate	Time	Interest ($i = prt$)
x	.055	1 yr	.055x
$x + 300$	.06	1 yr	$.06(x + 300)$

Write an equation. ──────────→ (Interest at $5\frac{1}{2}\%$) + (Interest at 6%) = (Total interest)
Substitute. ────────────────→ $.055x + .06(x + 300) = 133$
$.055x + .06x + 18 = 133$
Multiply each side by 1,000. ──→ $55x + 60x + 18,000 = 133,000$
$115x = 115,000$
Amount invested at $5\frac{1}{2}\%$ ────→ $x = 1,000$
$x + 300 = 1,000 + 300,$
Amount invested at 6% ────────→ or 1,300

Thus, Ellen invested $1,000 at $5\frac{1}{2}\%$ and $1,300 at 6%.

EXAMPLE 4 Irving borrowed $1,900, part from a bank at an interest rate of 8% and the rest from his father at 5%. At the end of 6 months, he owed $64 in interest. How much did he borrow from each?

Represent the amounts borrowed algebraically.

Let $x =$ amount (in dollars) borrowed at 8%
$1,900 - x =$ amount (in dollars) borrowed at 5%

Make a chart. ──────────────→
6 months = .5 yr

Principal	Rate	Time	Interest ($i = prt$)
x	.08	.5 yr	.04x
$1,900 - x$	.05	.5 yr	$.025(1,900 - x)$

Write an equation. ──────────→ (Interest at 8%) + (Interest at 5%) = (Total interest)
Substitute. ────────────────→ $.04x + .025(1,900 - x) = 64$
$.04x + 47.5 - .025x = 64$
Multiply each side by 1,000. ──→ $40x + 47,500 - 25x = 64,000$
$15x = 16,500$
Amount borrowed at 8% ────────→ $x = 1,100$
Amount borrowed at 5% ────────→ $1,900 - x = 1,900 - 1,100,$
or 800

Thus, he borrowed $1,100 at 8% and $800 at 5%.

EXAMPLE 5   Alba invested one-half of her money at $5\frac{3}{4}\%$ and one-fourth of her money at $5\frac{1}{2}\%$. If her total interest at the end of 1 year was $136, find her original sum of money.

Represent the amounts invested algebraically.

Let x = amount of original sum of money
$\frac{1}{2}x$ = amount (in dollars) invested at $5\frac{3}{4}\%$
$\frac{1}{4}x$ = amount (in dollars) invested at $5\frac{1}{2}\%$

Make a chart. ──────────→

$5\frac{3}{4}\% = 5.75\% = .0575$

$5\frac{1}{2}\% = 5.5\% = .055$

Principal	Rate	Time	Interest ($i = prt$)
$\frac{1}{2}x$	.0575	1 yr	$\frac{.0575}{2}x$
$\frac{1}{4}x$	.055	1 yr	$\frac{.055}{4}x$

Write an equation. ──────────→   (Interest at $5\frac{3}{4}\%$) + (Interest at $5\frac{1}{2}\%$) = (Total interest)

Substitute. ──────────→ $\dfrac{.0575}{2}x + \dfrac{.055}{4}x = 136$

Multiply each side by 4. ──────────→ $.115x + .055x = 544$
Multiply each side by 1,000. ──────────→ $115x + 55x = 544{,}000$
$$170x = 544{,}000$$
$$x = 3{,}200$$

Thus, Alba's original sum of money was $3,200.

EXAMPLE 6   Harry had $600. He invested part of it at 6% and the rest at 5%. At the end of 1 year, his total return on these investments was $34. How much did he invest at each rate?

Represent the amounts invested algebraically.

Let x = amount (in dollars) invested at 6%
$600 - x$ = amount (in dollars) invested at 5%

Make a chart. ──────────→

Principal	Rate	Time	Interest ($i = prt$)
x	.06	1 yr	$.06x$
$600 - x$	.05	1 yr	$.05(600 - x)$

Write an equation. ──────────→   (Interest at 6%) + (Interest at 5%) = (Total interest)
Substitute. ──────────→ $.06x + .05(600 - x) = 34$
$$.06x + 30 - .05x = 34$$
Multiply each side by 100. ──────────→ $6x + 3{,}000 - 5x = 3{,}400$
$$1x = 400$$
$$x = 400$$
$$600 - x = 600 - 400,$$
$$\text{or } 200$$

Thus, he invested $400 at 6% and $200 at 5%.

EXERCISES

1. Bill borrowed $5,000 at $7\frac{1}{2}$% interest for 1 year. How much interest did he pay at the end of 1 year?

2. Ms. Diaz invested $5,000 for 1 year. She earned $300 interest. What was the rate of return?

3. Liz invested $1,800, part at 5% and the rest at 6%. If her total interest at the end of 1 year was $96, find the amount she invested at each rate.

4. Mr. Susan had $2,500. He invested part of it at $5\frac{3}{4}$% and the rest at 5%. At the end of 3 years, his total return was $420. How much did he invest at each rate?

5. Tony borrowed some money from friends. He borrowed part of it at 4% and the rest at 6%. The amount borrowed at 6% was twice the amount borrowed at 4%. If the total interest after 1 year was $96, how much did he borrow at each rate?

6. Doris borrowed some money from friends. She borrowed part of it at 8% and the rest at 5%. The amount borrowed at 5% was $1,200 more than the amount borrowed at 8%. If the total interest after $\frac{1}{2}$ year was $160, find the amount of each loan.

7. Melba had $1,300. She invested part of it at 5% and the rest at 6%. At the end of 2 years, her total return was $146. How much did she invest at each rate?

8. Rodney invested $800, part of it at 4% and the rest at 5%. At the end of 3 years, his total return was $111. How much did he invest at each rate?

9. The Kickingbirds invested $10,000, part at 5% and the rest at $4\frac{1}{2}$%. At the end of 6 years, their total return was $2,880. How much did they invest at each rate?

10. The Yoshidas invested $5,000, part at 6% and the rest at $6\frac{1}{2}$%. At the end of 4 years, their total return was $1,245. How much did they invest at each rate?

11. Ann invested one-half of her money at $5\frac{1}{2}$% and one-fourth at 6%. At the end of 2 years, she had earned $595 in interest. What was the original sum of money?

12. Bob invested one-third of his money at 6% and three-fifths at $6\frac{1}{2}$%. At the end of 3 years, he had earned $531 in interest. What was the original sum of money?

Complex Fractions

▶ *REVIEW CAPSULE*

Simplify $6a^2\left(\dfrac{3}{a}+\dfrac{5}{2}\right)$.

$$6a^2\cdot\dfrac{3}{a}+6a^2\cdot\dfrac{5}{2}$$

$$3\cdot2\cdot\overset{1}{\cancel{a}}\cdot a\cdot\dfrac{3}{\underset{1}{\cancel{a}}}+3\cdot\overset{1}{\cancel{2}}\cdot a\cdot a\cdot\dfrac{5}{\underset{1}{\cancel{2}}}$$

$$18a+15a^2$$

or $\qquad 15a^2+18a$

Complex Fractions

$$\left.\dfrac{\dfrac{1}{2}}{6}\right\}\begin{array}{l}\text{numerator}\\[4pt]\text{denominator}\end{array}\qquad\qquad\dfrac{\left.\dfrac{2}{3}\right\}\text{numerator}}{\left.\dfrac{1}{5}\right\}\text{denominator}}$$

$$\dfrac{x+3}{\left.\dfrac{2}{x}\right\}}\begin{array}{l}\text{numerator}\\[10pt]\text{denominator}\end{array}$$

Definition of complex fraction ———→ | A *complex fraction* is one whose numerator or denominator or both contain a fraction.

EXAMPLE 1

Simplify $\dfrac{\dfrac{2}{3}}{\dfrac{1}{5}}$.

The LCD of $\dfrac{2}{3}$ and $\dfrac{1}{5}$ is $3\cdot5$.
Multiply both numerator and denominator
by $3\cdot5$; $\dfrac{a}{b}=\dfrac{a\cdot c}{b\cdot c}$

$$\dfrac{3\cdot5\cdot\dfrac{2}{3}}{3\cdot5\cdot\dfrac{1}{5}}=\dfrac{\overset{1}{\cancel{3}}\cdot5\cdot\dfrac{2}{\underset{1}{\cancel{3}}}}{3\cdot\overset{1}{\cancel{5}}\cdot\dfrac{1}{\underset{1}{\cancel{5}}}}$$

$$=\dfrac{10}{3}$$

EXAMPLE 2   Simplify $\dfrac{3a + \dfrac{2}{3}}{\dfrac{a}{2} + \dfrac{5}{6}}$.

$3a = \dfrac{3a}{1}$ —————————————————→

$$\dfrac{\dfrac{3a}{1} + \dfrac{2}{3}}{\dfrac{a}{2} + \dfrac{5}{3 \cdot 2}}$$

Factor the denominators. —————————→

The LCD of $\dfrac{3a}{1}, \dfrac{2}{3}, \dfrac{a}{2}, \dfrac{5}{3 \cdot 2}$ is $3 \cdot 2$.
Multiply both numerator and denominator
by $3 \cdot 2$.

$$\dfrac{3 \cdot 2\left(\dfrac{3a}{1} + \dfrac{2}{3}\right)}{3 \cdot 2\left(\dfrac{a}{2} + \dfrac{5}{3 \cdot 2}\right)}$$

Distribute $3 \cdot 2$. Divide out common
factors in each product.

$$\dfrac{3 \cdot 2 \cdot \dfrac{3a}{1} + \overset{1}{3} \cdot 2 \cdot \dfrac{2}{\underset{1}{\cancel{3}}}}{3 \cdot \overset{1}{\cancel{2}} \cdot \dfrac{a}{\underset{1}{\cancel{2}}} + \overset{1}{\cancel{3}} \cdot \overset{1}{\cancel{2}} \cdot \dfrac{5}{\underset{1}{\cancel{3}} \cdot \underset{1}{\cancel{2}}}}$$

Multiply remaining factors in each
product.

$$\dfrac{18a + 4}{3a + 5}$$

EXAMPLE 3   Simplify $\dfrac{\dfrac{3}{a} - \dfrac{5}{2}}{\dfrac{7}{3} + \dfrac{4}{a^2}}$.

$\dfrac{3}{a} - \dfrac{5}{2} = \dfrac{3}{a} + \dfrac{-1 \cdot 5}{2} = \dfrac{3}{a} + \dfrac{-5}{2}$ —————→

$$\dfrac{\dfrac{3}{a} + \dfrac{-5}{2}}{\dfrac{7}{3} + \dfrac{4}{a \cdot a}}$$

Factor the denominators. —————————→

The LCD of $\dfrac{3}{a}, \dfrac{-5}{2}, \dfrac{7}{3}, \dfrac{4}{a \cdot a}$ is $3 \cdot 2 \cdot a \cdot a$.
Multiply both numerator and denominator
by the LCD.

$$\dfrac{3 \cdot 2 \cdot a \cdot a\left(\dfrac{3}{a} + \dfrac{-5}{2}\right)}{3 \cdot 2 \cdot a \cdot a\left(\dfrac{7}{3} + \dfrac{4}{a \cdot a}\right)}$$

Distribute $3 \cdot 2 \cdot a \cdot a$. Divide out common
factors in each product.

$$\dfrac{3 \cdot 2 \cdot \overset{1}{\cancel{a}} \cdot a \cdot \dfrac{3}{\underset{1}{\cancel{a}}} + 3 \cdot \overset{1}{\cancel{2}} \cdot a \cdot a \cdot \dfrac{-5}{\underset{1}{\cancel{2}}}}{\overset{1}{\cancel{3}} \cdot 2 \cdot a \cdot a \cdot \dfrac{7}{\underset{1}{\cancel{3}}} + 3 \cdot 2 \cdot \overset{1}{\cancel{a}} \cdot \overset{1}{\cancel{a}} \cdot \dfrac{4}{\underset{1}{\cancel{a}} \cdot \underset{1}{\cancel{a}}}}$$

Multiply remaining factors in each
product.

$$\dfrac{18a - 15a^2}{14a^2 + 24}, \text{ or } \dfrac{-15a^2 + 18a}{14a^2 + 24}$$

EXERCISES

Simplify.

1. $\dfrac{\dfrac{2}{5}}{\dfrac{1}{7}}$ $\quad \frac{14}{5}$

2. $\dfrac{\dfrac{1}{2}}{\dfrac{3}{5}}$ $\quad \frac{5}{6}$

3. $\dfrac{\dfrac{2}{5}+\dfrac{1}{10}}{\dfrac{1}{2}+\dfrac{3}{5}}$ $\quad \frac{5}{11}$

4. $\dfrac{\dfrac{2}{3}+\dfrac{1}{2}}{\dfrac{1}{6}+\dfrac{1}{2}}$ $\quad \frac{7}{4}$

5. $\dfrac{3a+\dfrac{1}{2}}{\dfrac{a}{5}+\dfrac{3}{10}}$ $\quad \frac{30a+5}{2a+3}$

6. $\dfrac{\dfrac{3a}{2}+1}{\dfrac{a}{4}+\dfrac{1}{2}}$ $\quad \frac{6a+4}{a+2}$

7. $\dfrac{4a+\dfrac{1}{3}}{2a+\dfrac{1}{3}}$ $\quad \frac{12a+1}{6a+1}$

8. $\dfrac{\dfrac{3b}{5}+\dfrac{2}{3}}{\dfrac{b}{15}+\dfrac{3}{5}}$ $\quad \frac{9b+10}{b+9}$

9. $\dfrac{\dfrac{4}{a}-\dfrac{3}{5}}{\dfrac{3}{2}+\dfrac{7}{a^2}}$ $\quad \frac{40a-6a^2}{15a^2+70}$

10. $\dfrac{\dfrac{3}{5}-\dfrac{4}{b}}{\dfrac{2}{b^2}+\dfrac{3}{2}}$ $\quad \frac{6b^2-40b}{15b^2+20}$

11. $\dfrac{\dfrac{3}{a^2}-\dfrac{5}{a}}{\dfrac{2}{a}+\dfrac{1}{a^2}}$ $\quad \frac{3-5a}{2a+1}$

12. $\dfrac{\dfrac{4}{b^2}+\dfrac{3}{b}}{\dfrac{2}{b}+\dfrac{5}{3b^2}}$ $\quad \frac{9b+12}{6b+5}$

EXAMPLE

Simplify $\dfrac{1-\dfrac{5}{m}+\dfrac{4}{m^2}}{1-\dfrac{16}{m^2}}$.

$$\dfrac{m^2\left(1-\dfrac{5}{m}+\dfrac{4}{m^2}\right)}{m^2\left(1-\dfrac{16}{m^2}\right)} = \dfrac{m^2+\overset{m}{\cancel{m^2}}\cdot\dfrac{-5}{\cancel{m}_1}+\overset{1}{\cancel{m^2}}\cdot\dfrac{4}{\cancel{m^2}_1}}{m^2+\overset{1}{\cancel{m^2}}\cdot\dfrac{-16}{\cancel{m^2}_1}}$$

$$= \dfrac{m^2-5m+4}{m^2-16}$$

$$= \dfrac{(\overset{1}{\cancel{m-4}})\,(m-1)}{(\underset{1}{\cancel{m-4}})\,(m+4)}, \text{ or } \dfrac{m-1}{m+4}$$

Simplify.

13. $\dfrac{1+\dfrac{3}{x}+\dfrac{2}{x^2}}{\dfrac{1}{x}+\dfrac{2}{x^2}}$ $\quad x+1$

14. $\dfrac{1-\dfrac{9}{x}+\dfrac{14}{x^2}}{\dfrac{1}{x}-\dfrac{7}{x^2}}$ $\quad x-2$

15. $\dfrac{\dfrac{1}{m}+\dfrac{2}{m^2}}{1-\dfrac{6}{m}-\dfrac{16}{m^2}}$ $\quad \frac{1}{m-8}$

More Complex Fractions

▶ *REVIEW CAPSULE*

Simplify $\dfrac{\dfrac{c}{2} + \dfrac{3}{5}}{\dfrac{c}{10} + \dfrac{1}{2}}$.

$$\frac{5 \cdot 2\left(\dfrac{c}{2} + \dfrac{3}{5}\right)}{5 \cdot 2\left(\dfrac{c}{5 \cdot 2} + \dfrac{1}{2}\right)}$$

$$\frac{5 \cdot \overset{1}{2} \cdot \dfrac{c}{\underset{1}{2}} + \overset{1}{5} \cdot 2 \cdot \dfrac{3}{\underset{1}{5}}}{\overset{1}{5} \cdot \overset{1}{2} \cdot \dfrac{c}{\underset{1}{5 \cdot 2}} + 5 \cdot \overset{1}{2} \cdot \dfrac{1}{\underset{1}{2}}} = \frac{5c + 6}{c + 5}$$

EXAMPLE 1

Simplify $\dfrac{\dfrac{5}{m - 3} + \dfrac{7}{m + 2}}{\dfrac{7}{m^2 - m - 6} + \dfrac{1}{m - 3}}$.

$m^2 - m - 6 = (m - 3)(m + 2)$;
LCD $= (m - 3)(m + 2)$ ⟶

$$\frac{\dfrac{5}{m - 3} + \dfrac{7}{m + 2}}{\dfrac{7}{(m - 3)(m + 2)} + \dfrac{1}{m - 3}}$$

Multiply both numerator and denominator by the LCD, $(m - 3)(m + 2)$.

$$\frac{(m - 3)(m + 2)\left(\dfrac{5}{m - 3} + \dfrac{7}{m + 2}\right)}{(m - 3)(m + 2)\left[\dfrac{7}{(m - 3)(m + 2)} + \dfrac{1}{m - 3}\right]}$$

Use the distributive property. Divide out common factors in each product.

$$\frac{(\overset{1}{m - 3})(m + 2) \cdot \dfrac{5}{\underset{1}{m - 3}} + (m - 3)(\overset{1}{m + 2}) \cdot \dfrac{7}{\underset{1}{m + 2}}}{(\overset{1}{m - 3})(\overset{1}{m + 2}) \cdot \dfrac{7}{\underset{1}{(m - 3)(m + 2)}} + (\overset{1}{m - 3})(m + 2) \cdot \dfrac{1}{\underset{1}{m - 3}}}$$

Multiply remaining factors in each product. Combine like terms.

$$\frac{5m + 10 + 7m - 21}{7 + m + 2} = \frac{12m - 11}{m + 9}$$

EXAMPLE 2

Simplify $\dfrac{\dfrac{2}{a} + \dfrac{-16}{a^2 + 6a}}{\dfrac{4}{a+6} - \dfrac{1}{a}}$.

Factor: $a^2 + 6a = a(a+6)$.

$\dfrac{4}{a+6} - \dfrac{1}{a} = \dfrac{4}{a+6} + \dfrac{-1 \cdot 1}{a}$

$\qquad = \dfrac{4}{a+6} + \dfrac{-1}{a}$

$\dfrac{\dfrac{2}{a} + \dfrac{-16}{a(a+6)}}{\dfrac{4}{a+6} + \dfrac{-1}{a}}$ ← LCD is $a(a+6)$.

Multiply both numerator and denominator by the LCD, $a(a+6)$.

$\dfrac{a(a+6)\left[\dfrac{2}{a} + \dfrac{-16}{a(a+6)}\right]}{a(a+6)\left(\dfrac{4}{a+6} + \dfrac{-1}{a}\right)}$

Use the distributive property. Divide out common factors in each product.

$\dfrac{\overset{1}{a}(a+6) \cdot \dfrac{2}{\underset{1}{a}} + \overset{1}{a}(a+6) \cdot \dfrac{-16}{\underset{1}{a}(a+6)\underset{1}{}}}{a(a+6) \cdot \dfrac{4}{a+6} + \overset{1}{a}(a+6) \cdot \dfrac{-1}{\underset{1}{a}}}$

Multiply remaining factors in each product. Combine like terms.

$\dfrac{2a + 12 - 16}{4a - 1a - 6}$, or $\dfrac{2a - 4}{3a - 6}$

Factor numerator and denominator. Then write in simplest form.

$\dfrac{2(\overset{1}{a-2})}{3(\underset{1}{a-2})} = \dfrac{2}{3}$

EXAMPLE 3

Simplify $\dfrac{b + 8 + \dfrac{5}{b-3}}{1 + \dfrac{-1}{b-3}}$.

$b - 3$ cannot be factored. Multiply both numerator and denominator by the LCD, $b - 3$.

$\dfrac{(b-3)\left(\dfrac{b+8}{1} + \dfrac{5}{b-3}\right)}{(b-3)\left(1 + \dfrac{-1}{b-3}\right)}$

Use the distributive property. Divide out common factors in each product.

$b^2 + 5b - 24$

$\dfrac{(b-3)(b+8) + (\overset{1}{b-3}) \cdot \dfrac{5}{\underset{1}{b-3}}}{b - 3 + (\overset{1}{b-3}) \cdot \dfrac{-1}{\underset{1}{b-3}}}$

$\dfrac{b^2 + 5b - 24 + 5}{b - 3 - 1}$

Combine like terms.

$\dfrac{b^2 + 5b - 19}{b - 4}$

EXERCISES

PART A

Simplify.

1. $\dfrac{\dfrac{3}{a^2 - 7a + 10} + \dfrac{2}{a - 5}}{\dfrac{4}{a - 5} + \dfrac{2}{a - 2}}$ $\quad \frac{2a-1}{6a-18}$

2. $\dfrac{\dfrac{5}{x^2 - 9} + \dfrac{2}{x - 3}}{\dfrac{3}{x - 3} + \dfrac{2}{x + 3}}$ $\quad \frac{2x+11}{5x+3}$

3. $\dfrac{\dfrac{7}{x^2 - 7x + 12} + \dfrac{3}{x - 4}}{\dfrac{2}{x - 4} + \dfrac{7}{x - 3}}$ $\quad \frac{3x-2}{9x-34}$

4. $\dfrac{\dfrac{3}{m} + \dfrac{-12}{m^2 + 2m}}{\dfrac{2}{m + 2} - \dfrac{1}{m}}$ $\quad 3$

5. $\dfrac{\dfrac{2}{x} + \dfrac{-10}{x^2 + 7x}}{\dfrac{5}{x + 7} + \dfrac{2}{x}}$ $\quad \frac{2}{7}$

6. $\dfrac{\dfrac{6}{x} + \dfrac{-24}{x^2 + 3x}}{\dfrac{4}{x + 3} - \dfrac{1}{x}}$ $\quad 2$

7. $\dfrac{a + 6 + \dfrac{4}{a - 2}}{1 + \dfrac{-2}{a - 2}}$ $\quad \frac{a^2+4a-8}{a-4}$

8. $\dfrac{m + 2 + \dfrac{3}{m - 5}}{\dfrac{4}{m - 5} + 1}$ $\quad \frac{m^2-3m-7}{m-1}$

9. $\dfrac{\dfrac{2}{x - 4} + x - 2}{1 + \dfrac{1}{x - 4}}$ $\quad \frac{x^2-6x+10}{x-3}$

10. $\dfrac{\dfrac{4}{m + 5} + \dfrac{-20}{m^2 + 5m}}{\dfrac{2}{m + 5} - \dfrac{1}{m}}$ $\quad 4$

11. $\dfrac{5 + \dfrac{7}{x - 3}}{4 + \dfrac{3}{x - 3}}$ $\quad \frac{5x-8}{4x-9}$

12. $\dfrac{\dfrac{6b}{3b - 1} + \dfrac{1}{2}}{\dfrac{5}{2} + \dfrac{4}{3b - 1}}$ $\quad \frac{15b-1}{15b+3}$

13. $\dfrac{\dfrac{4}{x^2 - 6x - 16} - \dfrac{3}{x - 8}}{\dfrac{5}{x - 8} + \dfrac{2}{x + 2}}$ $\quad \frac{-3x-2}{7x-6}$

14. $\dfrac{\dfrac{4}{a - 2} + \dfrac{2}{2a + 1}}{\dfrac{5a}{2a^2 - 3a - 2}}$ $\quad 2$

15. $\dfrac{\dfrac{3x}{x^2 - 9}}{\dfrac{6}{x - 3} + \dfrac{6}{x + 3}}$ $\quad \frac{1}{4}$

PART B

Simplify.

16. $\dfrac{\dfrac{x + 1}{x} - \dfrac{5}{x + 2}}{\dfrac{x + 1}{x^2 + 2x} + \dfrac{3}{x + 2}}$ $\quad \frac{x^2-2x+2}{4x+1}$

17. $\dfrac{\dfrac{1}{x + 3} + \dfrac{1}{x - 7}}{\dfrac{2x^2 + x - 10}{x^2 - 4x - 21}}$ $\quad \frac{2}{2x+5}$

18. $\dfrac{\dfrac{x + 1}{x + 2} + \dfrac{x + 7}{x - 5}}{\dfrac{5}{x^2 - 3x - 10}}$ $\quad \frac{2x^2+5x+9}{5}$

PART C

Simplify.

19. $\dfrac{\dfrac{a}{b} + 2 + \dfrac{b}{a}}{\dfrac{a^2 - b^2}{ab}}$

20. $\dfrac{\dfrac{x}{y} - 6 + \dfrac{7y}{6}}{\dfrac{x^2 - 49y^2}{xy}}$

21. $\dfrac{\dfrac{x - y}{x - 2y} + \dfrac{x + 7y}{x + 5y}}{\dfrac{3x}{x^2 + 3xy - 10y^2}}$

Formulas

REVIEW CAPSULE

Solve for y. Then find y if $x = 3$.

$$2x + 3y = 10 \qquad \text{If } x = 3, \text{ then}$$
$$\underline{-2x \qquad\quad -2x}$$
$$3y = 10 - 2x \qquad y = \frac{10 - 2(3)}{3}$$
$$y = \frac{10 - 2x}{3} \qquad = \frac{10 - 6}{3}, \text{ or } \frac{4}{3}.$$

EXAMPLE 1 Solve $ax = b$ for x.

Divide each side by a. ⟶

Similar to $3x = 17$

$x = \dfrac{17}{3}$

$$ax = b$$
$$\frac{ax}{a} = \frac{b}{a}$$
$$x = \frac{b}{a}$$

EXAMPLE 2 The formula for perimeter of a rectangle is
$p = l + w + l + w$, or
$p = 2l + 2w$.
Solve $p = 2l + 2w$ for l.
Then find l if $p = 46$ cm and $w = 9$ cm.

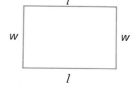

Get $2l$ alone on one side.
Add $-2w$ to each side.
l is alone on one side.
Divide each side by 2.
Formula is solved for l.

$$p = 2l + 2w$$
$$\underline{-2w \qquad\quad -2w}$$
$$p - 2w = 2l$$
$$\frac{p - 2w}{2} = l, \text{ or } l = \frac{p - 2w}{2}$$

Now, find l if $p = 46$ and $w = 9$.

Replace p with 46, w with 9. ⟶

$$l = \frac{p - 2w}{2}$$
$$= \frac{46 - 2(9)}{2}$$
$$= \frac{46 - 18}{2}, \text{ or } 14 \text{ cm}$$

EXAMPLE 3   Solve $pkt - m = 5m$ for k.

Get pkt alone on one side. ⎫
Add m to each side. ⎭

Rewrite pkt as $(pt)k$, since we can multiply in any order. ⟶

Divide each side by pt. ⟶

$$pkt - m = 5m$$
$$\underline{m \qquad m}$$
$$pkt = 6m$$
$$(pt)k = 6m$$
$$\frac{(pt)k}{pt} = \frac{6m}{pt}$$
$$k = \frac{6m}{pt}$$

EXAMPLE 4   Solve $R = \dfrac{5}{3}t + 40$ for t. Then find t if $R = 70$.

$$\frac{R}{1} = \frac{5}{3}t + \frac{40}{1} \qquad \longleftarrow \quad LCD \text{ is } 3.$$

Multiply each side by 3. ⟶

$$3 \cdot \frac{R}{1} = 3\left(\frac{5}{3}t + \frac{40}{1}\right)$$

Use the distributive property. ⎫
Divide out common factors. ⎭

$$3R = \overset{1}{3} \cdot \frac{5}{\underset{1}{3}}t + 3 \cdot 40$$

Get $5t$ alone on one side. ⎫
Add -120 to each side. ⎭

$$3R = 5t + 120$$
$$\underline{-120 \qquad\qquad -120}$$
$$3R - 120 = 5t$$

Divide each side by 5. ⟶

$$\frac{3R - 120}{5} = t, \text{ or } t = \frac{3R - 120}{5}$$

Now find t if $R = 70$.

$$t = \frac{3R - 120}{5}$$

$$\left.\frac{3(70) - 120}{5} = \frac{210 - 120}{5}\right.$$
$$= 18$$

$$= \frac{3(70) - 120}{5}$$
$$= 18$$

EXAMPLE 5   Solve $ax = c - bx$ for x.

Get all the x terms on one side. ⎫
Add bx to each side. ⎭

$$ax = c - bx$$
$$\underline{bx \qquad\qquad bx}$$
$$ax + bx = c$$

Factor out the common monomial, x. ⟶
Divide each side by $(a + b)$, since x is ⎫
multiplied by $(a + b)$. ⎭

$$x(a + b) = c$$
$$\frac{x(a + b)}{a + b} = \frac{c}{a + b}$$
$$x = \frac{c}{a + b}$$

EXERCISES

PART A

Solve for x.

1. $ax = 2$ $x = \frac{2}{a}$ 2. $rx = 5$ $x = \frac{5}{r}$ 3. $3x = 3a$ $x = a$ 4. $bc = 2x$ $x = \frac{bc}{2}$

5. $x + 3a = 0$ $x = -3a$ 6. $2c + x = a$ 7. $x - 4a = 0$ $x = 4a$ 8. $5 = x - 3c$

9. $2x - c = d$ $x = \frac{d+c}{2}$ 10. $bx - 7 = 3c$ 11. $4a + 2x = 3b$ 12. $7x + 2a = 6h$

13. $8 - 2x = kx$ 14. $ax = 4 - cx$ 15. $3ax = ax + b$ 16. $mx = px - t$

17. $\dfrac{x}{3} = \dfrac{b}{2} + \dfrac{c}{6}$ 18. $\dfrac{m}{5} + \dfrac{p}{3} = \dfrac{x}{15}$ 19. $\dfrac{x}{2a} = \dfrac{b}{c}$ $x = \frac{2ab}{c}$ 20. $\dfrac{x}{b} - c = a$

Solve each formula for the variable indicated. Then evaluate.

21. Solve $p = 4s$ for s. Then find s if $p = 28$. $\frac{p}{4}$; 7

22. Solve $A = pti$ for i. Then find i if $p = 180$, $A = 270$, and $t = \frac{1}{2}$. $\frac{A}{pt}$; 3

23. Solve $p = 2s + b$ for s. Then find s if $p = 52$ and $b = 14$. $\frac{p-b}{2}$; 19

24. Solve $l = a + 15d$ for d. Then find d if $l = 125$ and $a = 35$. $\frac{l-a}{15}$; 6

25. Solve $C = 2\pi r$ for r. Then find r if $C = 12.56$ m and $\pi \doteq 3.14$. $\frac{C}{2\pi}$; $2\ m$

26. Solve $i = prt$ for r. Then find r if $i = 30$, $p = 200$, and $t = 4$. $\frac{i}{pt}$; $\frac{3}{80}$

27. Solve $V = lwh$ for h. Then find h if $V = 48$ cm^3, $l = 2$ cm, and $w = 6$ cm. $\frac{V}{lw}$; $4\ cm$

28. Solve $C = \frac{1}{3}fd^2$ for f. Then find f if $C = 20$ and $d = 2$. $\frac{3C}{d^2}$; 15

PART B

Solve for x.

29. $5a + 2bx = 3c$ $\frac{3c-5a}{2b}$ 30. $6x - 6a = 2x + 10a$ $4a$ 31. $ax - c = 2d + 3c$ $\frac{2d+4c}{a}$

32. $3b - 3c = 2bx - 3c$ $\frac{3}{2}$ 33. $2 - 2bx = -4b + 3bx$ $\frac{4b+2}{5b}$ 34. $7a + 3x = 6a + 4x$ a

35. $a^2 - ax + 4 = 2x - 4a$ $a + 2$ 36. $4x - ax = 16 - a^2$ $a + 4$ 37. $ax + bx = a^2 + 2ab + b^2$ $a + b$

PART C

Solve each formula for the variable indicated. Then evaluate.

38. Solve $P = \dfrac{2}{3}(m - 16)$ for m. Then find m if $p = 8$.

39. Solve $V = \dfrac{1}{3}\pi r^2 h$ for h. Then find h if $V = 157$ km^3, $\pi \doteq 3.14$, and $r = 5$ km.

40. Solve $T = \pi r(r + l)$ for l. Then find l if $T = 942$, $r = 10$, and $\pi \doteq 3.14$.

41. Solve $A = p + prt$ for p. Then find p if $A = 134.40$, $r = .06$, and $t = 2$.

42. Solve $T = 2\pi r(r + h)$ for h. Then find h if $T = 301.44$, $r = 4$, and $\pi \doteq 3.14$.

43. Solve $A = \dfrac{b + c + a}{3}$ for a. Then find a if $A = 34$, $b = 39$, and $c = 32$.

Parallel Series Circuits

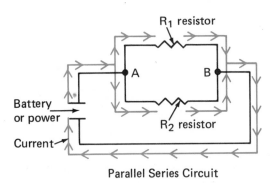

R$_1$ resistor

A   B

Battery or power

Current

R$_2$ resistor

Parallel Series Circuit

When you turn the power on, voltage from the battery forces current to flow. Current flows to A, then splits, part flowing through R$_1$ and part through R$_2$. The two branches join up again at B forming a single current flowing back to the battery. Resistors control the flow of current, that is, the greater the resistance, the less current.

A volume control on a radio is a resistor. Turning down the sound cuts or resists the flow of current.

Total resistance of two resistors in a parallel circuit

$$R = \frac{1}{\dfrac{1}{R_1} + \dfrac{1}{R_2}}$$

Resistance is measured in ohms: Ω.

PROBLEM

Two resistors in a parallel series circuit have resistances of $20\,\Omega$ and $30\,\Omega$. Find the total resistance.

Use $R = \dfrac{1}{\dfrac{1}{R_1} + \dfrac{1}{R_2}}$

where $R_1 = 20$ and $R_2 = 30$.

$$\frac{1}{\dfrac{1}{20} + \dfrac{1}{30}} \longleftarrow \text{A complex fraction}$$

$$\frac{60\,(1)}{60\left(\dfrac{1}{20} + \dfrac{1}{30}\right)}$$

LCD is 60.

Distribute 60. $\longrightarrow$

$$\frac{60\,(1)}{{}^{3}60\left(\dfrac{1}{20}_1\right) + {}^{2}60\left(\dfrac{1}{30}_1\right)}, \text{ or } \frac{60}{3+2}$$

Simplify. $\dfrac{60}{3+2} = \dfrac{60}{5} = 12.$ $\longrightarrow$ Thus, the total resistance is $12\,\Omega$.

PROJECT   Find the total resistance in a parallel circuit with these resistances.
1. $5\,\Omega, 10\,\Omega$ **2.** $25\,\Omega, 75\,\Omega$ **3.** $200\,\Omega, 150\,\Omega$ **4.** $4\,\Omega, 8\,\Omega, 6\,\Omega$

Chapter Thirteen Review

Solve and check for extraneous solutions. $[p.\ 341,\ 346]$

1. $\dfrac{2a-3}{6} = \dfrac{4a}{3} + \dfrac{1}{2}$

2. $\dfrac{3}{5} + \dfrac{6}{x} = 1$

3. $\dfrac{2}{3}(x-4) + \dfrac{x+5}{2} = \dfrac{2x-1}{3}$

4. $\dfrac{7}{y+3} + \dfrac{4}{y-7} = \dfrac{2}{y^2-4y-21}$

5. $\dfrac{x}{x-7} + \dfrac{3}{x} = \dfrac{-23}{x^2-7x}$

6. $\dfrac{2}{b+2} + \dfrac{13}{b^2-4} = \dfrac{b}{b-2}$

$[p.\ 350,\ 353]$

7. Working together, Mona and Martin can mow a lawn in 5 hours. It would take Mona 9 hours to do it alone. How long would it take Martin?

8. George can repair a radio in 5 hours. If Tina helps him, they can complete the job in 2 hours. How long would it take Tina to do it alone?

9. Working together, two women can build a house in 7 months. It would take one of them 3 times as long as the other to do it alone. How long would it take each alone?

10. By herself, Jane can build a table in 2 weeks. It would take Juan 5 weeks. How long would it take Irv if, working together, all three can complete the job in 1 week?

Solve. $[p.\ 358]$

11. $.03x = 7$

12. $.6x + 3 = .21x + 18$

13. $.01(2 - .5x) = .48 - .003x$

Show that each is a rational number. $[p.\ 361]$

14. -18 **15.** 0 **16.** $7\frac{1}{2}$ **17.** $4.6\overline{6}$ **18.** $.32\overline{2}$ **19.** $.18\overline{18}$

Simplify. $[p.\ 368,\ 371]$

20. $\dfrac{\dfrac{3}{5} + \dfrac{1}{2}}{\dfrac{3}{10} + \dfrac{2}{5}}$

21. $\dfrac{\dfrac{3}{b^2} + \dfrac{5}{b}}{\dfrac{2}{b} + \dfrac{7}{3b^2}}$

22. $\dfrac{1 - \dfrac{2}{x} - \dfrac{15}{x^2}}{\dfrac{1}{x} - \dfrac{5}{x^2}}$

23. $\dfrac{\dfrac{6}{a-3} + \dfrac{4}{a}}{\dfrac{7}{a^2-3a}}$

24. $\dfrac{\dfrac{3}{a-4} + \dfrac{5}{2a+3}}{\dfrac{4a}{2a^2-5a-12}}$

25. $\dfrac{x - 5 + \dfrac{3}{x-2}}{\dfrac{3}{x-2} + 2}$

Solve for x. $[p.\ 374]$

26. $bx - 8 = 3m$ **27.** $5a + mx = tr$ **28.** $8 - 5x = kx$ **29.** $6a + 5x = 4a + 3x$

Solve each formula for the variable indicated. Then evaluate. $[p.\ 374]$

30. Solve $a = mpq$ for p. Then find p if $a = 32$, $m = 2$, and $q = 7$.

31. Solve $k = \frac{1}{4}fd^2$ for f. Then find f if $k = 7$ and $d = 2$.

Chapter Thirteen Test

Solve and check for extraneous solutions.

1. $\dfrac{3a - 4}{15} = \dfrac{2a}{5} + \dfrac{1}{3}$

2. $\dfrac{2}{3} + \dfrac{6}{x} = 2$

3. $\dfrac{4}{y - 8} - \dfrac{3}{y + 2} = \dfrac{4}{y^2 - 6y - 16}$

4. $\dfrac{2}{7}(x - 2) + \dfrac{x + 4}{7} = \dfrac{x + 15}{14}$

5. Working together, Janice and Jack can mow a lawn in 4 hours. It would take Janice 7 hours to do it alone. How long would it take Jack?

6. Rodney can repair a T.V. set in 9 hours. If Lisa helps him, they can complete the job in 4 hours. How long would it take Lisa to do it alone?

7. Working together, two men can build a shed in 15 hours. It would take one of them 4 times as long as the other to do it alone. How long would it take each alone?

8. By herself, Joan can build a desk in 4 weeks. It would take José 5 weeks. How long would it take Sue if, working together, all three can complete the job in 2 weeks?

Solve.

9. $.05x = 4$

10. $.5x + 2 = .32x + 12$

11. $.01(3 - .4x) = .23 - .002x$

Show that each is a rational number.

12. -14

13. $8\frac{1}{3}$

14. $.4\overline{4}$

15. $.12\overline{12}$

Simplify.

16. $\dfrac{\dfrac{4}{7} + \dfrac{1}{3}}{\dfrac{2}{3} + \dfrac{5}{21}}$

17. $\dfrac{\dfrac{7}{a - 2} + \dfrac{5}{a}}{\dfrac{3}{a^2 - 2a}}$

18. $\dfrac{1 - \dfrac{5}{m} - \dfrac{14}{m^2}}{\dfrac{1}{m} - \dfrac{7}{m^2}}$

19. $\dfrac{x - 2 + \dfrac{5}{x + 3}}{\dfrac{7}{x + 3} + 5}$

Solve for x.

20. $mx - 4 = 2a$

21. $7 + 2x = tx$

22. $5x - 4b = 3x + 8b$

Solve each formula for the variable indicated. Then evaluate.

23. Solve $m = abd$ for b. Then find b if $m = 28$, $a = 2$, and $d = 7$.

24. Solve $I = \frac{1}{5}mp^2$ for m. Then find m if $p = 2$ and $I = 20$.

14 REAL NUMBERS

The Normal Curve

64 students were categorized according to their height. The results are given below.

Height	Number of Students
Under 152 cm	1
155 cm to under 160 cm	6
160 cm to under 165 cm	15
165 cm to under 170 cm	20
170 cm to under 175 cm	15
175 cm to under 180 cm	6
180 cm or over	1
	Total 64 students

The graph below, which is composed of rectangles, is called a histogram. It represents the data from the table.

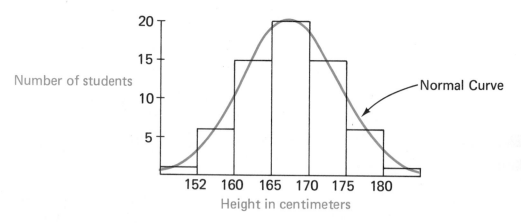

The smooth curve drawn through the graph is shaped like a bell. It is called the *normal curve*.

380

The Apex Lighting Company took a survey of 10,000, 150-watt light bulbs to determine the number of hours each bulb would burn. The results are given below.

MORTALITY RATE OF 150-WATT LIGHT BULBS

Number of Hours Burned	Number of Bulbs
100-299.9	3
300-499.9	321
500-699.9	1,108
700-899.9	2,193
900-1,099.9	2,745
1,100-1,299.9	2,196
1,300-1,499.9	1,113
1,500-1,699.9	319
1,700-1,899.9	2
	Total 10,000 bulbs

These results fit the normal curve.

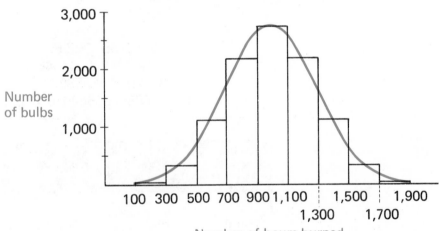

Number of bulbs

Number of hours burned

PROJECT   Survey each. Then see if the results fit the normal curve.

1. The batting averages of a large group of baseball players

2. The weights of thousands of apples

The Set of Real Numbers

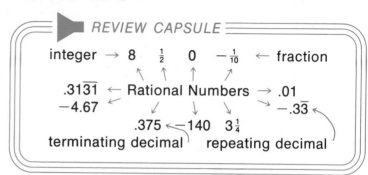

REVIEW CAPSULE

integer → 8 $\frac{1}{2}$ 0 $-\frac{1}{10}$ ← fraction

.31$\overline{31}$ ← Rational Numbers → .01

−4.67

.375 ←—140 $3\frac{1}{4}$

terminating decimal   repeating decimal $-.3\overline{3}$

EXAMPLE 1 If possible, write these decimals with a bar.
.311311311311. . .
.313113111311113111113. . .

This decimal repeats. ——————→ .311311311311. . . = .311$\overline{311}$

.313113111311113111113. . . cannot be written with a bar since no group of digits continues to repeat.

These cannot be written with a bar. ——————

These are nonrepeating decimals.
.57557555755557. . .
−7.40414243444546. . .
3.14159265358979. . .
43.00600660066600666600. . .

Decimal approximation for π ——————→

Nonrepeating decimals cannot be written in the form $\frac{a}{b}$, where a and b are integers and $b \neq 0$.

Nonrepeating decimals are *irrational* numbers.

repeating decimal	nonrepeating decimal
↓	↓
.399939993999. . .	.3939939993. . .
↓	↓
rational number	irrational number

EXAMPLE 2 Which are rational and which are irrational numbers?

Answers

Terminating decimal ——————→ −4.287   Rational
Nonrepeating decimal ——————→ 6.161161116. . .   Irrational
Repeating decimal ——————→ 37.237$\overline{237}$ Rational

The set of *real* numbers contains all the rational and all the irrational numbers.

EXERCISES

PART A

Which are rational and which are irrational numbers?

1. .424242. . . R **2.** .424424442. . . I **3.** $-.5639$ R **4.** $.68\overline{68}$ R

5. $-.31323334. . .$ I **6.** $.3083\overline{83}$ R **7.** .123123123. . . R **8.** $-.00009$ R

9. π I **10.** $7.1234\overline{1234}$ R **11.** $\frac{34}{3,434}$ R **12.** 0 R

13. $-2.101101110. . .$ **14.** $-.1121231234. . .$ **15.** 456,456 R **16.** 3.1416 R

17. $-.438438$ R **18.** $\frac{22}{7}R$ **19.** $-.682\overline{682}$ R **20.** .20212223. . . I

PART B

21. Make up five real numbers that are rational.

22. Make up decimal numerals for five real numbers that are irrational.

23. Name five real numbers that are integers.

24. Is every integer a real number? Why or why not? *yes*

25. A number called *e* is used in higher mathematics. $e \doteq 2.71828. . . .$ At no time does a group of digits repeat, no matter how far the decimal is carried out. Is *e* rational or irrational? *irrational*

26. Start with a decimal point. Flip a coin. If heads comes up, write 1. If tails comes up, write 2. Imagine doing this indefinitely. Does the numeral you are constructing name a rational or an irrational number?

27. Start with a decimal point. Toss a die. Record the number shown on the die. Imagine that this continues forever. Does the numeral you are constructing name a rational or an irrational number? *irrational*

28. Start with a decimal point. Toss two dice. Record the number that is the sum of the numbers shown on the dice. Imagine that this continues forever. Does the numeral you are constructing name a rational or an irrational number?

PART C

True or false?

29. {rationals} ∩ {irrationals} = {reals}

30. {integers} ⊆ {reals}

31. {rationals} ∩ {irrationals} = ϕ

32. {reals} = {rationals}

33. {reals} ∩ {rationals} = {rationals}

34. {rationals} ∪ {reals} = {reals}

Square Roots

REVIEW CAPSULE

$(2)(2) = 4$

$(-2)(-2) = 4$

$(15)(15) = 225$

$(-15)(-15) = 225$

$(3.1)(3.1) = 9.61$

$(-3.1)(-3.1) = 9.61$

$\left(\dfrac{3}{4}\right)\left(\dfrac{3}{4}\right) = \dfrac{9}{16}$

$\left(-\dfrac{3}{4}\right)\left(-\dfrac{3}{4}\right) = \dfrac{9}{16}$

Definition of square root ⟶ If $x \cdot x = n$, then x is a square root of n.

Every positive real number has two square roots, one positive and one negative.

2 is a square root of 4, since $(2)(2) = 4$. Also, -2 is a square root of 4, since $(-2)(-2) = 4$.

Number	Positive Square Root	Negative Square Root
4	2	-2
9.61	3.1	-3.1
$\frac{9}{16}$	$\frac{3}{4}$	$-\frac{3}{4}$

Definition of principal square root⟶ The positive square root of a number is called the *principal* square root. It is indicated by the symbol $\sqrt{}$.

The principal square root of 4 is 2.

$\sqrt{4} = 2$ $\qquad \sqrt{9.61} = 3.1$ $\qquad \sqrt{225} = 15$ $\qquad \sqrt{\dfrac{9}{16}} = \dfrac{3}{4}$

EXAMPLE 1   Are $\sqrt{16}$ and $\sqrt{33}$ whole numbers?

$(5)(5) = 25$ and $(6)(6) = 36$; so, $\sqrt{33}$ is not 5 or 6. ⟶ $\sqrt{16}$ is the whole number 4, since $(4)(4) = 16$. $\sqrt{33}$ is not a whole number.

Definition of a perfect square ──────→
16 is a perfect square.

> A *perfect square* is a number whose principal square root is a whole number.

The table on page 476 gives 3-decimal place values for square roots of whole numbers from 1 to 100.

$\doteq$ means is approximately equal to.

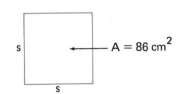

$\sqrt{33} \doteq 5.745$ $(5.745)(5.745) = 33.005025 \doteq 33$

$\sqrt{65} \doteq 8.062$ $(8.062)(8.062) = 64.995844 \doteq 65$

EXAMPLE 2   The area of a square is 86 square cm. Find the length of a side, to the nearest tenth of a cm.

Formula for area of a square ──────→ $s^2 = A$

Substitute 86 for A. ──────→ $s^2 = 86$

$s = \sqrt{86}$

From the table, $\sqrt{86} \doteq 9.274$. ──────→ $s \doteq 9.274$

Round to the nearest tenth. ──────→ $s \doteq 9.3$

s ←── $A = 86\ cm^2$

s

Thus, the length of a side is 9.3 cm, to the nearest tenth.

EXAMPLE 3   The area of a rectangle is 48 square meters. The length is 4 times the width. Find the length and the width, to the nearest tenth of a meter.

Let $x =$ width in meters

$4x =$ length in meters

Formula for area of a rectangle ──────→ $l \cdot w = A$

Substitute $4x$, x, and 48. ──────→ $(4x)(x) = 48$

$4x^2 = 48$

Divide each side by 4. ──────→ $x^2 = 12$

$x = \sqrt{12}$

From the table, $\sqrt{12} \doteq 3.464$. ──────→ $x \doteq 3.464$

Round to the nearest tenth. ──────→ $x \doteq 3.5$

Find the length, $4x$. ──────→ $4x \doteq 4(3.464)$

Multiply 3.464 by 4. ──────→ $4x \doteq 13.856$

Round to the nearest tenth. ──────→ $4x \doteq 13.9$

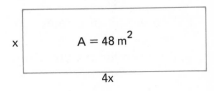

x $A = 48\ m^2$

$4x$

Thus, the length is 13.9 m and the width is 3.5 m, to the nearest tenth.

ORAL EXERCISES

Tell which are perfect squares. Then give the principal square root of each number. Approximate to the nearest tenth for nonperfect squares. Use the table on page 476.

1. 25 *5*
6. 38 *6.2*
11. 1 *1*
16. 74 *8.6*

2. 6 *2.4*
7. 42 *6.5*
12. 67 *8.2*
17. 39 *6.2*

3. 100 *10*
8. 49 *7*
13. 12 *3.5*
18. 78 *8.8*

4. 26 *5.1*
9. 11 *3.3*
14. 64 *8*
19. 9 *3*

5. 36 *6*
10. 59 *7.7*
15. 8 *2.8*
20. 92 *9.6*

EXERCISES

PART A

Give answers to the nearest tenth.

1.
$A = 37$ m^2, s, s

Find *s*.

2.
$A = 62$ cm^2, s, s

Find *s*.

3.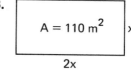
$A = 110$ m^2, x, $2x$

Find *x* and *2x*.

4.
$A = 94$ cm^2, s, s

Find *s*.

5.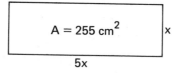
$A = 90$ m^2, x, $3x$

Find *x* and *3x*.

6.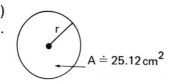
$A = 255$ cm^2, $5x$, x

Find *x* and *5x*.

7.
$A = 28$ cm^2, s, s

Find *s*.

8.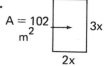
$A = 102$ m^2, $3x$, $2x$

Find *2x* and *3x*.

9. The length of a rectangle is 5 times the width. The area is 220 m². Find the length and the width. *w = 6.6 m* *l = 33 m*

10. The area of a rectangle is 166 cm². The length is twice the width. Find the length and the width. *w = 9.1 cm* *l = 18.2 cm*

PART B

Give answers to the nearest tenth.

11. Find *r*.
(Hint: $A = \pi r^2$.)
Use 3.14 for π.

r
$A \doteq 25.12$ cm^2

12. Find *3x* and *2x*.
(Hint: $A = \frac{1}{2}bh$.)

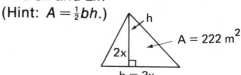
h
$A = 222$ m^2
$2x$
$b = 3x$

The Galton Board

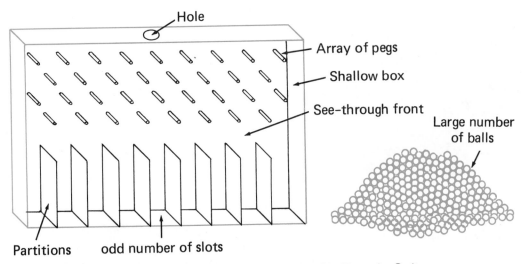

Hole

Array of pegs

Shallow box

See-through front

Large number of balls

Partitions

odd number of slots

The board was invented by a British mathematician, Sir Francis Galton
(1822-1911).

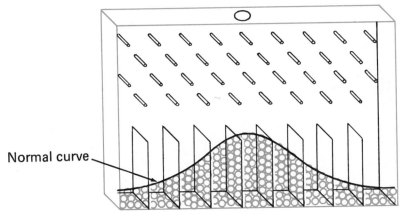

Normal curve

If the balls are poured into the hole, they will form a model of the
normal curve.

PROJECT Build a model of the Galton board.
(Suggested materials: wood, plastic, heavy cardboard)

Approximating Square Roots

 REVIEW CAPSULE

From the square root table:
$$\sqrt{4} = 2$$
$$\sqrt{5} \doteq 2.236$$
$$\sqrt{6} \doteq 2.449$$
$$\sqrt{7} \doteq 2.646$$
$$\sqrt{8} \doteq 2.828$$
$$\sqrt{9} = 3$$

The decimal for $\sqrt{5}$ is nonrepeating. $\sqrt{5}$ is an irrational number. ——→

If the square root of a whole number is not a whole number, then it is an irrational number.

EXAMPLE 1 Approximate $\sqrt{34}$ to the nearest tenth.

Step 1 ————————————→ Guess the square root.

$5 \times 5 = 25$ and $6 \times 6 = 36$ ————→ $\sqrt{34}$ is between 5 and 6. GUESS: 5.5.

Step 2 ————————————→ Divide the guess into the number. Carry to hundredths. Do not round.

Divide 5.5 into 34. Carry to two decimal places. }

$$
\begin{array}{r}
6.18 \\
5.5\overline{)34.000} \\
\underline{33\ 0} \\
1\ 00 \\
\underline{55} \\
450 \\
\underline{440}
\end{array}
$$

$\sqrt{34}$ is between 5.5 and 6.18.

$$5.5 < \sqrt{34} < 6.18$$

Step 3 ————————————→ Average the divisor and the quotient. Round to the nearest tenth.

To average 5.5 and 6.18, add them and divide by 2. Then round to the nearest tenth.

$$
\begin{array}{r}
5.5 \\
+6.18 \\
\hline
11.68
\end{array}
$$

$$
\begin{array}{r}
5.84 \doteq 5.8 \\
2\overline{)11.68} \\
\underline{10} \\
1\ 6 \\
\underline{1\ 6} \\
8 \\
\underline{8}
\end{array}
$$

5.8 is the average.

If they were the same, we would be finished. However, we must continue.

Check to see if the average is the same as the previous divisor: $5.8 \neq 5.5$.

Step 4

Divide the average into the number. Carry to hundredths. Do not round.

Divide 5.8 into 34. ⟶

$$
\begin{array}{r}
5.86 \\
5.8\,)\overline{34.000} \\
\underline{29\,0} \\
5\,00 \\
\underline{4\,64} \\
360 \\
\underline{348}
\end{array}
$$

If they were not the same, we would have to repeat Step 3.

The divisor and the quotient are the same in the tenths place: 5.8   5.86

$5.8 < \sqrt{34} < 5.86$

Thus, $\sqrt{34} = 5.8$ to the nearest tenth.

This method of approximating square roots is called the divide and average method.

To approximate a square root to the nearest tenth:
Step 1   Guess the square root.
Step 2   Divide the guess into the number. Carry to hundredths. Do not round.
Step 3   Average the divisor and quotient. Round to the nearest tenth.
Step 4   Divide the average into the number. Carry to hundredths. Do not round.
Repeat Steps 3 and 4 until the average is the same as the divisor in Step 3 or until the divisor and quotient agree in the tenths place in Step 4.

EXAMPLE 2   Approximate $\sqrt{86}$ to the nearest tenth.

Guess the square root.

Step 1
$9 \times 9 = 81$ and $10 \times 10 = 100$
$9 < \sqrt{86} < 10$ ⟶ GUESS: 9.5

Step 2

Divide the guess into the number. Carry to hundredths. Do not round.

Divide 9.5 into 86. Carry to two decimal places.

$$
\begin{array}{r}
9.05 \\
9.5\,)\overline{86.000} \\
\underline{85\,5} \\
500 \\
\underline{475}
\end{array}
$$

$\sqrt{86}$ is between 9.05 and 9.5.

$9.05 < \sqrt{86} < 9.5$

Step 3	Average the divisor and quotient. Round to the nearest tenth.	

Add and divide by 2. Then round to the nearest tenth.

$$9.5$$
$$+9.05$$
$$\overline{18.55}$$

$$\begin{array}{r} 9.27 \doteq 9.3 \\ 2\overline{)18.55} \\ \underline{18} \\ 5 \\ \underline{4} \\ 15 \end{array}$$

9.3 is the average.

$9.3 \neq 9.5$. We must continue.

Step 4

Divide the average into the number. Carry to hundredths. Do not round.

Divide 9.3 into 86. Carry to two decimal places.

$$\begin{array}{r} 9.24 \\ 9.3\overline{)86.000} \\ \underline{83\ 7} \\ 2\ 30 \\ \underline{1\ 86} \\ 440 \\ \underline{372} \end{array}$$

$\sqrt{86}$ is between 9.24 and 9.3.

$$9.24 < \sqrt{86} < 9.3$$

$9.3 \quad 9.27$ We must continue. ⟶
Repeat Step 3.

Divisor and quotient do not agree in the tenths place. Average divisor and quotient. Round to the nearest tenth.

Add and divide by 2. Then round to the nearest tenth.

$$9.3$$
$$+9.24$$
$$\overline{18.54}$$

$$\begin{array}{r} 9.27 \doteq 9.3 \\ 2\overline{)18.54} \\ \underline{18} \\ 5 \\ \underline{4} \\ 14 \end{array}$$

9.3 is the average.

Average equals previous quotient.

Thus, $\sqrt{86} = 9.3$ to the nearest tenth.

EXERCISES

PART A

Approximate to the nearest tenth. Use the divide and average method.

1. $\sqrt{26}$ *5.1* **2.** $\sqrt{1}$ *1* **3.** $\sqrt{48}$ *6.9* **4.** $\sqrt{25}$ *5* **5.** $\sqrt{89}$ *9.4* **6.** $\sqrt{62}$ *7.9* **7.** $\sqrt{18}$ *4.2*
8. $\sqrt{49}$ *7* **9.** $\sqrt{52}$ *7.2* **10.** $\sqrt{7}$ *2.6* **11.** $\sqrt{12}$ *3.5* **12.** $\sqrt{36}$ *6* **13.** $\sqrt{37}$ *6.1* **14.** $\sqrt{78}$ *8.8*
15. $\sqrt{32}$ *5.7* **16.** $\sqrt{90}$ *9.5* **17.** $\sqrt{67}$ *8.2* **18.** $\sqrt{58}$ *7.6* **19.** $\sqrt{70}$ *8.4* **20.** $\sqrt{100}$ *10* **21.** $\sqrt{82}$ *9.1*

PART B

Approximate to the nearest tenth. Use the divide and average method.

22. $\sqrt{243}$ *15.6* **23.** $\sqrt{116}$ *10.8* **24.** $\sqrt{255}$ *16.0* **25.** $\sqrt{200}$ *14.1* **26.** $\sqrt{378}$ *19.4*

Simplifying Radicals

▶ REVIEW CAPSULE

Factor 48 into primes.
$$48 = (2)(24)$$
$$= (2)(2)(12)$$
$$= (2)(2)(2)(6)$$
$$= (2)(2)(2)(2)(3)$$

Thus, 48 = (2)(2)(2)(2)(3).

EXAMPLE 1 Simplify $\sqrt{9} \cdot \sqrt{4}$. Then simplify $\sqrt{9 \cdot 4}$. What conclusion can you draw?

Results are the same. ———————→

$\sqrt{9} \cdot \sqrt{4}$		$\sqrt{9 \cdot 4}$
$3 \cdot 2$		$\sqrt{36}$
6		6

Thus, $\sqrt{9} \cdot \sqrt{4} = \sqrt{9 \cdot 4}$.

Example 1 suggests this. ———→
a is nonnegative if $a \geq 0$.

$\sqrt{a} \cdot \sqrt{b} = \sqrt{a \cdot b}$ and $\sqrt{a \cdot b} = \sqrt{a} \cdot \sqrt{b}$, for all nonnegative numbers *a* and *b*.

EXAMPLE 2 Simplify $\sqrt{5} \cdot \sqrt{11}$.

$\sqrt{a} \cdot \sqrt{b} = \sqrt{a \cdot b}$ ———→ $\sqrt{5} \cdot \sqrt{11} = \sqrt{5 \cdot 11} = \sqrt{55}$

Thus, $\sqrt{5} \cdot \sqrt{11} = \sqrt{55}$.

EXAMPLE 3 Simplify $\sqrt{5} \cdot \sqrt{5}$.   Simplify $\sqrt{8} \cdot \sqrt{8}$.

Multiply first. ———————→
Then simplify. ———————→

$\sqrt{5} \cdot \sqrt{5} = \sqrt{5 \cdot 5}$		$\sqrt{8} \cdot \sqrt{8} = \sqrt{8 \cdot 8}$
$= \sqrt{25}$		$= \sqrt{64}$
$= 5$		$= 8$

Thus, $\sqrt{5} \cdot \sqrt{5} = 5$ and $\sqrt{8} \cdot \sqrt{8} = 8$.

Example 3 suggests this. ───────→ $\sqrt{x} \cdot \sqrt{x} = x$, for each nonnegative number x.

EXAMPLE 4 Simplify $\sqrt{36 \cdot 81}$.

$\sqrt{a \cdot b} = \sqrt{a} \cdot \sqrt{b}$ ─────────────→
$$\begin{aligned} \sqrt{36 \cdot 81} &= \sqrt{36} \cdot \sqrt{81} \\ &= 6 \cdot 9 \\ &= 54 \end{aligned}$$

Thus, $\sqrt{36 \cdot 81} = 54$.

EXAMPLE 5 Simplify $\sqrt{72}$.

One way Factor into primes.	Another way Find greatest perfect square factor.

Group pairs of the same factors.⎫
$\sqrt{a \cdot b} = \sqrt{a} \cdot \sqrt{b}$ ⎬

$$\begin{aligned} \sqrt{72} &= \sqrt{3 \cdot 3 \cdot 2 \cdot 2 \cdot 2} \\ &= \underbrace{\sqrt{3} \cdot \sqrt{3}} \cdot \underbrace{\sqrt{2} \cdot \sqrt{2}} \cdot \sqrt{2} \end{aligned}$$

$\sqrt{x} \cdot \sqrt{x} = x$ ─────────────→

$$\begin{aligned} &= \quad 3 \quad \cdot \quad 2 \quad \cdot \sqrt{2} \\ &= 6\sqrt{2} \end{aligned}$$
Thus, $\sqrt{72} = 6\sqrt{2}$.

Another way:
$$\begin{aligned} \sqrt{72} &= \sqrt{36 \cdot 2} \\ &= \sqrt{36} \cdot \sqrt{2} \\ &= 6\sqrt{2} \end{aligned}$$
Simplest radical form

$\sqrt{72}$ is a *radical*. $\sqrt{}$ is the *radical sign*.
72 is the *radicand*. A radical is *simplified* when
the radicand does not have a perfect square
factor.

EXAMPLE 6 Simplify $\sqrt{90}$.

One way Factor into primes.	Another way Find greatest perfect square factor.

Factor 90 into primes. ─────────→
Group like factors.

$$\begin{aligned} \sqrt{90} &= \sqrt{2 \cdot 3 \cdot 5 \cdot 3} \\ &= \underbrace{\sqrt{3} \cdot \sqrt{3}} \cdot \sqrt{2} \cdot \sqrt{5} \end{aligned}$$

$\sqrt{a} \cdot \sqrt{a} = a$ ─────────────→

$$= \quad 3 \quad \cdot \underbrace{\sqrt{2} \cdot \sqrt{5}}$$

$\sqrt{a} \cdot \sqrt{b} = \sqrt{ab}$ ─────────────→

$$= \quad 3 \qquad \sqrt{10}$$
Thus, $\sqrt{90} = 3\sqrt{10}$.

Another way:
$$\begin{aligned} \sqrt{90} &= \sqrt{9 \cdot 10} \\ &= \sqrt{9} \cdot \sqrt{10} \\ &= 3\sqrt{10} \end{aligned}$$
Simplest radical form

EXAMPLE 7   Simplify $-5\sqrt{147}$. Then approximate to the nearest tenth.

$147 = 49 \cdot 3$. 49 is the greatest perfect square factor of 147. ⟶

$$\begin{aligned}
-5\sqrt{147} &= -5\sqrt{49 \cdot 3} \\
&= -5\sqrt{49} \cdot \sqrt{3} \\
&= -5 \cdot 7 \cdot \sqrt{3} \\
&= -35\sqrt{3} \\
&\doteq -35(1.732) \\
&\doteq -60.620 \\
&\doteq -60.6
\end{aligned}$$

Simplest radical form ⟶
From the table, $\sqrt{3} \doteq 1.732$. ⟶

Round to the nearest tenth. ⟶

Thus, $-5\sqrt{147} = -35\sqrt{3} \doteq -60.6$.

EXERCISES

PART A

Simplify.

1. $\sqrt{2} \cdot \sqrt{5}$ $\sqrt{10}$ 2. $\sqrt{3} \cdot \sqrt{7}$ $\sqrt{21}$ 3. $\sqrt{5} \cdot \sqrt{6}$ $\sqrt{30}$ 4. $\sqrt{3} \cdot \sqrt{11}$ 5. $\sqrt{7} \cdot \sqrt{2}$

Simplify.

6. $\sqrt{9 \cdot 25}$ 15 7. $\sqrt{64 \cdot 16}$ 32 8. $\sqrt{81 \cdot 4}$ 18 9. $\sqrt{49 \cdot 25}$ 35 10. $\sqrt{100 \cdot 121}$
11. $\sqrt{12}$ $2\sqrt{3}$ 12. $\sqrt{80}$ $4\sqrt{5}$ 13. $\sqrt{27}$ $3\sqrt{3}$ 14. $\sqrt{50}$ $5\sqrt{2}$ 15. $\sqrt{98}$ $7\sqrt{2}$
16. $\sqrt{28}$ $2\sqrt{7}$ 17. $-2\sqrt{60}$ 18. $4\sqrt{40}$ $8\sqrt{10}$ 19. $2\sqrt{32}$ $8\sqrt{2}$ 20. $3\sqrt{45}$ $9\sqrt{5}$
    $-4\sqrt{15}$

PART B

Simplify. Then approximate to the nearest tenth.

21. $\sqrt{75}$ 8.7 22. $2\sqrt{144}$ 23. $-3\sqrt{20}$ 24. $2\sqrt{54}$ 25. $3\sqrt{180}$ 26. $4\sqrt{160}$
                         24 -13.4 14.7 40.2

PART C

EXAMPLE   Simplify $\sqrt{675}$.

$$\begin{aligned}
\sqrt{675} &= \sqrt{3 \cdot 3 \cdot 3 \cdot 5 \cdot 5} \\
&= \sqrt{3} \cdot \sqrt{3} \cdot \sqrt{5} \cdot \sqrt{5} \cdot \sqrt{3} \\
&= \quad 3 \quad \cdot \quad 5 \quad \cdot \sqrt{3}, \text{ or } 15\sqrt{3}
\end{aligned}$$

Simplify.

                                                      $-306\sqrt{3}$ $102\sqrt{11}$
27. $-\sqrt{1,372}$ 28. $5\sqrt{1,014}$ 29. $-2\sqrt{1,805}$ 30. $-17\sqrt{972}$ 31. $6\sqrt{3,179}$
    $-14\sqrt{7}$ $65\sqrt{6}$ $-38\sqrt{5}$

Even Exponents

EXAMPLE 1   Simplify $\sqrt{a^6b^2}$.

$\sqrt{x \cdot y} = \sqrt{x} \cdot \sqrt{y}$ ⟶

a^6 and b^2 are perfect squares. ⟶

$\sqrt{x} \cdot \sqrt{x} = x$ ⟶

$$\sqrt{a^6b^2} = \sqrt{a^6} \cdot \sqrt{b^2}$$
$$= \sqrt{a^3 \cdot a^3} \cdot \sqrt{b^1 \cdot b^1}$$
$$= \sqrt{a^3} \cdot \sqrt{a^3} \cdot \sqrt{b} \cdot \sqrt{b}$$
$$= a^3b$$

EXAMPLE 2   Simplify $-\sqrt{49x^{10}y^4z^{18}}$.

x^{10} is a perfect square;
$\sqrt{x^{10}} = \sqrt{x^5} \cdot \sqrt{x^5} = x^5.$

$$-\sqrt{49} \cdot \sqrt{x^{10}} \cdot \sqrt{y^4} \cdot \sqrt{z^{18}} = -7x^5y^2z^9$$

EXAMPLE 3   Try to express $\sqrt{-64}$ as a real number.

Neither product is -64. ⟶

8 and -8 are not the same. ⟶

No real number squared is -64. ⟶

$$(8)(8) = 64 \text{ and } (-8)(-8) = 64$$
$$(8)(-8) = -64$$

It seems that $\sqrt{-64}$ is not a real number.

> The square root of a negative number is not a real number.

EXAMPLE 4   Simplify $\sqrt{-81}$ and $-\sqrt{81}$ if possible.

$\sqrt{-81}$ is not a real number.
$-\sqrt{81} = -9$

We will assume that variables under a radical sign represent only positive numbers or zero.

ORAL EXERCISES

Simplify, if possible.

1. $\sqrt{1}$ *1*   2. $\sqrt{-1}$ 3. $-\sqrt{1}$ *−1*   4. $-\sqrt{-1}$

5. $\sqrt{25}$ *5*   6. $-\sqrt{36}$ *−6*   7. $\sqrt{-100}$ 8. $\sqrt{49}$ *7*

9. $-\sqrt{-25}$ 10. $\sqrt{-16}$ 11. $-\sqrt{9}$ *−3*   12. $\sqrt{121}$ *11*

EXERCISES

PART A

Simplify.

1. $\sqrt{x^8 y^4}$ $x^4 y^2$ 2. $-\sqrt{a^6 b^{10}}$ $-a^3 b^5$ 3. $\sqrt{c^2 d^8}$ cd^4

4. $\sqrt{25x^2}$ $5x$ 5. $-\sqrt{9y^4}$ $-3y^2$ 6. $\sqrt{49a^{10}}$ $7a^5$

7. $-\sqrt{81a^2 b^6}$ $-9ab^3$ 8. $\sqrt{64x^4 y^8}$ $8x^2 y^4$ 9. $-\sqrt{4c^{10}d^2}$ $-2c^5 d$

10. $-\sqrt{16x^8 y^{12}}$ $-4x^4 y^6$ 11. $\sqrt{9a^6 b^8}$ $3a^3 b^4$ 12. $\sqrt{100x^4 y^{14}}$ $10x^2 y^7$

13. $\sqrt{a^4 b^6 c^8}$ $a^2 b^3 c^4$ 14. $\sqrt{x^2 y^6 z^{10}}$ $xy^3 z^5$ 15. $-\sqrt{c^4 d^2 e^{12}}$ $-c^2 de^6$

16. $-\sqrt{4x^2 y^8 z^2}$ $-2xy^4 z$ 17. $\sqrt{9a^6 b^8 c^2}$ $3a^3 b^4 c$ 18. $-\sqrt{49x^4 y^8 z^2}$ $-7x^2 y^4 z$

19. $\sqrt{64a^4 b^{12}c^2}$ $8a^2 b^6 c$ 20. $-\sqrt{81x^8 y^{12}z^4}$ $-9x^4 y^6 z^2$ 21. $\sqrt{36c^8 d^{10}e^{12}}$ $6c^4 d^5 e^6$

22. $-\sqrt{100x^2 y^{12}z^{10}}$ $-10xy^6 z^5$ 23. $\sqrt{25a^{12}b^{10}c^4}$ $5a^6 b^5 c^2$ 24. $-\sqrt{16c^2 d^6 e^{14}}$ $-4cd^3 e^7$

25. $\sqrt{121c^8 d^6 e^2}$ $11c^4 d^3 e$ 26. $-\sqrt{169x^8 y^2 z^{10}}$ $-13x^4 yz^5$ 27. $\sqrt{144a^8 b^2 c^{16}}$ $12a^4 bc^8$

PART B

             EXAMPLE   Simplify $\sqrt{12x^4 y^{16}z^2}$.

$$\begin{aligned} \sqrt{12} &= \sqrt{2 \cdot 2 \cdot 3} = \sqrt{2} \cdot \sqrt{2} \cdot \sqrt{3} \\ &= 2\sqrt{3} \end{aligned} \Bigg\}$$

$$\begin{aligned} \sqrt{12x^4 y^{16}z^2} &= \sqrt{12} \cdot \sqrt{x^4} \cdot \sqrt{y^{16}} \cdot \sqrt{z^2} \\ &= 2\sqrt{3}\, x^2 y^8 z \end{aligned}$$

Simplify.

28. $\sqrt{20x^2 y^8}$ $2xy^4 \sqrt{5}$ 29. $-\sqrt{27a^4 b^{10}}$ $-3a^2 b^5 \sqrt{3}$ 30. $-\sqrt{28c^8 d^2}$ $-2c^4 d\sqrt{7}$

31. $-\sqrt{32a^6 b^{12}}$ $-4a^3 b^6 \sqrt{2}$ 32. $\sqrt{50x^2 y^6}$ $5xy^3 \sqrt{2}$ 33. $-\sqrt{48a^{10}b^{12}}$

34. $\sqrt{200x^4 y^2 z^6}$ $10x^2 yz^3 \sqrt{2}$ 35. $\sqrt{45a^{12}b^{14}c^2}$ $3a^6 b^7 c\sqrt{5}$ 36. $\sqrt{75c^8 d^2 e^{12}}$

37. $-\sqrt{98a^4 b^8 c^{16}}$ 38. $\sqrt{128x^4 y^{10}z^8}$ 39. $-\sqrt{243x^8 y^2 z^{18}}$

      $-7a^2 b^4 c^8 \sqrt{2}$ $8x^2 y^5 z^4 \sqrt{2}$

PART C

Simplify.

40. $\sqrt{.04x^2 y^8}$ 41. $-\sqrt{1.69a^2 b^8 c^{20}}$ 42. $\sqrt{.000016x^4 y^2 z^{18}}$

43. $\sqrt{\dfrac{1}{25}x^{10}y^2 z^{12}}$ 44. $\sqrt{\dfrac{4}{49}x^8 y^{12}z^{24}}$ 45. $-\sqrt{\dfrac{81}{16}a^2 b^{36}c^{100}}$

Odd Exponents

REVIEW CAPSULE

$$x^6 \cdot x = x^6 \cdot x^1 = x^{6+1} = x^7$$
$$a^{10} \cdot a = a^{10} \cdot a^1 = a^{10+1} = a^{11}$$

Also, $y^9 = y^{8+1} = y^8 \cdot y^1 = y^8 \cdot y$
$$z^5 = z^{4+1} = z^4 \cdot z^1 = z^4 \cdot z$$

EXAMPLE 1   Simplify $\sqrt{x^5}$.

x^4 is a perfect square. $\longrightarrow$

$\sqrt{x^4} = \sqrt{x^2 \cdot x^2} = x^2$ $\longrightarrow$

$$\sqrt{x^5} = \sqrt{x^4 \cdot x^1}$$
$$= \sqrt{x^4} \cdot \sqrt{x^1}$$
$$= x^2 \sqrt{x}$$

EXAMPLE 2   Simplify $\sqrt{a^3b^7}$.

a^2 and b^6 are perfect squares. $\longrightarrow$
Group perfect squares together. $\longrightarrow$
$\sqrt{a^2b^6} = \sqrt{a^2} \cdot \sqrt{b^6} = ab^3$ $\longrightarrow$

$$\sqrt{a^3b^7} = \sqrt{a^2 \cdot a^1 \cdot b^6 \cdot b^1}$$
$$= \sqrt{a^2 \cdot b^6} \cdot \sqrt{ab}$$
$$= ab^3 \sqrt{ab}$$

EXAMPLE 3   Simplify $\sqrt{40xy^9}$.

The greatest perfect square factor of $40xy^9$ is $4y^8$.

$\sqrt{4y^8} = \sqrt{4} \cdot \sqrt{y^8} = 2y^4$ $\longrightarrow$

$$\sqrt{40xy^9} = \sqrt{4 \cdot 10 \cdot x \cdot y^8 \cdot y^1}$$
$$= \sqrt{4y^8} \cdot \sqrt{10xy}$$
$$= 2y^4 \sqrt{10xy}$$

EXAMPLE 4   Simplify $-4x^2y \sqrt{45x^3y^4}$.

The greatest perfect square factor of $45x^3y^4$ is $9x^2y^4$.

$\sqrt{9x^2y^4} = \sqrt{9} \sqrt{x^2} \sqrt{y^4} = 3xy^2$ $\longrightarrow$

$x^2 \cdot x^1 = x^3$; $y^1 \cdot y^2 = y^3$ $\longrightarrow$

$$-4x^2y \sqrt{45x^3y^4} = -4x^2y \sqrt{9 \cdot 5 \cdot x^2 \cdot x^1 \cdot y^4}$$
$$= -4x^2y \sqrt{9x^2y^4} \cdot \sqrt{5x}$$
$$= -4x^2y(3xy^2) \sqrt{5x}$$
$$= -12x^3y^3 \sqrt{5x}$$

Read: the cube root of 8 equals 2. $\longrightarrow$

$\sqrt[3]{8} = 2$, since $2 \cdot 2 \cdot 2 = 8$. $\qquad [2^3 = 8]$

$\sqrt[3]{-64} = -4$, since $(-4)(-4)(-4) = -64$.
$$[(-4)^3 = -64]$$

EXAMPLE 5   Simplify $\sqrt[3]{24x^3y^7}$

$$= \sqrt[3]{2 \cdot 2 \cdot 2 \cdot 3 \cdot x^1 \cdot x^1 \cdot x^1 \cdot y^2 \cdot y^2 \cdot y^2 \cdot y^1}$$
$$= \sqrt[3]{2 \cdot 2 \cdot 2 \cdot x^1 \cdot x^1 \cdot x^1 \cdot y^2 \cdot y^2 \cdot y^2} \ \sqrt[3]{3y^1}$$

Read: $2xy^2$ times the cube root of $3y$. $\longrightarrow$ $= 2xy^2 \ \sqrt[3]{3y}$

EXERCISES

PART A
Simplify.

1. $\sqrt{x^3}$ $x \sqrt{x}$
2. $-\sqrt{a^7}$ $-a^3 \sqrt{a}$
3. $\sqrt{9x^5}$ $3x^2 \sqrt{x}$
4. $\sqrt{25c}$ $5 \sqrt{c}$

5. $\sqrt{8x^5}$ $2x^2 \sqrt{2x}$
6. $\sqrt{18a^9}$ $3a^4 \sqrt{2a}$
7. $\sqrt{7x^3}$ $x \sqrt{7x}$
8. $-\sqrt{5x^{11}}$ $-x^5 \sqrt{5x}$

9. $\sqrt{x^4y^7}$ $x^2 y^3 \sqrt{y}$
10. $\sqrt{a^2b^5}$ $ab^2 \sqrt{b}$
11. $-\sqrt{c^6d^3}$ $-c^3 d \sqrt{d}$
12. $\sqrt{m^8n}$ $m^4 \sqrt{n}$

13. $\sqrt{x^5y^7}$ $x^2 y^3 \sqrt{xy}$
14. $\sqrt{a^9b^3}$ $a^4 b \sqrt{ab}$
15. $\sqrt{c^3d}$ $c \sqrt{cd}$
16. $\sqrt{mn^7}$ $n^3 \sqrt{mn}$

17. $\sqrt{a^5b^8}$ $a^2 b^4 \sqrt{a}$
18. $-\sqrt{4cd^2}$ $-2d \sqrt{c}$
19. $\sqrt{5x^3y^4}$ $xy^2 \sqrt{5x}$
20. $\sqrt{99m^3b^8}$

21. $\sqrt{36x^2y}$ $6x \sqrt{y}$
22. $-\sqrt{16m^8n^7}$
23. $\sqrt{6x^6y^9}$
24. $\sqrt{20a^4b^3}$

25. $\sqrt{19x^5y^9}$
26. $\sqrt{40xy^3}$ $2y \sqrt{10xy}$
27. $-\sqrt{50m^3n^4}$
28. $\sqrt{72ab^6}$ $6b^3 \sqrt{2a}$

29. $4\sqrt{44xy^2z^6}$ $8yz^3 \sqrt{11x}$
30. $-7\sqrt{90a^3b^6c^7}$
31. $6\sqrt{28a^4bc^{12}}$

32. $x\sqrt{x^3yz^8}$ $x^2 z^4 \sqrt{xy}$
33. $-cd\sqrt{c^4d^5e^6}$ $-c^3 d^3 e^3 \sqrt{d}$
34. $-a^2bc\sqrt{a^3b^8c^9}$

35. $-3y\sqrt{x^3y^5z}$ $-3xy^3 \sqrt{xyz}$
36. $4xz\sqrt{x^4y^7z^2}$ $4x^3 y^3 z^2 \sqrt{y}$
37. $-5c^2d\sqrt{b^7c^3d^6}$

38. $4a^2b\sqrt{75a^6b^7}$ $20a^5 b^4 \sqrt{3b}$
39. $-12xy^3\sqrt{32x^2y^5}$
40. $8e^3f^2\sqrt{128ef^2g^3}$

PART B
Simplify.

41. $\sqrt[3]{x^3y^9}$ xy^3
42. $\sqrt[3]{a^6b^{12}}$ $a^2 b^4$
43. $-\sqrt[3]{c^3d^{12}}$ $-cd^4$

44. $\sqrt[3]{-x^6y^9}$ $-x^2 y^3$
45. $\sqrt[3]{8a^3b^9}$ $2ab^3$
46. $\sqrt[3]{-27x^6y^3}$ $-3x^2 y$

47. $-\sqrt[3]{64a^4b^6}$ $-4ab^2 \sqrt[3]{a}$
48. $\sqrt[3]{-125x^7y^9}$ $-5x^2 y^3 \sqrt[3]{x}$
49. $-\sqrt[3]{40a^2b^8}$ $-2b^2 \sqrt[3]{5a^2 b^2}$

50. $\sqrt[3]{-56ab^6c^{10}}$ $-2b^2 c^3 \sqrt[3]{7ac}$
51. $-\sqrt[3]{-192x^7yz^{12}}$
52. $-\sqrt[3]{32x^9y^{10}z^{11}}$

PART C

Read:
The fourth root of 81 equals 3. $\longrightarrow$ $\sqrt[4]{81} = 3$, since $3 \cdot 3 \cdot 3 \cdot 3 = 81$. $[3^4 = 81]$
The fifth root of 32 equals 2. $\longrightarrow$ $\sqrt[5]{32} = 2$, since $2 \cdot 2 \cdot 2 \cdot 2 \cdot 2 = 32$. $[2^5 = 32]$

Simplify.

53. $\sqrt[4]{x^4y^{12}}$
54. $\sqrt[5]{a^5b^{10}}$
55. $-\sqrt[4]{16x^8y^4}$

56. $\sqrt[6]{64x^6y^{12}}$
57. $\sqrt[5]{243x^6y^{10}}$
58. $-\sqrt[4]{81a^3b^5}$

59. $\sqrt[5]{-96a^2b^7c^3}$
60. $\sqrt[4]{80x^3y^7z^{12}}$
61. $-2a\sqrt[5]{160c^5d^6e^7}$

62. $-3a^3b\sqrt[4]{162a^6bc^9}$
63. $6xy^2\sqrt[3]{54x^2yz^8}$
64. $-7c^2d^3\sqrt[4]{12c^9d^{21}e}$

Flow Chart: Finding Square Roots

This is a flow chart of a process used in computers to find square roots.

Find $\sqrt{x}$

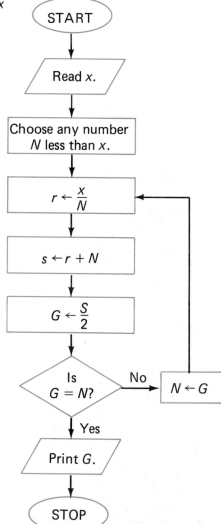

START

Read x.

Choose any number N less than x.

$r \leftarrow \dfrac{x}{N}$

$s \leftarrow r + N$

$G \leftarrow \dfrac{s}{2}$

Is $G = N$? ── No ── $N \leftarrow G$

Yes

Print G.

STOP

Find $\sqrt{3}$ to two decimal places.

Read 3.

- Choose 1.5 (1.5 < 3).
  Divide. $\dfrac{3}{1.5} = 2$
  Add. $2 + 1.5 = 3.5$
  Divide. $\dfrac{3.5}{2} = 1.75$
  Is 1.75 = 1.5? No

- Choose 1.75. (1.75 < 3)
  Divide. $\dfrac{3}{1.75} = 1.71$
  Add. $1.71 + 1.75 = 3.46$
  Divide. $\dfrac{3.46}{2} = 1.73$
  Is 1.73 = 1.75? No

- Choose 1.73 (1.73 < 3)
  Divide. $\dfrac{3}{1.73} = 1.73$
  Add. $1.73 + 1.73 = 3.46$
  Divide. $\dfrac{3.46}{2} = 1.73$
  Is 1.73 = 1.73? Yes
  Print 1.73.

Thus, $\sqrt{3} = 1.73$.

PROJECT Carry all calculations to 2 decimal places. Use the flow chart.
1. $\sqrt{5}$ **2.** $\sqrt{7}$

The Pythagorean Theorem

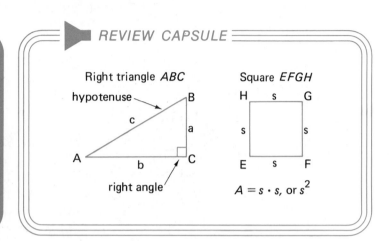

▶ REVIEW CAPSULE

Right triangle *ABC*

Square *EFGH*

$A = s \cdot s,$ or s^2

EXAMPLE 1 Examine right triangle *ABC* and the three squares shown. Find the area of each square. See what you can discover.

Area of Square I $= 3 \cdot 3 = 9$
Area of Square II $= 4 \cdot 4 = 16$
Area of Square III $= 5 \cdot 5 = 25$

$$9 \quad + \quad 16 \quad = \quad 25$$

This is true for all right triangles. ⟶ Area of Square I $+$ Area of Square II $=$ Area of Square III

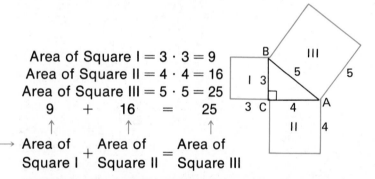

Pythagoras, a Greek philosopher and mathematician, discovered the relationship above in 500 B.C.

c is the length of the hypotenuse.
a and *b* are the lengths of the other two sides.

If △*ABC* is a right triangle, then $a^2 + b^2 = c^2$.

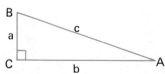

Pythagorean theorem ⟶
A *theorem* is a property which can be proved.

In any right triangle, the square of the length of the hypotenuse equals the sum of the squares of the lengths of the other two sides.

EXAMPLE 2 If the lengths of two sides of a right triangle are 5 meters and 12 meters, find the length of the hypotenuse.

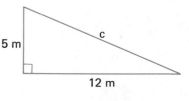

Pythagorean theorem ⟶ $a^2 + b^2 = c^2$

Substitute 5 for a, 12 for b. ⟶ $5^2 + 12^2 = c^2$

$25 + 144 = c^2$

$169 = c^2$

$\sqrt{169} = c$

$13 \cdot 13 = 169$ ⟶ $13 = c$

Thus, the length of the hypotenuse is 13 meters.

EXAMPLE 3 The length of the hypotenuse of a right triangle is 14 cm, and the length of one side is 7 cm. Find the length of the other side, in simplest radical form.

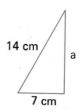

Pythagorean theorem ⟶ $a^2 + b^2 = c^2$

Substitute 7 for b, 14 for c. ⟶ $a^2 + 7^2 = 14^2$

$a^2 + 49 = 196$

Add -49 to each side. ⟶ $a^2 = 147$

$a = \sqrt{147}$

$\sqrt{147} = \sqrt{7 \cdot 7 \cdot 3} = 7\sqrt{3}$ ⟶ $a = 7\sqrt{3}$

Thus, the length of the other side is $7\sqrt{3}$ cm.

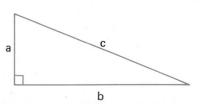

If $a^2 + b^2 = c^2$, then the triangle is a right triangle with c the hypotenuse.

Converse of the Pythagorean theorem ⟶

To form a converse of a statement, reverse the if and the then parts.

> If the sum of the squares of the lengths of two sides of a triangle equals the square of the length of the third side, then the triangle is a right triangle.

EXAMPLE 4 If the lengths of the sides of a triangle are 7, 24, and 25, is the triangle a right triangle?

See if $7^2 + 24^2 = 25^2$. ⟶ $7^2 = 49$ $24^2 = 576$ $25^2 = 625$ $49 + 576 = 625$

Thus, the triangle is a right triangle.

EXERCISES

PART A

Tell whether each triangle described is a right triangle. The lengths of the three sides are given.

1. 4, 5, 6 *no*　　　　**2.** 6, 8, 10 *yes*　　　　**3.** 3, 5, 7 *no*　　　　**4.** 12, 16, 20 *yes*

5. 12, 14, 16 *no*　　　**6.** 9, 40, 41 *yes*　　　**7.** 1, 3, $\sqrt{11}$ *no*　　　**8.** $\sqrt{2}$, $\sqrt{3}$, $\sqrt{5}$ *yes*

For each right triangle, find the missing length. Give answers in simplest radical form.

9. $a = 8$, $b = 6$　$c = 10$　　　**10.** $a = 12$, $b = 16$　$c = 20$　　　**11.** $a = 9$, $c = 15$　$b = 12$

12. $a = 2$, $b = 6$　$c = 2\sqrt{10}$　　**13.** $b = 4$, $c = 8$　$a = 4\sqrt{3}$　　**14.** $b = 1$, $c = 3$　$a = 2\sqrt{2}$

15. $a = 14$, $c = 50$　$b = 48$　　　**16.** $b = 4$, $c = 4\sqrt{5}$　$a = 8$　　　**17.** $a = 2\sqrt{2}$, $b = 2\sqrt{3}$

PART B

EXAMPLE　A rectangular field is 50 m wide by 100 m long. How long is a diagonal path connecting two opposite corners? Give the answer to the nearest tenth of a meter.

$a^2 + b^2 = c^2$ ⟶

$$50^2 + 100^2 = c^2$$
$$2{,}500 + 10{,}000 = c^2$$
$$12{,}500 = c^2$$
$$\sqrt{12{,}500} = c$$

$\sqrt{12{,}500} = \sqrt{2{,}500} \cdot \sqrt{5} = 50\sqrt{5}$ ⟶

$$50\sqrt{5} = c$$
$$50\,(2.236) = c$$
$$111.800 = c$$

Round to the nearest tenth. ⟶ **Thus,** the diagonal path is approx. 111.8 meters long.

Give answers to the nearest tenth.

18. Paul walked 8 km north and 3 km west. How far was he from his starting point? *8.5 km*

19. A 4-m ramp covers 3 m of ground. How high does it rise? *2.6 m*

20. A T.V. screen is 15 cm by 12 cm. What is its diagonal length? *19.2 cm*

21. A 6-m ladder is 2 m from *5.7 m* the base of a building. At what height does it touch the building?

PART C

22. Find the length of the side of a square if the length of the diagonal is 4 cm.

23. Find the length of the side of a square if the length of the diagonal is 6 m.

Combining Radicals

<table>
<tr>
<td>

OBJECTIVE
■ To combine like radicals

</td>
<td>

▶ REVIEW CAPSULE

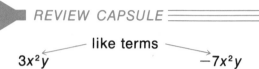

Simplify by using the distributive property.
$$3x^2y - 7x^2y = (3 - 7)x^2y$$
$$= -4x^2y$$

</td>
</tr>
</table>

$\sqrt{2}$ in each ⟶ 5 $\sqrt{2}$ and 2 $\sqrt{2}$ are *like radicals.*

EXAMPLE 1 Simplify $5\sqrt{2} + 2\sqrt{2}$.

Distributive Property ⟶ $5\sqrt{2} + 2\sqrt{2} = (5 + 2)\sqrt{2} = 7\sqrt{2}$

Illustration of $5\sqrt{2} + 2\sqrt{2} = 7\sqrt{2}$ ⟶

EXAMPLE 2 Simplify $5\sqrt{7} - 9\sqrt{13} + 6\sqrt{7}$.

Rearrange the terms. ⟶
$$5\sqrt{7} - 9\sqrt{13} + 6\sqrt{7} = 5\sqrt{7} + 6\sqrt{7} - 9\sqrt{13}$$
$$= (5 + 6)\sqrt{7} - 9\sqrt{13}$$
11 $\sqrt{7}$ and $-9\sqrt{13}$ are unlike radicals. ⟶ $\qquad = 11\sqrt{7} - 9\sqrt{13}$

EXAMPLE 3 Simplify $\sqrt{75} - \sqrt{27} + \sqrt{12}$.

Simplify each radical. ⟶ $\sqrt{75} - \sqrt{27} + \sqrt{12}$
$$= \sqrt{25 \cdot 3} - \sqrt{9 \cdot 3} + \sqrt{4 \cdot 3}$$
$$= \sqrt{25} \cdot \sqrt{3} - \sqrt{9} \cdot \sqrt{3} + \sqrt{4} \cdot \sqrt{3}$$
$\sqrt{3}$ is common to each term. ⟶ $\quad = 5\sqrt{3} - 3\sqrt{3} + 2\sqrt{3}$
Distributive property ⟶ $\qquad\quad = (5 - 3 + 2)\sqrt{3}$
$$= 4\sqrt{3}$$

EXAMPLE 4 Simplify $2\sqrt{cd} - 5\sqrt{cd} + 9\sqrt{cd}$.

Distributive property ⟶ $2\sqrt{cd} - 5\sqrt{cd} + 9\sqrt{cd} = (2 - 5 + 9)\sqrt{cd}$
$$= 6\sqrt{cd}$$

EXAMPLE 5 Simplify $\sqrt{ab^3} + \sqrt{9ab^3} - 5b\sqrt{16ab}$.

$$\sqrt{ab^3} + \sqrt{9ab^3} - 5b\sqrt{16ab}$$
$$= \sqrt{b^2 \cdot ab} + \sqrt{9b^2 \cdot ab} - 5b\sqrt{16 \cdot ab}$$
$$= b\sqrt{ab} + 3b\sqrt{ab} - 5b(4)\sqrt{ab}$$

$\sqrt{ab}$ is common to each term. $\longrightarrow$
$$= b\sqrt{ab} + 3b\sqrt{ab} - 20b\sqrt{ab}$$

Distributive Property $\longrightarrow$
$$= (b + 3b - 20b)\sqrt{ab} = -16b\sqrt{ab}$$

EXERCISES

PART A

Simplify.

1. $2\sqrt{5} + 7\sqrt{5}$ $9\sqrt{5}$
2. $5\sqrt{3} - 2\sqrt{3}$ $3\sqrt{3}$
3. $7\sqrt{6} + 8\sqrt{6}$ $15\sqrt{6}$
4. $9\sqrt{2} - 8\sqrt{2}$ $\sqrt{2}$
5. $4\sqrt{10} + 2\sqrt{10} - 5\sqrt{10}$ $\sqrt{10}$
6. $6\sqrt{7} - 10\sqrt{7} - 4\sqrt{7}$ $-8\sqrt{7}$
7. $5\sqrt{6} - 3\sqrt{6} + 6\sqrt{3}$ $2\sqrt{6} + 6\sqrt{3}$
8. $4\sqrt{3} - 8\sqrt{2} - 7\sqrt{2}$ $4\sqrt{3} - 15\sqrt{2}$
9. $4\sqrt{5} - 6\sqrt{7} + 8\sqrt{5}$ $12\sqrt{5} - 6\sqrt{7}$
10. $6\sqrt{5} - \sqrt{11} + 5\sqrt{11} - 10\sqrt{5}$
11. $\sqrt{5} + 3\sqrt{2} - 6\sqrt{2} + 7\sqrt{5}$ $8\sqrt{5} - 3\sqrt{2}$
12. $8\sqrt{7} - 7\sqrt{3} + 6\sqrt{7} + 9\sqrt{3}$
13. $3\sqrt{8} + \sqrt{2}$ $7\sqrt{2}$
14. $4\sqrt{3} + \sqrt{12}$ $6\sqrt{3}$
15. $2\sqrt{24} - 3\sqrt{54}$ $-5\sqrt{6}$
16. $6\sqrt{27} - 3\sqrt{48}$ $6\sqrt{3}$
17. $3\sqrt{44} - 7\sqrt{11} + \sqrt{99}$ $2\sqrt{11}$
18. $-\sqrt{32} + 5\sqrt{18} - 7\sqrt{98}$ $-38\sqrt{2}$
19. $\sqrt{a} + 8\sqrt{a}$ $9\sqrt{a}$
20. $6\sqrt{x} + 7\sqrt{x} - \sqrt{x}$ $12\sqrt{x}$
21. $4\sqrt{mn} - 2\sqrt{mn} + 5\sqrt{mn}$ $7\sqrt{mn}$
22. $3\sqrt{xy} - \sqrt{xy} + 8\sqrt{xy} + \sqrt{xy}$ $11\sqrt{xy}$
23. $\sqrt{xy} + \sqrt{4xy} - 2\sqrt{9xy}$ $-3\sqrt{xy}$
24. $-6\sqrt{9c} + 8\sqrt{16c} - 4c\sqrt{4c}$
25. $5x\sqrt{3z} + x\sqrt{5z} - x\sqrt{3z} - 2x\sqrt{5z}$
26. $2\sqrt{xy} - 5\sqrt{4xy} - \sqrt{25xy}$
27. $3\sqrt{a^3b^3} + 2b\sqrt{4a^3b} - 7a\sqrt{16ab^3}$
28. $c\sqrt{cd^3} + cd\sqrt{cd} + d\sqrt{c^3d}$

PART B

Simplify.

29. $\sqrt{27x} - \sqrt{48x} + \sqrt{75x}$ $4\sqrt{3x}$
30. $2\sqrt{24y} - 5\sqrt{54y} + 7\sqrt{96y}$ $17\sqrt{6y}$
31. $\sqrt{33a} + \sqrt{11a} - \sqrt{77a}$ *cannot simplify*
32. $2\sqrt{98z} + \sqrt{18z} - 5\sqrt{32z}$ $-3\sqrt{2z}$
33. $2\sqrt{10x} + \sqrt{40x} - 5\sqrt{90x}$ $-11\sqrt{10x}$
34. $\sqrt{3xy} + \sqrt{27xy} - \sqrt{12xy}$ $2\sqrt{3xy}$
35. $2x\sqrt{5xy^2} + 3\sqrt{20x^3y^2}$ $8xy\sqrt{5x}$
36. $7\sqrt{8a^2b^3} - 4b\sqrt{50a^2b}$ $-6ab\sqrt{2b}$

PART C

Simplify.

37. $\sqrt{.04xy^2} + y\sqrt{.16x}$
38. $3\sqrt{.25a^3b} + 4a\sqrt{.0001ab}$
39. $6x\sqrt{.0036xy^2} - 2yx\sqrt{.0049x}$
40. $2x\sqrt{.01xy^2} - 5\sqrt{.0025x^3y^2}$
41. $-2b\sqrt{.0004a^3b} + 6a\sqrt{.36ab^3}$
42. $7xy\sqrt{.64xy} - 8y\sqrt{.0081x^3y}$

Products of Radicals

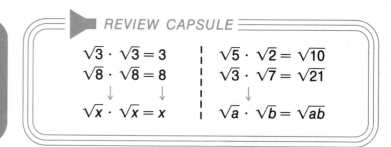

REVIEW CAPSULE

$$\sqrt{3} \cdot \sqrt{3} = 3 \qquad \sqrt{5} \cdot \sqrt{2} = \sqrt{10}$$
$$\sqrt{8} \cdot \sqrt{8} = 8 \qquad \sqrt{3} \cdot \sqrt{7} = \sqrt{21}$$
$$\downarrow \qquad \downarrow \qquad \qquad \downarrow$$
$$\sqrt{x} \cdot \sqrt{x} = x \qquad \sqrt{a} \cdot \sqrt{b} = \sqrt{ab}$$

EXAMPLE 1 Multiply $6\sqrt{5} \cdot 4\sqrt{3}$.

Rearrange factors. $\longrightarrow$
$6 \cdot 4 = 24$; $\sqrt{5} \cdot \sqrt{3} = \sqrt{5 \cdot 3}$ $\longrightarrow$
$\sqrt{5 \cdot 3} = \sqrt{15}$

$$6\sqrt{5} \cdot 4\sqrt{3} = 6 \cdot 4 \cdot \sqrt{5} \cdot \sqrt{3}$$
$$= 24 \cdot \sqrt{5 \cdot 3}$$
$$= 24\sqrt{15}$$

EXAMPLE 2 Multiply $-7\sqrt{6x} \cdot 2\sqrt{3x}$.

$$-7\sqrt{6x} \cdot 2\sqrt{3x} = -7 \cdot 2 \cdot \sqrt{6x} \cdot \sqrt{3x}$$
$$= -14\sqrt{6x \cdot 3x}$$
$$= -14\sqrt{2 \cdot 3x \cdot 3x}$$

$\sqrt{3x \cdot 3x} = 3x$ $\longrightarrow$
$-14 \cdot 3 = -42$ $\longrightarrow$

$$= -14 \cdot 3x \cdot \sqrt{2}$$
$$= -42x\sqrt{2}$$

EXAMPLE 3 Multiply $\sqrt{3}(\sqrt{5} + 4\sqrt{3})$.

Distribute the $\sqrt{3}$. $\longrightarrow$
$\sqrt{3} \cdot 4\sqrt{3} = 4\sqrt{3} \cdot \sqrt{3}$ $\longrightarrow$
$\sqrt{3 \cdot 5} = \sqrt{15}$; $\sqrt{3} \cdot \sqrt{3} = 3$ $\longrightarrow$

$$\sqrt{3}(\sqrt{5} + 4\sqrt{3}) = \sqrt{3} \cdot \sqrt{5} + \sqrt{3} \cdot 4\sqrt{3}$$
$$= \sqrt{3 \cdot 5} + 4\sqrt{3} \cdot \sqrt{3}$$
$$= \sqrt{15} + 4 \cdot 3$$
$$= \sqrt{15} + 12$$

EXAMPLE 4 Multiply $-6\sqrt{2}(\sqrt{10} - 7\sqrt{8})$.

Distribute the $-6\sqrt{2}$. $\longrightarrow$ $-6\sqrt{2}(\sqrt{10} - 7\sqrt{8})$

$$= (-6\sqrt{2})(\sqrt{10}) + (-6\sqrt{2})(-7\sqrt{8})$$

$\sqrt{a} \cdot \sqrt{b} = \sqrt{ab}$ $\longrightarrow$

$$= -6\sqrt{20} + 42\sqrt{16}$$

4 and 16 are perfect squares. $\longrightarrow$

$$= -6\sqrt{4 \cdot 5} + 42\sqrt{16}$$

$\sqrt{4} = 2$; $\sqrt{16} = 4$ $\longrightarrow$

$$= -6 \cdot 2\sqrt{5} + 42 \cdot 4$$
$$= -12\sqrt{5} + 168$$

EXAMPLE 5 Multiply $(2\sqrt{6} + \sqrt{5})(8\sqrt{6} - \sqrt{5})$.

Write vertically.
Multiply like two binomials.

$8\sqrt{6}(+\sqrt{5}) = +8 \cdot \sqrt{6} \cdot \sqrt{5} = +8\sqrt{30} \longrightarrow$
$-\sqrt{5}(2\sqrt{6}) = -2 \cdot \sqrt{5} \cdot \sqrt{6} = -2\sqrt{30} \longrightarrow$

$$\begin{array}{c} 2\sqrt{6} \qquad +\sqrt{5} \\ 8\sqrt{6} \qquad -\sqrt{5} \\ \hline \end{array}$$

$$2 \cdot 8 \cdot \sqrt{6} \cdot \sqrt{6} \quad \begin{array}{c} +8\sqrt{30} \\ -2\sqrt{30} \end{array} \qquad -\sqrt{5} \cdot \sqrt{5}$$

$+8\sqrt{30} - 2\sqrt{30} = +6\sqrt{30} \longrightarrow$

$$\begin{array}{ccccc} 16 & \cdot & 6 & +6\sqrt{30} & - & 5 \\ & 96 & & +6\sqrt{30} & - & 5 \end{array}$$

$96 - 5 = 91 \longrightarrow$

$$91 + 6\sqrt{30}$$

EXAMPLE 6 Multiply $(7\sqrt{2} - 3\sqrt{10})(7\sqrt{2} + 3\sqrt{10})$.

$$\begin{array}{c} 7\sqrt{2} \qquad -3\sqrt{10} \\ 7\sqrt{2} \qquad +3\sqrt{10} \\ \hline \end{array}$$

$7\sqrt{2}(-3\sqrt{10}) = 7(-3)\sqrt{2} \cdot \sqrt{10} = -21\sqrt{20}$
$+3\sqrt{10}(7\sqrt{2}) = +3 \cdot 7 \cdot \sqrt{10} \cdot \sqrt{2} = +21\sqrt{20}$

$$7 \cdot 7 \cdot \sqrt{2} \cdot \sqrt{2} \quad \begin{array}{c} -21\sqrt{20} \\ +21\sqrt{20} \end{array} \qquad -3 \cdot 3 \cdot \sqrt{10} \cdot \sqrt{10}$$

$-21\sqrt{20} + 21\sqrt{20} = 0 \longrightarrow$

$$\begin{array}{ccccccc} 49 & \cdot & 2 & & + & 0 & & - & 9 & \cdot & 10 \\ & 98 & & & & & & - & & 90 \end{array}$$

$$8$$

EXAMPLE 7 Multiply $(2\sqrt{3} + \sqrt{5})^2$.

$(a + b)^2$ means $(a + b)(a + b)$.

$$\begin{array}{c} 2\sqrt{3} \qquad +\sqrt{5} \\ 2\sqrt{3} \qquad +\sqrt{5} \\ \hline \end{array}$$

$$2 \cdot 2 \cdot \sqrt{3} \cdot \sqrt{3} \quad \begin{array}{c} +2\sqrt{15} \\ +2\sqrt{15} \end{array} \qquad +\sqrt{5} \cdot \sqrt{5}$$

$2\sqrt{15} + 2\sqrt{15} = 4\sqrt{15}$

$$\begin{array}{ccccc} 4 & \cdot & 3 & +4\sqrt{15} & + & 5 \\ & 12 & & +4\cdot\sqrt{15} & + & 5 \\ & 17 & & +4\sqrt{15} & & \end{array}$$

ORAL EXERCISES

Multiply.

1. $\sqrt{7} \cdot \sqrt{7}$ *7*
2. $(\sqrt{8})^2$ *8*
3. $(-\sqrt{5})^2$ *5*
4. $2\sqrt{3} \cdot 2\sqrt{3}$ *12*
5. $(4\sqrt{6})^2$ *96*
6. $(-5\sqrt{2})^2$ *50*
7. $3\sqrt{5} \cdot 4\sqrt{5}$ *60*
8. $-8\sqrt{2} \cdot 3\sqrt{2}$ *−48*
9. $-2\sqrt{3} \cdot 2\sqrt{3}$ *−12*
10. $2 \cdot 4\sqrt{7}$ *8√7*
11. $5 \cdot (-6\sqrt{2})$ *−30√2*
12. $4\sqrt{10} \cdot 6\sqrt{3}$ *24√30*

EXERCISES

Multiply.

1. $5\sqrt{6} \cdot 4\sqrt{2}$ $40\sqrt{3}$ **2.** $3\sqrt{7} \cdot 2\sqrt{5}$ $6\sqrt{35}$ **3.** $4\sqrt{10} \cdot 6\sqrt{3}$ $24\sqrt{30}$

4. $2\sqrt{7} \cdot 3\sqrt{14}$ $42\sqrt{2}$ **5.** $5\sqrt{3} \cdot 3\sqrt{10}$ $15\sqrt{30}$ **6.** $-8\sqrt{2} \cdot 4\sqrt{6}$ $-64\sqrt{3}$

7. $2\sqrt{x} \cdot \sqrt{x}$ $2x$ **8.** $5\sqrt{c} \cdot 3\sqrt{c}$ $15c$ **9.** $(-\sqrt{y})^2$ y

10. $3\sqrt{2x} \cdot \sqrt{2x}$ $6x$ **11.** $-4\sqrt{3y} \cdot 6\sqrt{3y}$ $-72y$ **12.** $8\sqrt{2x} \cdot 5\sqrt{6x}$ $80x\sqrt{3}$

Multiply.

13. $\sqrt{2}(\sqrt{18} - 3\sqrt{2})$ 0 **14.** $4\sqrt{2}(\sqrt{5} - 2\sqrt{2})$ $4\sqrt{10} - 16$

15. $-5\sqrt{6}(2\sqrt{2} + 4\sqrt{3})$ $-20\sqrt{3} - 60\sqrt{2}$ **16.** $2\sqrt{5}(2\sqrt{2} + 8\sqrt{10})$ $4\sqrt{10} + 80\sqrt{2}$

17. $(2\sqrt{3} - \sqrt{2})(3\sqrt{3} + \sqrt{2})$ $16 - \sqrt{6}$ **18.** $(\sqrt{5} - \sqrt{3})(2\sqrt{5} + 4\sqrt{3})$

19. $(6\sqrt{3} - 2\sqrt{2})(3\sqrt{3} + 5\sqrt{2})$ $34 + 2\sqrt{6}$ **20.** $(4\sqrt{7} - 2\sqrt{3})(3\sqrt{7} + 2\sqrt{3})$

21. $(\sqrt{5} + \sqrt{3})(\sqrt{5} - \sqrt{3})$ 2 **22.** $(\sqrt{7} + \sqrt{2})(\sqrt{7} - \sqrt{2})$ 5

23. $(3\sqrt{2} + 4\sqrt{3})(3\sqrt{2} - 4\sqrt{3})$ -30 **24.** $(2\sqrt{5} - 3\sqrt{6})(2\sqrt{5} + 3\sqrt{6})$ -34

25. $(2\sqrt{3} + \sqrt{7})^2$ $19 + 4\sqrt{21}$ **26.** $(3\sqrt{2} - \sqrt{5})^2$ $23 - 6\sqrt{10}$

27. $(\sqrt{6} - 2\sqrt{5})^2$ $26 - 4\sqrt{30}$ **28.** $(2\sqrt{5} + 3\sqrt{2})^2$ $38 + 12\sqrt{10}$

$72 + 2\sqrt{21}$

$-2 + 2\sqrt{15}$

EXAMPLE   Multiply $(2\sqrt{3} + \sqrt{6})^2$.

$$\underset{4}{2 \cdot 2 \cdot} \quad \underset{3}{\sqrt{3} \cdot \sqrt{3}} \quad \underset{+ 4\sqrt{18}}{+2\sqrt{18}} + \quad \underset{6}{\sqrt{6} \cdot \sqrt{6}}$$

$4\sqrt{18} = 4\sqrt{9 \cdot 2} = 4 \cdot 3\sqrt{2} \longrightarrow$

$$
\begin{array}{ccc}
4 & 3 & + 4\sqrt{18} + \quad 6 \\
& 12 & + 4 \cdot 3\sqrt{2} + \quad 6 \\
& 12 & + 12\sqrt{2} + \quad 6 \\
& 18 & + 12\sqrt{2}
\end{array}
$$

Multiply. $62 + 24\sqrt{3}$ $203 - 80\sqrt{6}$ $522 - 72\sqrt{7}$

29. $(3\sqrt{6} + 2\sqrt{2})^2$ **30.** $(5\sqrt{3} - 4\sqrt{8})^2$ **31.** $(6\sqrt{14} - 3\sqrt{2})^2$

32. $(2\sqrt{8} - 3\sqrt{2})^2$ 2 **33.** $(4\sqrt{5} - 2\sqrt{10})^2$ **34.** $(5\sqrt{6} + 3\sqrt{3})^2$

$120 - 80\sqrt{2}$ $177 + 90\sqrt{2}$

Multiply.

35. $(\sqrt{3} + \sqrt{2} - \sqrt{5})^2$ **36.** $(\sqrt{3} + \sqrt{2})(\sqrt{3} + \sqrt{6} + \sqrt{2})$ **37.** $\sqrt[3]{2}(\sqrt[3]{4} + \sqrt[3]{32})$

Points for Irrational Numbers

PROBLEM 1.

Find a point corresponding to $\sqrt{2}$ on a number line.

Construct a right triangle with each leg 1 unit in length. Use the Pythagorean theorem to find the length of the hypotenuse.

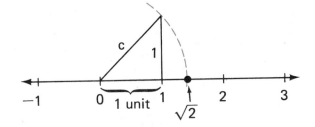

$$c^2 = 1^2 + 1^2$$
$$c^2 = 1 + 1$$
$$c^2 = 2$$
So, $c = \sqrt{2}$

Thus, the hypotenuse is $\sqrt{2}$ units long. Mark off a segment the length of the hypotenuse on the number line. The endpoint is $\sqrt{2}$.

PROBLEM 2.

Find a point corresponding to $\sqrt{3}$ on a number line.

Construct a right triangle with legs 1 and $\sqrt{2}$ units long. Again, use the Pythagorean theorem.

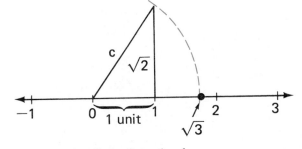

$$c^2 = 1^2 + (\sqrt{2})^2$$
$$c^2 = 1 + 2$$
$$c^2 = 3$$
So, $c = \sqrt{3}$

Thus, the hypotenuse is $\sqrt{3}$ units long. Mark off the length of the hypotenuse on the number line. The endpoint is $\sqrt{3}$.

PROJECT   Find the points corresponding to $\sqrt{5}$ and $\sqrt{6}$ on a number line.

Rationalizing Denominators

The examples in the Review suggest this rule. ⟶ $\dfrac{\sqrt{a}}{\sqrt{b}} = \sqrt{\dfrac{a}{b}}$, for all positive numbers a and b.

EXAMPLE 1   Simplify $\dfrac{\sqrt{15}}{\sqrt{3}}$.   Simplify $\dfrac{\sqrt{32x^3}}{\sqrt{8x}}$.

$\dfrac{\sqrt{a}}{\sqrt{b}} = \sqrt{\dfrac{a}{b}}$ ⟶

$$\frac{\sqrt{15}}{\sqrt{3}} = \sqrt{\frac{15}{3}}$$
$$= \sqrt{5}$$

$$\frac{\sqrt{32x^3}}{\sqrt{8x}} = \sqrt{\frac{32x^3}{8x}}$$
$$= \sqrt{4x^2}$$
$$= 2x$$

EXAMPLE 2   Rewrite $\dfrac{5}{\sqrt{7}}$ with no radical in the denominator.

$\dfrac{\sqrt{7}}{\sqrt{7}} = 1$; multiply by $\dfrac{\sqrt{7}}{\sqrt{7}}$. ⟶

$\sqrt{7} \cdot \sqrt{7} = 7$
There is no radical in the denominator.

$$\frac{5}{\sqrt{7}} = \frac{5}{\sqrt{7}} \cdot \frac{\sqrt{7}}{\sqrt{7}}$$
$$= \frac{5\sqrt{7}}{7}$$

Definition of rationalize ⟶ To *rationalize* the denominator of a fraction means to rewrite the fraction with no radical in the denominator.

EXAMPLE 3 Rationalize the denominator of $\dfrac{3}{\sqrt{12}}$.

First Method	Second Method
$\dfrac{3}{\sqrt{12}} \cdot \dfrac{\sqrt{12}}{\sqrt{12}} = \dfrac{3\sqrt{12}}{12}$	$\dfrac{3}{\sqrt{12}} \cdot \dfrac{\sqrt{3}}{\sqrt{3}} = \dfrac{3\sqrt{3}}{\sqrt{36}}$
$= \dfrac{3 \cdot 2\sqrt{3}}{12}$	$= \dfrac{3\sqrt{3}}{6}$
$= \dfrac{6\sqrt{3}}{12}$	$= \dfrac{\overset{1}{3}\sqrt{3}}{\underset{2}{6}}$
$= \dfrac{\sqrt{3}}{2}$	$= \dfrac{\sqrt{3}}{2}$

$\sqrt{12} = \sqrt{4 \cdot 3} = 2\sqrt{3}$

Second Method: Multiply by the smallest square root needed to make a perfect square in the denominator.

$\dfrac{6\sqrt{3}}{12} = \dfrac{\overset{1}{\cancel{2}} \cdot \overset{1}{\cancel{3}} \cdot \sqrt{3}}{\underset{1}{\cancel{2}} \cdot 2 \cdot \underset{1}{\cancel{3}}} = \dfrac{\sqrt{3}}{2}$

Both methods give the same result.

Thus, $\dfrac{3}{\sqrt{12}} = \dfrac{\sqrt{3}}{2}.$

EXAMPLE 4 Rationalize the denominator of $\dfrac{3}{\sqrt{x^3}}$.

$x^3 \cdot x^1 = x^4$, a perfect square.

$$\dfrac{3}{\sqrt{x^3}} \cdot \dfrac{\sqrt{x^1}}{\sqrt{x^1}} = \dfrac{3\sqrt{x^1}}{\sqrt{x^4}}$$
$$= \dfrac{3\sqrt{x}}{x^2}$$

EXAMPLE 5 Rationalize the denominator of $\dfrac{3ab}{\sqrt{a^4b}}$.

$a^4b^1 \cdot b^1 = a^4b^2$, a perfect square.

$a^4b^1 \cdot b^1 = a^4b^2$

$\sqrt{a^4b^2} = a^2b^1$

$$\dfrac{3ab}{\sqrt{a^4b^1}} = \dfrac{3ab}{\sqrt{a^4b^1}} \cdot \dfrac{\sqrt{b^1}}{\sqrt{b^1}}$$
$$= \dfrac{3ab\sqrt{b}}{\sqrt{a^4b^2}}$$
$$= \dfrac{3ab\sqrt{b}}{a^2b^1} = \dfrac{3 \cdot \overset{1}{\cancel{a}} \cdot \overset{1}{\cancel{b}} \cdot \sqrt{b}}{\underset{a^1}{a^2} \cdot \underset{1}{\cancel{b^1}}}$$

Thus, $\dfrac{3ab}{\sqrt{a^4b}} = \dfrac{3\sqrt{b}}{a}.$

EXAMPLE 6 Rationalize the denominator of $\dfrac{8y^2}{\sqrt{12y}}$.

Multiply by $\dfrac{\sqrt{3y}}{\sqrt{3y}}$. Then 36 and y^2 are perfect squares.

$\sqrt{36y^2} = 6y$

$$\dfrac{8y^2}{\sqrt{12y}} = \dfrac{8y^2}{\sqrt{12y}} \cdot \dfrac{\sqrt{3y}}{\sqrt{3y}}$$
$$= \dfrac{8y^2\sqrt{3y}}{\sqrt{36y^2}} = \dfrac{8y^2\sqrt{3y}}{6y} = \dfrac{\overset{4}{\cancel{8}}\overset{y}{\cancel{y^2}}\sqrt{3y}}{\underset{3\,1}{\cancel{6}\cancel{y}}} = \dfrac{4y\sqrt{3y}}{3}$$

EXERCISES

Rationalize the denominator.

1. $\dfrac{1}{\sqrt{2}}$ $\dfrac{\sqrt{2}}{2}$ **2.** $\dfrac{5}{\sqrt{3}}$ $\dfrac{5\sqrt{3}}{3}$ **3.** $\dfrac{5}{\sqrt{5}}$ $\sqrt{5}$ **4.** $\dfrac{28}{\sqrt{7}}$ $4\sqrt{7}$ **5.** $\dfrac{6}{\sqrt{3}}$ $2\sqrt{3}$

6. $\dfrac{3}{\sqrt{18}}$ $\dfrac{\sqrt{2}}{2}$ **7.** $\dfrac{6}{\sqrt{12}}$ $\sqrt{3}$ **8.** $\dfrac{4}{\sqrt{20}}$ $\dfrac{2\sqrt{5}}{5}$ **9.** $\dfrac{5}{\sqrt{10}}$ $\dfrac{\sqrt{10}}{2}$ **10.** $\dfrac{8}{\sqrt{50}}$ $\dfrac{4\sqrt{2}}{5}$

11. $\dfrac{4}{\sqrt{x^5}}$ $\dfrac{4\sqrt{x}}{x^3}$ **12.** $\dfrac{3}{\sqrt{x^7}}$ $\dfrac{3\sqrt{x}}{x^4}$ **13.** $\dfrac{2}{\sqrt{m^3}}$ $\dfrac{2\sqrt{m}}{m^2}$ **14.** $\dfrac{5}{\sqrt{m^9}}$ $\dfrac{5\sqrt{m}}{m^5}$ **15.** $\dfrac{6}{\sqrt{x}}$ $\dfrac{6\sqrt{x}}{x}$

16. $\dfrac{4}{\sqrt{12a^3}}$ $\dfrac{2\sqrt{3a}}{3a^2}$ **17.** $\dfrac{6}{\sqrt{8a^5}}$ $\dfrac{3\sqrt{2a}}{2a^3}$ **18.** $\dfrac{4}{\sqrt{18b^3}}$ $\dfrac{2\sqrt{2b}}{3b^2}$ **19.** $\dfrac{3x}{\sqrt{6x^3}}$ $\dfrac{\sqrt{6x}}{2x}$ **20.** $\dfrac{27a}{\sqrt{3a^5}}$ $\dfrac{9\sqrt{3a}}{a^2}$

Rationalize the denominator.

$12x^2y^2\sqrt{xy}$

21. $\dfrac{5xy}{\sqrt{x}}$ $5y\sqrt{x}$ **22.** $\dfrac{12ab}{\sqrt{a^2b}}$ $12\sqrt{b}$ **23.** $\dfrac{3x}{\sqrt{x^2y}}$ $\dfrac{3\sqrt{y}}{y}$ **24.** $\dfrac{5c^3d}{\sqrt{cd}}$ $5c^2\sqrt{cd}$ **25.** $\dfrac{12x^3y^3}{\sqrt{xy}}$ ↗

26. $\dfrac{6x^2y}{\sqrt{xy^2}}$ $6x\sqrt{x}$ **27.** $\dfrac{6y^2}{\sqrt{18y}}$ $y\sqrt{2y}$ **28.** $\dfrac{4m^3}{\sqrt{8m^7}}$ $\dfrac{\sqrt{2m}}{m}$ **29.** $\dfrac{2a^3}{\sqrt{20a^5}}$ $\dfrac{\sqrt{5a}}{5}$ **30.** $\dfrac{3x^5}{\sqrt{6x^3}}$ $\dfrac{x^3\sqrt{6x}}{2}$

EXAMPLE   Rationalize the denominator of $\dfrac{7}{5-\sqrt{3}}$.

Multiply by 1: $\dfrac{5+\sqrt{3}}{5+\sqrt{3}}$

$5+\sqrt{3}$ is the conjugate of $5-\sqrt{3}$. ⟶

$$\begin{array}{rrl} & 5 & -\sqrt{3} \\ \times & 5 & +\sqrt{3} \\ \hline 25 & & -5\sqrt{3} \\ & +5\sqrt{3} & -3 \\ \hline 25 & +0 & -3 = 22 \end{array}$$

$$\dfrac{7}{5-\sqrt{3}} = \dfrac{7}{5-\sqrt{3}} \cdot \dfrac{5+\sqrt{3}}{5+\sqrt{3}}$$

$$= \dfrac{7(5+\sqrt{3})}{(5-\sqrt{3})(5+\sqrt{3})}$$

$$= \dfrac{35+7\sqrt{3}}{22}$$

Thus, $\dfrac{7}{5-\sqrt{3}} = \dfrac{35+7\sqrt{3}}{22}$.

Rationalize the denominator of each.

31. $\dfrac{5}{3-\sqrt{3}}$ **32.** $\dfrac{-2}{3+\sqrt{2}}$ **33.** $\dfrac{\sqrt{3}}{\sqrt{10}-2}$ **34.** $\dfrac{5}{2\sqrt{5}+1}$ **35.** $\dfrac{-3}{\sqrt{7}-2}$

Fractional Radicands

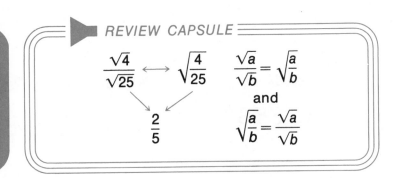

$\sqrt{10}$ ← radical
10 ← radicand

To simplify $\sqrt{\dfrac{3}{4}}$, rewrite it so that the radicand is not a fraction.

EXAMPLE 1   Simplify $\sqrt{\dfrac{3}{4}}$.

The radicand is 3; 3 is not a fraction. ⟶

$$\frac{\sqrt{3}}{\sqrt{4}} = \frac{\sqrt{3}}{2}$$

EXAMPLE 2   Simplify $\sqrt{\dfrac{24}{25}}$.

$\sqrt{24} = \sqrt{4 \cdot 6} = 2\sqrt{6}$ ⟶

$$\frac{\sqrt{24}}{\sqrt{25}} = \frac{2\sqrt{6}}{5}$$

EXAMPLE 3   Simplify $\sqrt{\dfrac{5}{8}}$.

Multiply by $\dfrac{\sqrt{2}}{\sqrt{2}}$, since $8 \cdot 2 = 16$, and 16 is a perfect square.

$$\frac{\sqrt{5}}{\sqrt{8}} = \frac{\sqrt{5}}{\sqrt{8}} \cdot \frac{\sqrt{2}}{\sqrt{2}}$$

$$= \frac{\sqrt{10}}{\sqrt{16}} = \frac{\sqrt{10}}{4}$$

EXAMPLE 4   Simplify $\sqrt{\dfrac{3}{2y^3}}$.

Rationalize the denominator of $\dfrac{\sqrt{3}}{\sqrt{2y^3}}$. ⟶

$$\frac{\sqrt{3}}{\sqrt{2y^3}} = \frac{\sqrt{3}}{\sqrt{2y^3}} \cdot \frac{\sqrt{2y}}{\sqrt{2y}}$$

$$= \frac{\sqrt{6y}}{\sqrt{4y^4}} = \frac{\sqrt{6y}}{2y^2}$$

EXAMPLE 5   Simplify $\sqrt{\dfrac{14x}{24x^2}}$.

$$\dfrac{14x}{24x^2}=\dfrac{\overset{1}{2}\cdot 7\cdot \overset{1}{x}}{\underset{1}{2}\cdot 12\cdot \underset{1}{x}\cdot x}=\dfrac{7}{12x} \qquad \sqrt{\dfrac{7}{12x}}=\dfrac{\sqrt{7}}{\sqrt{12x}}=\dfrac{\sqrt{7}}{\sqrt{12x}}\cdot\dfrac{\sqrt{3x}}{\sqrt{3x}}=\dfrac{\sqrt{21x}}{\sqrt{36x^2}}=\dfrac{\sqrt{21x}}{6x}$$

EXERCISES

PART A

Simplify.

1. $\sqrt{\dfrac{9}{16}}$ $\dfrac{3}{4}$
2. $\sqrt{\dfrac{25}{49}}$ $\dfrac{5}{7}$
3. $\sqrt{\dfrac{100}{81}}$ $\dfrac{10}{9}$
4. $\sqrt{\dfrac{64}{36}}$ $\dfrac{4}{3}$
5. $\sqrt{\dfrac{121}{25}}$ $\dfrac{11}{5}$

6. $\sqrt{\dfrac{7}{4}}$ $\dfrac{\sqrt{7}}{2}$
7. $\sqrt{\dfrac{54}{25}}$ $\dfrac{3\sqrt{6}}{5}$
8. $\sqrt{\dfrac{31}{49}}$ $\dfrac{\sqrt{31}}{7}$
9. $\sqrt{\dfrac{67}{81}}$ $\dfrac{\sqrt{67}}{9}$
10. $\sqrt{\dfrac{27}{16}}$ $\dfrac{3\sqrt{3}}{4}$

11. $\sqrt{\dfrac{3}{8}}$ $\dfrac{\sqrt{6}}{4}$
12. $\sqrt{\dfrac{4}{27}}$ $\dfrac{2\sqrt{3}}{9}$
13. $\sqrt{\dfrac{5}{12}}$ $\dfrac{\sqrt{15}}{6}$
14. $\sqrt{\dfrac{7}{20}}$ $\dfrac{\sqrt{35}}{10}$
15. $\sqrt{\dfrac{11}{40}}$ $\dfrac{\sqrt{110}}{20}$

16. $\sqrt{\dfrac{5}{y}}$ $\dfrac{\sqrt{5y}}{y}$
17. $\sqrt{\dfrac{16}{x^3}}$ $\dfrac{4\sqrt{x}}{x^2}$
18. $\sqrt{\dfrac{7}{3z^2}}$ $\dfrac{\sqrt{21}}{3z}$
19. $\sqrt{\dfrac{6}{5y^3}}$ $\dfrac{\sqrt{30y}}{5y^2}$
20. $\sqrt{\dfrac{27}{xy^3}}$ $\dfrac{3\sqrt{3xy}}{xy^2}$

21. $\sqrt{\dfrac{54x}{y^5}}$ $\dfrac{3\sqrt{6xy}}{y^3}$
22. $\sqrt{\dfrac{60}{x^2y^3}}$
23. $\sqrt{\dfrac{x}{2x^4}}$ $\dfrac{\sqrt{2x}}{2x^2}$
24. $\sqrt{\dfrac{12z^2}{3yz}}$ $\dfrac{2\sqrt{yz}}{y}$
25. $\sqrt{\dfrac{5xz}{15x^3z^2}}$ $\dfrac{\sqrt{3z}}{3xz}$

26. $\sqrt{\dfrac{3y}{18y^4}}$ $\dfrac{\sqrt{6y}}{6y^2}$
27. $\sqrt{\dfrac{22y}{14y^3}}$ $\dfrac{\sqrt{77}}{7y}$
28. $\sqrt{\dfrac{24a^2b^3}{6ab}}$
29. $\sqrt{\dfrac{56y^4z}{4yz^2}}$
30. $\sqrt{\dfrac{64a^2b^2}{20ab^3}}$

PART B

EXAMPLE   Simplify $\sqrt{\dfrac{3y+2}{y}}$.

$$\dfrac{\sqrt{3y+2}}{\sqrt{y}}=\dfrac{\sqrt{3y+2}}{\sqrt{y}}\cdot\dfrac{\sqrt{y}}{\sqrt{y}}=\dfrac{\sqrt{(3y+2)y}}{\sqrt{y^2}}=\dfrac{\sqrt{3y^2+2y}}{y}$$

Simplify.

31. $\sqrt{\dfrac{2x+3}{2}}$ $\dfrac{\sqrt{4x+6}}{2}$
32. $\sqrt{\dfrac{5z-3}{3}}$
33. $\sqrt{\dfrac{4x+7}{7}}$
34. $\sqrt{\dfrac{5x+5}{2}}$

35. $\sqrt{\dfrac{3-5z}{5}}$
36. $\sqrt{\dfrac{4x^2-7}{2}}$
37. $\sqrt{\dfrac{2z^2+3}{3}}$
38. $\sqrt{\dfrac{6y^2-y}{2}}$

PART C
Simplify.

39. $\sqrt{\dfrac{y+6}{y}+\dfrac{9}{y^2}}$

40. $\sqrt{1+\dfrac{10}{x}+\dfrac{25}{x^2}}$

412   FRACTIONAL RADICANDS

Mathematics in Banking

Pictured above are two bank managers studying a manual on interest rates.

PROJECT A checkbook showed a balance of $155 at the beginning of a month. During the month deposits of $50, $125, and $200 were made and checks were written for $15, $25.50, $48.75, $100, $10, $35, $40, and $200. When the bank sent its monthly statement, the balance was $340.75. Only the first four checks had cleared the bank.

1. Find the checkbook balance by adding the deposits to the original balance and deducting only the checks that have cleared the bank.

2. Does the checkbook balance agree with the bank balance?

Chapter Fourteen Review

Which are rational and which are irrational numbers? $[p.\ 382]$

1. .131131113. . .   **2.** .13$\overline{13}$ **3.** .468   **4.** $2\frac{7}{8}$
5. π **6.** $-\sqrt{81}$ **7.** $\sqrt{21}$ **8.** -3.6

Give answers to the nearest tenth. Use the table on page 476. $[p.\ 384]$

9.
s | $A = 46$ cm^2 | with side s

Find s.

10.
x | $A = 159\ \mathrm{m}^2$ | with base $3x$

Find x and 3x.

11. The length of a rectangle is twice the width. The area is 70 square cm. Find the length and the width.

Which are irrational numbers? For each irrational number, approximate the square root to the nearest tenth. Use the divide and average method. $[p.\ 388]$

12. $\sqrt{81}$ **13.** $\sqrt{74}$ **14.** $\sqrt{41}$ **15.** $\sqrt{16}$ **16.** $\sqrt{15}$ **17.** $\sqrt{62}$

Simplify. $[p.\ 391,\ 394,\ 396]$

18. $\sqrt{49} \cdot \sqrt{9}$ **19.** $\sqrt{16 \cdot 81}$ **20.** $-\sqrt{48}$ **21.** $\sqrt{64a^4b^{10}}$ **22.** $-\sqrt{49x^8y^2z^{10}}$
23. $\sqrt{144c^2d^4e^{10}}$ **24.** $\sqrt{xy^3}$ **25.** $-2x^2y\sqrt{27x^7y^9}$ **26.** $\sqrt[3]{27x^6y^{11}}$ **27.** $-\sqrt[3]{-64x^4y^5z^6}$

Tell whether each triangle described is a right triangle. The lengths of the three sides are given. $[p.\ 399]$

28. 5, 12, 13   **29.** 4, 5, 6   **30.** 15, 20, 25   **31.** 1, 5, $\sqrt{26}$

For each right triangle, find the missing length. Give answers in simplest radical form. $[p.\ 399]$

32. $a = 15,\ b = 8$ **33.** $b = 6,\ c = 3\sqrt{5}$ **34.** $a = 7,\ c = 9$

Simplify. $[p.\ 402]$

35. $4\sqrt{5} - 8\sqrt{5} + 3\sqrt{5}$ **36.** $5x\sqrt{4y} + 7x\sqrt{y} - 3\sqrt{16x^2y}$

Multiply. $[p.\ 404]$

37. $5\sqrt{x}(3\sqrt{x} - 2)$ **38.** $(2\sqrt{2} - 3\sqrt{3})^2$ **39.** $(\sqrt{3} - \sqrt{5})(\sqrt{3} + \sqrt{5})$

Rationalize the denominator. $[p.\ 408]$

40. $\dfrac{1}{\sqrt{3}}$ **41.** $\dfrac{12}{\sqrt{18}}$ **42.** $\dfrac{3x}{\sqrt{12x^3}}$ **43.** $\dfrac{24xy^4}{\sqrt{8xy^3}}$

Simplify. $[p.\ 411]$

44. $\dfrac{\sqrt{98}}{\sqrt{2}}$ **45.** $\dfrac{\sqrt{75x^3y}}{\sqrt{3xy}}$ **46.** $\sqrt{\dfrac{56a^2b^2}{4ab^3}}$ **47.** $\sqrt{\dfrac{4x + 2}{3}}$

Chapter Fourteen Test

Which are rational and which are irrational numbers?

1. .001

2. $\sqrt{64}$

3. $.123\overline{123}$

4. .123122312223. . .

5. -2.37

6. π

7. $-\sqrt{52}$

8. $-6\frac{5}{8}$

Give answers to the nearest tenth. Use the table on page 476.

9.
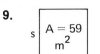
Find s.

10.

Find 3x and 4x.

11. The length of a rectangle is 3 times the width. The area is 216 square cm. Find the length and the width.

Which are irrational numbers? For each irrational number, approximate the square root to the nearest tenth. Use the divide and average method.

12. $\sqrt{10}$

13. $\sqrt{49}$

14. $\sqrt{52}$

15. $\sqrt{100}$

Simplify.

16. $\sqrt{5} \cdot \sqrt{13}$

17. $\sqrt{100 \cdot 16}$

18. $-\sqrt{80}$

19. $\sqrt{49a^4b^2}$

20. $-\sqrt{81x^6y^2z^{12}}$

21. $\sqrt{15cd^2}$

22. $-5x^2y\sqrt{54xy^3}$

23. $-\sqrt[3]{-27x^9y^{13}}$

Tell whether each triangle described is a right triangle. The lengths of the three sides are given.

24. 8, 6, 10

25. 7, 8, 9

26. 4, 4$\sqrt{3}$, 8

For each right triangle, find the missing length. Give answers in simplest radical form.

27. $a = 2, b = 4$

28. $a = 12, c = 13$

29. $b = 6, c = 6\sqrt{2}$

Simplify.

30. $2\sqrt{3} - 9\sqrt{3} + 6\sqrt{3}$

31. $2x\sqrt{16y} + 5x\sqrt{y} - 7\sqrt{25x^2y}$

Multiply.

32. $(1 - \sqrt{2})^2$

33. $(\sqrt{5} + \sqrt{7})(\sqrt{5} - \sqrt{7})$

34. $3\sqrt{x}(2\sqrt{x} - 5)$

Rationalize the denominator.

35. $\dfrac{7}{\sqrt{3}}$

36. $\dfrac{4}{\sqrt{8}}$

37. $\dfrac{15x^2}{\sqrt{5x}}$

38. $\dfrac{15cd^3}{\sqrt{3cd}}$

Simplify.

39. $\dfrac{\sqrt{48}}{\sqrt{3}}$

40. $\dfrac{\sqrt{54xy^5}}{\sqrt{2xy^2}}$

41. $\sqrt{\dfrac{34xy^3}{4x^2y}}$

42. $\sqrt{\dfrac{3x - 5}{7}}$

Pythagorean Triples

This is the symbol of the Order of the Pythagoreans, a society of ancient Greek mathematicians.

A Pythagorean triple is a group of positive integers a, b, and c which make the sentence $a^2 + b^2 = c^2$ true. 3, 4, 5 is a *Pythagorean triple* because $3^2 + 4^2 = 5^2$.

PROJECT

1. Verify that each is a Pythagorean triple.

3	4	5
5	12	13
7	24	25
9	40	41
11	60	61
•	•	•
•	•	•
•	•	•

2. All of the triples above start with an odd number. Can you see a pattern in the formation?

3. List the next three triples which fit the pattern.

Radical Equations

The equations in the Review Capsule suggest this property. ⟶

The solution of the equation $x = a$ is a solution of the equation $x^2 = a^2$. But, a solution of $x^2 = a^2$ may not be a solution of $x = a$.

$\sqrt{x} = 6$ is a radical equation since the variable is in the radicand.

EXAMPLE 1   Find the solution set of $\sqrt{x} = 6$.

Square each side of $\sqrt{x} = 6$. ⟶
$(\sqrt{x})^2 = \sqrt{x} \cdot \sqrt{x} = x$ ⟶

$$\sqrt{x} = 6$$
$$(\sqrt{x})^2 = 6^2$$
$$x = 36$$

Check.

$\sqrt{x}$	6
$\sqrt{36}$	6
6	

Thus, the solution set is $\{36\}$.

EXAMPLE 2   Find the solution set of $\sqrt{2x - 5} + 8 = 7$.

Add -8 to each side. Now the radical is by itself. ⟶

Square each side. ⟶
$(\sqrt{2x - 5})^2 = \sqrt{2x - 5} \cdot \sqrt{2x - 5} = 2x - 5 \rightarrow$

Add 5 to each side. ⟶
Divide each side by 2. ⟶

$$\sqrt{2x - 5} + 8 = 7$$
$$\sqrt{2x - 5} = -1$$
$$(\sqrt{2x - 5})^2 = (-1)^2$$
$$2x - 5 = 1$$
$$2x = 6$$
$$x = 3$$

Check.

$\sqrt{2x - 5} + 8$	7
$\sqrt{2(3) - 5} + 8$	7
$\sqrt{6 - 5} + 8$	
$\sqrt{1} + 8$	
$1 + 8$	
9	

3 doesn't check. $9 \neq 7$.
ϕ is the empty set. ⟶ **Thus,** the solution set is ϕ.

EXAMPLE 3 Solve $\sqrt{2y} = 4\sqrt{5}$.

$$\sqrt{2y} = 4\sqrt{5}$$

Square each side. $\longrightarrow$ $(\sqrt{2y})^2 = (4\sqrt{5})^2$

$(4\sqrt{5})^2 = (4\sqrt{5})(4\sqrt{5}) = 16 \cdot 5 = 80 \longrightarrow$ $2y = 80$

Divide each side by 2. $\longrightarrow$ $y = 40$

Check.

$\sqrt{2y}$	$4\sqrt{5}$
$\sqrt{2 \cdot 40}$	$4\sqrt{5}$
$\sqrt{80}$	
$4\sqrt{5}$	

40 checks. $\longrightarrow$ **Thus,** the solution is 40.

EXAMPLE 4 Solve $x - 2 = \sqrt{19 - 6x}$.

$$x - 2 = \sqrt{19 - 6x}$$

Square each side. $\longrightarrow$ $(x - 2)^2 = (\sqrt{19 - 6x})^2$

$(x - 2)^2 = (x - 2)(x - 2) \longrightarrow$ $x^2 - 4x + 4 = 19 - 6x$

Add -19 and $6x$ to each side. $\longrightarrow$ $x^2 + 2x - 15 = 0$

Factor. $\longrightarrow$ $(x - 3)(x + 5) = 0$

$$x - 3 = 0 \text{ or } x + 5 = 0$$
$$x = 3 \text{ or } \quad x = -5$$

Check 3.

$x - 2$	$\sqrt{19 - 6x}$
$3 - 2$	$\sqrt{19 - 6(3)}$
1	$\sqrt{19 - 18}$
	$\sqrt{1}$
	1

Check -5.

$x - 2$	$\sqrt{19 - 6x}$
$-5 - 2$	$\sqrt{19 - 6(-5)}$
-7	$\sqrt{19 + 30}$
	$\sqrt{49}$
	7

$$-7 \neq 7$$

-5 doesn't check. $\longrightarrow$ **Thus,** the solution is 3.

EXAMPLE 5 If 4 is added to 3 times a number, the square root is 5. Find the number.

Let x = the number.

Write an equation. $\longrightarrow$ $\sqrt{3x + 4} = 5$

Square each side. $\longrightarrow$ $(\sqrt{3x + 4})^2 = 5^2$

$$3x + 4 = 25$$
$$3x = 21$$
$$x = 7$$

Check 7 in the original problem; add 4 to 3 times 7. $\longrightarrow$

$$3(7) + 4 = 21 + 4$$
$$= 25$$

7 checks. $\longrightarrow$ Is $\sqrt{25} = 5$? Yes.

Thus, the number is 7.

EXERCISES

PART A

Find the solution set.

1. $\sqrt{y} = 3$ *{9}*   **2.** $\sqrt{x} = 8$ *{64}*   **3.** $\sqrt{5x} = 10$ *{20}*   **4.** $\sqrt{2y} = 24$ *{288}*

5. $\sqrt{4x} = \frac{1}{2}$ *$\{\frac{1}{16}\}$*   **6.** $\sqrt{3y} = \frac{1}{6}$ *$\{\frac{1}{108}\}$*   **7.** $\sqrt{18y} = 6$ *{2}*   **8.** $\sqrt{3x} = 3$ *{3}*

Solve.

9. $\sqrt{x} + 1 = 2$ *1*   **10.** $\sqrt{z} + 3 = 7$ *16*

11. $\sqrt{6x} + 5 = 2$ *no solution*   **12.** $\sqrt{2x} + 4 = 10$ *18*

13. $\sqrt{3x + 2} = 9$ *$\frac{79}{3}$*   **14.** $\sqrt{y + 2} = 4$ *14*

15. $\sqrt{2x - 1} = \sqrt{x + 3}$ *4*   **16.** $\sqrt{x - 3} = \sqrt{2x + 7}$ *no solution*

17. $\sqrt{x + 3} + 4 = 0$ *no solution*   **18.** $\sqrt{x - 5} - 8 = 0$ *69*

19. $\sqrt{x} = 2\sqrt{3}$ *12*   **20.** $2\sqrt{x} = \sqrt{48}$ *12*

PART B

Solve.

21. $\sqrt{3x + 10} = x + 4$ *−3, −2*   **22.** $\sqrt{x^2 - 9} = -4$ *no solution*

23. $x + 1 = \sqrt{17 - 4x}$ *2*   **24.** $\sqrt{2x - 20} = x - 1$ *no solution*

25. The square root of a number, decreased by 2, equals 3. Find the number. *25*

26. Twice the square root of a number is equal to 20. Find the number. *100*

27. A number is multiplied by 2 and 5 is added to the product. The square root of the result is equal to 3. Find the number. *2*

28. A number is increased by 6. The square root of the sum is multiplied by 3, resulting in 12. Find the number. *10*

PART C

            EXAMPLE   Solve $\sqrt{x} + 2 = \sqrt{x + 20}$.

Square each side. $\longrightarrow$ $(\sqrt{x} + 2)^2 = (\sqrt{x + 20})^2$ Check.

$$x + 4\sqrt{x} + 4 = x + 20$$

	$\sqrt{x} + 2$	$\sqrt{x + 20}$
Add $-x$ and -4 to each side. $\longrightarrow$ $4\sqrt{x} = 16$	$\sqrt{16} + 2$	$\sqrt{16 + 20}$
Divide each side by 4. $\longrightarrow$ $\sqrt{x} = 4$	$4 + 2$	$\sqrt{36}$
Square each side. $\longrightarrow$ $x = 16$	6	6

Thus, the solution is 16.

Solve.

29. $\sqrt{x} - 5 = -\sqrt{x + 15}$ **30.** $\sqrt{x} + 3 = \sqrt{x - 9}$ **31.** $\sqrt{x} = \sqrt{x + 77} - 7$

                                                                    [Hint: First add 7 to each side.]

The Solution Set of $x^2 = a$

▶ *REVIEW CAPSULE*

$$(\sqrt{25})^2 = \sqrt{25} \cdot \sqrt{25} = 5 \cdot 5 = 25$$
$$(-\sqrt{25})^2 = (-\sqrt{25})(-\sqrt{25}) = (-5)(-5)$$
$$= 25$$

$$(\sqrt{17})^2 = \sqrt{17} \cdot \sqrt{17} = 17$$
$$(-\sqrt{17})^2 = (-\sqrt{17})(-\sqrt{17}) = 17$$

$$\left.\begin{array}{l}(\sqrt{a})^2 = \sqrt{a} \cdot \sqrt{a} = a \\ (-\sqrt{a})^2 = (-\sqrt{a})(-\sqrt{a}) = a\end{array}\right\} \begin{array}{l}\text{for each} \\ a \geq 0.\end{array}$$

EXAMPLE 1 Find the solution set of $x^2 = 25$.

$$x^2 = 25$$

For $x = 5$ or $x = -5$, we could write
$x = \pm 5$.
└─ read: plus or minus

$$x = \sqrt{25} \quad \text{or} \quad x = -\sqrt{25}$$
$$x = 5 \quad \text{or} \quad x = -5$$

$(5)^2 = 25$ and $(-5)^2 = 25$. ——————→ **Thus,** the solution set is $\{5, -5\}$.

EXAMPLE 2 Solve $x^2 = 17$.

$$x^2 = 17$$

$$x = \sqrt{17} \quad \text{or} \quad x = -\sqrt{17}$$

$(\sqrt{17})^2 = 17$ and $(-\sqrt{17})^2 = 17$.——→ **Thus,** the solutions are $\sqrt{17}$ and $-\sqrt{17}$.

Examples 1 and 2 suggest this. ———→ If $x^2 = a$, then $x = \sqrt{a}$ or $x = -\sqrt{a}$, for each $a \geq 0$.

EXAMPLE 3 Find the solution set of $y^2 = 12$.

$$y^2 = 12$$

If $x^2 = a$, then $x = \sqrt{a}$ or $x = -\sqrt{a}$. ——→
$\sqrt{12} = \sqrt{4 \cdot 3} = 2\sqrt{3}$ ————————→

$$y = \sqrt{12} \quad \text{or} \quad y = -\sqrt{12}$$
$$y = 2\sqrt{3} \quad \text{or} \quad y = -2\sqrt{3}$$

Thus, the solution set is $\{2\sqrt{3}, -2\sqrt{3}\}$.

EXAMPLE 4 Solve $(y + 4)^2 = 49$.

$$(y + 4)^2 = 49$$

If $x^2 = a$, then $x = \sqrt{a}$ or $x = -\sqrt{a}$. ———→

$$y + 4 = \sqrt{49} \quad \text{or} \quad y = 4 = -\sqrt{49}$$

Solve each equation.

$$y + 4 = 7 \qquad\qquad y + 4 = -7$$

Add -4 to each side. ————————→

$$y = 3 \quad \text{or} \quad y = -11$$

Check 3 and -11 in $(y + 4)^2 = 49$. ———→ **Thus,** the solutions are 3 and -11.

EXAMPLE 5 Find the solution set of $(x - 3)^2 = 100$.

$$(x - 3)^2 = 100$$

$$x - 3 = \sqrt{100} \quad \text{or} \quad x - 3 = -\sqrt{100}$$

Solve each equation.

$$x - 3 = 10 \qquad\qquad x - 3 = -10$$

Add 3 to each side. ————————→

$$x = 13 \quad \text{or} \quad x = -7$$

Check 13 and -7 in $(x - 3)^2 = 100$. ———→ **Thus,** the solution set is $\{13, -7\}$.

EXAMPLE 6 Solve $3x^2 = 7$.

$$3x^2 = 7$$

Divide each side by 3. ————————→

$$\frac{3x^2}{3} = \frac{7}{3}$$

$$x^2 = \frac{7}{3}$$

$$x = \sqrt{\frac{7}{3}} \quad \text{or} \quad x = -\sqrt{\frac{7}{3}}$$

$\sqrt{\dfrac{7}{3}} = \dfrac{\sqrt{7}}{\sqrt{3}} \cdot \dfrac{\sqrt{3}}{\sqrt{3}} = \dfrac{\sqrt{21}}{3}$ ————————→

$$x = \frac{\sqrt{21}}{3} \quad \text{or} \quad x = -\frac{\sqrt{21}}{3}$$

Check $\dfrac{\sqrt{21}}{3}$ and $-\dfrac{\sqrt{21}}{3}$ in $3x^2 = 7$. ———→ **Thus,** the solutions are $\dfrac{\sqrt{21}}{3}$ and $-\dfrac{\sqrt{21}}{3}$.

EXERCISES

PART A

Find the solution set.

1. $x^2 = 1$ $\{1, -1\}$ ⎡Hint: What
4. $x^2 = -16$ ϕ ←⎜number squared
7. $x^2 = 9$ $\{3, -3\}$ ⎣equals -16?
10. $x^2 = 100$ $\{10, -10\}$
13. $x^2 = 15$ $\{\sqrt{15}, -\sqrt{15}\}$

2. $x^2 = 36$ $\{6, -6\}$
5. $x^2 = 49$ $\{7, -7\}$
8. $x^2 = -36$ ϕ
11. $x^2 = -100$ ϕ
14. $x^2 = 11$
$\{\sqrt{11}, -\sqrt{11}\}$

3. $x^2 = 4$ $\{2, -2\}$
6. $x^2 = 0$ $\{0\}$
9. $x^2 = 64$ $\{8, -8\}$
12. $x^2 = 144$ $\{12, -12\}$
15. $x^2 = 13$ $\{\sqrt{13}, -\sqrt{13}\}$

16. $x^2 = 28$ $\{2\sqrt{7}, -2\sqrt{7}\}$ **17.** $x^2 = 24$ $\{2\sqrt{6}, -2\sqrt{6}\}$ **18.** $x^2 = 32$ $\{4\sqrt{2}, -4\sqrt{2}\}$

19. $y^2 = 18$ $\{3\sqrt{2}, -3\sqrt{2}\}$ **20.** $m^2 = 44$ **21.** $x^2 = -24$

$\{2\sqrt{11}, -2\sqrt{11}\}$ *no solution*

Solve.

22. $(x - 7)^2 = 9$ $10, 4$ **23.** $(x + 5)^2 = 16$ $-1, -9$ **24.** $(x - 8)^2 = 1$ $9, 7$

25. $3x^2 = 5$ $\frac{\sqrt{15}}{3}, -\frac{\sqrt{15}}{3}$ **26.** $2x^2 = 7$ $\frac{\sqrt{14}}{2}, -\frac{\sqrt{14}}{2}$ **27.** $5x^2 = 13$ $\frac{\sqrt{65}}{5}, -\frac{\sqrt{65}}{5}$

28. $4a^2 = 64$ $4, -4$ **29.** $2x^2 = 50$ $5, -5$ **30.** $3x^2 = 36$

$2\sqrt{3}, -2\sqrt{3}$

PART B

EXAMPLE   Solve $(x - 4)^2 = 8$.

$$(x - 4)^2 = 8$$

$$x - 4 = +\sqrt{8} \quad \text{or} \quad x - 4 = -\sqrt{8}$$

Add 4 to each side. $\underline{\quad 4 \quad 4 \quad}$ $\underline{\quad 4 \quad 4 \quad}$

$$x = 4 + \sqrt{8} \quad \text{or} \quad x = 4 - \sqrt{8}$$

$\sqrt{8} = \sqrt{4 \cdot 2} = 2\sqrt{2}$ ⟶ $x = 4 + 2\sqrt{2}$ or $x = 4 - 2\sqrt{2}$

Thus, the solutions are $4 + 2\sqrt{2}$ and $4 - 2\sqrt{2}$.

Solve.

31. $(x + 3)^2 = 8$ $-3 \pm 2\sqrt{2}$ **32.** $(x - 4)^2 = 32$ $4 \pm 4\sqrt{2}$ **33.** $(x + 6)^2 = 28$ $-6 \pm 2\sqrt{7}$

34. $(x + 1)^2 = 12$ $-1 \pm 2\sqrt{3}$ **35.** $(x - 7)^2 = 24$ $7 \pm 2\sqrt{6}$ **36.** $(x - 3)^2 = 40$

$3 \pm 2\sqrt{10}$

PART C

EXAMPLE   Find the solution set of $3(2x - 3)^2 + 8 = 44$.

$$3(2x - 3)^2 + 8 = 44$$

Add -8 to each side. ⟶ $3(2x - 3)^2 = 36$

Divide each side by 3. ⟶ $(2x - 3)^2 = 12$

$$2x - 3 = +\sqrt{12} \quad \text{or} \quad 2x - 3 = -\sqrt{12}$$

Add 3 to each side. ⟶ $2x = 3 + \sqrt{12}$ or $2x = 3 - \sqrt{12}$

$\sqrt{12} = \sqrt{4 \cdot 3} = 2\sqrt{3}$ ⟶ $2x = 3 + 2\sqrt{3}$ or $2x = 3 - 2\sqrt{3}$

Divide each side by 2. ⟶ $x = \dfrac{3 + 2\sqrt{3}}{2}$ or $x = \dfrac{3 - 2\sqrt{3}}{2}$

Thus, the solution set is $\left\{\dfrac{3 + 2\sqrt{3}}{2}, \dfrac{3 - 2\sqrt{3}}{2}\right\}$.

Find the solution set of each.

37. $4(2x - 5)^2 + 6 = 54$ **38.** $3(2x + 3)^2 - 7 = 29$ **39.** $5(4x - 2)^2 - 6 = 94$

Completing the Square

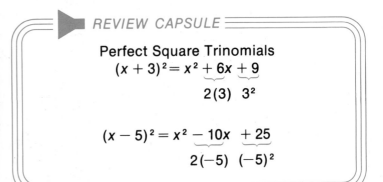

REVIEW CAPSULE

Perfect Square Trinomials
$$(x + 3)^2 = x^2 + \underbrace{6x}_{2(3)} + \underbrace{9}_{3^2}$$

$$(x - 5)^2 = x^2 \underbrace{- 10x}_{2(-5)} + \underbrace{25}_{(-5)^2}$$

The Review Capsule suggests this. ⟶ $$(a + b)^2 = a^2 + \underbrace{2ba}_{2(b)} + \underbrace{b^2}_{b^2}$$

twice b ⟶   ⟵ b squared

EXAMPLE 1 What number do we add to $x^2 + 14x$ to make a perfect square trinomial?

$$x^2 + \underbrace{14x}_{2(7)}$$

$14 = 2(7)$ ⟶

$7^2 = 49$ ⟶ Add 49: $x^2 + 14x + 49$

Check by squaring $(x + 7)$. ⟶ $(x + 7)^2 = x^2 + 14x + 49$, a perfect square trinomial.

EXAMPLE 2 What number do we add to $x^2 - 20x$ to make a perfect square trinomial?

$$x^2 \underbrace{- 20x}_{2(-10)}$$

$-20 = 2(-10)$ ⟶

$(-10)^2 = 100$ ⟶ Add 100: $x^2 - 20x + 100$

$(x - 10)^2 = x^2 - 20x + 100$, a perfect square trinomial.

In Example 3, we show a method called *completing the square* for finding the solution set of a quadratic equation.

EXAMPLE 3   Find the solution set of $x^2 - 6x = 27$ by completing the square.

$-6 = 2(-3)$ and $(-3)^2 = 9.$
Add 9 to each side.

$x^2 - 6x + 9$:

$x^2 - 6x + 9 = (x - 3)^2$

Add 3 to each side. ⟶

$$x^2 - 6x + \underline{} = 27 + \underline{}$$
$$x^2 - 6x + 9 = 27 + 9$$
$$(x - 3)^2 = 36$$

$$x - 3 = +\sqrt{36} \text{ or } x - 3 = -\sqrt{36}$$
$$x - 3 = +6 \qquad\qquad x - 3 = -6$$
$$\underline{\quad 3 \quad 3 \quad} \qquad\qquad \underline{\quad 3 \quad 3 \quad}$$
$$x = 9 \qquad\qquad\qquad x = -3$$

Thus, the solution set is $\{9, -3\}$.

EXAMPLE 4   Find the solution set of $x^2 + 16x + 55 = 0$ by completing the square.

To get $x^2 + 16x$ by itself on the left, add -55 to each side.

Complete the square. ⟶
$16 = 2(8)$ and $8^2 = 64$. Add 64 to each side.

$x^2 + 16x + 64$:

$x^2 + 16x + 64 = (x + 8)^2$

Add -8 to each side. ⟶

$$x^2 + 16x + 55 = 0$$
$$\underline{\qquad\qquad -55 \qquad -55}$$
$$x^2 + 16x = -55$$
$$x^2 + 16x + \underline{} = -55 + \underline{}$$
$$x^2 + 16x + 64 = -55 + 64$$
$$x^2 + 16x + 64 = 9$$
$$(x + 8)^2 = 9$$

$$x + 8 = +\sqrt{9} \text{ or } x + 8 = -\sqrt{9}$$
$$x + 8 = +3 \qquad\qquad x + 8 = -3$$
$$x = -5 \qquad\qquad\qquad x = -11$$

Check -5 and -11 in $x^2 + 16x + 55 = 0$. ⟶ **Thus,** the solution set is $\{-5, -11\}$.

EXAMPLE 5   Find the solution set of $x^2 + 10x - 4 = 0$ by completing the square.

Add 4 to each side. ⟶
Complete the square. ⟶
$10 = 2(5)$ and $5^2 = 25.$ ⟶
$x^2 + 10x + 25 = (x + 5)^2$ ⟶

Add -5 to each side. ⟶

We may show the solution set as $\{-5 \pm \sqrt{29}\}$.

$$x^2 + 10x - 4 = 0$$
$$x^2 + 10x = 4$$
$$x^2 + 10x + \underline{} = 4 + \underline{}$$
$$x^2 + 10x + 25 = 4 + 25$$
$$(x + 5)^2 = 29$$
$$x + 5 = +\sqrt{29} \text{ or } x + 5 = -\sqrt{29}$$
$$x = -5 + \sqrt{29} \text{ or } x = -5 - \sqrt{29}$$

Thus, the solution set is $\{-5 + \sqrt{29},\ -5 - \sqrt{29}\}$.

ORAL EXERCISES

What number should be added to each expression to make a perfect square trinomial?

1. $x^2 + 2x$ *1*   **2.** $x^2 - 6x$ *9*   **3.** $x^2 + 10x$ *25*   **4.** $x^2 - 4x$ *4*

5. $x^2 + 16x$ *64*   **6.** $x^2 - 8x$ *16*   **7.** $x^2 - 12x$ *36*   **8.** $x^2 + 18x$ *81*

EXERCISES

PART A

Find the solution set by completing the square.

{−1, −15}

1. $x^2 + 10x = -16$ **2.** $x^2 + 2x = 3$ **3.** $x^2 + 16x = -15$

4. $x^2 + 2x = 8$ **5.** $x^2 - 8x = -5$ **6.** $x^2 - 6x = 27$

7. $x^2 + 10x + 15 = 0$ **8.** $x^2 + 12x - 13 = 0$ **9.** $x^2 - 4x - 21 = 0$

10. $x^2 + 8x + 3 = 0$ **11.** $x^2 - 4x + 4 = 0$ **12.** $x^2 + 6x - 7 = 0$

13. $x^2 + 4x - 77 = 0$ **14.** $x^2 + 6x - 3 = 0$ **15.** $x^2 - 16x + 28 = 0$

16. $x^2 - 2x - 48 = 0$ **17.** $x^2 - 18x + 72 = 0$ **18.** $x^2 + 16x + 60 = 0$

19. $x^2 - 10x - 39 = 0$ **20.** $x^2 + 4x - 3 = 0$ **21.** $x^2 + 20x + 51 = 0$

22. $x^2 + 2x - 5 = 0$ **23.** $x^2 - 16x + 60 = 0$ **24.** $x^2 + 18x + 77 = 0$

25. $x^2 - 20x - 21 = 0$ **26.** $x^2 - 24x + 80 = 0$ *{4, 20}*   **27.** $x^2 + 30x + 155 = 0$

{21, −1}   *{−15 + √70, −15 − √70}*

PART B

EXAMPLE   Find the solution set of $x^2 + 3x - 40 = 0$ by completing the square.

$\left(\dfrac{1}{2}\right)(3) = \dfrac{3}{2}; \quad \left(\dfrac{3}{2}\right)^2 = \dfrac{9}{4}$

$$x^2 + 3x - 40 = 0$$
$$x^2 + 3x = 40$$

Add $\dfrac{9}{4}$ to each side. $\longrightarrow$

$$x^2 + 3x + \frac{9}{4} = 40 + \frac{9}{4}$$

$40\dfrac{9}{4} = \dfrac{169}{4}$ $\longrightarrow$

$$\left(x + \frac{3}{2}\right)^2 = \frac{169}{4}$$

$$x + \frac{3}{2} = \sqrt{\frac{169}{4}} \quad \text{or} \quad x + \frac{3}{2} = -\sqrt{\frac{169}{4}}$$

$$x + \frac{3}{2} = \frac{13}{2} \qquad\qquad x + \frac{3}{2} = -\frac{13}{2}$$

Add $-\dfrac{3}{2}$ to each side. $\longrightarrow$

$$x = \frac{13}{2} - \frac{3}{2} \qquad\qquad x = -\frac{13}{2} - \frac{3}{2}$$

$$x = \frac{10}{2} \qquad\qquad x = -\frac{16}{2}$$

Check 5 and −8 in

$x^2 + 3x - 40 = 0$. $\longrightarrow$

$$x = 5 \qquad \text{or} \qquad x = -8$$

Thus, the solution set is $\{5, -8\}$.

Find the solution set by completing the square.

28. $x^2 - 3x = 10$ $\{5, -2\}$ **29.** $x^2 + 9x = -8$ $\{-8, -1\}$ **30.** $x^2 - 7x = -6$ $\{6, 1\}$
31. $x^2 + 5x = 50$ $\{5, -10\}$ **32.** $x^2 - 3x = 4$ $\{4, -1\}$ **33.** $x^2 - x = 6$ $\{3, -2\}$
34. $x^2 - 11x + 28 = 0$ **35.** $x^2 + x - 30 = 0$ **36.** $x^2 + 5x + 6 = 0$
37. $x^2 + x - 12 = 0$ $\{3, -4\}$ **38.** $x^2 - 9x - 10 = 0$ **39.** $x^2 - 5x - 14 = 0$
40. $x^2 + 15x + 36 = 0$ **41.** $x^2 - 17x + 30 = 0$ **42.** $x^2 - 3x + 2 = 0$
43. $x^2 + x - 56 = 0$ $\{7, -8\}$ **44.** $x^2 - 7x - 8 = 0$ $\{8, -1\}$ **45.** $x^2 + 11 + 28 = 0$
46. $x^2 - 13x + 36 = 0$ **47.** $x^2 - 19x + 84 = 0$ **48.** $x^2 - 15x + 54 = 0$
49. $x^2 - 21x + 38 = 0$ **50.** $x^2 + 17x + 72 = 0$ **51.** $x^2 + 15x - 34 = 0$
52. $x^2 + 23x + 60 = 0$ **53.** $x^2 - 25x + 100 = 0$ $\{20, 5\}$ **54.** $x^2 - 21x - 46 = 0$
   $\{-3, -20\}$ $\{23, -2\}$

PART C

EXAMPLE Find the solution set of $x^2 + 7x - 2 = 0$ by completing the square.

$$x^2 + 7x - 2 = 0$$
$$x^2 + 7x \qquad = 2$$

$\left(\frac{1}{2}\right)(7) = \frac{7}{2};\ \left(\frac{7}{2}\right)^2 = \frac{49}{4}$ ⟶

$$x^2 + 7x + \frac{49}{4} = 2 + \frac{49}{4}$$

Add $\frac{49}{4}$ to each side.

$$\left(x + \frac{7}{2}\right)^2 = \frac{57}{4}$$

$$x + \frac{7}{2} = \sqrt{\frac{57}{4}} \qquad \text{or} \quad x + \frac{7}{2} = -\sqrt{\frac{57}{4}}$$

$\sqrt{\frac{57}{4}} = \frac{\sqrt{57}}{\sqrt{4}} = \frac{\sqrt{57}}{2}$ ⟶

$$x + \frac{7}{2} = \frac{\sqrt{57}}{2} \qquad\qquad x + \frac{7}{2} = -\frac{\sqrt{57}}{2}$$

Add $-\frac{7}{2}$ to each side. ⟶

$$x = -\frac{7}{2} + \frac{\sqrt{57}}{2} \qquad\qquad x = -\frac{7}{2} - \frac{\sqrt{57}}{2}$$

$$x = \frac{-7 + \sqrt{57}}{2} \quad \text{or} \qquad x = \frac{-7 - \sqrt{57}}{2}$$

We may show the solution set as $\left\{\frac{-7 \pm \sqrt{57}}{2}\right\}$.

Thus, the solution set is $\left\{\dfrac{-7 + \sqrt{57}}{2}, \dfrac{-7 - \sqrt{57}}{2}\right\}$.

Find the solution set by completing the square.

55. $x^2 + 7x + 3 = 0$ **56.** $x^2 + 11x + 20 = 0$ **57.** $x^2 + 5x + 1 = 0$
58. $x^2 - 3x - 5 = 0$ **59.** $x^2 + 5x - 1 = 0$ **60.** $x^2 - 7x - 2 = 0$
61. $x^2 - x - 3 = 0$ **62.** $x^2 + 2x + 2 = 0$ **63.** $x^2 + 7x + 4 = 0$
64. $x^2 + 3x - 1 = 0$ **65.** $x^2 - x + 1 = 0$ **66.** $x^2 - 9x + 3 = 0$

The Quadratic Formula

OBJECTIVES

■ To determine a, b, and c in a quadratic equation $ax^2 + bx + c = 0$

■ To solve a quadratic equation with integer solutions by using the quadratic formula

 REVIEW CAPSULE

Determine a, b, and c in $x^2 - 5x + 2 = 0$.

Standard form: $\quad ax^2 \; + \; bx \; + c = 0$
$$(1)x^2 + (-5)x + 2 = 0$$

Thus, $a = 1$, $b = -5$, and $c = 2$.

EXAMPLE 1   Find the solution set of $2x^2 + 3x - 1 = 0$ by completing the square.

$$2x^2 + 3x - 1 = 0$$

Add 1 to each side. ⟶ $\qquad 2x^2 + 3x \quad = 1$

Divide each side by 2. ⟶ $\qquad \dfrac{2x^2 + 3x}{2} \quad = \dfrac{1}{2}$

$\left(\dfrac{1}{2}\right)\left(\dfrac{3}{2}\right) = \dfrac{3}{4}; \left(\dfrac{3}{4}\right)^2 = \dfrac{9}{16}$ $\qquad x^2 + \dfrac{3}{2}x \quad = \dfrac{1}{2}$

Add $\dfrac{9}{16}$ to each side. ⟶ $\qquad x^2 + \dfrac{3}{2}x + \dfrac{9}{16} = \dfrac{1}{2} + \dfrac{9}{16}$

$$\left(x + \dfrac{3}{4}\right)^2 = \dfrac{17}{16}$$

Solve each equation. $\qquad x + \dfrac{3}{4} = \sqrt{\dfrac{17}{16}} \qquad$ or $\quad x + \dfrac{3}{4} = -\sqrt{\dfrac{17}{16}}$

$\sqrt{\dfrac{17}{16}} = \dfrac{\sqrt{17}}{\sqrt{16}} = \dfrac{\sqrt{17}}{4}$ ⟶ $\quad x + \dfrac{3}{4} = \dfrac{\sqrt{17}}{4} \qquad\qquad x + \dfrac{3}{4} = -\dfrac{\sqrt{17}}{4}$

Add $-\dfrac{3}{4}$ to each side. ⟶ $\quad x = -\dfrac{3}{4} + \dfrac{\sqrt{17}}{4} \qquad\quad x = -\dfrac{3}{4} - \dfrac{\sqrt{17}}{4}$

4 is the common denominator. $\quad x = \dfrac{-3 + \sqrt{17}}{4} \quad$ or $\qquad x = \dfrac{-3 - \sqrt{17}}{4}$

We may write the solution set as

$\left\{\dfrac{-3 \pm \sqrt{17}}{4}\right\}.$ ⟶ **Thus,** the solution set is $\left\{\dfrac{-3 + \sqrt{17}}{4}, \dfrac{-3 - \sqrt{17}}{4}\right\}.$

We now use this process to derive a formula for solving a quadratic equation.

EXAMPLE 2 Solve $ax^2 + bx + c = 0$, $(a > 0)$ by completing the square.

$$ax^2 + bx + c = 0$$

Add $-c$ to each side. ⟶ $$ax^2 + bx \qquad = -c$$

Divide each side by a. ⟶ $$\frac{ax^2 + bx}{a} = \frac{-c}{a}$$

$\left(\dfrac{1}{2}\right)\left(\dfrac{b}{a}\right) = \dfrac{b}{2a}; \left(\dfrac{b}{2a}\right)^2 = \dfrac{b^2}{4a^2};$

$$x^2 + \frac{b}{a}x = \frac{-c}{a}$$

Add $\dfrac{b^2}{4a^2}$ to each side. ⟶ $$x^2 + \frac{b}{a}x + \frac{b^2}{4a^2} = \frac{-c}{a} + \frac{b^2}{4a^2}$$

$4a^2$ is a common denominator on the right. ⟶ $$\left(x + \frac{b}{2a}\right)^2 = \frac{-4ac + b^2}{4a^2}$$

$$\left(x + \frac{b}{2a}\right)^2 = \frac{b^2 - 4ac}{4a^2}$$

$$x + \frac{b}{2a} \qquad\qquad\text{or}\qquad x + \frac{b}{2a}$$

$$= \sqrt{\frac{b^2 - 4ac}{4a^2}} \qquad\qquad = -\sqrt{\frac{b^2 - 4ac}{4a^2}}$$

Add $-\dfrac{b}{2a}$ to each side; $\sqrt{4a^2} = 2a$. ⟶ $$x = -\frac{b}{2a} + \frac{\sqrt{b^2 - 4ac}}{2a} \qquad x = -\frac{b}{2a} - \frac{\sqrt{b^2 - 4ac}}{2a}$$

$2a$ is a common denominator. ⟶ $$x = \frac{-b + \sqrt{b^2 - 4ac}}{2a} \qquad\text{or}\qquad x = \frac{-b - \sqrt{b^2 - 4ac}}{2a}$$

$\pm$ means $+$ or $-$. ⟶
A similar proof can be shown for $a < 0$.

Thus, $x = \dfrac{-b \pm \sqrt{b^2 - 4ac}}{2a}$.

Example 2 gives this formula. ⟶

> ### The Quadratic Formula
> The solutions of a quadratic equation of the form
> $$ax^2 + bx + c = 0$$
> may be found by the formula
> $$x = \frac{-b \pm \sqrt{b^2 - 4ac}}{2a}$$

EXAMPLE 3 Rewrite $5x = 6x^2 - 7$ in standard form. Then determine a, b, and c.

$$5x = 6x^2 - 7$$

Add $-5x$ to each side. ⟶ $$0 = 6x^2 - 7 - 5x$$

Rearrange in descending order. ⟶ $$0 = 6x^2 - 5x - 7$$

$$\uparrow \qquad \uparrow \quad \uparrow$$

Standard form ⟶ $$0 = ax^2 + bx + c$$

$$a = 6,\ b = -5,\ \text{and}\ c = -7.$$

EXAMPLE 4   Solve $x^2 - 9x + 14 = 0$ by using the quadratic formula.

Determine a, b, and c. $\longrightarrow$ $a = 1,\ b = -9,\ c = 14$

Quadratic formula $\longrightarrow$ $x = \dfrac{-b \pm \sqrt{b^2 - 4ac}}{2a}$

Substitute for a, b, and c. $\longrightarrow$ $x = \dfrac{-(-9) \pm \sqrt{(-9)^2 - 4(1)(14)}}{2(1)}$

$-(-9) = 9$ $\longrightarrow$ $x = \dfrac{9 \pm \sqrt{81 - 56}}{2}$

$x = \dfrac{9 \pm \sqrt{25}}{2}$

$x = \dfrac{9 \pm 5}{2}$

$\pm$ means $+$ or $-$. $\longrightarrow$ $x = \dfrac{9 + 5}{2}$ or $x = \dfrac{9 - 5}{2}$

$x = \dfrac{14}{2}$ or $x = \dfrac{4}{2}$ $\longrightarrow$ $x = 7$ or $x = 2$

Check 7 and 2 in $x^2 - 9x + 14 = 0$. $\longrightarrow$ **Thus,** the solutions are 7 and 2.

EXERCISES

PART A

Rewrite each equation in standard form. Then determine a, b, and c.
$2;\ -4;\ -8$

1. $2x^2 + 6x + 5 = 0$ $2;\ 6;\ 5$ 2. $4x^2 + 3x + 2 = 0$ $4;\ 3;\ 2$ 3. $2x^2 - 4x - 8 = 0$
4. $2x^2 - 4x = 0$ $2;\ -4;\ 0$ 5. $x^2 + 2x = 0$ $1;\ 2;\ 0$ 6. $3x^2 + 7 = 0$ $3;\ 0;\ 7$
7. $x^2 - 5 = 0$ $1;\ 0;\ -5$ 8. $x^2 = 6x - 3$ $1;\ -6;\ 3$ 9. $3x^2 - 6x = 2$
10. $x^2 = 4$ $1;\ 0;\ -4$ 11. $5x^2 = 3x$ $5;\ -3;\ 0$ 12. $2 + 6x = 4x^2$

Solve by using the quadratic formula.

13. $x^2 + 4x + 3 = 0$ $-3, -1$ 14. $x^2 - 5x + 6 = 0$ $3,\ 2$ 15. $x^2 - 2x + 1 = 0$ 1
16. $x^2 + 3x - 10 = 0$ $2, -5$ 17. $x^2 - 4x - 21 = 0$ $7, -3$ 18. $x^2 - 2x - 24 = 0$ $6, -4$
19. $x^2 + 3x - 40 = 0$ $5, -8$ 20. $x^2 - 12x - 13 = 0$ $13, -1$ 21. $x^2 - 8x + 16 = 0$ 4

PART B

Find the solution set by using the quadratic formula.
$\{15, -3\}$

22. $x^2 = 6 - x$ $\{2, -3\}$ 23. $x^2 - 11 = -10x$ $\{1, -11\}$ 24. $-12x = 45 - x^2$
25. $-30 = x - x^2$ $\{6, -5\}$ 26. $x^2 = -2x + 3$ $\{1, -3\}$ 27. $5x = -x^2 - 4$ $\{-1, -4\}$
28. $9x - x^2 = 8$ $\{8, 1\}$ 29. $16 = 4x^2$ $\{2, -2\}$ 30. $-3x = x^2 + 2$ $\{-1, -2\}$
31. $6x^2 = 12 + 6x$ $\{2, -1\}$ 32. $3x^2 = -9x$ $\{0, -3\}$ 33. $-36 = 16x - x^2$

Wet Mixture Problems *(optional)*

<table>
<tr>
<td>

OBJECTIVE

■ To solve problems about wet mixtures

</td>
<td>

 REVIEW CAPSULE

A 30-liter solution is made up of iodine and alcohol. The solution is 20% iodine. How many liters of iodine are in the solution?

$$\begin{pmatrix}\text{Number}\\\text{of liters}\\\text{of iodine}\end{pmatrix}=\begin{pmatrix}\text{Percent}\\\text{iodine}\end{pmatrix}\cdot\begin{pmatrix}\text{Total number}\\\text{of liters}\\\text{in solution}\end{pmatrix}$$

Liters of iodine = .20 · 30

Decimal is used for percent.

= 6.00

Thus, there are 6 liters (L) of iodine in the solution.

</td>
</tr>
</table>

EXAMPLE 1 A solution of 60 liters contains a mixture of alcohol and water. If 30% of the solution is alcohol, how many liters are water?

Total liters, 60 is 100%. ⟶ If 30% is alcohol, 100% − 30%, or 70%, is water.

$$\begin{aligned}\text{Liters of water} &= \text{Percent water} \cdot \text{Total liters}\\ &= .70\,(60)\\ &= 42.00\end{aligned}$$

Thus, there are 42 liters of water in the solution.

EXAMPLE 2 A chemist had 20 liters of a 65% salt solution. *X* liters of water were added to reduce it to a 45% salt solution. Write an algebraic solution for the number of liters of water in the 45% salt solution.

$$\begin{aligned}\text{L in new solution} &= \text{original total} + \text{water added}\\ &= \quad 20 \quad + \quad x\end{aligned}$$

Percent water = 100% − Percent salt ⎫
= 100% − 45% = 55% ⎭

$$\begin{aligned}\text{Liters of water} &= \text{Percent water} \cdot \text{Total liters}\\ &= .55\,(20 + x)\end{aligned}$$

Thus, there are .55 (20 + x) liters of water.

EXAMPLE 3 How many liters of water must be added to 32 liters of a 25% sulfuric acid solution to reduce it to a 20% acid solution?

Represent the amount needed algebraically.

Let x = number of liters of water to be added

Make a chart. —————————→
Total L in new solution:
original total, 32
    +
water added, x

	Total L	L of Acid	L of Water
25% solution	32	.25 (32)	.75 (32)
20% solution	32 + x	.20 (32 + x)	.80 (32 + x)

Only water is added. The amounts of acid are the same in both solutions.

Write an equation. —————————→

$$\left(\begin{array}{c}\text{Acid in 25\%}\\\text{solution}\end{array}\right) = \left(\begin{array}{c}\text{Acid in 20\%}\\\text{solution}\end{array}\right)$$

Substitute. —————————→

$$.25\,(32) = .20\,(32 + x)$$
$$8 = 6.4 + .2x$$

Multiply each side by 10.

$$80 = 64 + 2x$$
$$16 = 2x$$
$$8 = x$$

Thus, 8 liters of water must be added.

EXAMPLE 4 A solution is made of an antiseptic and distilled water. How many deciliters of antiseptic must be added to 80 deciliters of a 5% antiseptic solution to make it a 24% solution?

Represent the amount needed algebraically.

Let x = number of deciliters (dL) of antiseptic to be added

Make a chart. —————————→
Total dL in new solution:
original total, 80
    +
Antiseptic added, x

	Total dL	dL of Antiseptic	dL of Water
5% solution	80	.05 (80)	.95 (80)
24% solution	80 + x	.24 (80 + x)	.76 (80 + x)

Write an equation. —————————→
Only antiseptic is added.

$$\left(\begin{array}{c}\text{Water in}\\\text{5\% solution}\end{array}\right) = \left(\begin{array}{c}\text{Water in}\\\text{24\% solution}\end{array}\right)$$

Substitute. —————————→

$$.95\,(80) = .76\,(80 + x)$$
$$76 = 60.8 + .76x$$

Multiply each side by 100.

$$7,600 = 6,080 + 76x$$
$$1,520 = 76x$$
$$20 = x$$

Thus, 20 dL of antiseptic must be added.

EXAMPLE 5 How many liters of antifreeze must be added to 20 liters of a 15% antifreeze solution (antifreeze and water), to make a 40% antifreeze solution?

Represent the amount needed algebraically.

Let x = number of liters of antifreeze to be added

Make a chart. ──────────────►

	Total L	L of Antifreeze	L of Water
15% solution	20	.15(20)	.85(20)
40% solution	20 + x	.40(20 + x)	.60(20 + x)

Write an equation.
Since only antifreeze is added, amount of water in each stays the same.

Multiply each side by 100.

$$\left(\begin{array}{c}\text{L of water in}\\ \text{15\% solution}\end{array}\right) = \left(\begin{array}{c}\text{L of water in}\\ \text{40\% solution}\end{array}\right)$$
$$.85(20) = .60(20 + x)$$
$$17.00 = 12.00 + .60x$$
$$1{,}700 = 1{,}200 + 60x$$
$$500 = 60x$$
$$8\tfrac{1}{3} = x$$

Thus, $8\tfrac{1}{3}$ L of antifreeze must be added.

EXAMPLE 6 A chemist has one solution that is 20% alcohol and a more concentrated solution that is 85% alcohol. How much of the more concentrated solution must be added to 8 dL of the original solution to obtain a solution that is 45% alcohol?

Represent the amount needed algebraically.

Let x = number of dL of 85% solution to be added

Make a chart. ──────────────►
Total dL in new solution:
original total, 8
+
added concentrate, x

	Total dL	dL of Alcohol
20% solution	8	.20(8)
85% solution	x	.85(x)
45% solution	8 + x	.45(8 + x)

Write an equation. ──────────────►

Substitute. ──────────────►

Multiply each side by 100.

$$\left(\begin{array}{c}\text{Alcohol in}\\ \text{20\% solution}\end{array}\right) + \left(\begin{array}{c}\text{Alcohol in}\\ \text{85\% solution}\end{array}\right) = \left(\begin{array}{c}\text{Alcohol in}\\ \text{45\% solution}\end{array}\right)$$

$$
\begin{array}{rcl}
.20(8) & + & .85(x) = .45(8 + x) \\
1.6 & + & .85x = 3.6 + .45x \\
160 & + & 85x = 360 + 45x \\
 & & 40x = 200 \\
 & & x = 5
\end{array}
$$

Thus, 5 dL of the 85% solution must be added.

EXERCISES

1. How many liters of water must be added to 9 liters of a 40% solution of hydrochloric acid to make it a 30% acid solution?

2. A nurse has 4 liters of a mixture that is 20% medicine. How much more medicine must be added to make it a 36% mixture?

3. Dr. Rivers has 3 liters of a 60% salt solution. How many liters of water must be added to obtain a 20% solution?

4. A pharmacist has 100 deciliters of a 10% peroxide in water solution. How much peroxide must be added to obtain a 20% solution?

5. A farmer has 200 liters of milk that tests 9.2% butterfat. How many liters of skimmed milk (without butterfat) must be added to obtain milk that tests 6.4% butterfat?

6. A chemist has a solution of alcohol and water. How many cubic centimeters (cm^3) of alcohol must be added to 60 cm^3 of a 28% solution to make it a 46% solution?

7. How many liters of water must a chemist add to 24 liters of a sulfuric acid solution that is 30% acid to obtain a solution that is 10% acid?

8. A pharmacist has 3 deciliters of cough medicine that is 10% water. For children, it must be 40% water. How much water must be added?

9. How many liters of water must be added to 26 liters of a 15% antifreeze solution to dilute it to a 12% solution?

10. A solution of 40 milliliters is 50% acid. How many milliliters of water must be added to dilute it to a 20% acid solution?

11. A solution of 4 deciliters is 20% iodine. How many deciliters of a 50% iodine solution must be added in order to obtain a 30% iodine solution?

12. How many cubic centimeters of a solution that is 65% alcohol must be added to 50 cm^3 of a 25% alcohol solution to make a 40% solution?

13. Dr. Green has one solution that is 40% salt and another solution that is 65% salt. How much of the 65% solution must be added to 5 deciliters of the original solution to obtain a solution that is 55% salt?

14. A chemist wants to add a 15% acid solution to 30 deciliters of a 70% acid solution to reduce it to a 45% acid solution. How much of the 15% solution must be added?

Applying the Quadratic Formula

 REVIEW CAPSULE

Quadratic Equation	Standard Form	a	b	c
$x^2 - 7x + 2 = 0$	same	1	-7	2
$5x^2 = 3x$	$5x^2 - 3x + 0 = 0$	5	-3	0
$-x - 8 = -x^2$	$x^2 - x - 8 = 0$	1	-1	-8

Quadratic Formula

$$x = \frac{-b \pm \sqrt{b^2 - 4ac}}{2a}$$

EXAMPLE 1 Find the solution set of $2x^2 + x = 6$ by using the quadratic formula.

Add -6 to each side to get standard form. $\longrightarrow$
$$2x^2 + x = 6$$
$$2x^2 + 1x - 6 = 0$$

Determine a, b, and c. $\longrightarrow$
$$a = 2 \qquad b = 1 \qquad c = -6$$

Quadratic formula $\longrightarrow$
$$x = \frac{-b \pm \sqrt{b^2 - 4ac}}{2a}$$

Substitute for a, b, and c. $\longrightarrow$
$$x = \frac{-1 \pm \sqrt{1^2 - 4(2)(-6)}}{2(2)}$$

$-4(2)(-6) = 48$ $\longrightarrow$
$$x = \frac{-1 \pm \sqrt{1 + 48}}{4}$$

$$x = \frac{-1 \pm \sqrt{49}}{4}$$

$$x = \frac{-1 \pm 7}{4}$$

$$x = \frac{-1 + 7}{4} \quad \text{or} \quad x = \frac{-1 - 7}{4}$$

$$x = \frac{6}{4} \quad \text{or} \quad x = \frac{-8}{4}$$

$$x = \frac{3}{2} \quad \text{or} \quad x = -2$$

Rational solutions $\longrightarrow$ **Thus,** the solution set is $\left\{\dfrac{3}{2}, -2\right\}$.

EXAMPLE 2 Find the solution set of $3x^2 + x - 1 = 0$ by using the quadratic formula.

$$x = \frac{-b \pm \sqrt{b^2 - 4ac}}{2a}$$

$3x^2 + 1x - 1 = 0$

$a = 3, b = 1, c = -1$

$$x = \frac{-1 \pm \sqrt{1^2 - 4(3)(-1)}}{2(3)}$$

$$x = \frac{-1 \pm \sqrt{1 + 12}}{6}$$

Irrational solutions $\longrightarrow$

$$x = \frac{-1 \pm \sqrt{13}}{6}$$

Thus, the solution set is $\left\{ \dfrac{-1 \pm \sqrt{13}}{6} \right\}$.

EXAMPLE 3 Find the solution set of $3x^2 - x + 1 = 0$ by using the quadratic formula.

$$x = \frac{-b \pm \sqrt{b^2 - 4ac}}{2a}$$

$3x^2 - 1x + 1 = 0$

$a = 3, b = -1, c = 1.$

$$x = \frac{-(-1) \pm \sqrt{(-1)^2 - 4(3)(1)}}{2(3)}$$

$$x = \frac{1 \pm \sqrt{1 - 12}}{6}$$

$\sqrt{-11}$ is not a real number. $\longrightarrow$

$$x = \frac{1 \pm \sqrt{-11}}{6}$$

No real solutions $\longrightarrow$ **Thus,** the solution set is ϕ.

EXAMPLE 4 Find the solution set of $x^2 - 2x - 1 = 0$ by using the quadratic formula.

$$x = \frac{-b \pm \sqrt{b^2 - 4ac}}{2a}$$

$1x^2 - 2x - 1 = 0$

$a = 1, b = -2, c = -1.$

$$x = \frac{-(-2) \pm \sqrt{(-2)^2 - 4(1)(-1)}}{2(1)}$$

$$x = \frac{2 \pm \sqrt{4 + 4}}{2}$$

$$x = \frac{2 \pm \sqrt{8}}{2}$$

$\sqrt{8} = \sqrt{4 \cdot 2} = 2\sqrt{2}$ $\longrightarrow$

$$x = \frac{2 \pm 2\sqrt{2}}{2}$$

Factor numerator and denominator.}
Simplify. }

$$x = \frac{\overset{1}{2}(1 \pm \sqrt{2})}{\underset{1}{2}}$$

$$x = 1 \pm \sqrt{2}$$

Irrational solutions $\longrightarrow$ **Thus,** the solution set is $\{1 \pm \sqrt{2}\}$.

EXERCISES

PART A

Find the solution set by using the quadratic formula.

1. $2x^2 + 5x - 3 = 0$ $\{-3, \frac{1}{2}\}$
2. $3x^2 - 7x + 2 = 0$ $\{2, \frac{1}{3}\}$
3. $6x^2 - x - 2 = 0$ $\{-\frac{1}{2}, \frac{2}{3}\}, \{\frac{5}{4}, \frac{3}{2}\}$ $\{\frac{10}{3}\}$
4. $2x^2 - 7x + 3 = 0$ $\{\frac{1}{2}, 3\}$
5. $2x^2 - 11x + 12 = 0$ $\{\frac{3}{2}, 4\}$
6. $8x^2 - 22x + 15 = 0$
7. $3x^2 + 5x - 2 = 0$ $\{-2, \frac{1}{3}\}$
8. $2x^2 - 3x - 9 = 0$ $\{-\frac{3}{2}, 3\}$
9. $9x^2 - 60x + 100 = 0$
10. $x^2 - 5x - 2 = 0$ $\{\frac{5 \pm \sqrt{33}}{2}\}$
11. $x^2 - 7x + 3 = 0$ $\{\frac{7 \pm \sqrt{37}}{2}\}$
12. $x^2 - 7x - 3 = 0$ $\{\frac{7 \pm \sqrt{61}}{2}\}$
13. $2x^2 + 4x + 3 = 0$ ϕ
14. $x^2 + x - 1 = 0$ $\{\frac{-1 \pm \sqrt{5}}{2}\}$
15. $x^2 + 5x - 3 = 0$ $\{\frac{-5 \pm \sqrt{37}}{2}\}$
16. $x^2 + x - 5 = 0$ $\{\frac{-1 \pm \sqrt{21}}{2}\}$
17. $3x^2 - 7x + 9 = 0$ ϕ
18. $x^2 - 3x + 1 = 0$ $\{\frac{3 \pm \sqrt{5}}{2}\}$
19. $5x^2 - 3x + 2 = 0$ ϕ
20. $x^2 - 6x - 2 = 0$ $\{3 \pm \sqrt{11}\}$
21. $x^2 - 4x - 10 = 0$
22. $x^2 - 10x = -5$ $\{5 \pm 2\sqrt{5}\}$
23. $x^2 = 8x - 3$ $\{4 \pm \sqrt{13}\}$
24. $x^2 + 2x + 7 = 0$ ϕ
25. $2x^2 - 12 = -5x$ $\{\frac{3}{2}, -4\}$
26. $15x = 9x^2 + 4$ $\{\frac{4}{3}, \frac{1}{3}\}$
27. $x^2 + 1 = -4x$
28. $x^2 + 8 = 3x$ ϕ
29. $x^2 = 7x - 11$ $\{\frac{7 \pm \sqrt{5}}{2}\}$
30. $2x^2 + 9 = 9x$ $\{3, \frac{3}{2}\}$

$\{-2 \pm \sqrt{3}\}$
$\{2 \pm \sqrt{14}\}$

PART B

EXAMPLE Find the solution set of $\frac{1}{2}x^2 - \frac{3}{2}x + \frac{5}{6} = 0$.

Multiply by the LCD, 6. ————→

$$6\left(\frac{1}{2}x^2 - \frac{3}{2}x + \frac{5}{6}\right) = 6(0)$$

$$3x^2 - 9x + 5 = 0$$

$$x = \frac{-(-9) \pm \sqrt{(-9)^2 - 4(3)(5)}}{2(3)}$$

$$x = \frac{9 \pm \sqrt{21}}{6}$$

Thus, the solution set is $\left\{\frac{9 + \sqrt{21}}{6}, \frac{9 - \sqrt{21}}{6}\right\}$.

Find the solution set.

31. $x^2 + \frac{3}{2}x - \frac{5}{2} = 0$ $\{1, -\frac{5}{2}\}$
32. $x^2 - \frac{7}{4}x + \frac{3}{4} = 0$ $\{1, \frac{3}{4}\}$
33. $x^2 - \frac{3}{2}x + \frac{9}{16} = 0$
34. $x^2 + \frac{5}{2}x + 1 = 0$ $\{-2, -\frac{1}{2}\}$
35. $x^2 - \frac{4}{5}x - 1 = 0$ $\{\frac{2 \pm \sqrt{29}}{5}\}$
36. $\frac{1}{2}x^2 + \frac{1}{2}x - 2 = 0$

PART C

Find the solution set. Use the quadratic formula.

37. $x^2 - (2\sqrt{2})x - 2 = 0$
38. $(\sqrt{3})x^2 - 2x - 2\sqrt{3} = 0$
39. $\frac{x + 6}{2} = \frac{2}{x}$

Area Problems

▶ REVIEW CAPSULE

$$A = lw$$

w

l

Find the area of a rectangle whose length is 7 m and whose width is 3 m.

$$A = lw$$
$$= 7 \cdot 3, \text{ or 21 square meters or 21 m}^2$$

EXAMPLE 1 The length of a rectangle is 3 cm more than the width. The area is 70 square cm. Find the length and the width.

Represent length and width algebraically; draw a rough sketch. ───────→

Let x = width in cm
$x + 3$ = length in cm

x

x + 3

Formula for area ───────→
Substitute for A, l, and w. ───────→
$(x + 3)x = x \cdot x + 3 \cdot x = x^2 + 3x$ ───────→

Add −70 to each side to get standard form. ───────→

$$A = lw$$
$$70 = (x + 3)x$$
$$70 = x^2 + 3x$$
$$\underline{-70 = \qquad\qquad -70}$$
$$0 = x^2 + 3x - 70$$

Two ways to solve $x^2 + 3x - 70$

Factor   Quadratic formula

$$0 = (x + 10)(x - 7)$$
$$x + 10 = 0 \quad \text{or } x - 7 = 0$$

$a = 1, b = 3, c = 70.$

$$x = -10 \quad \text{or} \quad x = 7$$

−10 is an extraneous solution. ───────→

Reject −10, since a rectangle cannot have a negative number as its width.

$$x = \frac{-b \pm \sqrt{b^2 - 4ac}}{2a}$$
$$x = \frac{-3 \pm \sqrt{9 + 280}}{2}$$
$$x = \frac{-3 \pm \sqrt{289}}{2}$$
$$x = \frac{-3 \pm 17}{2}$$

$\dfrac{-3 \pm 17}{2}$ means $\dfrac{-3 + 17}{2}$ or $\dfrac{-3 - 17}{2}$

Width, x is 7.
Length, $x + 3$ is 10.

$$x = \tfrac{14}{2} \quad \text{or} \quad x = \tfrac{-20}{2}$$
$$x = 7 \quad \text{or} \quad x = -10$$

Check: $A = lw$
$= 10 \cdot 7 = 70.$ ───────→

Thus, the length is 10 cm and the width is 7 cm.

EXAMPLE 2

The length of a rectangle is twice the width. The area is 50 m². Find the length and the width.

Represent length and width algebraically; draw a rough sketch. ⟶

Let x = width in m
$2x$ = length in m
$A = lw$

Substitute for A, l, and w. ⟶

$50 = 2x(x)$
$50 = 2x^2$

Divide each side by 2. ⟶

$25 = x^2$

If $x^2 = a$, then $x = \sqrt{a}$ or $x = -\sqrt{a}$. ⟶

$x = \sqrt{25}$ or $x = -\sqrt{25}$
$x = 5$ or $x = -5$ ← Extraneous solution
Width, x is 5.
Length, $2x$ is 10.

Check: $A = lw$
$= 10 \cdot 5 = 50.$ ⟶

Thus, the length is 10 m and the width is 5 m.

EXAMPLE 3

The length of a rectangle is 8 cm more than the width. The area is 50 cm². Find the length and the width.

Represent length and width algebraically; draw a rough sketch. ⟶

Let x = width in cm
$x + 8$ = length in cm
$A = lw$

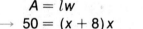

Substitute for A, l, and w. ⟶

$50 = (x + 8)x$

Distribute x. ⟶

$50 = x^2 + 8x$

Add -50 to each side. ⟶

$0 = x^2 + 8x - 50$

$$x = \frac{-b \pm \sqrt{b^2 - 4ac}}{2a}$$

Replace a with 1, b with 8, and c with -50.

$$x = \frac{-8 \pm \sqrt{(8)^2 - 4(1)(-50)}}{2(1)}$$

$\left.\begin{array}{l}(8)^2 = 64. -4(1)(-50) = 200; \\ 64 + 200 = 264\end{array}\right\}$

$$x = \frac{-8 \pm \sqrt{264}}{2}$$

$$x = \frac{-8 \pm \sqrt{4(66)}}{2}$$

$$x = \frac{-8 \pm 2\sqrt{66}}{2}$$

Divide numerator and denominator by the common factor, 2. ⟶

$x = -4 \pm \sqrt{66}$

From the table, $\sqrt{66} \doteq 8.12$. ⟶

$x = -4 + \sqrt{66} \doteq -4 + 8.12 = 4.12 \doteq 4.1$, or

Extraneous solution. ⟶

$x = -4 - \sqrt{66} \doteq -4 - 8.12 = -12.12$
Width, x is 4.1.
Length, $x + 8$ is 12.1.

Check: $(12.1)(4.1) = 49.61$, which is 50 to the nearest whole number. ⟶

Thus, the length is 12.1 cm and the width is 4.1 cm, to the nearest tenth.

ORAL EXERCISES

Give the area of each rectangle in terms of x.

1. $l = 7x$; $w = 2x$ $14x^2$ **2.** $l = x + 1$; $w = x$ $x^2 + x$ **3.** $l = 3x$; $w = x + 5$ ↗
$3x^2 + 15x$

4. $l = x + 3$; $w = x - 3$ $x^2 - 9$ **5.** $l = 2x + 5$; $w = 2x - 5$ **6.** $l = 3x + 2$; $w = 2x - 3$
$4x^2 - 25$ ↙ $6x^2 - 5x - 6$ ↙

EXERCISES

PART A

Find the length and the width of each rectangle.
$l = 10$, $w = 5$ ↘

1. The length is 3 m more than the width. The area is 40 m². $l = 8$, $w = 5$

2. The length is 5 cm less than 3 times the width. The area is 50 cm².

3. The length is twice the width. The area is 32 m². $l = 8$, $w = 4$

4. The length is 3 times the width. The area is 27 m². $l = 9$, $w = 3$

5. The length is 3 cm more than twice the width. The area is 44 cm².

6. The length is 2 m more than twice the width. The area is 60 m².

7. The length is 3 cm less than twice the width. The area is 20 cm².

8. The length is 1 m less than twice the width. The area is 28 m².

9. The length is 6 cm more than the width. The area is 20 cm². $l = 8.4$, $w = 2.4$

10. The length is 15 m more than the width. The area is 50 m².

11. The width is 2 m less than the length. The area is 44 m². $l = 7.7$, $w = 5.7$

12. The width is 4 km less than the length. The area is 6 km². ↘
$l = 5.2$, $w = 1.2$

PART B

Find the length and the width of each rectangle.
$l = 12$, $w = 8$ ↗ $l = 19$, $w = 8$ ↖

13. The length is 4 cm less than twice the width. The area is 96 cm².

14. The length is 5 m less than 3 times the width. The area is 152 m².

15. The length is 3 km greater than twice the width. The area is 90 km². $l = 15$, $w = 6$

16. The length is 1 cm less than twice the width. The area is 91 cm².

17. The length is 2 km more than 4 times the width. The area is 72 km².

18. The length is twice the width. The area is 128 cm². $l = 16$, $w = 8$

19. The width is 5 m less than the length. The area is 25 m². ↘
$l = 8.1$, $w = 3.1$

20. The width is 3 km less than twice the length. The area is 4 km². ↘
$l = 2.4$, $w = 1.8$

PART C

Find the length and the width of each rectangle.

21. The perimeter is 24. The area is 35.

22. The perimeter is 44. The area is 120.

Zeller's Congruence

ON WHAT DAY OF THE WEEK
DID JULY 4, 1776 FALL?

Almanacs have perpetual calendars to answer this question. A mathematical formula can also be used.

Zeller's Congruence

$$f = \left\{ [2.6m - 0.2] + k + D + \left[\frac{D}{4}\right] + \left[\frac{C}{4}\right] - 2C \right\} \bmod 7$$

m = month code number C = first two digits of year
k = date of month D = last two digits of year
f = day of week code number

Chart 1: Code Number for Month

Month	Code Number (m)
January	11*
February	12*
March	1
April	2
May	3
June	4
July	5
August	6
September	7
October	8
November	9
December	10

Chart 2: Code Number for Day

Day of Week	Code Number (f)
Sunday	0
Monday	1
Tuesday	2
Wednesday	3
Thursday	4
Friday	5
Saturday	6

*Use the last two digits of the preceding year.

PROBLEM

On what day of the week did July 4, 1776 fall? Use Zeller's congruence.

JULY	4	17	76
↓	↓	↓	↓
$m = 5$	$k = 4$	$C = 17$	$D = 76$
(See Chart 1.)			

$$[2.6m - 0.2] + k + D + \left[\frac{D}{4}\right] + \left[\frac{C}{4}\right] - 2C$$

$$[2.6(5) - 0.2] + 4 + 76 + \left[\frac{76}{4}\right] + \left[\frac{17}{4}\right] - 2 \cdot 17$$

$$[13.0 - 0.2] + 4 + 76 + \left[\frac{76}{4}\right] + \left[\frac{17}{4}\right] - 34$$

$$[12.8] + 4 + 76 + \left[\frac{76}{4}\right] + \left[\frac{17}{4}\right] - 34$$

[ ] means the greatest integer less than or equal to the number. →

$$12 + 4 + 76 + 19 + 4 - 34$$

$$81$$

$$\begin{array}{r} 11 \\ 7\overline{)81} \\ 77 \\ \hline 4 \end{array} \rightarrow \text{remainder}$$

The { } mod 7 around the formula means that we must find the remainder from dividing 81 by 7.

Now, use Chart 2. July 4, 1776 fell on a Thursday.

PROJECT

1. Check to see if Zeller's congruence works for today's date.

2. Use Zeller's congruence to find out on what day of the week you were born. Consult an almanac to check your answer.

3. Use Zeller's congruence to find out on what day of the week October 31, 2001 will fall. Consult an almanac to check your answer.

Chapter Fifteen Review

Find the solution set. [p. 417, 420]

1. $\sqrt{3x} = 15$

2. $\sqrt{y} + 5 = 11$

3. $\sqrt{4x - 5} = -2$

4. $4\sqrt{3x} = \sqrt{96}$

5. $\sqrt{x^2 - 4} = -8$

6. $\sqrt{19 + 3x} = x + 3$

7. $x^2 = 100$

8. $x^2 = -49$

9. $x^2 - 36 = 0$

10. $(x - 4)^2 = 64$

11. $(x + 8)^2 = 144$

12. $(x - 3)^2 = 8$

What number should be added to each expression to make a perfect square trinomial?

13. $x^2 + 8x$

14. $x^2 - 14x$

15. $x^2 - 2x$ [p. 423]

16. $x^2 + 20x$

17. $x^2 + 5x$

18. $x^2 - 15x$

Find the solution set by completing the square. [p. 423]

19. $x^2 - 12x - 13 = 0$

20. $x^2 + 2x - 3 = 0$

21. $x^2 - 14x + 45 = 0$

22. $x^2 + 8x - 48 = 0$

23. $x^2 - 4x - 21 = 0$

24. $x^2 - 10x + 24 = 0$

25. $x^2 + 6x + 8 = 0$

26. $x^2 - 20x + 51 = 0$

27. $x^2 + 16x + 60 = 0$

Rewrite each quadratic equation in standard form. Then determine a, b, and c.

28. $3x^2 - 5x + 4 = 0$

29. $x^2 - x + 6 = 0$

30. $3x^2 + 6x = 0$ [p. 427]

31. $x^2 - 7 = 0$

32. $4x^2 = 3x$

33. $7 = 5x^2 - 4$

34. $-4x + 3x^2 = 8$

35. $1 - 2x = -7x^2$

36. $\dfrac{x^2}{2} + 4x = \dfrac{1}{6}$

Find the solution set by using the quadratic formula. [p. 434]

37. $x^2 - 6x + 8 = 0$

38. $x^2 + 2x - 15 = 0$

39. $x^2 - 7x + 12 = 0$

40. $x^2 - 5x - 6 = 0$

41. $x^2 + 7x + 10 = 0$

42. $x^2 - 10x - 11 = 0$

43. $x^2 + 4x - 21 = 0$

44. $x^2 - 15x + 50 = 0$

45. $2x - 3 = -x^2$

46. $x^2 - 10x = -24$

47. $x^2 = 7x$

48. $x^2 = 3x + 54$

49. $3x^2 + 5x - 2 = 0$

50. $4x^2 - 10x - 24 = 0$

51. $4x^2 + 8x - 5 = 0$

52. $x^2 + 3x + 10 = 0$

53. $3x^2 + 2x - 4 = 0$

54. $x^2 + 6x - 1 = 0$

55. $x^2 - 7x + 11 = 0$

56. $2x^2 - x + 7 = 0$

57. $2x^2 - 4x - 7 = 0$

58. $x^2 = 1 - x$

59. $-5x + 1 = -2x^2$

60. $3 + 2x^2 = -5x$

61. $x^2 - \dfrac{5}{3}x - 2 = 0$

62. $x^2 - \dfrac{2}{7}x = \dfrac{1}{7}$

Solve each problem. [p. 437]

63. The length of a rectangle is 3 m less than twice the width. The area is 20 m². Find the length and the width.

64. The length of a rectangle is 5 times the width. The area is 80 m². Find the length and the width.

Chapter Fifteen Test

Find the solution set.

1. $\sqrt{7x - 3} = 5$ **2.** $\sqrt{3y} + 8 = 2$ **3.** $x - 2 = \sqrt{x + 10}$

4. $x^2 = 36$ **5.** $x^2 - 100 = 0$ **6.** $(x + 5)^2 = 12$

What number should be added to each expression to make a perfect square trinomial?

7. $x^2 + 10x$ **8.** $x^2 - 4x$

9. $x^2 - 18x$ **10.** $x^2 + 7x$

Find the solution set by completing the square.

11. $x^2 + 4x + 3 = 0$ **12.** $x^2 - 10x - 39 = 0$

13. $x^2 + 6x - 16 = 0$ **14.** $x^2 - 18x - 19 = 0$

Rewrite each quadratic equation in standard form. Then determine a, b, and c.

15. $2x^2 - 5x + 4 = 0$ **16.** $x^2 = x + 8$

17. $-3x = 7 - 2x^2$ **18.** $\dfrac{x^2}{3} = 6x + \dfrac{1}{9}$

Find the solution set by using the quadratic formula.

19. $x^2 + 9x + 18 = 0$ **20.** $x^2 + x - 30 = 0$

21. $x^2 + 7x - 2 = 0$ **22.** $6x^2 - 7x + 2 = 0$

23. $2x^2 - x - 3 = 0$ **24.** $3x^2 - 2x = 4$

25. $7x^2 + 15 = 2x$ **26.** $6x^2 + 3x + 5 = 0$

27. $x^2 - \dfrac{2}{3}x - 1 = 0$ **28.** $x^2 + \dfrac{7}{4}x + \dfrac{3}{4} = 0$

Solve each problem.

29. The length of a rectangle is 5 meters less than twice the width. The area is 12 m². Find the length and the width.

30. The length of a rectangle is 3 times the width. The area is 12 km². Find the length and the width.

Approximating Cube Roots

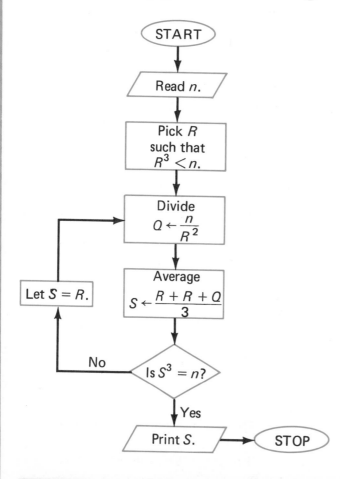

$n = 100$
Let $R = 4$. $(4)^3 < 100$

Divide by $(4)^2$, or 16.

$$\begin{array}{r} 6.2 = 6.3 \\ 16{\overline{\smash{\big)}\,100.0}} \\ \underline{96} \\ 40 \\ \underline{32} \\ 8 \end{array}$$ ← divide to one decimal place

Average. $\dfrac{4 + 4 + 6.3}{3} = \dfrac{14.3}{3}$ or 4.8

Is $(4.8)^3 = 100$? No
Divide by $(4.8)^2 = 23.04$

$$\begin{array}{r} 4.34 \\ 23.04{\overline{\smash{\big)}\,100.00{\wedge}00}} \\ \underline{92\ 16} \\ 7\ 84\ 0 \\ \underline{6\ 91\ 2} \\ 92\ 80 \\ \underline{92\ 16} \end{array}$$ ← divide to two decimal places

Average. $\dfrac{4.8 + 4.8 + 4.34}{3} = \dfrac{13.94}{3}$
$= 4.65$

$4.65^3 = 100.5$
Thus, $\sqrt[3]{100} = 4.7$ correct to one decimal place.

PROJECT Approximate $\sqrt[3]{n}$ to one decimal place.

1. 89   **2.** 21   **3.** 180   **4.** 300

Angles and Triangles

OBJECTIVES

■ To solve problems involving complementary angles
■ To solve problems involving the sum of the angle-measures of a triangle
■ To find the measure of an acute angle of a right triangle, given the measure of the other acute angle

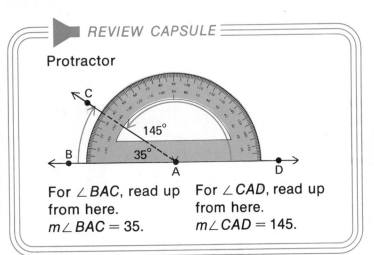

REVIEW CAPSULE

Protractor

For ∠BAC, read up from here.
m∠BAC = 35.

For ∠CAD, read up from here.
m∠CAD = 145.

Pairs of complementary angles ──────→

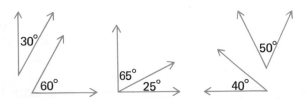

Definition of complementary angles ──────→

Complementary angles are two angles the sum of whose measures is 90°. Each is the *complement* of the other.

EXAMPLE 1

An angle is 12° greater in measure than its complement. Find the measure of the angle and its complement.

Let x = degree measure of the complement
$x + 12$ = degree measure of the angle

Write an equation: The sum of the degree measures is 90. ──────→
$$x + (x + 12) = 90$$
$$2x + 12 = 90$$
$$2x = 78$$

Measure of complement ──────→
$$x = 39$$

Measure of angle ──────→
$$x + 12 = 51$$

Check: $39 + 51 = 90$. ──────→

Thus, the angle measures 51° and its complement measures 39°.

EXAMPLE 2   Try this experiment. Cut a triangle out of paper. Tear off the three corners and fit them together, as shown below.

This is true for every triangle. ———————→ The three angles form a straight line, or 180°.

This can be proved in a geometry course. ———————→ | The sum of the measures of the three angles of a triangle is 180°.

EXAMPLE 3   The second angle of a triangle measures twice the first. The third angle measures 8 degrees more than the first. Find the measures of the three angles.

Let x = degree measure of first angle
   $2x$ = degree measure of second angle
$x + 8$ = degree measure of third angle

Sum of the measures of the three angles of a triangle is 180°. ———————→ $x + 2x + (x + 8) = 180$
$4x + 8 = 180$
Add −8 to each side. ———————→ $4x = 172$
Measure of first angle ———————→ $x = 43$
Measure of second angle ———————→ $2x = 86$
Measure of third angle ———————→ $x + 8 = 51$

Thus, the angles measure 43°, 86°, and 51°.

EXAMPLE 4   In right triangle ABC, $m\angle C = 90$, and $m\angle A = 32$. Find $m\angle B$.

Sum of the measures of the angles of a triangle is 180°. ———————→ $m\angle A + m\angle B + m\angle C = 180$
Let $x = m\angle B$. ———————→ $32 + x + 90 = 180$
$32 + 90 = 122$ ———————→ $122 + x = 180$
Add −122 to each side. ———————→ $x = 58$

Thus, $m\angle B = 58$.

In Example 4,
$m\angle A + m\angle B = 32 + 58 = 90$. ———————→ | $m\angle A + m\angle B = 90$

An acute angle has a measure of less than 90°. | *The acute angles of a right triangle are complementary.*

ORAL EXERCISES

Find the measure of the complement of the angle whose measure is given.

1. 20° *70°*   **2.** 35° *55°*   **3.** 15° *75°*   **4.** 60° *30°*   **5.** 85° *5°*   **6.** $x°$ ↘
                                                                                                                        $(90 - x)°$

In right triangle *ABC*, $m \angle C = 90$. Find $m \angle A$ for the given $m \angle B$.

7. 30° *60°*   **8.** 45° *45°*   **9.** 75° *15°*   **10.** 2° *88°*   **11.** 82° *8°*   **12.** $y°$ ↘
                                                                                                                        $(90 - y)°$

EXERCISES

PART A

1. An angle measures 24° less than its complement. Find the measure of the angle and its complement. *33°, 57°*

2. All three angles of an equilateral triangle have the same measure. What is the measure of each? *60°*

3. An angle measures 15° more than twice its complement. Find the measure of each angle. *65°, 25°*

4. The measures of the angles of a triangle are in the ratio 1:2:3. Find the measures. *30°, 60°, 90°*

5. The acute angles of a right triangle have the same measure. Find the measure of the acute angles. *45°*

6. One of two complementary angles measures 20° more than 4 times the other. Find the measures of the two angles. *14°, 76°*

7. Two angles of a triangle have the same measure. The third angle measures 20° more than 8 times the first, or second. Find the measures of the two acute angles. *16°*

8. The degree-measures of the angles of a triangle are consecutive even integers. Find the measures of the three angles. *58°, 60°, 62°*

9. One acute angle of a right triangle measures 30° more than 3 times the other acute angle. Find the measures of the two acute angles. *15°, 75°*

10. One of two complementary angles has $\frac{2}{3}$ the degree-measure of the other. Find the measures of the two angles. *54°, 36°*

PART B

11. One angle of a triangle measures 5° less than the second. The third angle measures 20° more than the complement of the second angle. Find the measures of the three angles. ↘
75°, 70°, 35°

12. One angle of a triangle measures 6° more than the second. The third angle measures 4° less than 3 times the sum of the measures of the first two angles. Find the measures of the three angles. *20°, 26°, 134°*

Similar Triangles

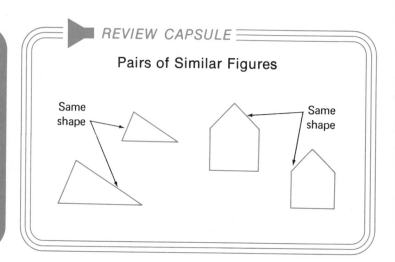
Read. ⟶

Write. ⟶

$\triangle ABC$ is similar to $\triangle DEF$.

$\triangle ABC \sim \triangle DEF$

$\triangle ABC \sim \triangle DEF$

$m\angle A = m\angle D$, $m\angle B = m\angle E$, $m\angle C = m\angle F$. The angles of each triangle are congruent, equal in measure, in the order given. $\cong$ means is congruent to.

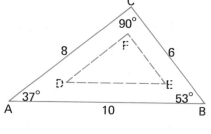

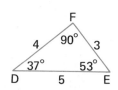

In $\triangle ABC$, $\overline{BC}$ is opposite $\angle A$.

In $\triangle DEF$, $\overline{EF}$ is opposite $\angle D$.

$$\angle A \cong \angle D$$

$$\angle B \cong \angle E$$

$$\angle C \cong \angle F$$

$$\frac{BC}{EF} = \frac{6}{3} = \frac{2}{1}$$

$$\frac{AC}{DF} = \frac{8}{4} = \frac{2}{1}$$

$$\frac{AB}{DE} = \frac{10}{5} = \frac{2}{1}$$

Corresponding sides are opposite corresponding angles in similar triangles.

Corresponding angles are congruent.

Lengths of corresponding sides have the same ratio.

Definition of similar triangles ⟶

First condition ⟶

Second condition ⟶

Two triangles are similar if the corresponding angles are congruent and the lengths of the corresponding sides have the same ratio.

EXAMPLE 1   △ABC ~ △DEF. Find x and y.

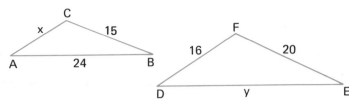

$\overline{AB}$ corresponds to $\overline{DE}$. ⟶
$\overline{BC}$ corresponds to $\overline{EF}$. ⟶
$\overline{AC}$ corresponds to $\overline{DF}$. ⟶

Lengths of corresponding sides have the same ratio. Write and solve these proportions. ⟶

$$\frac{x}{16} = \frac{15}{20}$$

$$\frac{y}{24} = \frac{20}{15}$$

Simplify $\frac{15}{20}$ to $\frac{3}{4}$. ⟶

$$\frac{x}{16} = \frac{3}{4}$$

$$\frac{y}{24} = \frac{4}{3}$$

$$4x = 3 \cdot 16$$

$$3y = 4 \cdot 24$$

$$4x = 48$$

$$3y = 96$$

$$x = 12$$

$$y = 32$$

Thus, x is 12 and y is 32.

EXAMPLE 2   △ABC ~ △DEF. AC = 9, BC = 10, and DF = 6. Find EF.

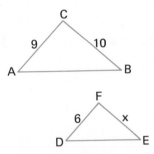

Let x = EF

$$\frac{x}{10} = \frac{6}{9}$$

$$\frac{x}{10} = \frac{2}{3}$$

$$3x = 2 \cdot 10$$

$$3x = 20$$

$$x = 6\frac{2}{3}$$

△ABC ~ △DEF
$\overline{AB}$ corresponds to $\overline{DE}$.
$\overline{BC}$ corresponds to $\overline{EF}$.
$\overline{AC}$ corresponds to $\overline{DF}$.

Thus, EF is $6\frac{2}{3}$.

EXAMPLE 3   A boy 2 m tall casts a shadow 8 m long. How tall is a nearby flagpole if its shadow is 50 m long?

Two similar triangles are formed.

Let x = height of flagpole

$$\frac{x}{2} = \frac{50}{8}$$

$$\frac{x}{2} = \frac{25}{4}$$

$$4x = 50$$

$$x = 12\frac{1}{2}$$

Thus, the flagpole is $12\frac{1}{2}$ m tall.

EXERCISES

PART A

In Exercises 1–8, △ABC ~ △DEF. Find the indicated measures.

1.

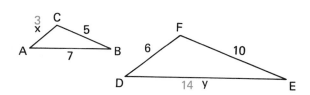

2.

3. $AB = 12$, $AC = 13$, $BC = 5$ and $DE = 8$. Find DF and EF. $8\frac{2}{3}$; $3\frac{1}{3}$

5. $AB = 7$, $AC = 9$, $BC = 12$, and $DF = 15$. Find DE and EF. $11\frac{2}{3}$; 20

7. $AB = 12$, $AC = 10$, $DE = 18$, and $FE = 20$. Find CB and DF. $13\frac{1}{3}$; 15

9. A vertical meterstick casts a 4-m shadow while a flagpole casts a 24-m shadow. How tall is the flagpole? *6 m*

4. $DE = 15$, $EF = 6$. $AB = 10$, $AC = 9$. Find BC and DF. 4; $13\frac{1}{2}$

6. $AC = 5$, $CB = 8$, $DF = 15$, and $DE = 18$. Find AB and FE. 6; 24

8. $DE = 16$, $FE = 14$, $DF = 11$, and $AB = 24$. Find CB and AC. 21; $16\frac{1}{2}$

10. A tree 2 m tall casts a shadow 4 m long while a tower casts a shadow 90 m long. How tall is the tower? *45 m*

PART B

11. A 10-m ladder touches the side of a building at a height of 8 m. At what height would a 12-m ladder touch the building if it makes the same angle with the ground? *9.6 m*

12. △VRS ~ △UTS. Find the width of the river. *64 m*

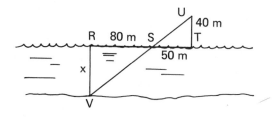

13. Jim walked 8 meters up a ramp and was 3 meters above the ground. If he walked 12 meters farther up the ramp, how far above the ground would he be? $7\frac{1}{2}$ *m*

14. Mary was standing 12 m from the base of a 10-m tree. She could spot the top of a 500-m building just beyond the top of the tree. How far was she from the base of the building? *600 m*

Trigonometric Ratios

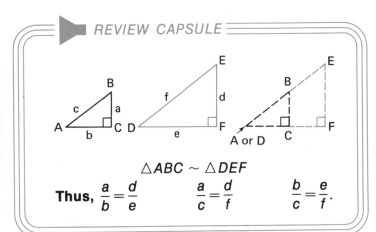

▶ REVIEW CAPSULE

$$\triangle ABC \sim \triangle DEF$$

Thus, $\dfrac{a}{b} = \dfrac{d}{e}$ $\qquad \dfrac{a}{c} = \dfrac{d}{f}$ $\qquad \dfrac{b}{c} = \dfrac{e}{f}$.

From the Greek language ⟶

Trigonometry means *triangle measurement.* We will work with right triangles.

Words associated with right triangles.

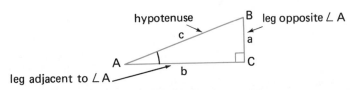

All right triangles with a given $m \angle A$ are similar: The ratios, $\dfrac{a}{b}, \dfrac{a}{c},$ and $\dfrac{b}{c}$ are the same for each $m \angle A$.

Ratio	Abbreviation
tangent of $m \angle A =$ $\dfrac{\text{measure of opposite leg}}{\text{measure of adjacent leg}}$	$\tan A = \dfrac{a}{b}$
sine of $m \angle A =$ $\dfrac{\text{measure of opposite leg}}{\text{measure of hypotenuse}}$	$\sin A = \dfrac{a}{c}$
cosine of $m \angle A =$ $\dfrac{\text{measure of adjacent leg}}{\text{measure of hypotenuse}}$	$\cos A = \dfrac{b}{c}$

EXAMPLE 1 For $\triangle ABC$, find tan A, sin A, and cos A.

$\tan = \dfrac{\text{opp.}}{\text{adj.}}$; opp. means opposite.
adj. means adjacent.

$\sin = \dfrac{\text{opp.}}{\text{hyp.}}$; hyp. means hypotenuse.

$\cos = \dfrac{\text{adj.}}{\text{hyp.}}$

$\tan A = \dfrac{3}{4}$, or .75

$\sin A = \dfrac{3}{5}$, or .6

⟶ $\cos A = \dfrac{4}{5}$, or .8

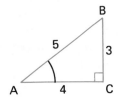

EXAMPLE 2 For △*ABC*, find tan *B*, sin *B*, and cos *B*, to three decimal places.

$\overline{AC}$ is opposite ∠*B*. $\overline{BC}$ is adjacent to ∠*B*.

$\tan = \dfrac{\text{opp.}}{\text{adj.}}$ ──────────→ $\tan B = \dfrac{12}{5} = 2.400$

$\sin = \dfrac{\text{opp.}}{\text{hyp.}}$ ──────────→ $\sin B = \dfrac{12}{13} = .923$

$\cos = \dfrac{\text{adj.}}{\text{hyp.}}$ ──────────→ $\cos B = \dfrac{5}{13} = .385$

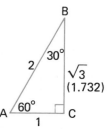

EXAMPLE 3 Use △*ABC* to find tan 60°, sin 60°, and cos 60°, to three decimal places.

These ratios will be the same for ──────→ all 30°–60° right triangles.

$\tan 60° = \dfrac{\sqrt{3}}{1} \doteq \dfrac{1.732}{1} = 1.732$

$\sin 60° = \dfrac{\sqrt{3}}{2} \doteq \dfrac{1.732}{2} = .866$

$\cos 60° = \dfrac{1}{2} \quad = .500$

EXAMPLE 4 Use the figure in Example 3 to find tan 30°, sin 30°, cos 30° to three decimal places.

First rationalize the denominator. ──────→ $\tan 30° = \dfrac{1}{\sqrt{3}} = \dfrac{1}{\sqrt{3}} \cdot \dfrac{\sqrt{3}}{\sqrt{3}} = \dfrac{\sqrt{3}}{3} \doteq \dfrac{1.732}{3} \doteq .577$

$\sin 30° = \dfrac{1}{2} \quad = .500$

$\cos 30° = \dfrac{\sqrt{3}}{2} \doteq \dfrac{1.732}{2} = .866$

ORAL EXERCISES

Refer to the figure at the right.

1. Name the leg adjacent to ∠*P*. *q*
2. Name the leg opposite ∠*Q*. *q*
3. Name the hypotenuse. *r*
4. Name the leg opposite ∠*P*. *p*
5. Name the leg adjacent to ∠*Q*. *p*
6. What is sin *P*? $\frac{p}{r}$
7. What is cos *Q*? $\frac{p}{r}$
9. What is cos *P*? $\frac{q}{r}$

8. What is tan *Q*? $\frac{q}{p}$
10. What is sin *Q*? $\frac{q}{r}$

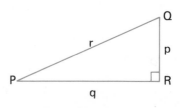

EXERCISES

PART A

Find tan *A*, sin *A*, cos *A*, tan *B*, sin *B*, and cos *B* to three decimal places.

1.

2.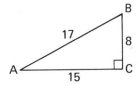

3.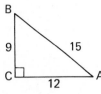

4.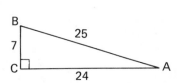

5.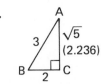

6.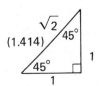

Find the value of each, to three decimal places.
Use the figure at the right.

7. tan 45° *1.000* **8.** sin 45° *.707* **9.** cos 45° *.707*

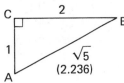

PART B ●

Show that each statement is true. Use the
figure at the right.

10. sin *A* = cos *B* $sin\ A = \frac{a}{c}; \ cos\ B = \frac{a}{c} \therefore sin\ A = cos\ B$

11. sin *B* = cos *A* $sin\ B = \frac{b}{c}; \ cos\ A = \frac{b}{c} \therefore sin\ B = cos\ A$

12. $\tan A = \dfrac{1}{\tan B}$ $tan\ A = \frac{a}{b}; \ tan\ B = \frac{b}{a}; \ \frac{1}{tan\ B} = \frac{1}{\frac{b}{a}} = \frac{a}{b}$

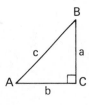

13. (sin *A*)² + (cos *A*)² = 1 (Hint: Use the Pythagorean theorem.)

$$a^2 + b^2 = c^2, \ \frac{a^2}{c^2} + \frac{b^2}{c^2} = \frac{c^2}{c^2} = 1. \ Also \ \frac{a^2}{c^2} + \frac{b^2}{c^2} = sin^2\ A + cos^2\ A.$$

PART C *By substitution sin² A + cos² A = 1.*

Find tan *A*, sin *A*, cos *A*, tan *B*, sin *B*, and cos *B*, to three decimal places.

14.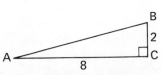

15.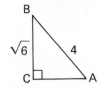

16.

17. Show that the sine of an angle is
equal to the cosine of its complement.

18. Explain why the sine of an angle is
between 0 and 1.

Graphing in Space

We add a z-axis perpendicular to both the x- and y-axes in order to plot points in space.

The points are described by ordered triples (x, y, z).

To plot point
$E(-5, -2, 4)$

x-coordinate / z-coordinate
y-coordinate

First plot the point
$B(-5, -2)$ in the
xy-plane, then move
the point to the 4
position on the z-axis.

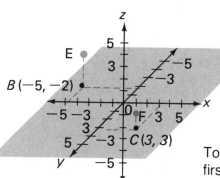

The z-axis is
perpendicular to
the xy-plane.

To plot point $F(3, 3, -1)$,
first plot the point $C(3, 3)$
on the xy-plane then
move the point to the -1
position on the z-axis.

Plot $(-5, -1)$ in xy-plane
then move point to 2
position on z-axis.

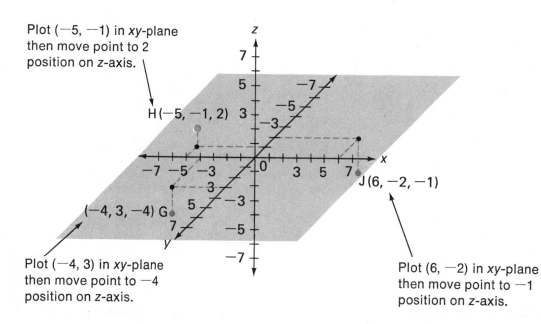

Plot $(-4, 3)$ in xy-plane
then move point to -4
position on z-axis.

Plot $(6, -2)$ in xy-plane
then move point to -1
position on z-axis.

What does the graph of the equation $z = 4$ look like?

Graph $\{(x, y, z) \mid z = 4\}$.

the set of all ordered triples | such that | $z = 4$

All points in space which have z-coordinate 4 lie in a plane parallel to the xy-plane and 4 units above it.

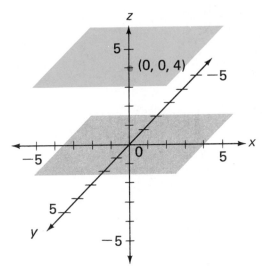

Similarly, the graph of $\{(x, y, z) \mid y = -2\}$ is a plane parallel to the xz-plane and perpendicular to the xy-plane.

line of equation $y = -2$

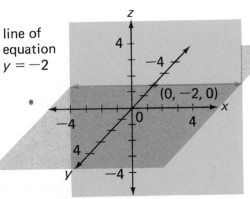

PROJECT   What do you think the graph of $\{(x, y, z) \mid x = -3\}$ looks like? Draw a three-dimensional system and graph $x = -3$.

455

Tables of Trigonometric Ratios

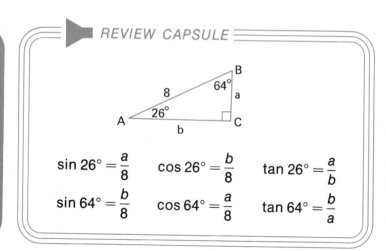

REVIEW CAPSULE

$$\sin 26° = \frac{a}{8} \qquad \cos 26° = \frac{b}{8} \qquad \tan 26° = \frac{a}{b}$$

$$\sin 64° = \frac{b}{8} \qquad \cos 64° = \frac{a}{8} \qquad \tan 64° = \frac{b}{a}$$

The table gives decimal approximations. ⟶ The table on page 477 gives the values of sine, cosine, and tangent for angles from 0° to 90°.

Part of the table ⟶

Angle Measure	Sin	Cos	Tan	Angle Measure	Sin	Cos	Tan
10°	.1736	.9848	.1763	56°	.8290	.5592	1.483
11°	.1908	.9816	.1944	57°	.8387	.5446	1.540
12°	.2079	.9781	.2126	58°	.8480	.5299	1.600
13°	.2250	.9744	.2309	59°	.8572	.5150	1.664
14°	.2419	.9703	.2493	60°	.8660	.5000	1.732
15°	.2588	.9659	.2679	61°	.8746	.4848	1.804
16°	.2756	.9613	.2867	62°	.8829	.4695	1.881
17°	.2924	.9563	.3057	63°	.8910	.4540	1.963

EXAMPLE 1 Use the table to find sin 61°, cos 61°, and tan 61°.

Find 61° in the angle column. ⟶ sin 61° = .8746   cos 61° = .4848   tan 61° = 1.804

EXAMPLE 2 Find $m \angle A$ if tan A = .3249.

Find .3249 in the tan column. ⟶

$$\tan 18° = .3249$$

Thus, $m \angle A = 18$.

EXAMPLE 3 Find $m \angle B$ to the nearest degree, if cos B = .5392.

Find the closest value to .5392 in the cos column. ⟶

$$\cos 57° = .5446$$

Thus, $m \angle B = 57$, to the nearest degree.

ORAL EXERCISES

Use the table on page 477 to find each value.

1. sin 5°   **2.** tan 21°   **3.** cos 78°   **4.** tan 36°   **5.** sin 59° *.8572*
6. cos 48° *.6691* **7.** cos 8° *.9903* **8.** tan 12° *.2126* **9.** sin 86° *.9976* **10.** tan 53° *1.327*

Use the table on page 477 to find $m \angle A$.

11. sin A = .2250 *13°*   **12.** tan A = 1.428 *55°*   **13.** sin A = .6428 *40°*
14. cos A = .9998 *1°*   **15.** tan A = 28.64 *88°*   **16.** cos A = .7193 *44°*

EXERCISES

PART A

Use the table on page 477 to find each value.

1. sin 74° *.9613* **2.** cos 81° *.1564* **3.** sin 26° *.4384* **4.** cos 30° *.8660* **5.** tan 89° *57.29*
6. cos 18° *.9511* **7.** tan 65° *2.145* **8.** sin 42° *.6691* **9.** sin 15° *.2588* **10.** cos 61°

Find $m \angle B$, to the nearest degree. Use the table on page 477.

11. tan B = .1398 *8°*   **12.** cos B = .7452 *42°*   **13.** sin B = .3915 *23°*
14. cos B = .9281 *22°*   **15.** tan B = .6637 *34°*   **16.** cos B = .5099 *59°*
17. sin B = .7583 *49°*   **18.** tan B = 1.396 *54°*   **19.** sin B = .9725 *77°*
20. tan B = 1.126 *48°*   **21.** cos B = .1186 *83°*   **22.** sin B = .0716 *4°*

PART B

True or false? Use the figure at the right.

23. $\tan A = \dfrac{b}{a}$ *F*   **24.** $\sin B = \dfrac{b}{c}$ *T*   **25.** $\cos A = \dfrac{b}{c}$ *T*

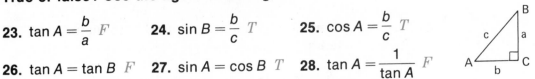

26. tan A = tan B *F* **27.** sin A = cos B *T* **28.** $\tan A = \dfrac{1}{\tan A}$ *F*

29. sin B = cos B *F* **30.** $a^2 + b^2 = c^2$ *T* **31.** $a + b = c$ *F*
32. ∠A and ∠B are complementary. *T*   **33.** ∠A and ∠B are acute. *T*
34. If $m \angle A > m \angle B$, then sin A > sin B. *T*   **35.** If $m \angle A > m \angle B$, then cos A > cos B.
36. If tan A < tan B, then $m \angle A > m \angle B$. *F* **37.** $(\sin A)^2 + (\cos A)^2 = 1$ *T*
38. sin 45° = cos 45° *T*   **39.** $(\cos A)^2 = 1 - (\sin A)^2$ *T*

PART C

Suppose $m \angle A$ increases from 0° to 90°.

40. What happens to   **41.** What happens to   **42.** What happens to
   sin A? Why?   cos A? Why?   tan A? Why?

Solving Right Triangles

▶ REVIEW CAPSULE

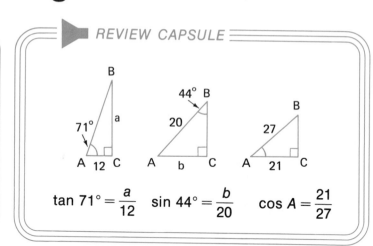

$$\tan 71° = \frac{a}{12} \qquad \sin 44° = \frac{b}{20} \qquad \cos A = \frac{21}{27}$$

EXAMPLE 1 If $m\angle A = 65$ and $c = 15$, find a, to the nearest tenth.

Sketch the figure. Use sin A, since we are dealing with a and c. Substitute 65° for A, 15 for c. ⟶

Use the table to get sin 65°. ⟶

Multiply each side by 15. ⟶

Round to the nearest tenth. ⟶

$$\sin A = \frac{a}{c}$$

$$\sin 65° = \frac{a}{15}$$

$$.9063 = \frac{a}{15}$$

$$(.9063)(15) = a$$
$$13.5945 = a$$
$$13.6 \doteq a$$

Thus, a is 13.6, to the nearest tenth.

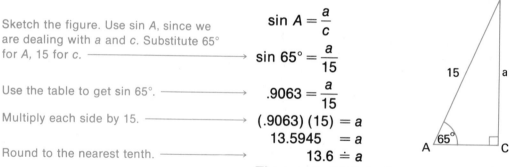

EXAMPLE 2 If $m\angle B = 51$ and $a = 10$, find c, to the nearest tenth.

$$\cos B = \frac{a}{c}$$

Substitute 51° for B, 10 for a. ⟶ $\cos 51° = \dfrac{10}{c}$

Use the table. ⟶ $.6293 = \dfrac{10}{c}$

Multiply each side by c. ⟶ $.6293c = 10$

Divide each side by .6293. ⟶ $c = \dfrac{10}{.6293}$

$$c \doteq 15.9$$

Thus c is 15.9, to the nearest tenth.

EXAMPLE 3   If $m\angle A = 27$ and $a = 18$, find b, to the nearest tenth.

Sketch the figure. ⟶

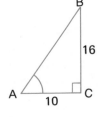

First way

$$\tan A = \frac{a}{b}$$

$$\tan 27° = \frac{18}{b}$$

$$.5095 = \frac{18}{b}$$

$$.5095b = 18$$

$$b = \frac{18}{.5095}$$

$$b \doteq 35.3$$

Second way

$$m\angle B = 90 - 27 = 63$$

$$\tan B = \frac{b}{a}$$

$$\tan 63° = \frac{b}{18}$$

$$1.963 = \frac{b}{18}$$

$$(1.963)(18) = b$$

$$35.334 = b$$

$$35.3 \doteq b$$

We can use tan A or tan B. ⟶

$$\tan A = \frac{18}{b}$$

$$\tan B = \frac{b}{18}$$

Note: In the second way, we multiply rather than divide.

Thus, b is 35.3, to the nearest tenth.

EXAMPLE 4   If $a = 16$ and $b = 10$, find $m\angle A$, to the nearest degree.

$$\tan A = \frac{a}{b}$$

Substitute 16 for a, 10 for b. ⟶ $\tan A = \dfrac{16}{10}$

$$\tan A = 1.600$$

Use the tan column: $\tan 58° = 1.600$. ⟶ $m\angle A \doteq 58$

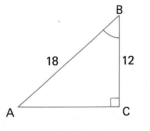

Thus, $m\angle A$ is 58, to the nearest degree.

EXAMPLE 5   If $a = 12$ and $c = 18$, find $m\angle B$, to the nearest degree.

Note: An alternate way is to use sin A.

$$\cos B = \frac{a}{c}$$

Substitute 12 for a, 18 for c. ⟶ $\cos B = \dfrac{12}{18}$

$$\cos B = \frac{2}{3}$$

$$\cos B = .6667$$

Use the cos column: $\cos 48° = .6691$. ⟶ $m\angle B \doteq 48$

Thus, $m\angle B$ is 48, to the nearest degree.

EXERCISES

PART A

Find the indicated measure (side, to the nearest tenth or angle, to the nearest degree).

1.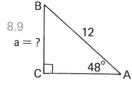

8.9
a = ?
12
48°

2.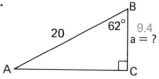

20
62°
9.4
a = ?

3.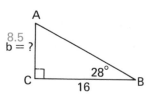

A
8.5
b = ?
28°
16

4.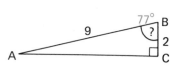

9
77°
B
?
2
A
C

5.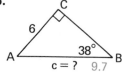

C
6
38°
A
c = ? 9.7
B

6.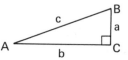

C
8
A
?
13
B
38°

Find the indicated measure (side to the nearest
tenth or angle to the nearest degree).
Use the figure at the right.

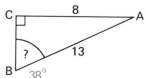

B
c
a
A
b
C

7. If $c = 7$ and $m\angle A = 42$, find a.
9. If $b = 18$ and $m\angle A = 10$, find c.
11. If $a = 2$ and $c = 4$, find $m\angle A$.
13. If $b = 18$ and $m\angle B = 35$, find a.

8. If $b = 8$ and $c = 13$, find $m\angle B$.
10. If $b = 28$ and $m\angle B = 82$, find a.
12. If $b = 16$ and $c = 20$, find $m\angle A$.
14. If $c = 30$ and $m\angle A = 27$, find a.

PART B

Find all the missing measures (sides to the nearest tenth
or angles to the nearest degree).

15.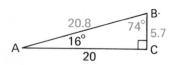

20.8
74°
B
5.7
16°
A
20
C

16.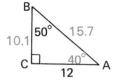

B
50°
15.7
10.1
C
40°
A
12

17.

B
10.2
54°
C
17.3
36°
14
A

18.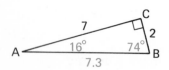

7
C
2
16°
74°
B
A
7.3

19.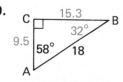

C
15.3
B
32°
9.5
58°
18
A

20.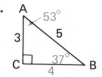

A
53°
3
5
37°
C
4
B

Applications of Trigonometry

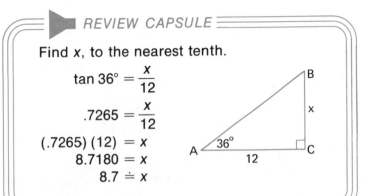

▶ REVIEW CAPSULE

Find x, to the nearest tenth.

$$\tan 36° = \frac{x}{12}$$

$$.7265 = \frac{x}{12}$$

$$(.7265)(12) = x$$

$$8.7180 = x$$

$$8.7 \doteq x$$

EXAMPLE 1   Find the height of the tree, to the nearest tenth of a meter.

Let x = height of tree in meters.

$\tan = \dfrac{\text{opp.}}{\text{adj.}}$ ⟶

Use tan column. ⟶

Multiply each side by 25. ⟶

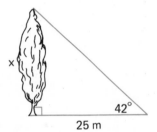

$$\tan 42° = \frac{x}{25}$$

$$.9004 = \frac{x}{25}$$

$$(.9004)(25) = x$$

$$22.5100 = x$$

$$22.5 \doteq x$$

Thus, the tree is 22.5 meters tall, to the nearest tenth.

EXAMPLE 2   Find the distance across the lake from P to Q, to the nearest tenth of a meter.

Let x = PQ in meters.

$\cos = \dfrac{\text{adj.}}{\text{hyp.}}$ ⟶

Use cos column. ⟶

Multiply each side by x. ⟶

Divide each side by .3746. ⟶

$$\cos 68° = \frac{36}{x}$$

$$.3746 = \frac{36}{x}$$

$$.3746x = 36$$

$$x = \frac{36}{.3746}$$

$$x \doteq 96.1$$

Thus, the distance from P to Q is 96.1 meters, to the nearest tenth.

An angle of elevation is the angle between the horizontal and the line of sight.
An angle of depression is the angle between the horizontal and the line of sight.
Angle of depression = angle of elevation

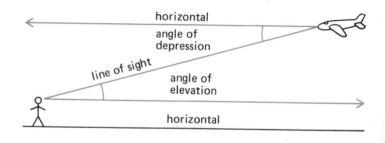

EXAMPLE 3   A power-line tower casts a 160-m shadow when the angle of elevation of the sun measures 20°. How high is the tower?

$\tan = \dfrac{\text{opp.}}{\text{adj.}}$ ⟶

$\tan 20° = \dfrac{x}{160}$

Use tan column. ⟶

$.3640 = \dfrac{x}{160}$

$(.3640)(160) = x$

$58.2400 = x$

Round to the nearest tenth. ⟶

$58.2 \doteq x$

Thus, the power-line tower is about 58.2 m high.

EXAMPLE 4   A lighthouse is 55 meters high. The angle of depression from the top of the lighthouse to a boat out at sea is 72°. How far from the base of the lighthouse is the boat?

Angle of depression = angle of elevation

Let x = distance between boat and lighthouse in meters; $\tan = \dfrac{\text{opp.}}{\text{adj.}}$ ⟶

$\tan 72° = \dfrac{55}{x}$

Use the tan column. ⟶

$3.077 = \dfrac{55}{x}$

$3.077x = 55$

$x = \dfrac{55}{3.077}$

Divide and round to the nearest tenth. ⟶

$x \doteq 17.9$

Thus, the boat is about 17.9 meters from the lighthouse.

EXERCISES

PART A

Find x, to the nearest tenth.

1.
52°
36 m

2.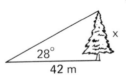
28°
42 m

3.
80 km
54°
x

4.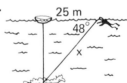
25 m
48°
x

5.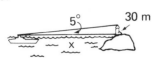
5°
30 m
x

6.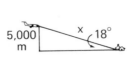
5,000 m
x 18°

7.
x 32° 55 m

8.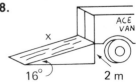
ACE VAN
x
16° 2 m

Give answers to the nearest tenth or to the nearest degree.

9. The angle of elevation from a ship to the top of a 50-m lighthouse on the coast measures 13°. How far from the coast is the ship? *216.6 m*

10. A kite is flying at the end of a 200-m string (straight). The string makes an angle of 68° with the ground. How high above the ground is the kite? *185.4 m*

11. A tree casts a 60-m shadow when the angle of elevation of the sun measures 58°. How tall is the tree? *96.0 m*

12. A ramp is 400 m long. It rises a vertical distance of 32 m. Find the measure of its angle of elevation. *5°*

13. Each step of a stairway rises 15 cm for a tread width of 24 cm. What angle does the stairway make with the floor? *32°*
24
24 15
15 Floor

14. A 30-m ladder makes an angle of 55° with the ground as it leans against a building. At what height does it touch the building? *24.6 m*

15. A plane is flying at an altitude of 10,000 m. The angle of elevation from an object on the ground to the plane measures 28°. How far is the object from the plane? *21,299.3 m*

16. A cliff is 150 m above the sea. From the cliff the angle of depression of a boat in the sea measures 8°. How far is the boat from the base of the cliff? *1,067.3 m*

PART B

17. The leg opposite the 20° angle in a right triangle measures 6 km. Find the area of the triangle. [Hint: $A = \frac{1}{2}bh$.] *49.5 km²*

18. A 12-m diagonal of a rectangle makes an angle of 56° with a side of the rectangle. Find the dimensions of the rectangle. *6.7 m; 9.9 m*

Chapter Sixteen Review

In each case, △ABC ~ △DEF. Find x and y. $[p.\ 448]$

1.

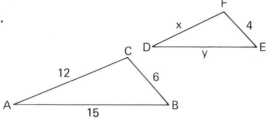

2.

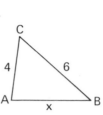

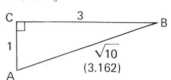

For △ABC, find the following, to three decimal places, or to the nearest degree. Use the table on page 477. $[p.\ 451,\ 456]$

3. tan A   **4.** cos B

5. sin A   **6.** sin B

7. $m \angle A$ **8.** $m \angle B$

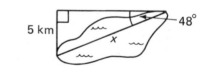

Find the indicated measure (side to the nearest tenth or angle to the nearest degree). Use the figure at the right. $[p.\ 458]$

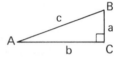

9. If $b = 12$ and $m \angle B = 36$, find c.

11. If $c = 8$ and $m \angle A = 59$, find a.

10. If $a = 20$ and $m \angle B = 16$, find b.

12. If $b = 6$ and $c = 10$, find $m \angle A$.

Find x, to the nearest tenth.

13.

25 meters

15°

x

14.

5 km

x

48°

15. Two angles of a triangle have the same measure. The third angle measures 4° more than the sum of the first two. Find the measures of the three angles. $[p.\ 445]$

16. One acute angle of a right triangle measures 10° more than 4 times the other. Find the measures of the two acute angles. $[p.\ 445]$

17. An angle measures 15° less than twice its complement. Find the measure of the angle and its complement. $[p.\ 445]$

18. A pole 2 m tall casts a shadow 10 m long while a tree casts a shadow 13 m long. How tall is the tree? $[p.\ 448]$

19. The angle of elevation from point A to the top of a building measures 38°. Point A is 40 meters from the base of the building. How tall is the building? $[p.\ 461]$

20. A ramp is to be constructed so that it rises 6 m and makes an angle of 12° with the ground. How long should the ramp be? $[p.\ 461]$

Chapter Sixteen Test

In each case, △ABC ~ △DEF. Find x and y.

1.

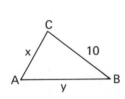

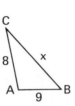

2.

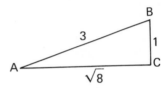

For △ABC, find the following, to three decimal places, or to the nearest degree. Use the table on page 477.

3. cos A   **4.** cos B
5. sin A   **6** tan B
7. m∠A   **8.** m∠B

Find the indicated measure (side to the nearest tenth or angle to the nearest degree). Use the figure at the right.

9. If c = 16 and m∠A = 38, find a.
11. If a = 15 and m∠B = 47, find b.
10. If b = 22 and m∠A = 71, find c.
12. If a = 17 and c = 22, find m∠B.

Find x, to the nearest tenth.

13.

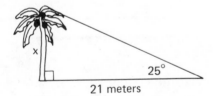

21 meters

14.

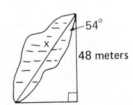

48 meters

15. The complement of an angle measures 14° less than 3 times the measure of the angle. Find the measure of the angle and its complement.

16. One angle of a triangle measures 5° more than the second. The third angle measures 25° less than twice the measure of the second. Find the measures of the three angles.

17. A 7-m flagpole casts a shadow 25 m long while a tree casts a shadow 40 m long. How tall is the tree?

18. A building casts a 200-m shadow when the angle of elevation of the sun measures 55°. How tall is the building?

Distance Formula

Find the distance between $A\,(3, 2)$ and $B\,(7, 5)$.

Plot the points.

Draw a right triangle.

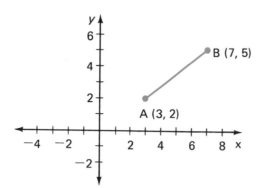

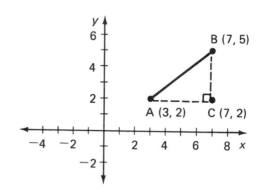

Use the Pythagorean theorem.
$$(AB)^2 = (AC)^2 + (BC)^2$$

$$(AB)^2 = 4^2 + 3^2$$
$$AB = \sqrt{16 + 9}$$
$$AB = \sqrt{25}$$
$$AB = 5$$

Distance Formula
The distance between points A and B is
$$d = \sqrt{(x\text{-coord. } B - x\text{-coord. } A)^2 + (y\text{-coord. } B - y\text{-coord. } A)^2}.$$

PROJECT

Use the distance formula to show that the triangles with these given vertices are isosceles.

1. $A(1,0)\ B(5,0)\ C(3,4)$ **2.** $A(2,3)\ B(5,7)\ C(1,4)$

GLOSSARY

The explanations given in this glossary are intended to be brief descriptions of the terms listed. They are not necessarily definitions.

Absolute value   The absolute value of a positive number or zero is the number itself. The absolute value of a negative number is the opposite of the number. We read $|x|$ as the absolute value of x.
Examples $|-3| = 3$, $|2| = 2$, $|0| = 0$

Acute   An angle is an acute angle if its measure is less than 90°.
Example $m \angle A = 72$; $\angle A$ is an acute angle.

Addition property for equations   We can add the same number to each side of an equation. If $a = b$ is true, then $a + c = b + c$ is also true, for all numbers a, b, and c.

Addition property for inequalities   We can add the same number to each side of a true inequality, and the result is another true inequality of the same order. If $a < b$, then $a + c < b + c$.

Additive identity   Zero is the additive identity since adding zero to a number gives the same number.

Additive inverse   The additive inverse of a number is the opposite of the number. -6 is the additive inverse of 6. 8 is the additive inverse of -8. 0 is its own additive inverse.

Adjacent side   In a triangle, a side is adjacent to an angle if it is contained in the angle.

Angle   An angle is a figure formed by two rays with a common endpoint.

Area of a rectangle   The area of a rectangle is given by the formula $A = l \cdot w$, where l is the length and w is the width.

Associative property of addition   When adding, we can change the grouping of the addends. $(a + b) + c = a + (b + c)$, for all numbers a, b, and c.

Associative property of multiplication   When multiplying, we can change the grouping of the factors. $(a \cdot b) \cdot c = a \cdot (b \cdot c)$, for all numbers a, b, and c.

Base   In 3^4, the 3 is the base. $3^4 = 3 \cdot 3 \cdot 3 \cdot 3$. The base is used 4 times as a factor.

Binomial   A binomial is a polynomial with two terms.

Coefficient   A coefficient is the multiplier of a variable. In $6a - 3b + 8$, 6 is the coefficient of a, and -3 is the coefficient of b.

Combine   To combine like terms in an expression such as $5y - 9y$, we use the distributive property.

$$5y - 9y = (5 - 9)y$$
$$= -4y$$

Commutative property of addition   When adding, we can change the order of the addends. $a + b = b + a$, for all numbers a and b.

Commutative property of multiplication   When multiplying, we can change the order of the factors. $a \cdot b = b \cdot a$, for all numbers a and b.

Complement   If the sum of the measures of two angles is 90°, then each angle is the complement of the other.

Complementary angles   Two angles are complementary if the sum of their measures is 90°.

Completing the square   Completing the square is a method for finding the solution set of a quadratic equation.

Complex fraction   A complex fraction is one whose numerator or denominator or both contain a fraction. $\frac{\frac{3}{4}}{\frac{1}{3}}$ is a complex fraction.

Consecutive even integers   Consecutive even integers have a factor of 2 and follow each other from smallest to largest. 6, 8, and 10 are consecutive even integers.

Consecutive integers   Consecutive integers follow each other from smallest to largest.

Examples 4, 5, 6; $-23, -22, -21, -20$

Consecutive odd integers   Consecutive odd integers do not have a factor of 2, and they follow each other from smallest to largest. 7, 9, and 11 are consecutive odd integers.

Constant function   A constant function is a function whose graph is a horizontal line or a subset of a horizontal line.

Constant of variation   For a direct variation $\frac{y}{x} = k$, k is the constant of variation, or constant of proportionality. For an inverse variation $xy = k$, k is the constant of variation.

Convenient form   A polynomial is in convenient form if its terms are in descending order of exponents, and the coefficient of the first term is positive. $6x - 2x^2 + 3$ is in convenient form when it is expressed as $-1(2x^2 - 6x - 3)$.

Converse   The converse of an if–then statement is formed by reversing the if and the then parts.

Converse of the pythagorean theorem   If the sum of the squares of the lengths of two sides of a triangle equals the square of the length of the third side, then the triangle is a right triangle. In a triangle, if $a^2 + b^2 = c^2$, then the triangle is a right triangle.

Coordinate(s) of a point   On a number line, the coordinate of a point is the number which corresponds to the point. In a coordinate plane, the coordinates of a point make up the ordered pair which corresponds to the point.

Coordinate plane   Two perpendicular number lines in a plane make up a coordinate plane, or a coordinate system. Each point in a coordinate plane corresponds to an ordered pair of numbers, and vice versa.

Correspond   A number corresponds to a point on a number line, and vice versa. An ordered pair corresponds to a point in a coordinate plane, and vice versa. "Corresponds to" means "is associated with."

Corresponding angles   The corresponding angles of two similar figures are the pairs of angles which have the same measure.

Corresponding sides   The pairs of corresponding sides of two similar figures are the sides which lie opposite the pairs of corresponding angles.

Cosine of an angle   The cosine of an acute angle of a right triangle is the ratio of the length of the side adjacent to the angle to the length of the hypotenuse.

Decrease   12 decreased by 8 means $12 - 8$, or 4.

Denominator   In the fraction $\frac{7}{8}$, 8 is the denominator.

Descending order   A polynomial is in descending order of exponents if the terms are arranged so that the exponents decrease from highest to lowest.
$7x^3 - 4x^2 + x - 8$ is in descending order.

Diagonal   A diagonal of a figure is a line segment joining opposite corners.

Difference   The difference is the result of a subtraction. In $17 - 8 = 9$, 9 is the difference.

Difference of two squares $a^2 - b^2$ represents the difference of two squares. $a^2 - b^2$ may be factored as $(a + b)(a - b)$.

Directed distance   The directed distance from P to Q on a number line is equal to the coordinate of Q minus the coordinate of P. $\vec{d}(PQ) =$ coordinate of $Q -$ coordinate of P.

Direct variation   A direct variation is a function in which the ratio y to x is always the same. $\frac{y}{x} = k$, or $y = kx$ is a direct variation. y varies directly as x, or y is directly proportional to x.

Distributive property of multiplication over addition   Multiplication is distributive over addition. $a(b + c) = a \cdot b + a \cdot c$ and $(b + c)a = b \cdot a + c \cdot a$, for all numbers a, b, and c.

Division property for equations   We can divide each side of an equation by the same nonzero number. If $a = b$ is true, then $\frac{a}{c} = \frac{b}{c}$ is also true, for all numbers a, b, and c, $[c \neq 0]$.

Division property for inequalities   We can divide each side of a true inequality by the same positive number, and the result is another true inequality of the same order. If $a < b$ and $c > 0$, then $\frac{a}{c} < \frac{b}{c}$.
We can divide each side of a true inequality by the same negative number, and the result is another true inequality of the reverse order. If $a < b$ and $c < 0$, then $\frac{a}{c} > \frac{b}{c}$.

Domain of a relation   The domain of a relation is the set of all first elements of the ordered pairs in the relation. For the relation $\{(0, 1), (2, -5), (4, 3)\}$, the domain is $\{0, 2, 4\}$.

Elements   The objects which belong to a set are the elements, or members of the set.

Empty set   The empty set is the set containing no elements. The symbol ϕ means the empty set.

Equal sets   Two sets are equal if they have the same elements.

Equation   A sentence with $=$ is an equation.

Equation of a line $y = mx + b$ is an equation of a line in a coordinate plane. m is the slope of the line and b is the y-intercept.

Equivalent equations   Equivalent equations are equations which have the same solution.

Evaluate   To evaluate an expression means to find its value. To evaluate $7x + 4$ if $x = 3$, we replace x with 3 and compute.
Example $7x + 4$
  $7(3) + 4$
  $21 + 4$
  25

Even integer   An even integer has a factor of 2. $\ldots, -4, -2, 0, 2, 4, 6, \ldots$ are even integers.

Exponent   In 3^4, the 4 is an exponent. $3^4 = 3 \cdot 3 \cdot 3 \cdot 3$. A positive integer tells how many times the base (3) is used as a factor.

Extraneous solution   An extraneous solution of an equation is an apparent solution that does not check.

Extremes   In the proportion $\frac{a}{b} = \frac{c}{d}$, a and d are the extremes.

Factors   Factors are numbers which are multiplied. In $5 \cdot 8 = 40$, 5 and 8 are factors.

Factor a number   To factor a number means to rename the number as a product of whole numbers. We may factor 12 as $12 \cdot 1$, $6 \cdot 2$, or $3 \cdot 4$.

Factor a trinomial   To factor a trinomial means to express it as the product of two binomials. $x^2 - 5x + 6$ can be factored as $(x - 2)(x - 3)$.

Finite set   A set is finite if it contains a definite number of elements. $\{2, 4, 6\}$ is a finite set.

Fraction   A fraction is an indicated quotient of two numbers.

Fractional equation   A fractional equation is an equation which contains one or more fractions.

Fulcrum   The fulcrum of a lever is the point where the lever balances.

Function   A function is a relation in which no two ordered pairs have the same first element.

Graph of an equation (inequality)   In a coordinate plane, the graph of an equation (inequality) is the set of all points and only those points whose coordinates satisfy the equation (inequality).

Graph of a number   On a number line, the graph of a number is the point which corresponds to the number.

Graph of an ordered pair   In a coordinate plane, the graph of an ordered pair is the point which corresponds to the ordered pair.

Graph of a set   The graph of a set is the graph of all the numbers or all the ordered pairs in the set.

Greatest common factor (GCF)   The greatest common factor of two numbers is the greatest number which is a factor of both numbers. 8 is the GCF of 16 and 24.

Horizontal line   A horizontal line in a coordinate plane is parallel to the x-axis.

Hypotenuse   The hypotenuse of a right triangle is the side opposite the right angle.

Increase   3 increased by 7 means $3 + 7$, or 10.

Inequality   An inequality is a sentence with $\neq, <, >, \leq$, or $\geq$. $x + 3 < 7$ is an inequality.

Infinite set   A set is infinite if it contains no definite number of elements. $\{1, 2, 3, 4, \ldots\}$ is an infinite set.

Integer   The numbers $\ldots, -4, -3, -2, -1, 0, 1, 2, 3, 4, \ldots$ are integers.

Intersection of sets   The intersection of two sets A and B is the set of all elements common to both sets A and B. $\cap$ is the symbol for intersection.

Inverse of a relation   Relation B is the inverse of relation A if the first and second elements of the ordered pairs in A are interchanged to form B.

Inverse variation   An inverse variation is a function in which the product xy is always the same. $xy = k$, or $y = \frac{k}{x}$ is an inverse variation. y varies inversely as x, or y is inversely proportional to x.

Irrational number   An irrational number cannot be expressed in the form $\frac{a}{b}$, where a and b are integers and $b \neq 0$. Nonrepeating decimals are irrational numbers.

Least common denominator (LCD) The least common denominator of two or more fractions is the smallest number which has each denominator as a factor. The LCD of $\frac{1}{2}$, $\frac{2}{3}$, and $\frac{3}{4}$ is 12.

Leg The legs of a right triangle are the two sides which form the right angle.

Less than 7 less than 9 means $9 - 7$, or 2.

Like radicals Like radicals are expressions which contain the same radical. $5\sqrt{2x}$ and $-3\sqrt{2x}$ are like radicals.

Like terms Like terms contain the same variable or variables. $5xy$ and $-3xy$ are like terms. $-8b$ and $11b^2$ are unlike terms.

Linear function A linear function is a function whose graph is a line or a subset of a line which is neither vertical nor horizontal.

Means In the proportion $\frac{a}{b} = \frac{c}{d}$, b and c are the means.

Member of a set The objects which belong to a set are the members (elements) of the set. In $\{3, -1, 0\}$, the members of the set are 3, -1, and 0.

Monomial A monomial is a polynomial with one term.

More than 8 more than 5 means $5 + 8$, or 13.

Multiplication property for equations We can multiply each side of an equation by the same number. If $a = b$ is true, then $a(c) = b(c)$ is also true, for all numbers a, b, and c.

Multiplication property for inequalities We can multiply each side of a true inequality by the same *positive* number, and the result is another true inequality of the *same order*. If $a < b$ and $c > 0$, then $a \cdot c < b \cdot c$.
We can multiply each side of a true inequality by the same *negative* number, and the result is another true inequality of the *reverse order*.
If $a < b$ and $c < 0$, then $a \cdot c > b \cdot c$.

Multiplication property of -1 Multiplying any number by -1 gives the opposite of that number. $(-1)(a) = -a$ and $(a)(-1) = -a$, for each number a.

Multiplicative inverse Two numbers are multiplicative inverses (reciprocals) if their product is 1.

Negative number A number is negative if it lies to the left of zero on a number line. $-5, -1, -\frac{1}{2}$, and $-\frac{4}{3}$ are negative numbers.

Nonrepeating decimal A nonrepeating decimal has no digit or group of digits which repeats forever. The decimal .010110111011110 . . . is a nonrepeating decimal.

Nonterminating decimal A nonterminating decimal has an infinite number of digits.

Numerator In the fraction $\frac{7}{8}$, 7 is the numerator.

Odd integer An odd integer does not have a factor of 2. $\ldots, -5, -3, -1, 0, 1, 3, 5, 7, \ldots$ are odd integers.

Open sentence An open sentence is a sentence which contains a variable. $7y - 3 = 5$ is an open sentence because it contains the variable y.

Opposite numbers Opposite numbers are the same distance from zero on the number line. -5 is the opposite of 5. 12 is the opposite of -12. 0 is its own opposite. The symbol $-x$ is read the opposite of x.

Opposite side In a triangle, a side is opposite an angle if it is not contained in the angle.

Ordered pair $(-4, 1)$ is an ordered pair of numbers. Each ordered pair of numbers corresponds to a point in a coordinate plane, and vice versa.

Order of inequalities   Two inequalities are of the same order if both contain $<$ or if both contain $>$. Two inequalities are of the reverse order if one contains $>$ and the other contains $<$.

Order of operations   When both multiplications and additions occur, we agree to multiply first and then add.
Example $5 + 7 \cdot 3 = 5 + 21$
$$= 26$$

Origin   The origin is the point for zero on a number line. The origin is the point for $(0, 0)$ in a coordinate plane.

Parallel   Lines are parallel if they lie in the same plane and never meet.

Perfect square   A perfect square is a number whose principal square root is a whole number. 36 is a perfect square since its principal square root is 6, and 6 is a whole number. 37 is not a perfect square.

Perimeter   The perimeter of a figure is the distance around the figure. If a triangle has sides measuring 6 meters, 7 meters, and 10 meters, then its perimeter is $6 + 7 + 10$, or 23 meters.

Perpendicular lines   Two lines are perpendicular if they form right angles $(90°)$. $\perp$ means is perpendicular to.

Plane   A plane is a flat surface.

Plot   To plot a point in a coordinate plane means to mark the point which corresponds to a given ordered pair of numbers.

Polynomial   A polynomial contains one or more terms.
Examples $2x^2$, $5x + 3$, $7a^2 - 5a - 2$

Positive number   A number is positive if it lies to the right of zero on a number line. 8, 2, $\frac{1}{3}$, and $\frac{16}{5}$ are positive numbers.

Power 3^4 means the fourth power of 3. $3^4 = 3 \cdot 3 \cdot 3 \cdot 3$. 3 is used 4 times as a factor.

Power of a power   To raise a power to a power, we can multiply the exponents. $(x^m)^n = x^{m \cdot n}$.

Power of a product   To raise a product to a power, we can raise each factor in the product to that power. $(x^m \cdot y^n)^p = x^{m \cdot p} \cdot y^{n \cdot p}$.

Prime factorization   The prime factorization of 20 is $2 \cdot 2 \cdot 5$, since $2 \cdot 2 \cdot 5 = 20$, and 2 and 5 are prime numbers.

Prime number   A prime number is a whole number greater than 1 whose only factors are itself and 1. 2, 3, 5, 7, 11, . . . are prime numbers.

Principal square root   The principal square root of a number is the positive square root of the number. 6 is the principal square root of 36. We use the symbol $\sqrt{}$ to indicate the principal square root of a number.

Product   The product is the result of a multiplication. In $5 \cdot 6 = 30$, 30 is the product.

Product of powers   When multiplying two powers, if the bases are the same, we can add the exponents. $x^m \cdot x^n = x^{m+n}$.

Property of additive identity   Adding zero to a number gives the same number. $a + 0 = a$ and $0 + a = a$, for each number a.

Property of additive inverse   Adding two opposite numbers (additive inverses) gives zero. $a + (-a) = 0$, for each number a.

Property of multiplicative identity
Multiplying any number by 1 gives the same number. $(1)(a) = a$ and $(a)(1) = a$, for each number a.

Property of zero for multiplication
Multiplying any number by zero gives zero. $a \cdot 0 = 0$ and $0 \cdot a = 0$, for each number a.

Proportion   A proportion is an equation which states that two ratios are equal. $\frac{a}{b} = \frac{c}{d}$ is a proportion.

Protractor   A protractor is a tool for measuring angles.

Pythagorean theorem In any right triangle, the square of the length of the hypotenuse equals the sum of the squares of the lengths of the other two sides. If $\triangle ABC$ is a right triangle, then $a^2 + b^2 = c^2$.

Quadrant The x- and y-axes divide the coordinate plane into four quadrants.

Quadratic equation In a quadratic equation, the variable in one term is raised to the second power, but no higher. $3x^2 - 5x + 4 = 0$, $x^2 - 49 = 0$, and $6x^2 = 2$ are quadratic equations.

Quadratic formula The solutions of a quadratic equation of the form $ax^2 + bx + c = 0$ may be found by the formula $x = \dfrac{-b \pm \sqrt{b^2 - 4ac}}{2a}$. The formula is called the quadratic formula.

Quotient The quotient is the result of a division. In $54 \div 9 = 6$, 6 is the quotient.

Radical equation In a radical equation, the variable is in the radicand. $\sqrt{2x} = 6$ is a radical equation.

Range of a relation The range of a relation is the set of all second elements of the ordered pairs in the relation. For the relation $\{(0, 1), (2, -5), (4, 3)\}$, the range is $\{1, -5, 3\}$.

Ratio The ratio of a to b is the quotient $\dfrac{a}{b}$, or $a:b$. A ratio is a comparison of two numbers by division.

Rationalize the denominator To rationalize the denominator of a fraction means to write the fraction with no radical in the denominator. To rationalize the denominator of $\dfrac{\sqrt{5}}{\sqrt{3}}$, we multiply by $\dfrac{\sqrt{3}}{\sqrt{3}}$.
$$\frac{\sqrt{5}}{\sqrt{3}} \cdot \frac{\sqrt{3}}{\sqrt{3}} = \frac{\sqrt{15}}{3}.$$

Rational number A rational number is a number which can be written in the form $\dfrac{a}{b}$, where a and b are integers and $b \neq 0$. $\dfrac{3}{5}, \dfrac{-24}{7}$, 8, and .63 are rational numbers.

Real number The set of real numbers contains all the rational and all the irrational numbers. $\{\text{rationals}\} \cup \{\text{irrationals}\} = \{\text{reals}\}$.

Rearrange In an expression like $9x + 8 - 12x + 7$, we can rearrange the terms to simplify.
$$9x + 8 - 12x + 7 = (9x - 12x) + (8 + 7)$$
$$= -3x + 15$$
In an expression like $7 \cdot x \cdot 5 \cdot y$, we can rearrange the factors to simplify.
$$7 \cdot x \cdot 5 \cdot y = (7 \cdot 5) \cdot (x \cdot y)$$
$$= 35xy$$

Reciprocal Two numbers are reciprocals (multiplicative inverses) if their product is 1. 5 and $\dfrac{1}{5}$ are reciprocals since $5\left(\dfrac{1}{5}\right) = 1$.

Rectangle A rectangle is a four-sided figure with opposite sides the same length and four right angles.

Relation A relation is a set of ordered pairs. $\{(0, 1), (2, -5), (-4, 2)\}$ is a relation.

Relatively prime Two numbers are relatively prime if their only common factor is 1.

Repeating decimal A repeating decimal has a digit or a group of digits which repeats forever. The decimal .5858585858..., or $.58\overline{58}$, is a repeating decimal. The bar indicates that the digits repeat forever.

Replacement set A replacement set is the set of all numbers which may replace the variable in an open sentence or expression.

Right triangle A right triangle is a triangle with one right angle.

Root A root of an equation is a solution of the equation.

Satisfy If a variable in an equation is replaced with a number, and the result is a true statement, then the number satisfies the equation.

Sentence A mathematical sentence contains either $=$, $\neq$, $>$, $<$, $\geq$, or $\leq$. $4 + 5 = 9$ and $7 \leq x - 3$ are mathematical sentences.

Set A set is a collection of objects. We use braces $\{\ \}$ to show a set.

Similar Two figures are similar if the corresponding angles are congruent and the lengths of the corresponding sides have the same ratio.

Simplest radical form An expression is in simplest radical form if it contains no factor which is a perfect square.

Simplify To simplify an expression means to replace it with the least complicated equivalent expression.

Sine of an angle The sine of an acute angle of a right triangle is the ratio of the length of the side opposite the angle to the length of the hypotenuse.

Slope of a line The slope of a line in a coordinate plane is the slope of any segment on the line. The slope of a horizontal line is zero. The slope of a vertical line is undefined.

Slope of a segment The slope of a segment in a coordinate plane is
$$\frac{\text{difference of } y\text{-coordinates}}{\text{difference of } x\text{-coordinates}}.$$

Solution A solution of an open sentence is a replacement of the variable which makes the sentence true. In $5x - 3 = 32$, 7 is a solution since $5(7) - 3 = 35 - 3 = 32$.

Solution set The solution set of an open sentence is the set of all members of the replacement set which are solutions of the sentence.

Solve To solve an open sentence means to find all of its solutions.

Square To square a number means to multiply it by itself.

Square of a number The square of a number is the product of the number and itself.

Square root x is a square root of n if $x \cdot x = n$. 6 is a square root of 36 since $6 \cdot 6 = 36$. Also, -6 is a square root of 36 since $(-6)(-6) = 36$.

Standard form A quadratic equation is in standard form if the coefficient of the x^2 term is positive, the polynomial is equal to zero, and the terms are arranged in descending order of exponents. $3x^2 - 6x + 1 = 0$ is in standard form. We use $ax^2 + bx + c = 0$ to represent the standard form of a quadratic equation.

Subset Set B is a subset of set A if every element of B is also in A. $B \subseteq A$ means B is a subset of A.

Substitute To substitute a value for a variable means to replace the variable with the particular value. For $8y - 9$, we can substitute the value 5 for y.
$$8y - 9$$
$$8(5) - 9$$
$$40 - 9$$
$$31$$

Subtract To subtract b from a means to add the opposite of b to a. $a - b = a + (-b)$, for all numbers a and b.

Sum The sum is the result of an addition. In $7 + 8 = 15$, 15 is the sum.

System of equations Two equations in two variables form a system of equations.
$$\begin{array}{l} 2x + 3y = 6 \\ x - 4y = -3 \end{array} \text{ is a system.}$$

System of inequalities Two inequalities in two variables form a system of inequalities.
$$\begin{array}{l} 3x - 2y < 8 \\ x - y > 4 \end{array} \text{ is a system.}$$

Tangent of an angle The tangent of an acute angle of a right triangle is the ratio of the length of the side opposite the angle to the length of the side adjacent to the angle.

Terminating decimal   A terminating decimal has a finite number of digits.

Terms   In $7x - 3y + 8$, the terms are $7x$, $-3y$, and 8. Terms are added.

Theorem   A theorem is a property which can be proved.

Triangle   A triangle is a three-sided figure.

Trinomial   A trinomial is a polynomial with three terms.

Twice   Twice a number means two times the number. Twice x means $2x$.

Undefined fraction   A fraction is undefined if its denominator is zero.

Union of sets   The union of two sets A and B is the set of all elements belonging to set A or to set B or to both sets A and B. $\cup$ is the symbol for union.

Value of a function   If (x, y) is an ordered pair in function f, then the value of f at x is y. We read $f(x) = y$ as the value of f at x is y, or as f at x is y.

Variable   A variable takes the place of a number. In $5x - 3 = 7$, x is a variable.

Vertical line   A vertical line in a coordinate plane is parallel to the y-axis.

Vertical line test   A relation is a function if no vertical line crosses its graph in more than one point.

Whole number   The numbers 0, 1, 2, 3, . . . are whole numbers.

x-axis   The x-axis is the horizontal number line in a coordinate plane.

x-coordinate   The x-coordinate of an ordered pair of numbers is the first number in the pair. For $(5, -2)$, 5 is the x-coordinate.

y-axis   The y-axis is the vertical number line in a coordinate plane.

y-coordinate   The y-coordinate of an ordered pair of numbers is the second number in the pair. For $(5, -2)$, -2 is the y-coordinate.

y-intercept   The y-intercept of a line in a coordinate plane is the y-coordinate of the point of intersection of the line with the y-axis. In the equation of a line, $y = mx + b$, b is the y-intercept.

Zero   Zero (0) lies between the positive and the negative numbers on a number line. Zero is neither positive nor negative.

Table of Roots and Powers

No.	Sq.	Sq. Root	Cube	Cu. Root	No.	Sq.	Sq. Root	Cube	Cu. Root
1	1	1.000	1	1.000	51	2,601	7.141	132,651	3.708
2	4	1.414	8	1.260	52	2,704	7.211	140,608	3.733
3	9	1.732	27	1.442	53	2,809	7.280	148,877	3.756
4	16	2.000	64	1.587	54	2,916	7.348	157,564	3.780
5	25	2.236	125	1.710	55	3,025	7.416	166,375	3.803
6	36	2.449	216	1.817	56	3,136	7.483	175,616	3.826
7	49	2.646	343	1.913	57	3,249	7.550	185,193	3.849
8	64	2.828	512	2.000	58	3,364	7.616	195,112	3.871
9	81	3.000	729	2.080	59	3,481	7.681	205,379	3.893
10	100	3.162	1,000	2.154	60	3,600	7.746	216,000	3.915
11	121	3.317	1,331	2.224	61	3,721	7.810	226,981	3.936
12	144	3.464	1,728	2.289	62	3,844	7.874	238,328	3.958
13	169	3.606	2,197	2.351	63	3,969	7.937	250,047	3.979
14	196	3.742	2,744	2.410	64	4,096	8.000	262,144	4.000
15	225	3.875	3,375	2.466	65	4,225	8.062	274,625	4.021
16	256	4.000	4,096	2.520	66	4,356	8.124	287,496	4.041
17	289	4.123	4,913	2.571	67	4,489	8.185	300,763	4.062
18	324	4.243	5,832	2.621	68	4,624	8.246	314,432	4.082
19	361	4.359	6,859	2.668	69	4,761	8.307	328,509	4.102
20	400	4.472	8,000	2.714	70	4,900	8.357	343,000	4.121
21	441	4.583	9,261	2.759	71	5,041	8.426	357,911	4.141
22	484	4.690	10,648	2.802	72	5,184	8.485	373,248	4.160
23	529	4.796	12,167	2.844	73	5,329	8.544	389,017	4.179
24	576	4.899	13,824	2.884	74	5,476	8.602	405,224	4.198
25	625	5.000	15,625	2.924	75	5,625	8.660	421,875	4.217
26	676	5.099	17,576	2.962	76	5,776	8.718	438,976	4.236
27	729	5.196	19,683	3.000	77	5,929	8.775	456,533	4.254
28	784	5.292	21,952	3.037	78	6,084	8.832	474,552	4.273
29	841	5.385	24,389	3.072	79	6,241	8.888	493,039	4.291
30	900	5.477	27,000	3.107	80	6,400	8.944	512,000	4.309
31	961	5.568	29,791	3.141	81	6,561	9.000	531,441	4.327
32	1,024	5.657	32,768	3.175	82	6,724	9.055	551,368	4.344
33	1,089	5.745	35,937	3.208	83	6,889	9.110	571,787	4.362
34	1,156	5.831	39,304	3.240	84	7,056	9.165	592,704	4.380
35	1,225	5.916	42,875	3.271	85	7,225	9.220	614,125	4.397
36	1,296	6.000	46,656	3.302	86	7,396	9.274	636,056	4.414
37	1,369	6.083	50,653	3.332	87	7,569	9.327	658,503	4.431
38	1,444	6.164	54,872	3.362	88	7,744	9.381	681,472	4.448
39	1,521	6.245	59,319	3.391	89	7,921	9.434	704,969	4.465
40	1,600	6.325	64,000	3.420	90	8,100	9.487	729,000	4.481
41	1,681	6.403	68,921	3.448	91	8,281	9.539	753,571	4.498
42	1,764	6.481	74,088	3.476	92	8,464	9.592	778,688	4.514
43	1,849	6.557	79,507	3.503	93	8,649	9.644	804,357	4.531
44	1,936	6.633	85,184	3.530	94	8,836	9.695	830,584	4.547
45	2,025	6.708	91,125	3.557	95	9,025	9.747	857,375	4.563
46	2,116	6.782	97,336	3.583	96	9,216	9.798	884,736	4.579
47	2,209	6.856	103,823	3.609	97	9,409	9.849	912,673	4.595
48	2,304	6.928	110,592	3.634	98	9,604	9.899	941,192	4.610
49	2,401	7.000	117,649	3.659	99	9,801	9.950	970,299	4.626
50	2,500	7.071	125,000	3.684	100	10,000	10.000	1,000,000	4.642

Trigonometric Ratios

Angle Measure	Sin	Cos	Tan	Angle Measure	Sin	Cos	Tan
0°	0.000	1.000	0.000	46°	.7193	.6947	1.036
1°	.0175	.9998	.0175	47°	.7314	.6820	1.072
2°	.0349	.9994	.0349	48°	.7431	.6691	1.111
3°	.0523	.9986	.0524	49°	.7547	.6561	1.150
4°	.0698	.9976	.0699	50°	.7660	.6428	1.192
5°	.0872	.9962	.0875	51°	.7771	.6293	1.235
6°	.1045	.9945	.1051	52°	.7880	.6157	1.280
7°	.1219	.9925	.1228	53°	.7986	.6018	1.327
8°	.1392	.9903	.1405	54°	.8090	.5878	1.376
9°	.1564	.9877	.1584	55°	.8192	.5736	1.428
10°	.1736	.9848	.1763	56°	.8290	.5592	1.483
11°	.1908	.9816	.1944	57°	.8387	.5446	1.540
12°	.2079	.9781	.2126	58°	.8480	.5299	1.600
13°	.2250	.9744	.2309	59°	.8572	.5150	1.664
14°	.2419	.9703	.2493	60°	.8660	.5000	1.732
15°	.2588	.9659	.2679	61°	.8746	.4848	1.804
16°	.2756	.9613	.2867	62°	.8829	.4695	1.881
17°	.2924	.9563	.3057	63°	.8910	.4540	1.963
18°	.3090	.9511	.3249	64°	.8988	.4384	2.050
19°	.3256	.9455	.3443	65°	.9063	.4226	2.145
20°	.3420	.9397	.3640	66°	.9135	.4067	2.246
21°	.3584	.9336	.3839	67°	.9205	.3907	2.356
22°	.3746	.9272	.4040	68°	.9272	.3746	2.475
23°	.3907	.9205	.4245	69°	.9336	.3584	2.605
24°	.4067	.9135	.4452	70°	.9397	.3420	2.747
25°	.4226	.9063	.4663	71°	.9455	.3256	2.904
26°	.4384	.8988	.4877	72°	.9511	.3090	3.077
27°	.4540	.8910	.5095	73°	.9563	.2924	3.270
28°	.4695	.8829	.5317	74°	.9613	.2756	3.487
29°	.4848	.8746	.5543	75°	.9659	.2588	3.732
30°	.5000	.8660	.5774	76°	.9703	.2419	4.010
31°	.5150	.8572	.6009	77°	.9744	.2250	4.331
32°	.5299	.8480	.6249	78°	.9781	.2079	4.704
33°	.5446	.8387	.6494	79°	.9816	.1908	5.145
34°	.5592	.8290	.6745	80°	.9848	.1736	5.671
35°	.5736	.8192	.7002	81°	.9877	.1564	6.314
36°	.5878	.8090	.7265	82°	.9903	.1392	7.115
37°	.6018	.7986	.7536	83°	.9925	.1219	8.144
38°	.6157	.7880	.7813	84°	.9945	.1045	9.514
39°	.6293	.7771	.8098	85°	.9962	.0872	11.43
40°	.6428	.7660	.8391	86°	.9976	.0698	14.30
41°	.6561	.7547	.8693	87°	.9986	.0523	19.08
42°	.6691	.7431	.9004	88°	.9994	.0349	28.64
43°	.6820	.7314	.9325	89°	.9998	.0175	57.29
44°	.6947	.7193	.9657	90°	1.000	0.000	
45°	.7071	.7071	1.000				

INDEX

Problems

age, 206–209 • area, 437–439 • coin, 80–82 • consecutive integer, 168–170 • digit, 326–329 • direct variation, 333 • dry mixture, 304–309 • equations, 72–79 • fractional equations, 350–355 • inverse variation, 337 • investment and loan, 364–367 • motion, 108–111 • number, 72–79 • number relation, 310–313 • perimeter, 84–86, 313 • quadratic equations, 437–439 • similar triangles, 448–450 • systems of equations, 306–313 • translating English phrases to algebra, 70–71 • trigonometry, 461–463 • using integers, 34–35 • wet mixture, 430–433 • work, 350–355

Product(s)

of a positive number and a negative number, 28–30 • of extremes, 262–264 • of fractions, 176–183 • of means, 262–264 • of powers, 121–123 • of radicals, 404–406 • of two negative numbers, 28–30 • of two positive numbers, 28–30 • power of a, 122–123 • rectangle, 144 • simplifying for fractions, 194–196

Property(ies)

addition for equations, 59–62 • addition for inequalities, 99–101 • additive identity, 24–26 • additive inverses, 25–26 • associative of addition, 6–8, 24–26, 36–38 • associative of multiplication, 6–8, 30 • commutative of addition, 6–8, 24–26, 36–38 • commutative of multiplication, 6–8, 30 • distributive of multiplication over addition, 9–11, 14–17, 30 • distributive of multiplication over subtraction, 11 • division for equations, 60–62 • division for inequalities, 100–101 • multiplication for equations, 60–62 • multiplication for inequalities, 99–101 • multiplicative identity, 44–45 • multiplicative inverse, 177 • of equations, 59–62 • of exponents, 121–123 • of inequalities, 98–101 • of negative a, 48–49 • of negative one for multiplication, 44–45 • of zero for multiplication, 28–30

Proportion(s), 261–264 • extremes of, 262–264 • means of, 262–264

Pythagoras, 399

Pythagorean theorem, 399–401

Pythagorean triples, 416

Q

Quadrant, 241

Quadratic equation(s), 158–164 • roots of, 159 • standard form of, 162–164

Quadratic formula, 427–429, 434–436

Quotient(s)

of two numbers with like signs, 31–33 • of two numbers with unlike signs, 31–33

R

Radical(s)

combining, 402–403 • division of, 408–410 • even exponents, 394–395 • odd exponent(s), 396–397 • products of, 404–406 • simplifying, 391–393

Radical equations, 417–422

Radicand, 392 • fractional, 411–412

Range

of a function, 323–324 • of a relation, 317–319

Ratio(s), 261–264 • trigonometric, 451–453, 456–457

Ratio and proportion, 261–264, 271

Rationalization of denominators, 408–410

Rational numbers, 176, 361–363

Real number(s), 382–383

Reciprocal of a fraction, 175–178

Rectangle

area of, 385 • vertices of, 244

Relation(s)

domain of, 317–319 • inverse of, 319 • range of, 317–319

Relatively prime numbers, 184

Replacement set, 57

S

Scientific notation, 140

Sentence(s)

false, 56–58 • open, 56–58 • solution of open, 57–58 • true, 56–58

Sequences, 90

Set(s)

as subset of itself, 105–107 • element of, 91–93 • empty, 92–93, 105–107 • empty set as subset of every set, 105–107 • equal, 91–93 • finite, 91–93 • infinite, 91–93 • intersection of, 105–107, 112–114 • member of, 91–93 • replacement, 57, 92 • solution, see Solution set(s) • subset of, 105–107 • union of, 105–107, 112–114

Set notation, 91–93

Sine, 451

Slant of a line, 255–257

Slope

of a line, 255–257 • of line segments, 251–254

Solution, 57 • extraneous, 349

ANSWERS

Page x
3. Turn both hourglasses over and start the egg when the 3-minute hourglass runs out. When the 8-minute hourglass runs out (5 minutes later), turn it over again to get 8 more minutes.

Page 2
1. 25 **3.** 30 **5.** 29 **7.** 35 **9.** 18 **11.** 68
13. 26 **15.** 10 **17.** 73 **19.** 32 **21.** 76
23. 69 **25.** 19 **27.** 79 **29.** 73 **31.** 53
33. 57 **35.** 220 **37.** 1.1835 **39.** .1017

Page 5
1. 13 **3.** 49 **5.** 55 **7.** 18 **9.** 14 **11.** 46
13. 31 **15.** 78 **17.** 73 **19.** 93 **21.** 95
23. 416 **25.** 222

Page 8
1. 77 **3.** 96 **5.** 105 **7.** 1,700 **9.** 1,640
11. 49,000 **13.** Comm. Prop. Add.
15. Assoc. Prop. Add. **17.** Assoc. Prop. Mult.
19. Comm. Prop. Add. **21.** Comm. Prop. Mult.
23. 210 **25.** 600 **27.** 390 **29.** 18,700
31. no; no

Page 11
1. $4 \cdot 6 + 4 \cdot 2$; 32 **3.** $2 \cdot 9 + 2 \cdot 4$; 26
5. $2 \cdot 6 + 9 \cdot 6$; 66 **7.** $98 = 98$ **9.** $6(3) + 6(5)$
11. $3(8) + 3(1)$ **13.** $4(2) + 4(7) + 4(6)$
15. $4(6 + 2)$ **17.** $(5 + 9)6$ **19.** $(3 + 7)8$
21. $5(4 + 2 + 7)$ **23.** $(6 + 4 + 7)8$
25. $4(3 + 7 + 1)$ **27.** $7(8 + 4 + 2)$
29. $7(5) + 7(1) + 7(9) + 7(2)$ **31.** $4(1) + 4(9) + 4(7) + 4(2)$ **33.** $7(8) + 7(4) + 7(3) + 7(5)$
35. $4 \cdot 8 + 4 \cdot 1 + 4 \cdot 3 + 4 \cdot 5 + 4 \cdot 9$
37. $3(8) + 3(9) + 3(1) + 3(4) + 3(6)$
39. $4(7 + 7 + 2 + 7)$ **41.** no **43.** yes

Page 12
1. 3,000 mm **3.** 70,000 dm **5.** .08 m
7. 300 cL **9.** 6,000,000 mL **11.** .008 kL
13. 5,000 mg **15.** 8,000,000 mg
17. .007 kg

Page 15
1. $10x + 3$ **3.** $7y + 9$ **5.** $11a + 9$ **7.** $6z + 12$
9. $9b + 7$ **11.** $9k + 7$ **13.** $5y + 1$ **15.** $11z + 4$
17. $10t + 16$ **19.** $8z + 13$ **21.** $9x + 9y$
23. $7m + 9q$ **25.** $11x + 8y + 1$
27. $16a + 8b + 6$ **29.** $7x + 2y + 5z + 1$
31. 25 **33.** 64 **35.** 54 **37.** 86

Page 17
1. $43y + 7$ **3.** $29m + 36$ **5.** $36c + 14$
7. $29x + 12$ **9.** $42r + 56$ **11.** $27y + 30$
13. $39c + 5$ **15.** $8x + 11$ **17.** $13x + 24$
19. $18c + 11$ **21.** $14x + 26$ **23.** $22r + 29$
25. $38e + 38$ **27.** $170c + 70$ **29.** $87x + 120$

Page 18
1. 22 **3.** 4 **5.** 25 **7.** 65 **9.** 44 **11.** 85
13. 5, $9x$; x; 9 **15.** $8a$, $7b$, $2c$; a, b, c; 8, 7, 2
17. 80 **19.** 4,700 **21.** 8,200 **23.** Assoc. Prop. Mult. **25.** Comm. Prop. Mult. **27.** $6 \cdot 3 + 8 \cdot 3$
29. $8 \cdot 3 + 8 \cdot 7 + 8 \cdot 5$ **31.** $9(8 + 2)$
33. $4(5 + 8 + 3 + 1)$ **35.** $45 = 45$ **37.** $12y + 9$
39. $11p + 14q + 3$ **41.** $20y + 24$
43. $14z + 14$ **45.** $57y + 101$ **47.** $13 + 9y$; 31
49. $4 + 12x + 11y$; 166

Page 20
1. 15°C   **3.** 0°C

Page 23
1. +10   **3.** −14   **5.** −10   **7.** +7   **9.** +5
11. −3   **13.** −1   **15.** −9   **17.** −10   **19.** −4
21. −13   **23.** +3   **25.** +5   **27.** −11   **29.** −23
31. +20   **33.** +9   **35.** −7   **37.** +5   **39.** −4
41. +6   **43.** −10   **45.** −2   **47.** +8   **49.** 0
51. 0   **53.** 0   **55.** 0   **57.** −22   **59.** +24
61. +67   **63.** −81   **65.** +8   **67.** −75
69. −131   **71.** 0   **73.** +22   **75.** −787
77. −132   **79.** +994   **81.** Drop the signs;
add the numbers; give a positive sign to the
result.   **83.** Drop the signs; subtract the smaller
number from the larger; give the result the
same sign as the larger.   **85.** −.83
87. −1.074   **89.** +1.87   **91.** +85.63

Page 25
1. +1 = +1   **3.** −13 = −13   **5.** Comm.
7. Add. Iden.   **9.** Add. Iden.   **11.** Comm.
13. Assoc.   **15.** Add. Inv.   **17.** Comm.   **19.** −3
21. +2   **23.** −7   **25.** Opposite of neg. is pos.

27.

Expression	Reason
$(-9 + +4) + -8$	Given
$-8 + (-9 + +4)$	Comm.
$-8 + (+4 + -9)$	Comm.
$(-8 + +4) + -9$	Assoc.

29.

Expression	Reason
$(-3 + +5) + +3$	Given
$(+5 + -3) + +3$	Comm.
$+5 + (-3 + +3)$	Assoc.
$+5 + 0$	Add. Inv.
$+5$	Add. Iden.

31.

Expression	Reason
$(x + y) + z$	Given
$(y + x) + z$	Comm.
$y + (x + z)$	Assoc.
$y + (z + x)$	Comm.
$(y + z) + x$	Assoc.
$(z + y) + x$	Comm.

Page 27
1. {H1, H2, H3, H4, H5, H6, T1, T2, T3, T4,
T5, T6}   **3.** $\frac{5}{36}$; $\frac{1}{2}$

Page 30
1. +21   **3.** −48   **5.** −45   **7.** −28   **9.** −7
11. −16   **13.** +27   **15.** 0   **17.** −8   **19.** +60
21. +72   **23.** −18   **25.** 0   **27.** +100
29. 0   **31.** −100   **33.** −39   **35.** −120
37. −32   **39.** +72   **41.** +250   **43.** −480
45. −720   **47.** −1,600   **49.** +900   **51.** 0
53. +90   **55.** +144   **57.** +1,512   **59.** −5,040
61. $(-4)(+2) = (+2)(-4)$; $(-6)(-5) = (-5)(-6)$
63. $-8(-6 + +3) = (-8)(-6) + (-8)(+3)$;
$+2(-7 + -9) = (+2)(-7) + (+2)(-9)$

Page 32
1. +2   **3.** −5   **5.** +7   **7.** +9   **9.** −9   **11.** 0
13. +6   **15.** +3   **17.** +4   **19.** −3   **21.** +1
23. +5   **25.** −42   **27.** −4   **29.** +7   **31.** −9
33. −8   **35.** +15   **37.** +5   **39.** +6   **41.** −32
43. +1   **45.** +1   **47.** +9   **49.** +1   **51.** −3
53. −5   **55.** −2   **57.** +.0002

Page 34
1. 60 m above sea level   **3.** yes   **5.** $.62

Page 38
1. −6   **3.** 13   **5.** 0   **7.** −44   **9.** 12   **11.** 7
13. 19   **15.** 10   **17.** 17   **19.** −21   **21.** 5
23. 34   **25.** −126   **27.** −83   **29.** 16
31. −102   **33.** −94   **35.** 0

Page 39
1.

1	12	7	14
8	13	2	11
10	3	16	5
15	6	9	4

Page 41
1. 14   **33.** −2   **5.** 11   **7.** 12   **9.** 63   **11.** 3
13. −32   **15.** −68   **17.** −74   **19.** −41   **21.** 94
23. 71   **25.** −211   **27.** $13x + 36y + 8$; 90

Page 43

1. $5y$ **3.** $2b$ **5.** $-2z$ **7.** $-5r$ **9.** $-7r$
11. $-4z - 8$ **13.** $-2q - 9$ **15.** $-9y - 4$
17. $-12x + 1$ **19.** $2x + 6y + 3$
21. $4r - 6s - 6$ **23.** $-14x + 4y + 8$
25. $-10x + 3y - 4$ **27.** $13a - 4c - 16$
29. $-6a + 3b + 1$ **31.** $2x + 6y - 3; -25$
33. $6x + 4y - 4z; -56$ **35.** $-11x + 6y - 6; -2$
37. $1.2x - 1.193y - 4; -7.3425$

Page 45

1. 0 **3.** $3b$ **5.** $12r$ **7.** $-a + 2$ **9.** $c - 1$
11. $-e - 3$ **13.** $-9q + 15$ **15.** $2p - 7$
17. $-5d - 10$ **19.** $-3a + 2$ **21.** $-7z + 16$
23. $14b - 14$ **25.** $2x - 4y - 8; -36$
27. $-x - y + 8z; -28$ **29.** $x - 8y - z; -47$
31. $x - 9y - 6z + 1; -37$ **33.** $.7x + .002y - z;$
-1.98692

Page 47

1. $29x - 16$ **3.** $14y - 14$ **5.** $-8a + 38$
7. $2x - 27$ **9.** $-39a - 63$ **11.** $-29a - 21$
13. $-6x - 11$ **15.** $25c - 27$ **17.** $17x$
19. $-38y - 74$ **21.** $17y - 32; 104$
23. $-37x - 6; 142$ **25.** $10x - 7; -97$
27. $31d - 26; 67$ **29.** $-17x - 1; 16$
31. $-33x + 14$ **33.** $-29y + 33$ **35.** $87z + 19$
37. $-20x - 48$ **39.** $-20x + 2$

Page 49

1. $-11y - 2$ **3.** $-5z - 12$ **5.** $-2c + 8$
7. $3f - 8$ **9.** $9y - 9$ **11.** $8y - 17$
13. $-6e - 13$ **15.** $-6d - 1$ **17.** $4y - 4$
19. $-11z + 6$ **21.** $-19b - 10$ **23.** -12
25. -23 **27.** 39 **29.** -7 **31.** -7
33. $-23y + 33$ **35.** $-4z - 2$ **37.** $9r - 2$
39. $-8x + 10$

Page 51

1. 3 **3.** -2 **5.** -14 **7.** 9 **9.** -18
11. $3b + 8$ **13.** $-x - 12$ **15.** $2y + 17$
17. $-5x + 3$ **19.** $20z + 10$ **21.** $3y - 27$
23. $18z - 6$ **25.** $-3x - 11$

Page 52

1. $+10$ **3.** $+3$ **5.** -18 **7.** -5 **9.** -9 **11.** 8
13. 6 **15.** -9 **17.** -16 **19.** 105 **21.** -75
23. -120 **25.** 7 **27.** -6 **29.** -5 **31.** -27
33. 49 **35.** $-3x$ **37.** $-5p + 20$ **39.** $5a + 16$
41. $-9z - 5$ **43.** $-30k + 16; 166$ **45.** 15
47. $4x + 12$ **49.** $2a - 8$ **51.** Comm.

Page 54

1. Start. Insert first key. Does it work? No: Insert second key. Yes: Stop. Does second key work? No: Insert third key. Yes: Stop.

Page 58

1. 5 **3.** 9 **5.** 5 **7.** 9 **9.** 7 **11.** 4 **13.** 5
15. 7 **17.** 4 **19.** 3 **21.** 4 **23.** 2 **25.** 6
27. 3 **29.** 0 **31.** $\frac{1}{4}$ **33.** -3 **35.** none **37.** $\frac{1}{2}$

Page 62

1. 4 **3.** 6 **5.** -1 **7.** -3 **9.** -2 **11.** -8
13. -1 **15.** -5 **17.** -3 **19.** 1 **21.** -2
23. 0 **25.** $\frac{1}{5}$ **27.** $\frac{1}{6}$ **29.** $\frac{1}{8}$ **31.** $\frac{2}{5}$ **33.** $\frac{1}{4}$ **35.** $\frac{3}{8}$
37. $-.176$ **39.** $.406$

Page 63

1. 7

Page 66

1. 3 **3.** 3 **5.** 8 **7.** 15 **9.** 4 **11.** 7 **13.** -11
15. 6 **17.** 1 **19.** 4 **21.** 5 **23.** 2 **25.** 6
27. 7 **29.** -4 **31.** 1 **33.** 3 **35.** 4 **37.** -3
39. $\frac{1}{4}$ **41.** $\frac{3}{5}$ **43.** $\frac{5}{6}$ **45.** $\frac{5}{4}$ **47.** $-\frac{7}{5}$ **49.** $\frac{3}{2}$
51. $\frac{3}{2}$ **53.** $\frac{5}{2}$ **55.** $.3$ **57.** $.64$

Page 67

1. $x; 2x; 2x + 6; 3x + 6; x + 2; x + 2$

Page 69

1. 7 **3.** -7 **5.** 8 **7.** -6 **9.** 20 **11.** -8
13. 9 **15.** -1 **17.** 10 **19.** 5 **21.** -3
23. -4 **25.** 2 **27.** 2 **29.** -1 **31.** 1 **33.** 11
35. 3 **37.** -2 **39.** 1 **41.** $\frac{16}{5}$ **43.** $\frac{1}{13}$ **45.** $-\frac{1}{6}$
47. $-\frac{3}{19}$ **49.** 2 **51.** 9 **53.** $\frac{42}{11}$ **55.** $-\frac{3}{8}$
57. $-\frac{4}{9}$

Page 71

1. $8 - 5$ **3.** $12 + 6$ **5.** $23 + 2$ **7.** $y + 4$
9. $n - 8$ **11.** $5y + 3$ **13.** $3n - 6$ **15.** $25 - 4n$
17. $4x + 8$ **19.** $14 + 2n$ **21.** $9n - 7$
23. $x + y$ **25.** $7x - 2y$ **27.** $xy + 9$ **29.** $y - 5x$
31. $5 + 7y + 8$, or $7y + 13$ **33.** $5n - 2 + 9$, or
$5n + 7$

Page 74

1. 4 **3.** 3 **5.** 1 **7.** 3 **9.** -2 **11.** -3 **13.** 1
15. -36 **17.** 5 **19.** 7 **21.** -8 **23.** -10
25. 7 **27.** -9 **29.** 1 **31.** -3

Page 78

1. 7, 35 **3.** 39, 11 **5.** 37, 46 **7.** 51, 17
9. \$31, \$58 **11.** 8, 11, 15 **13.** 9, 12
15. 26, 13

Page 82

1. 3 dimes, 12 nickels **3.** 1 dime, 3 quarters
5. 7 dimes, 4 quarters **7.** 14 pennies,
21 nickels **9.** 502 tickets **11.** 3 nickels,
18 dimes, 20 pennies **13.** 44 dimes

Page 83

1. 326 km **3.** Bus tour is more economical
by \$6.

Page 86

1. 13 m; 7 m **3.** 19 km; 8 km **5.** 15 cm;
13 cm; 21 cm **7.** 9 cm; 12 cm; 17 cm
9. 11 m; 11 m **11.** 16 m **13.** 18 cm; 9 cm
15. 6 cm; 9 cm

Page 88

1. 7 **3.** 3 **5.** none **7.** -11 **9.** $-\frac{8}{5}$ **11.** 5
13. 1 **15.** $\frac{23}{2}$ **17.** 3 **19.** 22 **21.** -4
23. -13 **25.** -5 **27.** -3 **29.** 8 **31.** -2
33. $6 + x$ **35.** $n - 3$ **37.** $2y - 5$ **39.** 4 **41.** 5,
22 **43.** 26 cm; 8 cm

Page 90

1. $-11, -12, -13$ **3.** $-3, -3, -3$ **5.** .00001,
.000001, .0000001 **7.** 13, 14, 16 **9.** 125, 216,
343 **11.** $\frac{5}{6}, \frac{6}{7}, \frac{7}{8}$ **13.** 24, 35, 48 **15.** 124, 215,
342

Page 93

1. equal **3.** not equal **5.** equal **7.** finite
9. infinite **11.** finite **13.** {1, 2, 3, 4, 5}
15. {$-3, -2$} **17.** {7} **19.** {7} **21.** {4}
23. {4} **25.** {9} **27.** {-1} **29.** {all numbers}
31. {all numbers} **33.** {all numbers}

Page 96

1. all points to the left of 3 **3.** 5 and all
points to the left **5.** -2 and all points to the
left **7.** all points to the right of 2 **9.** -6 and
all points to the right **11.** all points to the left
of 2 **13.** all points to the right of 4 **15.** 4 and
all points to the right **17.** all points to the left
of -3 **19.** 1 and all points to the right
21. -3 and all points to the left **23.** all points
to the left of -2 **25.** -1 and all points to the
right **27.** -4 and all points to the left **29.** all
points to the right of -2 **31.** 2 and all points
to the right **33.** 1 and all points to the right
35. 5 and all points to the left **37.** all points to
the right and left of $2\frac{1}{2}$ **39.** all points to the left
of $\frac{5}{4}$ **41.** $\frac{1}{2}$ and all points to the left **43.** $-\frac{2}{3}$
and all points to the right **45.** all points to the
right of 5 **47.** all points to the right of -2.5

Page 97

1. -6 **3.** 6

Page 101

1. $10 > 9$ **3.** $-24 < 4$ **5.** $-4 < -1$
7. $-21 < 14$ **9.** $0 > -15$ **11.** $-8 < 4$
13. $-42 < 6$ **15.** $2 \leq 3$ **17.** $2 > -2$ **19.** $3 \geq$
-10 **21.** $0 \leq 15$ **23.** $7 \leq 11$ **25.** $6 > 5$
27. Add -3 **29.** Multiply by -3. **31.** Add 5.
33. Divide by -3 **35.** Multiply by -3.

Page 104

1. $\{x \mid x > -2\}$ **3.** $\{y \mid y > -1\}$ **5.** $\{x \mid x > 7\}$
7. $\{a \mid a \leq 8\}$ **9.** $\{d \mid d < -3\}$ **11.** $\{r \mid r \geq 4\}$
13. $\{x \mid x \leq 3\}$ **15.** $\{x \mid x < 4\}$ **17.** $\{x \mid x \leq 6\}$
19. $\{y \mid y > 3\}$ **21.** $\{x \mid x \geq 8\}$ **23.** $\{y \mid y > 9\}$
25. $\{x \mid x > 5\}$ **27.** {all numbers}

1. $A \nsubseteq B$; $B \subseteq A$ 3. $A \subseteq B$; $B \nsubseteq A$ 5. $A \subseteq B$; $B \nsubseteq A$ 7. $A \subseteq B$; $B \nsubseteq A$ 9. $A \subseteq B$; $B \subseteq A$
11. $A \nsubseteq B$; $B \nsubseteq A$ 13. $A \nsubseteq B$; $B \subseteq A$
15. $A \subseteq B$; $B \nsubseteq A$ 17. $\{1, 2\}, \{1\}, \{2\}, \phi$; 4
19. $\{8\}, \phi$; 2   21. $\{-1, 0\}, \{-1\}, \{0\}, \phi$; 4
23. $\{3, 5\}$; $\{1, 3, 5\}$ 25. ϕ; $\{4, 5, 6, 7\}$
27. ϕ; $\{0, 2, 4\}$ 29. ϕ; $\{-3, -2, -1, 1, 2, 3\}$
31. $\{1, 4, 5\}$; $\{1, 2, 3, 4, 5\}$ 33. $\{6\}$;
$\{2, 4, 6, 8, 10\}$ 35. $\{2, 5, 8, 9\}$; $\{2, 5, 8, 9\}$
37. ϕ; $\{0, 1, 2, 3, \ldots\}$ 39. $\{0, 6, 12, 18, \ldots\}$;
$\{0, 2, 3, 4, 6, 8, 9, 10, 12, \ldots\}$ 41. $\{0\}$;
{integers}   43. {positive integers};
{whole numbers}   45. $\{0, 1, 2, 3, 4, 5, 6\}$
47. ϕ 49. $\{0, 2, 4\}$

1. 4 hr   3. 3 hr   5. 3 hr   7. 48 km   9. 5 hr

1. $\{x \mid x > -2 \text{ and } x < 5\}$; {all numbers}
3. $\{x \mid x \geq -4 \text{ and } x < 2\}$; {all numbers}
5. $\{x \mid x \geq -1\}$; $\{x \mid x > -3\}$
7. $\{x \mid x \geq -1 \text{ and } x \leq 3\}$; {all numbers}
9. $\{x \mid x < 0\}$; $\{x \mid x < 4\}$ 11. $\{1\}$; {all numbers}
13. $\{x \mid x > -4\}$; $\{x \mid x > -5\}$
15. $\{x \mid x \leq 2 \text{ and } x > -1\}$; {all numbers}
17. $\{x \mid x > 3\}$; $\{x \mid x \geq 3\}$ 19. ϕ;
{all numbers}   21. ϕ; $\{x \mid x \geq 5\}$
23. $\{x \mid x \geq -3 \text{ and } x \leq 3\}$; {all numbers}
25. $\{-3\}$; $\{x \mid x \leq -3\}$ 27. $\{x \mid x > 3 \text{ and } x \leq 4\}$;
{all numbers}   29. $\{x \mid x > 2\}$; {all numbers}
31. $\{x \mid x \geq 1 \text{ and } x \leq 4\}$
33. $\{x \mid x > -4 \text{ and } x < 3\}$
35. $\{x \mid x \leq -2 \text{ or } x \geq 0\}$
37. $\{x \mid x > 2 \text{ and } x \leq 3\}$ 39. segment with
endpoints 0 and 5   41. all points to the right
of -4

1. equal   3. not equal   5. infinite; the set of all
positive odd integers   7. infinite; the set of all
negative integers   9. ϕ 11. $\{-13\}$
13. all points to the right of -2 15. all points
to the right and left of $-\frac{1}{2}$ 17. all points to the
right of 2   19. $1 \geq -3$ 21. $3 > -6$
23. Add -2.   25. $\{x \mid x \leq -2\}$ 27. $\{x \mid x < 1\}$
29. $A \subseteq B$; $B \nsubseteq A$ 31. $\{3\}, \phi$; 2   33. $\{9\}, \{8\}$,
$\{7\}, \{9, 8\}, \{9, 7\}, \{8, 7\}, \{9, 8, 7\}, \phi$; 8
35. ϕ; $\{1, 2, 3, 4, 5, 6\}$ 37. $\{x \mid x > 3 \text{ and } x \leq 4\}$;
{all numbers}   39. $\{x \mid -4 \leq x \leq 2\}$

1. $x \cdot x \cdot x \cdot x \cdot x$ 3. $a \cdot a \cdot a \cdot a$ 5. $4 \cdot n \cdot n \cdot n$
7. $-3 \cdot a \cdot a$ 9. -27 11. 16   13. -24
15. 64   17. 243   19. 24   21. -27 23. -4
25. 64   27. 11,664   29. 1,048,576   31. -216

1. $12a^8$ 3. $6m^{11}$ 5. $28x^{12}$ 7. $15a^9$ 9. $4a^5$
11. $6a^{11}$ 13. $-8a^8$ 15. $-8m^8$ 17. $8a^4$
19. $-15b^8$ 21. $12a^5b^6$ 23. $-20m^4n^7$
25. $6a^5b^4$ 27. a^6 29. x^{12} 31. z^{30} 33. r^{30}
35. g^{45} 37. c^{28} 39. $16x^8$ 41. $-8z^{12}$
43. $256x^{12}$ 45. $9a^4x^6$ 47. $8m^9n^{12}$
49. $-64a^9m^{12}$ 51. $8x^3a^6$ 53. $-243x^5y^{10}m^5$
55. $a^{10}b^{20}c^{15}$ 57. $27a^9b^6$ 59. $-27x^9y^{12}z^6$
61. y^{4b} 63. x^{6a} 65. $2^a x^{5a^2}$

1. $3x^2 - 3x - 8$ 3. $9x^2 + 4x + 5$
5. $5x^2 - 11x + 3$ 7. $m^2 - 9$ 9. $7x^3 - 9x^2 + 9x$
11. $-m^3 + 5m$ 13. $8a^4 + a^2$ 15. $2a^2 + a - 1$
17. $7b^3 - 2b^2 - b + 8$ 19. $10a^3 + 2a^2 -$
$12a - 4$ 21. $3a^4 - 7a^3 + 2a^2 + a - 6$
23. $-22m^9 - m^6 - 3$ 25. $a^4 + 12a^3 - 10a^2 +$
$13a - 19$

1. 6, 8, 10   3. $-8, -2, 6, 20$ 5. Follow the
flow chart on page 126, but change $x > y$ to
$y > x$; or after the question, "Is $x > y$?",
exchange Yes and No branches; so Yes branch
becomes No branch, No branch becomes Yes
branch.

1. $3f^4 - 5f^3 + 4f^2$ 3. $2a^3 - 5a^2 + 4a$
5. $6x^5 - 14x^4$ 7. $24b^3 - 30b^2$ 9. $20c^4 - 25c^3$
11. $-4x^2 + 5x$ 13. $-2x^2 - 5x + 7$
15. $b^2 - 2b$ 17. $-a^2 + a + 4$
19. $9a^3 + 15a^2 - 6a$ 21. $-4a^4 + 12a^3 + 16a^2$
23. $m^3 + m^2 + 5m$ 25. $x^3 + 8x^2 - 12x + 9$
27. $2x^3 + x - 9$ 29. $x^5 + x^3 - 8x + 7$
31. $3a^2 - 2a - 7$ 33. $4x^2 - 9x + 17$
35. $6a^2 - 11a$ 37. $5x^4 - 2x^3 + 4x^2 - 3$
39. $x^4 + x^3 + 3x^2 - 3x + 3$ 41. $2m^5n^2 -$
$3m^4n^3 + m^3n^4$ 43. $2a^3b - 6a^2b^2 + 10ab^3$
45. $-2x^3y^2 + x^2y^3 - xy^4$ 47. $-2a^4c +$
$2a^3c^2 - 2a^2c^3 + 2ac^4$ 49. $3m^5n^2 - 5m^4n^3 +$
$4m^3n^4$ 51. $-2x^3y^2 + x^2y^3 - 6xy^4$

Page 131
1. no   **3.** no   **5.** 8,128

Page 133
1. $2 \cdot 2 \cdot 3$ **3.** $3 \cdot 3 \cdot 2$ **5.** $3 \cdot 3 \cdot 5$ **7.** $2 \cdot 13$
9. $5 \cdot 5 \cdot 2$ **11.** $2 \cdot 2 \cdot 11$ **13.** $5 \cdot 2 \cdot 2 \cdot 2 \cdot 2$
15. $3 \cdot 2 \cdot 2 \cdot 2 \cdot 2$ **17.** a^3 **19.** $6m^3$ **21.** $-9x^2$
23. $7x^5$ **25.** $-10x^4$ **27.** b^5 **29.** $-2b$
31. $9a^3b$ **33.** $-8a^2m^2$ **35.** $-ab$ **37.** $-x^2y^4$
39. x **41.** a^{3m} **43.** a^{2m+4}

Page 137
1. $3(x^2 + 9x + 3)$ **3.** $6(b^2 + 3b + 5)$
5. $7(a^2 - 3a + 7)$ **7.** $x^3(x^2 + x - 1)$
9. $a(2a^2 - a + 1)$ **11.** $7a(a - 4)$
13. $4a^2(a + 2)$ **15.** $6a(a - 4)$
17. $4a(a^2 - 3a + 2)$ **19.** $6x(2x^2 - x + 3)$
21. $4(m^2 - 5)$ **23.** $4m^2(m - 8)$
25. $7a^3(a^2 - 5a + 3)$ **27.** $3(a^2 + 4ab + 12b^2)$
29. $9m(2m^3 - 3m^2 - 5m + 4)$

Page 138
1. -8 **3.** 16   **5.** 36   **7.** 64   **9.** 64   **11.** a^{16}
13. $15b^3$ **15.** $-21a^5b^7$ **17.** $16b^2$
19. binomial   **21.** trinomial   **23.** $5a^2 - 2a + 8$
25. $9b^3 + 5b^2 + 5b + 7$
27. $2b^8 + 2b^7 + 2b^6$ **29.** $m^3 + 5m^2 + 2m$
31. $a^4 + 3a^3 - 3a^2 - 11a + 7$
33. $3c^2 + 2c - 1$ **35.** $-3a^4c^2 + 6a^3c^3 - 3a^2c^4 + 3ac^5$ **37.** $-3a^2 - 6a + 5$
39. $2y^3 + 2y^2 - 2y + 4$ **41.** $2 \cdot 2 \cdot 2 \cdot 2 \cdot 2$
43. a^5 **45.** a **47.** $-9ab^4$ **49.** $2(2a^2 - 4a + 3)$
51. $x(4x - 7)$ **53.** $4y(y^2 - 2y + 3)$

Page 140
1. 400   **3.** 26,300,000   **5.** 6.3×10^4
7. 1.75×10^6, or 1,750,000
9. 4.3902×10^8, or 439,020,000

Page 143
1. $6x^2 + 25x + 14$ **3.** $6m^2 + 13m + 5$
5. $8a^2 + 10a - 7$ **7.** $m^2 - 25$ **9.** $4r^2 - 9$
11. $3a^2 - 5a + 2$ **13.** $2y^2 + 3y - 20$
15. $2b^2 - b - 10$ **17.** $3x^2 - 16x - 35$
19. $9y^2 - 1$ **21.** $6a^2 + 7a - 10$
23. $4y^2 + 16my - 9m^2$ **25.** $9y^2 - 30y + 25$
27. $4x^2 + 12x + 9$ **29.** $6x^3 + 10x^2 + 5x - 3$
31. $3x^3 + 20x^2 - 2x + 35$ **33.** $3x^4 - 19x^3 - 5x^2 + 6x$ **35.** $x^2 - 14x + 49$
37. $4m^2 - 4m + 1$

Page 144
1. $a^2 + 5a + 6$ **3.** $x^2 + 7x + 10$

Page 147
1. $(2x + 5)(x + 1)$ **3.** $(5x + 2)(x + 1)$
5. $(3x - 1)(2x - 5)$ **7.** $(x + 3)(x - 2)$
9. $(x + 6)(x - 5)$ **11.** $(3x + 5)(x - 5)$
13. $(x + 5)(x + 2)$ **15.** $(a + 3)(a + 1)$
17. $(m - 5)(m - 4)$ **19.** $(a - 5)(a + 4)$
21. $(a - 9)(a + 2)$ **23.** $(b - 3)(b - 3)$
25. $(2a - 3)(a - 2)$ **27.** $(2a + 1)(a - 4)$
29. $(2a + 3)(a + 5)$ **31.** $(3x - 5)(x + 5)$
33. $(2m - 5)(m - 1)$ **35.** $(3y - 5)(y + 4)$
37. $(2b + 5)(b + 6)$ **39.** $(4y + 1)(3y + 1)$
41. $(2x + 5)(x + 9)$ **43.** $(2a - 5)(a - 10)$
45. $(2b - 5)(b - 12)$ **47.** $(5x + 3)(x - 9)$
49. $(5d - 3)(3d - 2)$ **51.** $(7b + 3)(2b - 3)$
53. $(3a - 2)(3a - 2)$ **55.** $(5x - 3)(3x - 4)$
57. $(6a + 7)(3a - 5)$

Page 149
1. $x = 3$

Page 152
1. $(x - 4)(x + 4)$ **3.** $(b - 5)(b + 5)$
5. $(b - 1)(b + 1)$ **7.** $(m + 8)(m - 8)$
9. $(2b - 7)(2b + 7)$ **11.** $(5a + 6)(5a - 6)$
13. $(7y - 2)(7y + 2)$ **15.** $(5m - 2)(5m + 2)$
17. $(2t - 5)(2t + 5)$ **19.** $(5 + x)(5 - x)$
21. $(9 - t)(9 + t)$ **23.** $(7 + b)(7 - b)$
25. $(1 - y)(1 + y)$ **27.** $(8 - 9c)(8 + 9c)$
29. $(4 - 9y)(4 + 9y)$ **31.** $(12a - 9)(12a + 9)$
33. $(5m - 12)(5m + 12)$ **35.** $(6x + 5)(6x - 5)$
37. $(13p - 4)(13p + 4)$ **39.** $(7 + 15x)(7 - 15x)$
41. $(4t - 15)(4t + 15)$
43. $(15a - 13)(15a + 13)$
45. $(11m - 15)(11m + 15)$

Page 155
1. $2(a-4)(a-1)$ 3. $2(a+7)(a-5)$
5. $x(3x-2)(x+2)$ 7. $2x(x+1)(x-1)$
9. $2m(2m+5)(2m-5)$ 11. $2m(m-9)(m-1)$
13. $4a(a-5)(a+2)$ 15. $3b(2b-5)(b+2)$
17. $2a(a+3)(a+5)$ 19. $(2a-1)(a+7)$
21. $(2a+1)(a+1)$ 23. $3(2x-7)(x+5)$
25. $y^2(3y+5)(y-4)$ 27. $3a(2a-1)(2a-11)$
29. $3a(3a-2)(a+8)$ 31. $(x-a)(m+n)$
33. $(r+t)(p-2)$ 35. $(y+1)(p+5)(p-5)$

Page 157
1. $(a+b)(a+3b)$ 3. $(c+6d)(c+d)$
5. $5(x-3y)(x+3y)$ 7. $(2m-5b)(m+2b)$
9. $(2a+b)(a-5b)$ 11. $(a-2b)(a-b)$
13. $2(a+7b)(a+3b)$ 15. $2(y+z)(y+9z)$
17. $2(3x+2y)(x-5y)$ 19. $b(ab-5)(ab+5)$
21. $ab(a+b)(a-b)$ 23. $3(2x-5y)(x-7y)$
25. $2(2k-5r)(k-8r)$ 27. $(3a-5b)(a+6b)$
29. $(3a+7b)(2a-3b)$ 31. $(5x+3y)(2x+3y)$
33. $xy(3x-4y)(2x+5y)$

Page 160
1. 2, 3 3. 1, 8 5. 6, -6 7. $\left\{\frac{1}{2}, -5\right\}$
9. $\left\{\frac{1}{2}, -3\right\}$ 11. $\left\{\frac{3}{2}, -5\right\}$ 13. $\left\{\frac{1}{3}, 7\right\}$ 15. $\left\{\frac{1}{2}, 5\right\}$
17. $\left\{\frac{5}{2}, -\frac{5}{2}\right\}$ 19. $\left\{\frac{3}{2}, 5\right\}$ 21. $\left\{0, \frac{5}{3}\right\}$ 23. $\frac{5}{3}, -7$
25. $\frac{7}{2}, -6$ 27. $-\frac{7}{2}, -8$ 29. 10 31. 0, 3, -3
33. 0, 2, -2 35. 0, 7, -7

Page 161
1. 5,625 3. 9,025 5. 42,025

Page 164
1. $-3, -5$ 3. $-4, -8$ 5. 2, -6 7. 0, -9
9. 0, -7 11. $\left\{\frac{2}{3}, -\frac{2}{3}\right\}$ 13. $\{0, -13\}$
15. $\{7, -7\}$ 17. $\left\{\frac{2}{3}, 1\right\}$ 19. $\left\{\frac{1}{2}, -1\right\}$
21. $\left\{\frac{1}{3}, -1\right\}$ 23. $\left\{-\frac{3}{2}, 7\right\}$ 25. $\left\{\frac{1}{2}, -6\right\}$
27. $\left\{\frac{5}{2}, -\frac{5}{2}\right\}$ 29. $\frac{3}{5}, \frac{2}{3}$ 31. $\frac{2}{3}, -\frac{5}{2}$ 33. $\frac{5}{3}, -\frac{7}{2}$
35. $\frac{7}{2}, -\frac{5}{2}$ 37. 0, -8 39. $\frac{2}{5}, \frac{5}{2}$ 41. 3, -3

Page 167
1. $x + (x+1) + (x+2) = 27$ 3. $x + (x+1) + (x+2) = -15$ 5. $x(x+2) = 35$
7. $x(x+2)(x+4) = 48$ 9. $x + (x+2) + (x+4) + (x+6) = 40$ 11. $2(x+1) + x = 35$
13. $2(x+2) + x = 19$ 15. $3(x+2) + 2x = 46$
17. $x(x+1)(x+2) = 8[x + (x+1) + (x+2)]$

Page 170
1. 22, 23 3. 29, 30, 31, 32, 33 5. 7, 8, 9
7. 37, 39, 41 9. $-4, -3$ or 3, 4 11. 4, 6 or $-6, -4$ 13. 7, 9 or $-9, -7$ 15. $-3, -2, -1$ or 2, 3, 4 17. 5, 6, 7 or $-4, -3, -2$
19. $-5, -3$ 21. $-2, -1, 0, 1$ 23. $-7, -6, -5, -4$ or 4, 5, 6, 7

Page 171
1. 38.4 m

Page 172
1. $x^2 + 8x + 15$ 3. $2x^2 + 13x + 15$
5. $2b^2 + 5b - 12$ 7. $12z^2 - 11z + 2$
9. $15x^2 + 7x - 4$ 11. $2x^3 + 3x^2 - 17x + 12$
13. $9a^2 - 30a + 25$ 15. $4x^2 + 12x + 9$
17. $(x-3)(x-4)$ 19. $(2a-1)(a+5)$
21. $(3y+2)(y+5)$ 23. $(2m-5)(m+4)$
25. $(2x-3)(x-3)$ 27. $(3x+1)(2x-1)$
29. $(a-2)(a+2)$ 31. $(2a+5)(2a-5)$
33. $3(x+3)(x+4)$ 35. $2(a-5)(a+4)$
37. $3k(k+6)(k-5)$ 39. $6x(x-3)(x-1)$
41. $(x+y)(x+2y)$ 43. $(a-7b)(a+4b)$
45. $(12x-13y)(12x+13y)$
47. $(3x-7y)(x-8y)$ 49. $3(2x+3)(2x-3)$
51. 1, 2 53. $-3, 12$ 55. 4, 6 57. $\{0, 5\}$
59. $\left\{\frac{1}{2}, -5\right\}$ 61. $\{0, 6\}$ 63. 8, 9 or $-9, -8$
65. 7, 8, 9 or $-2, -1, 0$

Page 178
1. $\frac{1}{7}$ 3. $\frac{1}{x}$ 5. $-\frac{1}{3}$; no reciprocal; 1; -1; -5
7. $-\frac{2}{3}$ 9. $\frac{6}{1}$ 11. $\frac{12}{3}$ 13. $-\frac{6}{12}$ 15. $-\frac{5}{17}$
17. $\frac{a-4}{a+2}$ 19. 5 21. 3, -3 23. 0, 5, -5
25. 2, -2

Page 179

1. 1 **3.** 1 **5.** $\frac{1}{6}$ **7.** $\frac{1}{3}$ **9.** 1

Page 183

1. $\frac{6}{48}$ **3.** $-\frac{8}{45}$ **5.** $\frac{10a^5}{18b^9}$ **7.** $-\frac{20a^5}{9b^9}$ **9.** $-\frac{x^5}{y^{11}}$

11. $\frac{x^{11}}{y^6}$ **13.** $-\frac{2x^2 - x - 3}{2x^2 + 7x + 6}$

15. $-\frac{2x^2 + x - 15}{2x^2 + 15x + 25}$ **17.** $\frac{10x - 5}{x + 4}$

19. $\frac{2x^2 - 11x - 21}{x - 4}$ **21.** $\frac{2a^2 + 7a - 15}{3a - 7}$

23. $\frac{x^7}{m^3}$ **25.** $\frac{a^2 - b^2}{x^2 + xy - 2y^2}$ **27.** $\frac{12r^2 - rt - t^2}{r^2 + 3rt + 2t^2}$

29. $-\frac{a^2 - 4b^2}{x^2 - y^2}$ **31.** $\frac{9a^2 + 6ab + b^2}{4a^2 + 4ab + b^2}$

33. $-\frac{4a^2 + 11ab - 3b^2}{2a^2 + ab - b^2}$

35. $\frac{x^3 - 8x^2 + 5x + 50}{x^3 + 6x^2 - 15x - 100}$

Page 186

1. $\frac{1}{3}$ **3.** $-\frac{5}{12}$ **5.** $\frac{a - 5}{2a - 1}$ **7.** $\frac{b + 5}{b - 2}$ **9.** $\frac{1}{4}$

11. $\frac{3}{b - 2}$ **13.** $\frac{4}{b + 3}$ **15.** $\frac{y - 4}{y}$ **17.** $\frac{3(x + 2)}{2}$

19. $\frac{b}{b + 7}$ **21.** $\frac{3p - 1}{5}$ **23.** $\frac{x + 4}{x - 4}$ **25.** $x + 4$

27. $x + 5$ **29.** $3a - 1$ **31.** $-11x - 3$

33. $a^2 - a - 2$

Page 190

1. $-\frac{1}{x + 4}$ **3.** $-\frac{1}{2}$ **5.** $\frac{a + 5}{4}$ **7.** $-(x - 4)$

9. -2 **11.** $-\frac{1}{c - 2}$ **13.** $-(a + 2)$ **15.** $-\frac{a + 3}{a + 8}$

17. $-\frac{y + 6}{y + 2}$ **19.** $-\frac{x + 2}{x - 4}$ **21.** $-\frac{n - 4}{2(n - 3)}$

23. $-\frac{a - b}{a + 2b}$ **25.** $-\frac{a - b}{2a - b}$ **27.** $-\frac{a^2 - b^2}{a}$

29. $-\frac{x^2 - 5}{x}$ **31.** $-(b + 3)(b + 2)$

Page 193

1. $\frac{2m^3}{3n^2}$ **3.** $\frac{a^5}{2b}$ **5.** $-\frac{n^2(n - 1)}{m^5}$

7. $2a^3b^2(x - 2)$ **9.** $\frac{b - 2}{2x}$ **11.** $\frac{1}{k(a + 4)}$

13. $\frac{a + 2}{n(a - 1)}$ **15.** $\frac{b^3(x + 3)}{x - 1}$ **17.** $\frac{a(2x - 1)}{b^2(2x - 3)}$

19. $\frac{y - 1}{x^4}$ **21.** $\frac{x^5}{b + y}$ **23.** $\frac{x - 2}{b^3}$

Page 195

1. $3(x - 2)$ **3.** $\frac{3}{n + 2}$ **5.** $\frac{b + 4}{2(b + 2)}$ **7.** $\frac{2b^2}{5x}$

9. $\frac{3x^2}{5y}$ **11.** $\frac{-3a(x + 6)}{2b^4}$ **13.** $\frac{2(b - 4)}{b - 2}$

15. $\frac{b - 5}{b - 7}$ **17.** $\frac{a + 5}{2}$ **19.** $\frac{4x}{3y^3(2a + 3)}$

21. $\frac{3(a + 2)}{a + 3}$ **23.** $\frac{6(2x + 5)}{x + 8}$ **25.** $-\frac{2(c + 1)}{c}$

27. $\frac{2(a + 2)}{a - 4}$ **29.** $\frac{c}{c + d}$ **31.** $\frac{2(x + 2y)}{a^2b}$

33. $-\frac{3(a + 3b)}{a - 2b}$ **35.** $-\frac{m + 2}{2m + 1}$ **37.** $-\frac{m + 1}{2}$

Page 197

1.

$$\begin{array}{r} 573 \\ 219 \\ 5\,157 \\ 5\,73 \\ 114\,6 \\ \hline 125{,}487 \end{array}$$

3.

$$\begin{array}{r} 384. \\ 26\overline{)9{,}984} \\ 7\,8 \\ \hline 2\,18 \\ 2\,08 \\ \hline 104 \\ 104 \end{array}$$

Page 199

1. $\frac{x - 2}{3(x + 6)}$ **3.** $2(a - 5)$ **5.** $\frac{5}{3a^2(a + 2)}$

7. $\frac{-35b^4}{3a^6}$ **9.** $-\frac{6m(5 + m)}{n}$ **11.** $\frac{5(b - 2)}{2(b - 3)}$

13. $-\frac{x - 1}{x + 1}$ **15.** -1 **17.** $\frac{2y(x + 5)}{x^2}$

19. $-\frac{m^7(m + 1)}{8}$ **21.** $\frac{a + 3}{a + 4}$

Page 200

1. $\frac{4}{5}$ **3.** $\frac{3}{2}$ **5.** $\frac{1}{a+7}$ **7.** $\frac{1}{4}$; no reciprocal;

$-\frac{1}{5}$; -3 **9.** 4 **11.** $\frac{20}{63}$ **13.** $\frac{x^2 + 2x - 15}{2x - 3}$

15. $\frac{2}{5}$ **17.** $\frac{b}{2}$ **19.** $x - 2$ **21.** -3 **23.** $-\frac{3a + 5}{a + 7}$

25. $\frac{b - 1}{x}$ **27.** $5(x - 2)$ **29.** $\frac{x^3}{y}$ **31.** $\frac{a - 9}{5(a + 7)}$

33. $-\frac{21b^5}{5a^6}$

Page 204

1. $\frac{2}{3}$ **3.** $\frac{1}{a}$ **5.** $\frac{7y}{y - 3}$ **7.** $\frac{17m}{m + 7}$ **9.** $\frac{1}{6}$

11. $\frac{1}{m - 5}$ **13.** $\frac{1}{a}$ **15.** $\frac{1}{a - 3}$ **17.** $\frac{1}{2}$

19. $\frac{3a + 2b}{7}$ **21.** $\frac{1}{x + 5}$ **23.** $\frac{a + 3}{3a + 5}$

25. $a + 3$ **27.** $4x + 3y$

Page 209

1. Joe 15, Tom 22 **3.** Louis 3, Dorothy 12
5. Sylvia 11, Martin 27 **7.** 4 yr **9.** 6 yr
11. Mona 6, Pedro 12 **13.** 13 yr **15.** 6 yr

Page 213

1. $\frac{3}{2}$ **3.** $\frac{3}{2}$ **5.** $\frac{b}{2}$ **7.** $\frac{23a}{8}$ **9.** $\frac{23a + 10}{12}$

11. $\frac{23m + 21}{28}$ **13.** $\frac{2m - 2}{3m}$ **15.** $\frac{5a + 3}{4a}$

17. $\frac{7}{3}$ **19.** $\frac{31x - 11}{15}$ **21.** $\frac{29a - 2}{6a}$

23. $\frac{23a^2 + 20a - 33}{30a}$

Page 216

1. $\frac{9a + 23}{(a - 4)(a + 4)}$ **3.** $\frac{x + 2}{x}$ **5.** $\frac{3x + 22}{x(x + 5)}$

7. $\frac{2x + 11}{(x - 3)(x + 3)}$ **9.** $\frac{3x + 11}{(x - 8)(x + 2)}$

11. $\frac{9a + 1}{(a - 1)(a + 1)}$ **13.** $\frac{10a + 12}{(2a - 5)(a + 3)}$

15. $\frac{k^2 + 3k - 5}{(k - 3)(k - 2)}$ **17.** $\frac{2m^2 + 5m - 11}{m(2m + 5)}$

Page 217

1. 9; 7 **3.** 25; 25 **5.** 1: comm., not assoc.;
2: not comm., not assoc.; 3: comm., not assoc.

Page 219

1. $\frac{2m + 3}{m}$ **3.** $\frac{3m + 2}{m}$ **5.** $\frac{7x - 10}{(x + 2)(x - 4)}$

7. $\frac{17a + 4}{(a - 3)(2a + 5)}$ **9.** $\frac{7x^2 + 8x + 3}{x^3}$

11. $\frac{7a^2 + 9a + 10}{6a^3}$ **13.** $\frac{5m^2 + 3m + 2}{m^2}$

15. $\frac{a^2 + 2a + 3}{a^2}$ **17.** $\frac{-9b^2 + 50b - 45}{15b^3}$

19. $\frac{6a^3 + 11a^2 + 14a - 2}{12a^3}$ **21.** $\frac{2m^2 + 9m - 2}{m + 5}$

23. $\frac{4x^2 - 3x - 6}{2x - 1}$ **25.** $\frac{3x^2 - 13x - 3}{3x + 2}$

27. $\frac{x^3 - 2x^2 - 14x - 1}{x - 5}$

Page 223

1. $\frac{-2}{a + 5}$ **3.** $\frac{-x^2 + 3x}{x^2 + 5x + 1}$ **5.** $\frac{-3a + 13}{(a - 5)(a - 2)}$

7. $\frac{10x - 3}{2x}$ **9.** $\frac{2a - 11}{a - 2}$ **11.** $\frac{x - 9}{(x - 2)(x - 4)}$

13. $\frac{-2b + 39}{(3b - 1)(2b + 7)}$ **15.** $\frac{9y - 10}{24y^3}$ **17.** $\frac{6}{a - 4}$

19. $\frac{-2a^2 - 2a + 7}{(a + 3)(a + 2)}$ **21.** $\frac{a^2 + 15a - 25}{(2a + 3)(a - 5)}$

23. $\frac{2a^2 - 12a - 6}{a(a - 5)}$ **25.** $\frac{a^2 - 10a + 22}{(2a - 5)(a + 4)}$

27. $\frac{y^2 - 4y - 8}{(y - 4)(2y + 3)}$

Page 226

1. $\frac{3}{x + 7}$ **3.** $\frac{2}{b - 1}$ **5.** $\frac{-b - 5}{(b - 2)(b + 1)}$

7. $\frac{a}{a - 4}$ **9.** $\frac{a}{a + 2}$ **11.** $\frac{8m + 1}{m(m - 1)}$

13. $\frac{-k^2 + 3k + 2}{(k - 6)(k - 2)}$ **15.** $\frac{m}{m - 5}$

17. $\frac{-2m^2 + 7m - 2}{(m - 5)(m - 2)}$ **19.** $\frac{6n^2 - 5n + 9}{(n + 3)(n - 3)}$

21. $\frac{a^2 + 2ab + 2a + 2b - 3b^2 + 7}{(a - b)(a + b)}$

23. $\frac{b^2 + bc + c^2}{(b + c)(b - c)}$

Page 227
1. not a group   **3.** not a group

Page 228
1. $\frac{2}{3}$ **3.** $\frac{5}{8}$ **5.** $\frac{7m}{3}$ **7.** $\frac{2b+5}{2b}$ **9.** $\frac{x+6}{x}$

11. $\frac{5a+4}{(a-6)(a+4)}$ **13.** $\frac{35m+4}{5m}$

15. $\frac{-6x^2+35x+3}{14x^3}$ **17.** $\frac{x^2+2x-11}{x-3}$

19. $\frac{-4x+15}{(x-4)(x-3)}$ **21.** $\frac{8}{x-5}$ **23.** $\frac{5}{x+3}$

25. $\frac{m}{m-9}$

Page 232
1. 3   **3.** 6   **5.** 15   **7.** 10   **9.** 7   **11.** 18   **13.** 4, −4
15. 2, −2   **17.** $\frac{18}{5}$ **19.** $\frac{8}{3}$ **21.** $\{x \mid -2 < x < 2\}$
23. $\{x \mid -1 < x < 1\}$ **25.** $\{x \mid x \le -2 \text{ or } x \ge 2\}$

Page 235
1. −1, 7   **3.** 3, −1   **5.** −3, 2   **7.** $\{1, 5\}$
9. $\{3, -11\}$ **11.** $\left\{-\frac{2}{3}, 4\right\}$ **13.** $\left\{\frac{13}{2}, \frac{15}{2}\right\}$ **15.** $\{1, 6\}$
17. 0, 7   **19.** 2, −2

Page 238
1. 4   **3.** 10   **5.** 6   **7.** 18   **9.** 4   **11.** $\frac{5}{6}$ **13.** 3
15. −2

Page 241
1. (1, 3)   **3.** (1, 1)   **5.** (−2, −3)   **7.** (−2, 2)
9. (2, −1)   **11.** (4, −3)   **13.** (3, 4)   **15.** (−3, 1)
17. 1   **19.** 3   **21.** 2

Page 244
1. right 2, up 3   **3.** left 3, down 1   **5.** right 3
7. left 3   **9.** down 7   **11.** right 4, down 1
13. up 3   **15.** left 8   **17.** left $2\frac{1}{2}$, up $4\frac{1}{2}$ **19.** left $1\frac{1}{4}$
21. (−4, 8)

Page 245
1. coefficients of powers of $a + b$ **3.** $a^6 + 6a^5b +$
$15a^4b^2 + 20a^3b^3 + 15a^2b^4 + 6ab^5 + b^6$;
$a^7 + 7a^6b + 21a^5b^2 + 35a^4b^3 + 35a^3b^4 +$
$21a^2b^5 + 7ab^6 + b^7$

Page 247
1. x-axis   **3.** x-axis   **5.** y-axis   **7.** x-axis
9. y-axis   **11.** 2   **13.** 4   **15.** 3   **17.** 3, 4

Page 250
1. −7   **3.** 1   **5.** −8   **7.** −3   **9.** −11   **11.** 8
13. −6   **15.** −23   **17.** 29   **19.** $-\frac{5}{4}$ **21.** $\frac{13}{6}$
23. $\frac{19}{15}$ **25.** .8   **27.** $-\frac{23}{8}$ **29.** −8a   **31.** −3k
33. $-\frac{5m}{6}$

Page 254
1. $\frac{3}{4}$ **3.** $\frac{2}{3}$ **5.** $\frac{3}{10}$ **7.** $-\frac{4}{15}$ **9.** 0   **11.** $-\frac{2t}{7i}$
13. $-\frac{k}{b}$

Page 257
1. undefined; vertical   **3.** 0; horizontal
5. $\frac{5}{8}$; up to the right   **7.** undefined; vertical
9. 0; horizontal   **11.** yes   **13.** yes   **15.** no
17. no   **19.** yes

Page 258
1. 6   **3.** 14   **5.** 7, −7   **7.** 1, $\frac{7}{3}$ **9.** 9   **11.** $-\frac{3}{2}$
13. (5, 1)   **15.** (1, −3)   **17.** (−4, −1)
19. (−3, 2)   **21.** (−2, 0)   **23.** 2; left 3, up 2
25. on y-axis; up 3   **27.** y-axis   **29.** −5   **31.** 11
33. 5   **35.** 0; horizontal   **37.** undefined; vertical
39. yes

Page 263
1. $\frac{10}{3}$ **3.** $\frac{21}{2}$ **5.** $\frac{15}{4}$ **7.** 4   **9.** $\frac{15}{16}$ **11.** 2,310
13. 320   **15.** 8, −8   **17.** 2, 5   **19.** 9, 24
21. 49, 21

Page 267
1. $y = 2x - 1$ **3.** $y = 2x - 5$ **5.** $y = x + 4$
7. $y = 4x - 2$ **9.** $y = -2x - 2$ **11.** $y = 3x + 4$
13. $y = -3x + 4$ **15.** $y = 2x - 8$
17. $-2(-3) - 5 = 1$ **19.** $y = 4x$; $12 = 4(3)$
21. $y = 3x - 5$; $4 = 3(3) - 5$ **23.** $y = 2x + 5$
25. $y = x$

Page 269

1. $y = \frac{3}{2}x + \frac{1}{2}$ 3. $y = \frac{1}{4}x + \frac{9}{2}$ 5. $y = -\frac{2}{5}x + \frac{21}{5}$
7. $y = \frac{4}{5}x + \frac{8}{5}$ 9. $y = \frac{5}{2}x + 5$ 11. $y = \frac{2}{3}x - 3$; 1
13. $y = \frac{3}{2}x + 2$; -1 15. $(-1, -5)$, $(0, -3)$,
$(1, -1)$ 17. $(-2, -3)$, $(0, -2)$, $(2, -1)$
19. $(-4, 0)$, $(0, -1)$, $(4, -2)$ 21. $y = \frac{1}{2}x + 5$;
$(-2, 4)$, $(0, 5)$, $(2, 6)$ 23. $y = \frac{1}{2}x - 6$; $(-2, -7)$,
$(0, -6)$, $(2, -5)$ 25. $y = \frac{2}{3}x + 1$; $(-3, -1)$,
$(0, 1)$, $(3, 3)$ 27. $-\frac{1}{2}$ 29. $-\frac{1}{8}$

Page 271

1. $20.83

Page 275

1. $\frac{1}{2}$; -7 3. $-\frac{4}{5}$; 7 5. $y = 2x + 4$ 7. $y = 5x$
9. $(-4, 5)$, $(4, -1)$ 11. $(0, 1)$, $(1, 4)$
13. $(1, 2)$, $(2, 0)$ 15. $(1, 1)$, $(2, -3)$
17. $(-3, 7)$, $(3, -3)$ 19. $(0, 0)$, $(2, 4)$
21. $(-3, 9)$, $(3, -9)$ 23. $y = -\frac{4}{5}x - 2$; $(0, -2)$,
$(5, -6)$

Page 278

1. $\left(2, \frac{3}{2}\right)$, $\left(4, \frac{9}{2}\right)$ 3. $(-5, 0)$, $(5, -4)$
5. $(0, 6)$, $(2, 6)$ 7. $(-3, 2)$, $(3, 6)$ 9. $(-1, 6)$,
$(1, 2)$ 11. $(2, 10)$, $(4, 15)$ 13. $(-1, 2)$, $(1, 4)$
15. $(-1, 2)$, $(1, -2)$ 17. $\left(-3, -\frac{10}{3}\right)$, $\left(3, \frac{2}{3}\right)$

Page 280

1. $(-2, -1)$, $(-2, 0)$, $(-2, 1)$ 3. $(-3, -1)$,
$(-3, 0)$, $(-3, 1)$ 5. $(3, -1)$, $(3, 0)$, $(3, 1)$
7. $(7, -1)$, $(7, 0)$, $(7, 1)$ 9. $(3, -1)$, $(3, 0)$,
$(3, 1)$ 11. $(6, -1)$, $(6, 0)$, $(6, 1)$

Page 284

1. $y < -x + 3$ 3. $y > -x - 3$ 5. $y > -\frac{3}{2}x$
7. $y < 3x + 4$ (Two points of the boundary line
are given.) 9. above; $(0, 3)$, $(2, 3)$
11. below and including; $(0, -4)$, $(2, -4)$
13. below; $(0, 0)$, $(1, 3)$ 15. below and
including; $(0, 0)$, $(2, 2)$ 17. below and
including; $(0, 5)$, $(2, 7)$ 19. below; $(0, -3)$,
$(2, -5)$ 21. below and including; $(0, 1)$, $(2, 5)$
23. to the left of; $(0, 0)$, $(0, 2)$ 25. below;
$(0, 1)$, $(3, 3)$ 27. below and including; $(0, 1)$,
$(2, 2)$ 29. above; $(0, 1)$, $(2, 1)$; $(3, 7)$
31. above; $(0, -6)$, $(2, -4)$; $(3, 8)$ 33. below
and including; $(0, 1)$, $(2, 7)$; $(3, 0)$ 35. below;
$(0, 4)$, $(2, 4)$ 37. below and including; $(0, 0)$,
$(2, 3)$ 39. above and including; $(0, -3)$, $(2, 0)$
41. below and including; $(0, -2)$, $(3, 2)$
43. above and including; $(0, -3)$, $(5, 0)$
45. above; $\left(0, \frac{1}{2}\right)$, $\left(2, -\frac{7}{2}\right)$ 47. above and
including; $(0, 3)$, $(4, 6)$ 49. above $y = 6$;
below and including $y = 9$

Page 286

1. extremes x, 3; means 4, 6; 8 3. extremes
$x + 2$, 3; means 4, $x - 5$; 26 5. extremes
$2x + 1$, 4; means 5, x; $-\frac{4}{3}$ 7. extremes x, x;
means 1, 9; 3, -3 9. 6,000 11. $y = 2x - 5$
13. $y = -2x + 6$ 15. $y = \frac{1}{3}x + \frac{11}{3}$ 17. $y = 2x$;
$8 = 2(4)$ 19. $y = \frac{2}{3}x - 5$ 21. $y = 3x - 1$
23. $-\frac{4}{5}$; 2; $(-5, 6)$, $(5, -2)$ 25. 2; 1; $(-1, -1)$,
$(1, 3)$ 27. 0; -6; $(-1, -6)$, $(1, -6)$
29. $(-1, 3)$, $(1, 5)$ 31. $(3, 0)$, $(3, 3)$
33. $(-2, 0)(-2, 1)$ 35. below; $(4, 2)$, $(0, -4)$

Page 291
1. (2, −3)   **3.** (0, 4)   **5.** (2, 6)   **7.** (2, 5)
9. (3, 6)   **11.** inconsistent   **13.** inconsistent
15. 3   **17.** 10

Page 293
For each of the following, the two points given
lie on the line. They are not necessarily part of
the graph.   **1.** to the left of the line containing
(4, 0), (4, 1) and above and including the line
containing (0, −2), (1, −2); (3, 1)   **3.** above
and including the line containing (0, 2), (1, 2)
and to the left of the line containing (−5, 0),
(−5, 1)   **5.** above the line containing (0, 5),
(1, 6) and to the left of and including the line
containing (2, 0), (2, 1)   **7.** below the line
containing (1, 1)(2, 2) and above and including
the line containing (3, −3), (0, −5)   **9.** above
the line containing (0, −3), (1, −1) and above
the line containing (0, −3), (9, 0)

Page 296
1. (3, 6)   **3.** (3, 1)   **5.** (3, 0)   **7.** (2, 0)
9. $\left(\frac{11}{2}, -\frac{1}{2}\right)$ **11.** $\left(\frac{5}{2}, 5\right)$ **13.** $\left(-1, -\frac{2}{5}\right)$
15. $\left(-3, -\frac{8}{5}\right)$

Page 299
1. (6, 2)   **3.** (2, 2)   **5.** (2, 1)   **7.** (2, 2)
9. (3, 2)   **11.** (3, 2)   **13.** (3, 6)   **15.** (15, 10)

Page 302
1. (2, 1)   **3.** (2, 2)   **5.** (5, 1)   **7.** (1, 1)
9. (2, 1)   **11.** (2, 2)   **13.** (−2, 6)   **15.** $\left(1, \frac{13}{2}\right)$
17. (3, 2)   **19.** (−18, 8)   **21.** $\left(\frac{58}{27}, \frac{1}{9}\right)$
23. $\left(\frac{4}{5}, -\frac{4}{25}\right)$

Page 305
1. 11 kg; 1,260¢   **3.** (x + y) kg; (158x + 210y)¢
5. (x + y) kg; (4x + 78y)¢   **7.** (x + y) kg;
(135x + my)¢   **9.** (x + y) kg; (px + qy)¢

Page 308
1. x + y = 7; 90x + 130y = 750   **3.** y = x + 2;
5x + 15y = 130   **5.** x = y − 2; 230x +
170y = 740   **7.** 5 kg at $.50, 4 kg at $.70
9. 2 at $.15, 9 at $.35   **11.** 4 kg at $1.60,
8 kg at $1.80   **13.** 3 at $.20, 4 at $.15
15. 8 kg at $.80, 5 kg at $1.60   **17.** 5 kg at
$1.20, 2 kg at $1.80

Page 312
1. 10, 40   **3.** 6, 12   **5.** 4, 13   **7.** 5, 17
9. 8, 12   **11.** width 7 m, length 14 m
13. width 10 km, length 68 km

Page 314
1. (5, 3)   **3.** (4,4)   **5.** inconsistent
7. consistent   **9.** (3, 1)   **11.** (5, −1)   **13.** (3, 6)
15. (6, 0)   **17.** 3 kg at $1.50, 2 kg at $1.90
19. 2 sheets at $.40, 4 sheets at $.30
21. 16, 24   **23.** 5, 13

Page 316
1. They land at the same time.   **3.** 5 seconds

Page 319
1. {(−4, 5), (−2, −2), (3, 2), (3, 4), (5, 1)};
D = {−4, −2, 3, 5}; R = {5, −2, 2, 4, 1}; no
3. {(−1, −3), (0, −2), (2, 0), (3, 1), (4, 2)};
D = {−1, 0, 2, 3, 4}; R = {−3, −2, 0, 1, 2}; yes
5. D = {3, 4, −1, 0}; R = {2}; yes
7. D = {3, −3, 0}; R = {0, 3, −3}; no
9. D = {−1, −2, 0, 1, 2}; R = {−1, −2, 0, 1, 2};
yes   **11.** {(4, −2), (1, −1), (4, 0)}; yes; no
13. {(1, −1), (1, −2), (1, 0), (1, 1), (1, 2)}; yes;
no   **15.** −6, 6

Page 321

(Two points belonging to each relation are given.) **1.** (0, 0), (1, 3); function; linear function **3.** (0, 0), (1, 1); function; linear function **5.** (−4, 0), (−4, −2) **7.** (3, 0), (3, 2) **9.** (0, −3), (2, 1); function; linear function **11.** (−1, 0), (2, 1); function; linear function **13.** (0, 0), (2, 0); function; constant function **15.** (0, −2), (1, 1); function; linear function **17.** (−1, 0), (1, −1); function; linear function **19.** (4, 0), (0, 4); function; linear function **21.** (4, 0), (4, 2) **23.** $\left(1, -\frac{3}{4}\right)$, $\left(-2, \frac{3}{4}\right)$; function; linear function **25.** (−4, 0), (2, 2); function; linear function **27.** (0, −3), (2, −3); function; constant function **29.** (0, 5), (−1, 2); function; linear function **31.** (−2, 4), (0, 0), (2, 4); function **33.** (−1, −2), (0, −3), (1, −2); function **35.** (−2, −12), (0, 0), (2, −12); function **37.** (4, 2), (0, 0), (4, −2) **39.** (12, 2), (0, 0), (12, −2) **41.** (6, −2), (2, 0), (6, 2) **43.** (−2, −8), (−1, −1), (0, 0), (1, 1), (2, 8); function **45.** (−2, −24), (−1, −3), (0, 0), (1, 3), (2, 24); function **47.** (1, −1), (0, 0), (1, 1)

Page 324

1. −2 **3.** −8 **5.** −68 **7.** −13 **9.** 35 **11.** −5 **13.** 11 **15.** 395 **17.** $R = \{-16, 8, 26\}$ **19.** $R = \{18, 32, 46\}$ **21.** $R = \{131, 101, 75\}$ **23.** $R = \{-3, 7, 52\}$ **25.** $R = \{5.5, 5.2, 4.9\}$ **27.** $R = \{25, 49, 81\}$ **29.** $R = \left\{-4\frac{3}{4}, -4\frac{15}{16}\right\}$ **31.** 20 **33.** 54 **35.** 172 **37.** 151

Page 329

1. 96 **3.** 84 **5.** 93 **7.** 38 **9.** 49 **11.** 72

Page 332

1. 6 or $\frac{1}{6}$ **3.** −4 or $-\frac{1}{4}$ **5.** −2 or $-\frac{1}{2}$ **7.** 14 **9.** −54 **11.** 437.5 km **13.** \$208.33 **15.** 10 cups **17.** $13\frac{1}{3}$ m by $16\frac{2}{3}$ m **19.** $\frac{135}{4}$ **21.** 550 m

Page 336

1. 18 **5.** −1 **7.** 4 **9.** 180 cm **11.** 9 m **13.** $4\frac{1}{6}$ hr **15.** \$750 **17.** 24 cm **19.** $5\frac{1}{3}$ m **21.** 2.2 m **23.** 18

Page 338

1. {(−1, −3), (0, −1), (1, 1), (2, 3), (3, 5)}; $D = \{-1, 0, 1, 2, 3\}$; $R = \{-3, -1, 1, 3, 5\}$; yes **3.** {(−4, 1), (−2, −2), (3, 1), (4, −2)}; $D = \{-4, -2, 3, 4\}$; $R = \{-2, 1\}$; yes **5.** $D = \{-2, -1, 0, 1, 2\}$; $R = \{1\}$; yes (Two points of the boundary line are given.) **7.** (4, 0), (4, 2) **9.** (0, −1), (1, 2); function; linear function **11.** (0, 1), (2, 9), (−1, 3); function **13.** 12 **15.** 39 **17.** $R = \{-2, 1, -5\}$ **19.** direct variation; 3 **25.** −10 **27.** 150 cm

Page 344

1. −3 **3.** $\frac{5}{4}$ **5.** $\frac{41}{10}$ **7.** $-\frac{10}{9}$ **9.** −84 **11.** {13} **13.** {1} **15.** {1}

Page 345

1. 24.96 **3.** 11.78 **5.** \$2.99

Page 348

1. $\frac{27}{2}$ **3.** −19 **5.** $\frac{11}{5}$ **7.** $\left\{\frac{45}{2}\right\}$ **9.** $\left\{\frac{15}{13}\right\}$ **11.** {11} **13.** {1, 3} **15.** −1 **17.** 5

Page 352

1. Jake $\frac{3}{5}$; Bill $\frac{3}{x}$ **3.** Maria $\frac{12}{x}$; Todd $\frac{6}{x}$ **5.** Lester $\frac{7}{m}$; Jim $\frac{14}{m + 1}$ **7.** Mark $\frac{3}{3m + 1}$; Stuart $\frac{3}{m - 4}$ **9.** Joan $\frac{5}{7}$; Helene $\frac{2}{7}$ **11.** Eleanor $\frac{x}{5}$; Ted $\frac{x}{10}$ **13.** Donald $\frac{5}{x}$; Merv $\frac{5}{3x}$

Page 355

1. $1\frac{5}{7}$ hr **3.** $7\frac{1}{2}$ hr **5.** $1\frac{1}{3}$ hr **7.** Josephine 8 hr; Lois 24 hr **9.** $1\frac{13}{47}$ hr **11.** $2\frac{2}{5}$ hr **13.** 10 hr

Page 356

1. 20% **3.** 58% **5.** 50 **7.** \$200

Page 360

1. $\frac{20}{3}$ **3.** 1,805   **5.** .31   **7.** 307.5   **9.** -140

11. 10.02   **13.** $\frac{15}{2}$ **15.** 5   **17.** $-296\frac{1}{3}$ **19.** .033

Page 363

1. $\frac{-1}{1}$ **3.** $\frac{-16}{1}$ **5.** $\frac{-24}{36}$ **7.** $\frac{-364}{100}$ **9.** $\frac{4}{9}$

11. $\frac{34}{45}$ **13.** $\frac{32}{9}$ **15.** $\frac{16}{99}$ **17.** $\frac{83}{99}$ **19.** $\frac{98}{99}$

21. $\frac{306,483}{99,900}$

Page 367

1. \$375   **3.** \$1,200 at 5%, \$600 at 6%
5. \$600 at 4%, \$1,200 at 6%   **7.** \$500 at 5%,
\$800 at 6%   **9.** \$6,000 at 5%, \$4,000 at
$4\frac{1}{2}$%   **11.** \$7,000

Page 370

1. $\frac{14}{5}$ **3.** $\frac{5}{11}$ **5.** $\frac{5(6a + 1)}{2a + 3}$ **7.** $\frac{12a + 1}{6a + 1}$

9. $\frac{40a - 6a^2}{15a^2 + 70}$ **11.** $\frac{3 - 5a}{2a + 1}$ **13.** $x + 1$

15. $\frac{1}{m - 8}$

Page 373

1. $\frac{2a - 1}{6a - 18}$ **3.** $\frac{3x - 2}{9x - 34}$ **5.** $\frac{2}{7}$ **7.** $\frac{a^2 + 4a - 8}{a - 4}$

9. $\frac{x^2 - 6x + 10}{x - 3}$ **11.** $\frac{5x - 8}{4x - 9}$ **13.** $\frac{-3x - 2}{7x - 6}$

15. $\frac{1}{4}$ **17.** $\frac{2}{2x + 5}$ **19.** $\frac{a + b}{a - b}$

21. $\frac{2x^2 + 9xy - 19y^2}{3x}$

Page 376

1. $x = \frac{2}{a}$ **3.** $x = a$ **5.** $x = -3a$ **7.** $x = 4a$

9. $x = \frac{d + c}{2}$ **11.** $x = \frac{3b - 4a}{2}$ **13.** $x = \frac{8}{k + 2}$

15. $\frac{b}{2a}$ **17.** $x = \frac{3b + c}{2}$ **19.** $x = \frac{2ab}{c}$

21. $\frac{p}{4}$; 7   **23.** $s = \frac{p - b}{2}$; 19   **25.** $r = \frac{C}{2\pi}$; 2m

27. $h = \frac{V}{lw}$; 4 cm   **29.** $x = \frac{3c - 5a}{2b}$

31. $x = \frac{2d + 4c}{a}$ **33.** $x = \frac{4b + 2}{5b}$ **35.** $x = a + 2$

37. $x = a + b$ **39.** $h = \frac{3V}{\pi r^2}$; 6 km

41. $p = \frac{A}{rt + 1}$; 120   **43.** $a = 3A - b - c$; 31

Page 377

1. $\frac{10}{3}\Omega$ **3.** $\frac{600}{7}\Omega$

Page 378

1. -1 **3.** $\frac{-1}{3}$ **5.** $-1, -2$ **7.** $\frac{45}{4}$ hr   **9.** $\frac{28}{3}$ mo;

28 mo   **11.** $\frac{700}{3}$ **13.** -230 **15.** $\frac{0}{1}$ **17.** $\frac{42}{9}$

19. $\frac{2}{11}$ **21.** $\frac{9 + 15b}{6b + 7}$ **23.** $\frac{10a - 12}{7}$

25. $\frac{x^2 - 7x + 13}{2x - 1}$ **27.** $\frac{tr - 5a}{m}$ **29.** $-a$

31. $\frac{4k}{d^2}$; 7

Page 383
1. R 3. R 5. I 7. R 9. I 11. R 13. I
15. R 17. R 19. R 21. Answers may vary.
23. Answers may vary. 25. irrational
27. irrational 29. F 31. T 33. T

Page 386
1. 6.1 m 3. 7.4 m, 14.8 m 5. 5.5 m,
16.5 m 7. 5.3 cm 9. 33.0 m, 6.6 m
11. 2.8 cm

Page 390
1. 5.1 3. 6.9 5. 9.4 7. 4.2 9. 7.2 11. 3.5
13. 6.1 15. 5.7 17. 8.2 19. 8.4 21. 9.1
23. 10.8 25. 14.1

Page 393
1. $\sqrt{10}$ 3. $\sqrt{30}$ 5. $\sqrt{14}$ 7. 32 9. 35
11. $2\sqrt{3}$ 13. $3\sqrt{3}$ 15. $7\sqrt{2}$ 17. $-4\sqrt{15}$
19. $8\sqrt{2}$ 21. $5\sqrt{3}$; 8.7 23. $-6\sqrt{5}$; -13.4
25. $18\sqrt{5}$; 40.2 27. $-14\sqrt{7}$ 29. $-38\sqrt{5}$
31. $102\sqrt{11}$

Page 395
1. x^4y^2 3. cd^4 5. $-3y^2$ 7. $-9ab^3$
9. $-2c^5d$ 11. $3a^3b^4$ 13. $a^2b^3c^4$ 15. $-c^2de^6$
17. $3a^3b^4c$ 19. $8a^2b^6c$ 21. $6c^4d^5e^6$
23. $5a^6b^5c^2$ 25. $11c^4d^3e$ 27. $12a^4bc^8$
29. $-3a^2b^5\sqrt{3}$ 31. $-4a^3b^6\sqrt{2}$
33. $-4a^5b^6\sqrt{3}$ 35. $3a^6b^7c\sqrt{5}$
37. $-7a^2b^4c^8\sqrt{2}$ 39. $-9x^4yz^9\sqrt{3}$
41. $-1.3ab^4c^{10}$ 43. $\frac{1}{5}x^5yz^6$ 45. $-\frac{9}{4}ab^{18}c^{50}$

Page 397
1. $x\sqrt{x}$ 3. $3x^2\sqrt{x}$ 5. $2x^2\sqrt{2x}$ 7. $x\sqrt{7x}$
9. $x^2y^3\sqrt{y}$ 11. $-c^3d\sqrt{d}$ 13. $x^2y^3\sqrt{xy}$
15. $c\sqrt{cd}$ 17. $a^2b^4\sqrt{a}$ 19. $xy^2\sqrt{5x}$
21. $6x\sqrt{y}$ 23. $x^3y^4\sqrt{6y}$ 25. $x^2y^4\sqrt{19xy}$
27. $-5mn^2\sqrt{2m}$ 29. $8yz^3\sqrt{11x}$
31. $12a^2c^6\sqrt{7b}$ 33. $-c^3d^3e^3\sqrt{d}$
35. $-3xy^3\sqrt{xyz}$ 37. $-5b^3c^3d^4\sqrt{bc}$
39. $-48x^2y^5\sqrt{2y}$ 41. xy^3 43. $-cd^4$
45. $2ab^3$ 47. $-4ab^2\sqrt[3]{a}$ 49. $-2b^2\sqrt[3]{5a^2b^2}$
51. $4x^2z^4\sqrt[3]{3xy}$ 53. xy^3 55. $-2x^2y$
57. $3xy^2\sqrt[5]{x}$ 59. $-2b\sqrt[5]{3a^2b^2c^3}$
61. $-4acde\sqrt[5]{5de^2}$ 63. $18xy^2z^2\sqrt[3]{2x^2yz^2}$

Page 398
1. 2.24

Page 401
1. no 3. no 5. no 7. no 9. $c = 10$
11. $b = 12$ 13. $a = 4\sqrt{3}$ 15. $b = 48$
17. $c = 2\sqrt{5}$ 19. 2.6 m 21. 5.7 m 23. 4.2 m

Page 403
1. $9\sqrt{5}$ 3. $15\sqrt{6}$ 5. $\sqrt{10}$ 7. $2\sqrt{6} + 6\sqrt{3}$
9. $12\sqrt{5} - 6\sqrt{7}$ 11. $8\sqrt{5} - 3\sqrt{2}$
13. $7\sqrt{2}$ 15. $-5\sqrt{6}$ 17. $2\sqrt{11}$ 19. $9\sqrt{a}$
21. $7\sqrt{mn}$ 23. $-3\sqrt{xy}$ 25. $4x\sqrt{3z} - x\sqrt{5z}$
27. $-21ab\sqrt{ab}$ 29. $4\sqrt{3x}$ 31. cannot
simplify 33. $-11\sqrt{10x}$ 35. $8xy\sqrt{5x}$
37. $.6y\sqrt{x}$ 39. $.22xy\sqrt{x}$ 41. $3.56ab\sqrt{ab}$

Page 405
1. $40\sqrt{3}$ 3. $24\sqrt{30}$ 5. $15\sqrt{30}$ 7. $2x$ 9. y
11. $-72y$ 13. 0 15. $-20\sqrt{3} - 60\sqrt{2}$
17. $16 - \sqrt{6}$ 19. $34 + 24\sqrt{6}$ 21. 2
23. -30 25. $19 + 4\sqrt{21}$ 27. $26 - 4\sqrt{30}$
29. $62 + 24\sqrt{3}$ 31. $522 - 72\sqrt{7}$
33. $120 - 80\sqrt{2}$ 35. $10 + 2\sqrt{6} - 2\sqrt{15} - 2\sqrt{10}$

Page 410
1. $\frac{\sqrt{2}}{2}$ 3. $\sqrt{5}$ 5. $2\sqrt{3}$ 7. $\sqrt{3}$ 9. $\frac{\sqrt{10}}{2}$
11. $\frac{4\sqrt{x}}{x^3}$ 13. $\frac{2\sqrt{m}}{m^2}$ 15. $\frac{6\sqrt{x}}{x}$ 17. $\frac{3\sqrt{2a}}{2a^3}$
19. $\frac{\sqrt{6x}}{2x}$ 21. $5y\sqrt{x}$ 23. $\frac{3\sqrt{y}}{y}$
25. $12x^2y^2\sqrt{xy}$ 27. $y\sqrt{2y}$ 29. $\frac{\sqrt{5a}}{5}$
31. $\frac{15 + 5\sqrt{3}}{6}$ 33. $\frac{\sqrt{30} + 2\sqrt{3}}{6}$ 35. $-\sqrt{7} - 2$

Page 412

1. $\frac{3}{4}$ **3.** $\frac{10}{9}$ **5.** $\frac{11}{5}$ **7.** $\frac{3\sqrt{6}}{5}$ **9.** $\frac{\sqrt{67}}{9}$ **11.** $\frac{\sqrt{6}}{4}$

13. $\frac{\sqrt{15}}{6}$ **15.** $\frac{\sqrt{110}}{20}$ **17.** $\frac{4\sqrt{x}}{x^2}$ **19.** $\frac{\sqrt{30y}}{5y^2}$

21. $\frac{3\sqrt{6xy}}{y^3}$ **23.** $\frac{\sqrt{2x}}{2x^2}$ **25.** $\frac{\sqrt{3z}}{3xz}$ **27.** $\frac{\sqrt{77}}{7y}$

29. $\frac{y\sqrt{14yz}}{z}$ **31.** $\frac{\sqrt{4x+6}}{2}$ **33.** $\frac{\sqrt{28x+49}}{7}$

35. $\frac{\sqrt{15-25z}}{5}$ **37.** $\frac{\sqrt{6z^2+9}}{3}$ **39.** $\frac{y+3}{y}$

Page 413
1. $340.75

Page 414
1. I **3.** R **5.** I **7.** I **9.** 6.8 cm **11.** 5.9 cm; 11.8 cm **13.** yes; 8.6 **15.** no **17.** yes; 7.9 **19.** 36 **21.** $8a^2b^5$ **23.** $12cd^2e^5$ **25.** $-6x^5y^5\sqrt{3xy}$ **27.** $4xyz^2\sqrt[3]{xy^2}$ **29.** no **31.** yes **33.** $a=3$ **35.** $-\sqrt{5}$ **37.** $15x-10\sqrt{x}$ **39.** -2 **41.** $2\sqrt{2}$ **43.** $6y^2\sqrt{2xy}$ **45.** $5x$ **47.** $\frac{\sqrt{12x+6}}{3}$

Page 416
1. $3^2+4^2=5^2$, $5^2+12^2=13^2$, $7^2+24^2=25^2$, $9^2+40^2=41^2$, $11^2+60^2=61^2$ **3.** 13, 84, 85; 15, 112, 113; 17, 144, 145

Page 419
1. {9} **3.** {20} **5.** $\left\{\frac{1}{16}\right\}$ **7.** {2} **9.** 1 **11.** no solution **13.** $\frac{79}{3}$ **15.** 4 **17.** no solution **19.** 12 **21.** $-3, -2$ **23.** 2 **25.** 25 **27.** 2 **29.** 1 **31.** 4

Page 421
1. $\{1, -1\}$ **3.** $\{2, -2\}$ **5.** $\{7, -7\}$ **7.** $\{3, -3\}$ **9.** $\{8, -8\}$ **11.** ϕ **13.** $\{\sqrt{15}, -\sqrt{15}\}$ **15.** $\{\sqrt{13}, -\sqrt{13}\}$ **17.** $\{2\sqrt{6}, -2\sqrt{6}\}$ **19.** $\{3\sqrt{2}, -3\sqrt{2}\}$ **21.** ϕ **23.** $-1, -9$ **25.** $\frac{\sqrt{15}}{3}, -\frac{\sqrt{15}}{3}$ **27.** $\frac{\sqrt{65}}{5}, -\frac{\sqrt{65}}{5}$ **29.** $5, -5$ **31.** $-3+2\sqrt{2}, -3-2\sqrt{2}$ **33.** $-6+2\sqrt{7}, -6-2\sqrt{7}$ **35.** $7+2\sqrt{6}, 7-2\sqrt{6}$ **37.** $\left\{\frac{5+2\sqrt{3}}{2}, \frac{5-2\sqrt{3}}{2}\right\}$ **39.** $\left\{\frac{1+\sqrt{5}}{2}, \frac{1-\sqrt{5}}{2}\right\}$

Page 425
1. $\{-8, -2\}$ **3.** $\{-1, -15\}$ **5.** $\{4+\sqrt{11}, 4-\sqrt{11}\}$ **7.** $\{-5+\sqrt{10}, -5-\sqrt{10}\}$ **9.** $\{7, -3\}$ **11.** $\{2\}$ **13.** $\{7, -11\}$ **15.** $\{2, 14\}$ **17.** $\{6, 12\}$ **19.** $\{13, -3\}$ **21.** $\{-3, -17\}$ **23.** $\{6, 10\}$ **25.** $\{21, -1\}$ **27.** $\{-15+\sqrt{70}, -15-\sqrt{70}\}$ **29.** $\{-8, -1\}$ **31.** $\{5, -10\}$ **33.** $\{3, -2\}$ **35.** $\{5, -6\}$ **37.** $\{3, -4\}$ **39.** $\{7, -2\}$ **41.** $\{15, 2\}$ **43.** $\{7, -8\}$ **45.** $\{-4, -7\}$ **47.** $\{12, 7\}$ **49.** $\{2, 19\}$ **51.** $\{2, -17\}$ **53.** $\{20, 5\}$ **55.** $\left\{\frac{-7\pm\sqrt{37}}{2}\right\}$ **57.** $\left\{\frac{-5\pm\sqrt{21}}{2}\right\}$ **59.** $\left\{\frac{-5\pm\sqrt{29}}{2}\right\}$ **61.** $\left\{\frac{1\pm\sqrt{13}}{2}\right\}$ **63.** $\left\{\frac{-7\pm\sqrt{33}}{2}\right\}$ **65.** ϕ

Page 429
1. $2x^2+6x+5=0$; $a=2$, $b=6$, $c=5$
3. $2x^2-4x-8=0$; $a=2$, $b=-4$, $c=-8$
5. $x^2+2x+0=0$; $a=1$, $b=2$, $c=0$
7. $x^2+0x-5=0$; $a=1$, $b=0$, $c=-5$
9. $3x^2-6x-2=0$; $a=3$, $b=-6$, $c=-2$
11. $5x^2-3x+0=0$; $a=5$, $b=-3$, $c=0$
13. $-3, -1$ **15.** 1 **17.** $7, -3$ **19.** $5, -8$
21. 4 **23.** $\{1, -11\}$ **25.** $\{6, -5\}$ **27.** $\{-1, -4\}$
29. $\{2, -2\}$ **31.** $\{2, -1\}$ **33.** $\{18, -2\}$

Page 433
1. 3 L **3.** 6 L **5.** 87.5 L **7.** 48 L **9.** 6.5 L
11. 2 dL **13.** 7.5 dL

Page 436

1. $\left\{-3, \frac{1}{2}\right\}$ 3. $\left\{-\frac{1}{2}, \frac{2}{3}\right\}$ 5. $\left\{\frac{3}{2}, 4\right\}$ 7. $\left\{-2, \frac{1}{3}\right\}$

9. $\left\{\frac{10}{3}\right\}$ 11. $\left\{\frac{7 \pm \sqrt{37}}{2}\right\}$ 13. ϕ

15. $\left\{\frac{-5 \pm \sqrt{37}}{2}\right\}$ 17. ϕ 19. ϕ

21. $\{2 \pm \sqrt{14}\}$ 23. $\{4 \pm \sqrt{13}\}$ 25. $\left\{-4, \frac{3}{2}\right\}$

27. $\{-2 \pm \sqrt{3}\}$ 29. $\left\{\frac{7 \pm \sqrt{5}}{2}\right\}$ 31. $\left\{1, -\frac{5}{2}\right\}$

33. $\left\{\frac{3}{4}\right\}$ 35. $\left\{\frac{2 \pm \sqrt{29}}{5}\right\}$ 37. $\{\sqrt{2} \pm 2\}$

39. $\{-3 \pm \sqrt{13}\}$

Page 439

1. $l = 8$ m, $w = 5$ m   3. $l = 8$ m, $w = 4$ m
5. $l = 11$ cm, $w = 4$ cm   7. $l = 5$ cm, $w = 4$ cm
9. $l = 8.4$ cm, $w = 2.4$ cm   11. $l = 7.7$ m,
$w = 5.7$ m   13. $l = 12$ cm, $w = 8$ cm
15. $l = 15$ km, $w = 6$ km   17. $l = 18$ km,
$w = 4$ km   19. $l = 8.1$ m, $w = 3.1$ m
21. $l = 7$, $w = 5$

Page 440

1. yes   3. Wednesday

Page 442

1. $\{75\}$ 3. ϕ 5. ϕ 7. $\{10, -10\}$
9. $\{6, -6\}$ 11. $\{4, -20\}$ 13. 16   15. 1
17. $\frac{25}{4}$ 19. $\{13, -1\}$ 21. $\{9, 5\}$ 23. $\{7, -3\}$
25. $\{-4, -2\}$ 27. $\{-6, -10\}$
29. $x^2 - x + 6 = 0$; $a = 1$, $b = -1$, $c = 6$
31. $x^2 + 0x - 7 = 0$; $a = 1$, $b = 0$, $c = -7$
33. $5x^2 + 0x - 11 = 0$; $a = 5$, $b = 0$, $c = -11$
35. $7x^2 - 2x + 1 = 0$; $a = 7$, $b = -2$, $c = 1$
37. $\{4, 2\}$ 39. $\{3, 4\}$ 41. $\{-2, -5\}$
43. $\{3, -7\}$ 45. $\{-3, 1\}$ 47. $\{7, 0\}$
49. $\left\{-2, \frac{1}{3}\right\}$ 51. $\left\{\frac{1}{2}, -\frac{5}{2}\right\}$ 53. $\left\{\frac{-1 \pm \sqrt{13}}{3}\right\}$
55. $\left\{\frac{7 \pm \sqrt{5}}{2}\right\}$ 57. $\left\{\frac{2 \pm 3\sqrt{2}}{2}\right\}$
59. $\left\{\frac{5 \pm \sqrt{17}}{4}\right\}$ 61. $\left\{\frac{5 \pm \sqrt{97}}{6}\right\}$
63. $l = 5$ m, $w = 4$ m

Page 444

1. 4.5   3. 5.6

Page 447

1. 33°, 57°   3. 65°, 25°   5. 45°   7. 16°
9. 15°, 75°   11. 75°, 70°, 35°

Page 450

1. $x = 3$, $y = 14$ 3. $EF = 3\frac{1}{3}$, $DF = 8\frac{2}{3}$
5. $DE = 11\frac{2}{3}$, $EF = 20$ 7. $CB = 13\frac{1}{3}$, $DF = 15$
9. 6 m   11. 9.6 m   13. $7\frac{1}{2}$ m

Page 452

1. $\tan A = 1.333$, $\sin A = .800$, $\cos A = .600$,
$\tan B = .750$, $\sin B = .600$, $\cos B = .800$
3. $\tan A = .750$, $\sin A = .600$, $\cos A = .800$,
$\tan B = 1.333$, $\sin B = .800$, $\cos B = .600$
5. $\tan A = .894$, $\sin A = .667$, $\cos A = .745$,
$\tan B = 1.118$, $\sin B = .745$, $\cos B = .667$

7. 1.000   9. .707   11. $\sin B = \dfrac{b}{c}$; $\cos A = \dfrac{b}{c}$;

thus $\sin B = \cos A$

13. $a^2 + b^2 = c^2$, $\dfrac{a^2}{c^2} + \dfrac{b^2}{c^2} = \dfrac{c^2}{c^2} = 1$.

Also, $\dfrac{a^2}{c^2} + \dfrac{b^2}{c^2} = \sin^2 A + \cos^2 A$. By

substitution, $\sin^2 A + \cos^2 A = 1$.   15. $\tan A = .775$, $\sin A = .612$, $\cos A = .791$, $\tan B = 1.291$, $\sin B = .791$, $\cos B = .612$ 17. Any two complementary angles may be represented as the acute angles of a right triangle ABC.

$\sin A = \dfrac{a}{c}$; $\cos B = \dfrac{a}{c}$; thus, $\sin A = \cos B$,

or the sine of an angle is equal to the cosine of its complement.

Page 457
1. .9613 **3.** .4384 **5.** 57.29 **7.** 2.145
9. .2588 **11.** 8° **13.** 23° **15.** 34° **17.** 49°
19. 77° **21.** 83° **23.** F **25.** T **27.** T **29.** F
31. F **33.** T **35.** F **37.** T **39.** T **41.** Cos A
decreases from 1 to 0. The ratio of b to c
approaches 0.

Page 460
1. $a = 8.9$ **3.** $b = 8.5$ **5.** $c = 9.7$ **7.** $a = 4.7$
9. $c = 18.3$ **11.** $m\angle A = 30$ **13.** $a = 25.7$
15. $m\angle B = 74$, $BC = 5.7$, $AB = 20.8$
17. $m\angle B = 54$, $BC = 10.2$, $AB = 17.3$
19. $m\angle B = 32$, $BC = 15.3$, $AC = 9.5$

Page 463
1. $x = 58.5$ m **3.** $x = 64.7$ km **5.** $x = 342.9$ m
7. $x = 46.6$ m **9.** 216.6 m **11.** 96.0 m
13. 32° **15.** 21,299.3 m **17.** 49.5 km²

Page 464
1. $x = 8$, $y = 10$ **3.** 3.000 **5.** .949 **7.** 72°
9. $c = 20.4$ **11.** $a = 6.9$ **13.** 93.3 m
15. 44°, 44°, 92° **17.** 35°, 55° **19.** 31.3 m

Page 466
1. $BC = 2\sqrt{5}$, $AC = 2\sqrt{5}$